D0671168

PLANE TRIGONOMETRY

PLANE TRIGONOMETRY

A TEXTBOOK FOR SCHOOLS AND COLLEGES

BY

RAYMOND W. BRINK, Ph.D.

PROFESSOR OF MATHEMATICS IN
THE UNIVERSITY OF MINNESOTA

THE CENTURY CO.

NEW YORK   LONDON

PREFACE

The special features of this book, which are described below, originate in a certain underlying purpose. This is to keep clearly before the student the values which he may expect to receive in return for his effort. An understanding of this sort is necessary for intelligent work. And, if he is to work with enthusiasm, the modern student is inclined to insist on it. Certainly this is not a new idea in the writing of textbooks. Nevertheless the technical methods by which this principle is carried out form the feature that most distinguishes this book from other books in the same field and that motivates most of the other features described below. Whether the reward for labor be immediate and obvious, or whether it be more remote, by example and by explanation it is held before the student as a guide and an incentive. This principle is present from the first problem which sets forth a reason for the introduction of the trigonometric functions before the functions themselves are defined, to the more algebraic parts of the book where clear explanations are given for the methods employed.

1. Originating in this general idea is the **discussion of the significance of numerical data,** and of the criteria for determining the accuracy of results. This material gives the student a sense of the reality of the things with which he is dealing and of the validity of his results. It is a feature of the book most valuable both for its direct applications and for its general cultural benefit.

2. In addition to formal exercises there is a **great variety of applied problems,** an unusual number of which have some real interest to the student and correspond to conditions that he can conceive of as occurring in actual experience.

3. Throughout the book there is an **immediate application of principles to problems.** These take the form both of illustrative examples worked out in the text and of exercises for the student.

v

A comparison of this book with other texts will show that to an unusual degree the passages devoted to the accumulation of principles and formulas are broken into short sections followed by exercises. This arrangement, besides immediately revealing the usefulness of a method just learned, enables a class to make continuous daily progress in the theory and at the same time to have ample time and material for drill work. Noticeable instances of this method will be found in the work on the logarithmic solution of right triangles, the proofs of identities involving multiple angles, and the formulas for the solution of the oblique triangle.

4. While no formal analysis is given of the various types of **trigonometric identities and equations,** general suggestions are offered which are very helpful in this most puzzling portion of the course. Sufficient justification is given for the introduction of this work and for the methods on which the book insists to dispel the gloomy indifference with which a class frequently struggles with this material.

5. The book may be said to be **self-contained.** (i) It contains a treatment of logarithms. (ii) It defines the terms and explains the principles involved in applied problems, with a saving of time for the class and teacher. (iii) It gives such abundant drill exercises as to make other exercises unnecessary, the problem lists and illustrative examples being complete even for such mechanical work as the use of tables. (iv) The text and tables are designed to be used together, so that the units involved and the methods of interpolation will correspond.

6. The book is especially **adaptable to courses of various lengths and purposes.** Certain sections are starred for omission in short courses. Exercises are given in duplicate with answers supplied where practicable for the odd-numbered examples. Either the odd- or even-numbered examples are more than sufficient for an ordinary class. The exercises are so carefully graded that a simple course may be planned, using only the earlier exercises in each section. Many types of applied problems are segregated so that certain types may be omitted to suit the time or purpose of a class.

7. It has been intended to make the book **concise but sufficiently complete,** and to include only such material as is justified by its true value rather than by tradition. No attempt has been made to reduce it to a mere outline, which, in the end, is wasteful of time and unsatisfying to the student.

8. While the book is modern in its purpose and material, it is **conservative in the details of presentation.** It avoids peculiar methods which may be useful for some individual instructor but are dangerous in the hands of an inexperienced teacher and offensive or inconvenient to an experienced one. On the contrary, the book should prove helpful to an inexperienced teacher by revealing the purpose behind each detail, and should lend itself to the methods of any teacher who has already developed his own technique of presentation, by furnishing ample material with which his class may work.

The author wishes to express his gratitude to Professor Leon Archibald for drawing the figures, and to Doctor Elizabeth Carlson for suggestions and problems. He is especially grateful to Professor Anthony L. Underhill who read the entire manuscript, used parts of it in the classroom, and made innumerable criticisms and suggestions which have added immensely to the value of the book.

R. W. B.

CONTENTS

ix

                ✸ Sections marked with a ★ may be omitted.

★ Sections marked with a ★ may be omitted.

★ Sections marked with a ★ may be omitted.

PLANE TRIGONOMETRY

GREEK ALPHABET

A, α — Alpha	I, ι — Iota	P, ρ — Rho
B, β — Beta	K, κ — Kappa	Σ, σ, s — Sigma
Γ, γ — Gamma	Λ, λ — Lambda	T, τ — Tau
Δ, δ — Delta	M, μ — Mu	Υ, υ — Upsilon
E, ε — Epsilon	N, ν — Nu	Φ, φ — Phi
Z, ζ — Zeta	Ξ, ξ — Xi	X, χ — Chi
H, η — Eta	O, o — Omicron	Ψ, ψ — Psi
Θ, θ — Theta	Π, π — Pi	Ω, ω — Omega

PLANE TRIGONOMETRY

CHAPTER I

THE TRIGONOMETRIC FUNCTIONS*

1. A problem of measurement and a graphical solution. — It is desired to build a bridge across a certain river, and in order to do so it is necessary to find the width of the river. Instruments are available, of course, for measuring angles and distances on land with the necessary accuracy. The problem is to devise a method by which, from such measurements, one can find the distance across the stream, where no direct measurement is possible.

To carry out the solution, place marks at two points, A and B, on opposite banks of the stream. With an instrument placed at A, establish a line AM at right angles to AB, and along AM measure any convenient distance, AC. With an instrument at C then measure the angle ACB. Suppose that in the present case the distance AC is taken equal to 800 feet, and that, on measurement, the angle ACB is found to be equal to 71°. The distance AB can now be found graphically as follows: Construct on paper a triangle $A'B'C'$

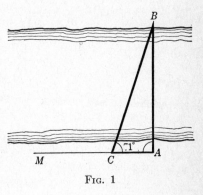

Fig. 1

similar to ABC, making the angle at A' a right angle, and with

---

* After reading Articles 1 and 2, the reader may proceed at once to Chapter II, and complete Chapter I after reading Chapters II, III, and IV. This order is recommended for those wishing a very short course.

1

a protractor make the angle at C' equal to 71°. The side $A'B'$ can be measured. And since the triangles are similar, AB can be found from the proportion

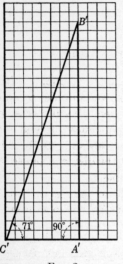

(1) $AB : AC = A'B' : A'C'$

where AB is the only unknown.

For convenience use paper ruled into squares and allow one space on the paper to represent some distance, say 100 feet, of the problem. Then $A'C'$, which corresponds to 800 feet, is 8 spaces. We read off the distance $A'B'$, which is about 23.2 spaces, and conclude that, approximately,

(2) $AB = 2320$ feet.

The accuracy of this result is limited by errors made in measuring the angles at A and C and the distance AC, and also, probably to even a greater extent, by inaccuracies in constructing the angle at C' and reading the distance $A'B'$.

Fig. 2

EXERCISES

Using Figure 2, determine AB for each of the following measurements of AC, assuming that angle $ACB = 71°$.

1. $AC = 1000$ ft.   *Ans.* $AB = 2900$ ft.   **2.** $AC = 1000$ yds.

3. $AC = 300$ rds.   *Ans.* $AB = 870$ rds.   **4.** $AC = 30$ rds.

Using Figure 3, determine AB for each of the following pairs of measurements. Do not draw lines nor mark on the figure, but indicate angles by a celluloid ruler or a thread stretched through the center of the circle.

5. $AC = 1000$ ft., $\angle ACB = 61°$.   *Ans.* 1800 ft.

6. $AC = 700$ ft., $\angle ACB = 58°$.

7. $AC = 1100$ ft., $\angle ACB = 42°$.   *Ans.* 990 ft.

8. $AC = 900$ ft., $\angle ACB = 39°$.

9. $AC = 800$ ft., $\angle ACB = 52° 30'$. *Ans.* 1040 ft.
10. $AC = 650$ ft., $\angle ACB = 31°$.

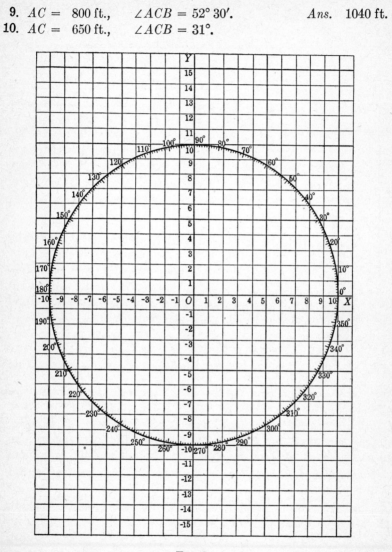

Fig. 3

2. Another solution. — From equation (2), Article **1**, we have:

$$\frac{AB}{AC} = \frac{2320}{800} = 2.9.$$

From the results of Exercise 1, Article **1**, we find

$$\frac{AB}{AC} = \frac{2900}{1000} = 2.9,$$

and from Exercise 3,

$$\frac{AB}{AC} = \frac{870}{300} = 2.9.$$

The ratio AB/AC evidently retains the value 2.9, regardless of the length of AC. Indeed, since the right triangles are similar, this ratio must remain constant so long as the angle ACB remains equal to 71°. A change in the value of the angle ACB carries with it a change in the ratio AB/AC. This ratio, then, is a number which is independent of the dimensions of the triangle, and is determined solely by the magnitude of the angle ACB. The ratio AB/AC, since it depends for its value on the value of the angle, is said to be a *function* of the angle ACB.

This function is called *the tangent of the angle ACB*, a statement which we may write in the following form:

(1) $$\frac{AB}{AC} = \tan \angle ACB.$$

A general definition of the tangent of an angle is given in Article **8**. We have seen that when $\angle ACB = 71°$, $AB/AC = 2.9$, so that $\tan 71° = 2.9$.

Had we but known this value for $\tan 71°$, we could have solved the problem of Article **1**, without incurring the inaccuracy and inconvenience of the graphical method. For, since $AC = 800$ ft., by equation (1)

$$AB = 800 \times \tan 71° = 800 \times 2.9 = 2320 \text{ ft.}$$

The solution which uses the tangent of the angle ACB is both more accurate and more convenient than the graphical method, for tables have been made which give very exactly the value of the tangent of any angle.

EXERCISES

1. A table gives tan $71° = 2.9042$. Use this value to obtain a better answer to the problem of Article **1**.   *Ans.* 2323 ft.

2. Solve Exercises **5** to **10**, Article **1**, using the following values:

$$\text{tan } 31° = .601, \qquad \text{tan } 39° \quad = .810,$$
$$\text{tan } 42° = .9004, \qquad \text{tan } 52° \ 30' = 1.303,$$
$$\text{tan } 58° = 1.600, \qquad \text{tan } 61° \quad = 1.804.$$

Ans.   **(5)** 1804 ft.,   **(7)** 990 ft.,   **(9)** 1042 ft.

Using Figure 3, find the values of

3. tan 27° 30′.   *Ans.*   .52.   **4.** tan 11°.
5. tan 55°.   *Ans.*   1.43.   **6.** tan 45°.
7. tan 60°.   *Ans.*   1.7.   **8.** tan 75°.
9. tan 32°.   *Ans.*   .62.   **10.** tan 25°.

Using Figure 3, find an angle C, such that

11. tan $C = 1.1$.   *Ans.* $C = 48°$.   **12.** tan $C = .51$.
13. tan $C = .65$.   *Ans.* $C = 33°$.   **14.** tan $C = .36$.
15. tan $C = .70$.   *Ans.* $C = 35°$.   **16.** tan $C = .23$.
17. tan $C = 4.0$.   *Ans.* $C = 76°$.   **18.** tan $C = .87$.

3. Directed distances.* — The next five articles deal with topics necessary for understanding a general definition of the tangent and of certain other functions of an angle.

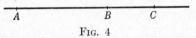

FIG. 4

If a point moves in a straight line from a point A to a point C, it traces out the *line-segment* AC. We call A the *initial point* and C the

* See footnote, page 1.

terminal point of the segment. We also denote by AC the distance from A to C or the length of AC expressed in some chosen unit. If B is a point on the line between A and C, in tracing AC the moving point traces the segments AB and BC, and

$$AB + BC = AC.$$

In order that this rule may hold even when B is not between A and C, distances measured in one direction along any given line will be counted positive, and distances in the opposite direction will be counted negative. That is, $AB = -BA$, or

(1) $$AB + BA = 0.$$

If a point starts at A and, after moving back and forth along the line in any way, ultimately arrives at C, the algebraic sum of all the distances traversed by the point is AC. For every segment except AC is traversed the same number of times in each direction, and the sum of the lengths of these other segments is zero. In particular, if the tracing point moves from A to B and then to C, we have

(2) $$AB + BC = AC,$$

for all arrangements of the points on a straight line.

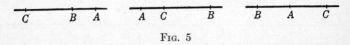

FIG. 5

4. The coördinate system. — Consider two straight lines drawn at right angles to each other in a plane. One of them, OX, usually taken horizontally, we shall call the x-axis, while the vertical line, OY, will be called the y-axis. Their point of intersection, O, is the *origin*. We choose some unit of length in which to express distances, and agree that distances measured along any line which is parallel to OX are to be counted positive if measured to the right, and negative if measured to the left. Distances along any line parallel to OY are positive if measured upward, negative if measured downward.

Now let P be any point of the plane, and let its distance from OY be x and its distance from OX be y. Then x is said to be the *abscissa* of the point P, and y is the *ordinate* of P. The position of P is determined if these two numbers or *coördinates*, x and y, are known, and P is commonly denoted as the point (x, y). The points $(-4, 6)$, $(-6, -5)$ and $(7, -3)$ are marked in Figure 6.

The distance of the point P from the origin is called the *radius vector* of P. This distance r is counted

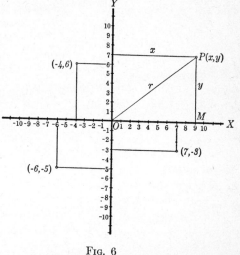

FIG. 6

positive, regardless of the signs of x and y. From the triangle OMP, $r = \sqrt{x^2 + y^2}$.

The axes of coördinates divide the plane into four *quadrants* which are numbered as in Figure 7. This figure also shows the signs of the coördinates of points in the different quadrants.

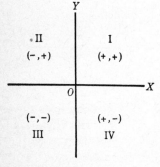

FIG. 7

EXERCISES

For careful plotting, the student should use printed "cross-section" or "coördinate" paper. For hurried work, or at the blackboard, mark a scale of points on each axis, and then estimate distances by the eye or with a measure.

1. Plot the points: $(2, 1), (4, 7), (6, 6), (-2, 4), (-5, 2), (-4, -3),$ $(-5, -5), (4, -1), (2, -8), (\sqrt{5}, 3), (-1, -\sqrt{3}), (\pi, 4), (2, \pi), (0, 3),$ $(0, 0), (6, 0), (-3, 0), (0, -4), (7/2, 2), (-2/3, 5/2).$

2. In Figure 3, give the coördinates for the point at which the degree sign (°) is printed for each of the angles 0°, 10°, 20°, etc.

Using Figure 3, find the value of the angle XOP to the nearest degree for each of the following positions of P.

3. $(10, 4)$.	*Ans.*	22°.	**4.** $(8, 7)$.
5. $(4, 8)$.	*Ans.*	63°.	**6.** $(2, 4)$.
7. $(13, 0)$.	*Ans.*	0°.	**8.** $(0, 5)$.
9. $(-3, 10)$.	*Ans.*	107°.	**10.** $(-12, 5)$.
11. $(-9, 3)$.	*Ans.*	162°.	**12.** $(-12, 4)$.
13. $(-6, 2)$.	*Ans.*	162°.	**14.** $(-3/2, 12)$.

Denote by A the foot of the perpendicular drawn from a point B to the x-axis, and find the value of tan $\angle AOB$ for each of the following positions of B.

15. $(4, 12)$.	*Ans.*	tan $\angle AOB = 3$.	**16.** $(3, 9)$.
17. $(4, 5)$.	*Ans.*	tan $\angle AOB = 5/4$.	**18.** $(3, 3)$.
19. $(\pi, 1)$.	*Ans.*	tan $\angle AOB = 1/\pi$.	**20.** $(5, 10)$.

Find the radius vector of each of the following points.

21. $(3, 4)$.	*Ans.*	5.	**22.** $(12, 5)$.
23. $(15, 8)$.	*Ans.*	17.	**24.** $(2, 1)$.
25. $(5, -12)$.	*Ans.*	13.	**26.** $(-4, 3)$.
27. $(-1, 1)$.	*Ans.*	$\sqrt{2}$.	**28.** (x, y).

5. The generation of angles. — If a straight line, l, revolves in a plane about a point O from the position OA to the position OC, it sweeps out or generates the *angle AOC*. The lines OA and OC are called the *sides* of the angle AOC, OA being the *initial side*, and OC being the *terminal side* of the angle.

When there is no possibility of confusion, an angle may be denoted by the same single letter as its vertex, or by some different letter (usually a Greek letter) designated for the purpose. For example, we may say

$$\angle AOC = \angle O = \theta.$$

If *OB* is a line lying between *OA* and *OC*, in revolving from the position *OA* to *OC*, the generating line sweeps out first the angle *AOB*, then the angle *BOC*, and in all, the angle *AOC*. We can thus add angles and write

$$\angle AOB + \angle BOC = \angle AOC.$$

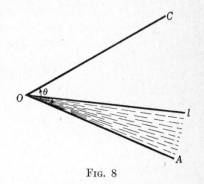

FIG. 8

6. General and directed angles. — It has been customary in elementary geometry to consider all angles as positive and as limited to values less than four right angles. These restrictions are not necessary and it is now desirable to do away with them.

We shall call certain angles positive and others negative, the sign of an angle depending on the direction of rotation of the line which generated it. An angle which is generated by a line revolving in a *counter-clockwise* sense (that is, in the opposite direc-

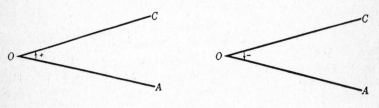

FIG. 9

tion from that in which a hand of a clock moves) is counted positive. And an angle generated by a line turning in a clockwise direction is negative.

In Figure 9, $\angle AOC$ is positive and $\angle COA$ is negative. In fact
$$\angle COA = -\angle AOC.$$

We shall place no limit on the magnitude of an angle. During one complete counter-clockwise revolution a line sweeps out all angles from 0° to 360°. But it may continue to turn. During its second revolution it completes the generation of angles between 360° and 720°; during the next revolution it finishes generating the angles from 720° to 1080°, etc., without arbitrary limit.

We thus see that two lines OA and OC may serve as the initial and terminal sides respectively not merely of a single angle AOC, but of countless angles, some positive and some negative.

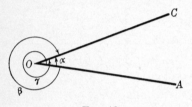

In Figure 10, for example, the angle AOC may have any one of the values $\alpha = 30°$, $\beta = -330°$, $\gamma = 390°$, etc.

The value of an angle AOC therefore depends not only on the positions of the initial side

Fig. 10

OA and of the terminal side OC, but also on the direction and extent of rotation of the generating line. Any two values of AOC will differ by some multiple of 360°.

Thus, in the figure, $\alpha - \gamma = 30° - 390° = -360°$; $\alpha - \beta = 30° - (-330°) = 360°$; $\gamma - \beta = 390° - (-330°) = 2 \times 360°$.

EXERCISES

Draw the following angles, and indicate by arrows, as in Figure 10, the direction and extent of the rotation. In each case name two other angles, one positive and one negative, having the same initial and terminal sides.

1. 90°.	**2.** −90°.	**3.** 135°.
4. −135°.	**5.** 180°.	**6.** −180°.
7. 270°.	**8.** −270°.	**9.** 300°.
10. 360°.	**11.** −390°.	**12.** 450°.
13. −600°.	**14.** 1035°.	**15.** −120°.

7. The standard position of an angle. — An angle is said to be in *standard position* with reference to a system of coördinates, if its vertex is at the origin and if its initial side extends along the positive *x*-axis. We speak of an angle as being in, say, the second quadrant, if, when it is placed in standard position, its terminal side lies in the second quadrant. We use similar expressions, of course, for the other quadrants.

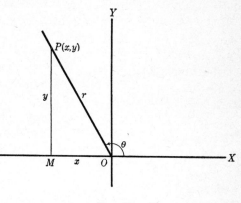

Fig. 11

The angles 120°, −210°, and 510°, for example, are in the second quadrant, while 65° is in the first, −100° is in the third, and 300° is in the fourth quadrant. Positive angles between 0° and 90° are in the first quadrant; angles between 90° and 180° are in the second, angles between 180° and 270° are in the third, and angles between 270° and 360° are in the fourth quadrant.

EXERCISES

Using Figure 3, find one positive and one negative value of the angle *XOP*, for each of the following positions of *P*, giving the results correctly to the nearest degree.

1. $(-7, 7)$.   *Ans.* 135°, −225°.   **2.** $(-6, 6)$.

3. $(5, -7)$.   *Ans.* 306°, −54°.   **4.** $(10, -3)$.

5. $(8, 0)$.   *Ans.* 360°, −360°.   **6.** $(0, -3)$.

7. $(-7, -10)$.   *Ans.* 235°, −125°.   **8.** $(8, 1)$.

8. Definition of the trigonometric functions of an angle. — In Article **2** we defined, for any *acute* angle, a number which we called its tangent. Now we shall give definitions of the tangent and of five other functions of an angle which will be applicable to *any* angle, θ, whatsoever. These six quantities, called trigonometric functions of θ, are the sine, the cosine, the tangent, the cotangent, the secant, and the cosecant of θ, which are written $\sin \theta$, $\cos \theta$, $\tan \theta$, $\cot \theta$, $\sec \theta$, $\csc \theta$, respectively. *Definition: Place the angle θ in standard position with reference to a coördinate system, and choose any point, P, on the terminal side of θ. Let the coördinates of this point be (x, y) and its distance from the origin be r. Then*

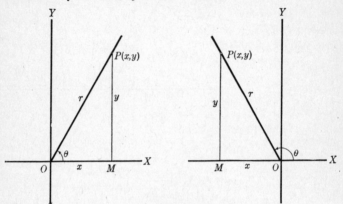

FIG. 12

$$\sin \theta = \frac{\text{ordinate of } P}{\text{radius vector of } P} = \frac{y}{r},$$

$$\cos \theta = \frac{\text{abscissa of } P}{\text{radius vector of } P} = \frac{x}{r},$$

$$\tan \theta = \frac{\text{ordinate of } P}{\text{abscissa of } P} = \frac{y}{x},$$

$$\cot \theta = \frac{\text{abscissa of } P}{\text{ordinate of } P} = \frac{x}{y},$$

$$\sec \theta = \frac{\text{radius vector of } P}{\text{abscissa of } P} = \frac{r}{x},$$

$$\csc \theta = \frac{\text{radius vector of } P}{\text{ordinate of } P} = \frac{r}{y}.$$

These quantities,* although defined in terms of the coördinates of the point P, are nevertheless true functions of θ. That is, their values depend solely on the value of θ, and not on the particular point P which we choose on the terminal side of θ. For if we choose any other point, P', on OP, with coördinates (x', y') and radius vector r', from the similarity of the triangles OMP and $OM'P'$, we have

$$\frac{y'}{r'} = \frac{y}{r},$$

so that the value of $\sin \theta$ is the same whether we obtain it using P' or using P. The

Fɪɢ. 13

student should write the corresponding equations for the other functions.

Two numbers are said to be *reciprocals* each of the other, if their product is equal to 1. Thus 3 and 1/3, and 2/5 and 5/2 are pairs of reciprocals. If a and b are reciprocals $a = 1/b$.

Since, by definition, $\sin \theta = y/r$ and $\csc \theta = r/y$, these functions are reciprocals each of the other. That is,

$$\csc \theta = \frac{1}{\sin \theta}.$$

* Two other functions are sometimes used, particularly in laying out railroad curves. They are the *versed sine* of θ and the *coversed sine* of θ, defined as

$$vers\ \theta = 1 - \cos \theta,$$
$$covers\ \theta = 1 - \sin \theta.$$

We shall make no further reference to these functions.

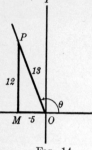

Fig. 14

Likewise $\qquad \sec \theta = \dfrac{1}{\cos \theta}$,

and $\qquad \cot \theta = \dfrac{1}{\tan \theta}$.

EXAMPLE 1. Find the trigonometric functions of the angle XOP, if the coördinates of P are $(-5,12)$.

The radius vector is

$$r = \sqrt{x^2 + y^2} = \sqrt{(-5)^2 + (12)^2} = 13.$$

Therefore, by definition,

$$\sin \theta = \frac{y}{r} = \frac{12}{13} = .923, \qquad \cos \theta = \frac{x}{r} = \frac{-5}{13} = -.385,$$

$$\tan \theta = \frac{y}{x} = \frac{12}{-5} = -\frac{12}{5} = -2.40, \qquad \cot \theta = \frac{x}{y} = \frac{-5}{12} = -.417,$$

$$\sec \theta = \frac{r}{x} = -\frac{13}{5} = -2.60, \qquad \csc \theta = \frac{r}{y} = \frac{13}{12} = 1.083.$$

The last three values might have been obtained from the first three by the reciprocal relations. That is, since

$$\sin \theta = 12/13, \qquad \csc \theta = 13/12;$$

since $\qquad \cos \theta = -5/13, \qquad \sec \theta = -13/5;$

since $\qquad \tan \theta = -12/5, \qquad \cot \theta = -5/12.$

EXAMPLE 2. Find the trigonometric functions of $270°$.

Place the angle in standard position, and as P choose a convenient point, say $(0,-8)$. Then $r = +8$, since r is always counted positive. Then, from the definitions,

$$\sin 270° = \frac{y}{r} = \frac{-8}{8} = -1, \qquad \cos 270° = \frac{x}{r} = \frac{0}{8} = 0.$$

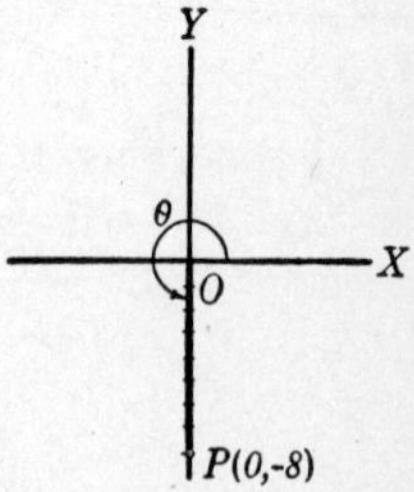

If we try to find $\tan \theta$, we are tempted to write

$$\tan \theta = \frac{y}{x} = \frac{-8}{0};$$

Fig. 15

but, since division by zero has no meaning, evidently there is no such thing as tan 270°. Likewise sec 270° does not exist, since r/x or $8/0$ is without meaning. But

$$\cot 270° = \frac{x}{y} = \frac{0}{-8} = 0, \qquad \csc 270° = \frac{r}{y} = \frac{8}{-8} = -1.$$

EXAMPLE 3. Find the trigonometric functions of 214°. From Figure 3, we see that the point $(-9, -6)$ lies on the terminal side of the angle 214°. Let us use $(-9, -6)$ as the point P. Then

$$r = \sqrt{(-9)^2 + (-6)^2} = \sqrt{117} = 10.8.$$

Therefore

$$\sin 214° = \frac{y}{r} = \frac{-6}{10.8} = -.56, \qquad \cos 214° = \frac{x}{r} = \frac{-9}{10.8} = -.83,$$

$$\tan 214° = \frac{y}{x} = \frac{-6}{-9} = .67, \qquad \cot 214° = \frac{x}{y} = \frac{-9}{-6} = 1.5,$$

$$\sec 214° = \frac{r}{x} = \frac{10.8}{-9} = -1.2, \qquad \csc 214° = \frac{r}{y} = \frac{10.8}{-6} = -1.8.$$

Second solution. — In Figure 3, the radius of the circle is 10. As the point P, take the point on the circle corresponding to 214°. Its coördinates are $(-8.3, -5.6)$ and $r = 10$. Therefore $\sin 214° = y/r = -.56$, $\cos 214° = -.83$. To find the tangent take P as the point where the terminal side of 214° meets the line for which $x = -10$, the vertical tangent to the circle. Its coördinates are $(-10, -6.7)$. Therefore $\tan 214° = y/x = .67$. If we take P on the horizontal tangent to the circle, its coördinates are $(-15, -10)$, and $\cot \theta = x/y = 1.5$.

EXERCISES

ORAL EXERCISES

Find the value of r for each of the following positions of P, and then find the trigonometric functions of the angle XOP. Do not reduce the answers to decimal form.

1. $(3, -4)$.

Ans. $r = 5$, $\sin \theta = -4/5$, $\cos \theta = 3/5$, $\tan \theta = -4/3$, etc.

2. $(-8, 6)$. **3.** $(2, 3)$. **4.** $(-4, -3)$.

5. $(5, 12)$. **6.** $(-12, 5)$. **7.** $(-5, -12)$.

8. $(1, 1)$. **9.** $(-1, 1)$. **10.** $(1, -1)$.

11. (2, 2).   12. (−2, 2).   13. (2, −2).
14. (−3, 4).   15. (−3, −4).   16. (−12, −5).
17. (6, 8).   18. (−6, 8).   19. (−6, −8).
20. (0, 2).   21. (2, 0).   22. (−3, 0).

23. For which quadrants is

     (a) sin θ positive;   (b) sin θ negative;
     (c) cos θ positive;   (d) cos θ negative;
     (e) tan θ positive;   (f) cot θ negative;
     (g) sec θ positive;   (h) csc θ positive?

24. The signs of sin θ and csc θ are always the same. (a) Why is this true? (b) What other function always has the same sign as cos θ? (c) What function has the same sign as tan θ?

25. In what quadrant is θ in each of the following cases?

     (a) sin θ and cos θ are both positive.
     (b) sin θ is positive, cos θ is negative.
     (c) sin θ and cos θ are negative.
     (d) sin θ is negative, cos θ is positive.

26. Work Exercise 25 using tan θ first instead of cos θ and then instead of sin θ.

WRITTEN EXERCISES

Using Figure 3, find the values of the sine, cosine, tangent and cotangent of the following angles correctly to one figure in every case and correctly to two figures when possible.

27.	49°.	*Ans.*	.75, .66, 1.2, .87.	28.	65°.	
29.	29°.	*Ans.*	.48, .87, .55, 1.8.	30.	14°.	
31.	148°.	*Ans.*	.53, −.85, −.62, −1.6.	32.	165°.	
33.	240°.	*Ans.*	−.87, −.50, 1.7, .58.	34.	209°.	
35.	0°.	*Ans.*	0, 1, 0, —.	36.	180°.	
37.	90°.	*Ans.*	1, 0, —, 0.	38.	−90°.	
39.	301°.	*Ans.*	−.86, .52, −1.7, −.60.	40.	339°.	
41.	−50°.	*Ans.*	−.77, .64, −1.2, −.84.	42.	−69°.	
43.	421°.	*Ans.*	.87, .48, 1.8, .55.	44.	824°.	

9. The determination of one function from another. — If we know the quadrant in which an angle lies, and have the value of one of its trigonometric functions, we can find the values of its other trigonometric functions. Formulas by which this can be done algebraically will be given in Article **68**. The geometrical method is illustrated in the following examples.

EXAMPLE 1. Given that θ is an angle in the second quadrant and that $\tan \theta = -4/5$, find the other functions of θ. Any point (x,y) in the second quadrant is a point on the terminal side of θ, if $y/x = \tan \theta = -4/5$. In particular, the point $(-5,4)$ is such a point. The point $(-10,8)$ or the point $(-5/2,2)$ would serve equally well, but we prefer $(-5,4)$ as being simpler. Then $r = \sqrt{16 + 25} = \sqrt{41}$. Therefore,

$$\sin \theta = \frac{y}{r} = \frac{4}{\sqrt{41}}, \qquad \cos \theta = \frac{x}{r} = \frac{-5}{\sqrt{41}},$$

$$\cot \theta = \frac{-5}{4}, \qquad \sec \theta = \frac{\sqrt{41}}{-5}, \qquad \csc \theta = \frac{\sqrt{41}}{4}.$$

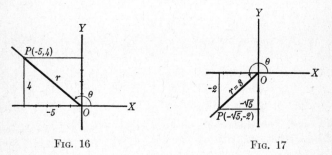

FIG. 16   FIG. 17

EXAMPLE 2. Given that $\sin \theta = -2/3$ and that θ is in the third quadrant. Find the other functions of θ. The point in the third quadrant for which $y = -2$ and $r = 3$ must lie on the terminal side of θ. From the relation $x^2 + y^2 = r^2$, $x = -\sqrt{r^2 - y^2} = -\sqrt{9 - 4} = -\sqrt{5}$. Therefore $\sin \theta = \frac{-2}{3}$, $\cos \theta = \frac{-\sqrt{5}}{3}$, $\tan \theta = \frac{2}{\sqrt{5}} = \frac{2}{5}\sqrt{5}$, $\cot \theta = \frac{\sqrt{5}}{2}$, $\sec \theta = \frac{-3}{\sqrt{5}} = -\frac{3}{5}\sqrt{5}$, $\csc \theta = \frac{-3}{2}$.

In general, the method consists in finding from the given conditions a point on the terminal side of the angle, and then using the coordinates and radius vector of this point in the definitions of the functions of an angle in order to obtain their values.

EXERCISES

In each of the following examples, find the functions of an angle which satisfies the given conditions.

1. $\tan \theta = \frac{2}{3}$, θ in first quadrant.

Ans. $\frac{2}{13}\sqrt{13}$, $\frac{3}{13}\sqrt{13}$, $\frac{3}{2}$, $\frac{1}{3}\sqrt{13}$, $\frac{1}{2}\sqrt{13}$.

2. $\cot \theta = \frac{4}{3}$, θ in first quadrant.

3. $\sin \theta = .4$, θ in first quadrant.

Ans. $\frac{1}{5}\sqrt{21}$, $\frac{2}{21}\sqrt{21}$, $\frac{1}{2}\sqrt{21}$, $\frac{5}{21}\sqrt{21}$, $\frac{5}{2}$.

4. $\cos \theta = \frac{6}{11}$, θ in first quadrant.

5. $\sin \theta = \frac{3}{5}$, θ in second quadrant. *Ans.* $-\frac{4}{5}$, $-\frac{3}{4}$, $-\frac{4}{3}$, $-\frac{5}{4}$, $\frac{5}{3}$.

6. $\cos \theta = -\frac{2}{5}$, θ in second quadrant.

7. $\tan \theta = 2$, θ in third quadrant.

Ans. $-\frac{2}{5}\sqrt{5}$, $-\frac{1}{5}\sqrt{5}$, $\frac{1}{2}$, $-\sqrt{5}$, $-\frac{1}{2}\sqrt{5}$.

8. $\cos \theta = -\frac{1}{2}$, θ in third quadrant.

9. $\sin \theta = -\frac{5}{13}$, θ in fourth quadrant.

Ans. $\frac{12}{13}$, $-\frac{5}{12}$, $-\frac{12}{5}$, $\frac{13}{12}$, $-\frac{13}{5}$.

10. $\cos \theta = \frac{8}{17}$, θ in fourth quadrant.

11. $\sin \theta = \frac{4}{5}$, $\cos \theta = -\frac{3}{5}$. *Ans.* $-\frac{4}{3}$, $-\frac{3}{4}$, $-\frac{5}{3}$, $\frac{5}{4}$.

12. $\tan \theta = \frac{8}{15}$, $\cos \theta$ negative.

CHAPTER II

THE TRIGONOMETRIC FUNCTIONS OF AN ACUTE ANGLE*

10. The trigonometric functions of an acute angle. — Consider a right triangle, ABC, in which the right angle is at C. Let α denote the angle at the vertex A, and β the angle at the vertex B. Denote by a, b, and c the lengths of the sides which are opposite the vertices A, B, and C respectively.

Note: This notation will be used regularly. Unless it is otherwise stated, in a triangle whose vertices are the points A, B, C, the letters α, β, γ will denote the angles at those vertices, and a, b, c will denote the lengths of the respectively opposite sides. In a *right* triangle, γ will ordinarily be the right angle.

The six trigonometric functions of the acute angle α are then

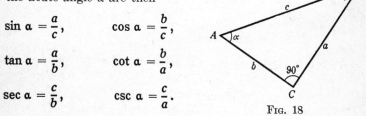

$$\sin \alpha = \frac{a}{c}, \qquad \cos \alpha = \frac{b}{c},$$

$$\tan \alpha = \frac{a}{b}, \qquad \cot \alpha = \frac{b}{a},$$

$$\sec \alpha = \frac{c}{b}, \qquad \csc \alpha = \frac{c}{a}.$$

Fig. 18

These statements may be expressed as follows: *For an acute angle of any **right** triangle,*
the sine equals the ratio of the opposite side to the hypotenuse;
the cosine equals the ratio of the adjacent side to the hypotenuse;
the tangent equals the ratio of the opposite side to the adjacent side;
the cotangent equals the ratio of the adjacent side to the opposite side;
the secant equals the ratio of the hypotenuse to the adjacent side;
the cosecant equals the ratio of the hypotenuse to the opposite side.

* See footnote, page 1.

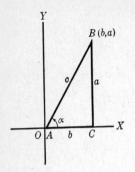

Students who have not read the latter part of Chapter I may accept the foregoing statements as *definitions* of the trigonometric functions of an acute angle. They are valid for all acute angles, since any acute angle may be taken as one of the angles of a right triangle. Definitions that apply to *all* angles are given in Article **8** of Chapter I.

Students who have learned the general definition of Article **8** should consider the statements above as a *theorem*, which may be proved as follows. Draw a set of coördinate axes with the origin at A and the x-axis in the direction AC, placing angle α in standard position. The coördinates of B are (b,a), and its radius vector is c. Therefore, by Article **8**,

$$\sin \alpha = \frac{a}{c}, \qquad \cos \alpha = \frac{b}{c}, \text{ etc.}$$

The relations of this article should be remembered, also, in the following forms:

$$a = c \sin \alpha, \qquad\qquad a = b \tan \alpha,$$
$$b = c \cos \alpha, \qquad\qquad b = a \cot \alpha,$$
$$c = a \csc \alpha, \qquad\qquad c = b \sec \alpha.$$

11. The variation of the functions of an acute angle. — For a hypotenuse, c, of given length, the larger the angle α, the larger is the value of a and the smaller is the value of b. Therefore, by the relations of Article **10**, when an acute angle increases, its sine, tangent, and secant increase, and its cosine, cotangent, and cosecant decrease. Since a and b are always less than c, the sine and cosine of an acute angle are always less than 1 and the secant and cosecant are always greater than 1. The tangent and cotangent have no such fixed limits.

12. The functions of complementary angles. — If we apply the statements of Article **10** to the angle β instead of to α, since a is now the adjacent side and b is the opposite side, we find that

$$\sin \beta = \frac{b}{c} = \cos \alpha, \qquad\qquad \cos \beta = \frac{c}{c} = \sin \alpha,$$

$$\tan \beta = \frac{b}{a} = \cot \alpha, \qquad\qquad \cot \beta = \frac{a}{b} = \tan \alpha,$$

$$\sec \beta = \frac{c}{a} = \csc \alpha, \qquad\qquad \csc \beta = \frac{c}{b} = \sec \alpha.$$

The sine and cosine are said to be *cofunctions,* each of the other, as are also the tangent and cotangent, and the secant and cosecant. Inasmuch as any two complementary acute angles can be taken as the acute angles, α and β, of a right triangle, we have the

Theorem. *Any trigonometric function of a positive acute angle is equal to the corresponding cofunction of the complementary angle.*

13. The trigonometric functions of 45°. —
It is very easy to compute the values of the trigonometric functions of the angles 30°, 45° and 60°, and it is useful to remember them. In this article we compute the values for 45°.

Draw a right triangle with the acute angle, α, equal to 45°, the length of the opposite side a equal to one unit. Then we also have $\beta = 45°$ and $b = 1$. Since $a^2 + b^2 = c^2$, $c = \sqrt{1 + 1} = \sqrt{2}$.

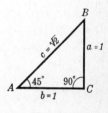

Fig. 20

From Article **10**, we have

$$\sin 45° = \frac{a}{c} = \frac{1}{\sqrt{2}} = \tfrac{1}{2}\sqrt{2}, \qquad \cos 45° = \frac{b}{c} = \tfrac{1}{2}\sqrt{2},$$

$$\tan 45° = \frac{a}{b} = 1, \qquad\qquad\qquad \cot 45° = \frac{b}{a} = 1,$$

$$\sec 45° = \frac{c}{b} = \frac{\sqrt{2}}{1} = \sqrt{2}, \qquad\qquad \csc 45° = \frac{c}{a} = \sqrt{2}.$$

14. The trigonometric functions of 60° and 30°. — Draw an equilateral triangle, ABD, making the length of each side equal to 2 units. From B draw BC perpendicular to AD. It will bisect AD at C. Then in the *right* triangle ABC, $\alpha = 60°$, $\beta = 30°$, $c = 2$, $b = 1$. Moreover $a^2 + b^2 = c^2$, so that $a = \sqrt{c^2 - b^2} = \sqrt{4 - 1} = \sqrt{3}$.

From Article **10**, we get

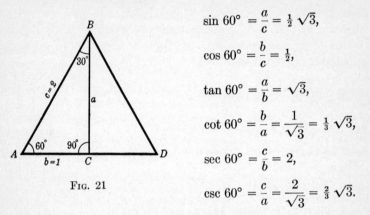

$$\sin 60° = \frac{a}{c} = \tfrac{1}{2}\sqrt{3},$$

$$\cos 60° = \frac{b}{c} = \tfrac{1}{2},$$

$$\tan 60° = \frac{a}{b} = \sqrt{3},$$

$$\cot 60° = \frac{b}{a} = \frac{1}{\sqrt{3}} = \tfrac{1}{3}\sqrt{3},$$

$$\sec 60° = \frac{c}{b} = 2,$$

$$\csc 60° = \frac{c}{a} = \frac{2}{\sqrt{3}} = \tfrac{2}{3}\sqrt{3}.$$

Fig. 21

Functions of 30° are equal to the corresponding cofunctions of 60°, which is the complementary angle. Therefore

$$\sin 30° = \tfrac{1}{2}, \qquad\qquad \cos 30° = \tfrac{1}{2}\sqrt{3},$$
$$\tan 30° = \tfrac{1}{3}\sqrt{3}, \qquad\qquad \cot 30° = \sqrt{3},$$
$$\sec 30° = \tfrac{2}{3}\sqrt{3}, \qquad\qquad \csc 30° = 2.$$

The student should memorize the following table:

θ	30°	45°	60°
$\sin \theta$	$\tfrac{1}{2}\sqrt{1}$	$\tfrac{1}{2}\sqrt{2}$	$\tfrac{1}{2}\sqrt{3}$
$\cos \theta$	$\tfrac{1}{2}\sqrt{3}$	$\tfrac{1}{2}\sqrt{2}$	$\tfrac{1}{2}\sqrt{1}$

15. Tables of trigonometric functions. — *Four-place tables.* In Table IV, pages 92–96 of the tables, are columns headed "Sine," "Tangent," "Cotangent," "Cosine." These give the values of these four functions to four decimal places for acute angles at intervals of

10′. The secant and cosecant, if needed, can be found as reciprocals of the cosine and sine.

There are two problems involved in the use of the tables: (*a*) given an angle, to find the corresponding value of a function, and (*b*) given the value of a function, to find the angle to which it corresponds. The methods are illustrated in the following examples.

16. A function of a given angle. —

EXAMPLE 1. Find sin 28° 20′. On page 95, in the column headed "Degrees," we find the entry 28° 20′ and opposite this entry, in the column headed "Sine," we find the number .4746. So sin 28° 20′ = .4746. In the same line, in the other columns, we find tan 28° 20′ = .5392, cot 28° 20′ = 1.8546, cos 28° 20′ = .8802.

EXAMPLE 2. Find sin 56° 40′. In the column marked "Degrees" at the top the entries go only to 45°. But in the column at the right, marked "Degrees" at the bottom, the entries read *upward* from 45° to 90°. In fact, for any row in the table, the angle at the left and the angle at the right are complementary angles, and consequently an entry in any column gives one function of the angle marked at the left and the corresponding cofunction of the complementary angle which is marked at the right. By this arrangement each entry of the table is made to do double service, with consequent economy in printing and using the table. In seeking a function of an angle entered in the column at the right, we must use the designation of the function which is printed at the bottom. The entry for 56° 40′ is on page 95, and we find sin 56° 40′ = .8355. Likewise tan 56° 40′ = 1.5204, cot 56° 40′ = .6577, cos 56° 40′ = .5495.

EXERCISES

From Table IV find the sine, cosine, tangent and cotangent of each of the following angles.

1. sin 11° 20′.	**2.** cos 6° 50′.	**3.** tan 17° 0′.
4. cot 23° 40′.	**5.** sin 33° 30′.	**6.** cos 40° 10′.
7. sin 81° 40′.	**8.** cos 69° 0′.	**9.** tan 49° 50′.
10. cot 76° 50′.	**11.** tan 61° 0′.	**12.** cot 52° 20′.

17. Interpolation. — When we wish to find a number which is not given in the tables, but lies between two entries of a table, we resort to the method of *interpolation*.

EXAMPLE 1. Find sin 34° 27′. The angle 34° 27′ lies between the two entries 34° 20′ and 34° 30′. The difference between two successive entries in the table is called the *tabular difference*. From the tables we find

$$\text{sin } 34° 20' = .5640$$
$$\text{sin } 34° 30' = .5664$$

Tabular Difference = .0024.

It is not correct to say that the sine of an angle is proportional to the angle. But for small changes in the angle, the change in the sine is nearly proportional to the change in the angle. And we may assume that *since* 34° 27′ *is* "*seven-tenths of the way*" *from* 34° 20′ *to* 34° 30′ *then* sin 34° 27′ *will also be* "*seven-tenths of the way*" *from* .5640 *to* .5664. We must therefore add to .5640 seven-tenths of the tabular difference .0024. That is

$$\text{sin } 34° 27' = .5640 + .7 \times .0024 = .5640 + .00168 = .56568.$$

We must remember, however, that the tables themselves are accurate only to four decimal places. When we say that sin 34° 20′ = .5640 we mean that sin 34° 30′ is nearer to this number than it is either to .5639 or to .5641. In other words, the entries in the table have been "rounded off" to four places. We should be wrong to expect greater accuracy in our interpolated result than exists in the tables themselves. We therefore "round off" our number to four places, and write sin 34° 27′ = .5657. The work of interpolation should be done mentally about as follows: "Sin 34° 20′ = .5640; the tabular difference is 24 (in the last places); .7 of 24 is 16.8, which we call 17; this number added to .5640 gives sin 34° 27′ = .5657." Only the result is to be written down.

EXAMPLE 2. Find cos 34° 27′. The process is the same as in the preceding example, except that since the cosine *decreases* when the angle increases, we must now *subtract* seven-tenths of the tabular difference from cos 34° 20′. We find cos 34° 20′ = .8258; the tabular difference is (8258 − 8241) = 17; .7 × 17 = 11.9, which we call 12 and subtract from 8258. The result is cos 34° 27′ = .8246. The student should verify the following results: tan 34° 27′ = .6860, cot 34° 27′ = 1.4577.

EXAMPLE 3. Find cot 64° 45′. From the table cot 64° 40′ = .4734. The tabular difference is 35, and five-tenths of the difference is 17.5. This number is equally near to 17 and to 18, and there is no logical reason for choosing one in preference to the other. It is well, however, to have some fixed practice, and it is the custom among computers in interpolating to *round off* .5 *so that the result written down is the even rather than the possible odd number. We shall adhere to this rule throughout the book.* In a long piece of computation, the cases in which the result is increased are likely to be nearly balanced by the cases in which the result is diminished. In the present case, if we round off 17.5 to 18, the result is cot 64° 45′ = .4716, which, being even, is accepted as the result. It is the result, rather than the added difference (17 or 18), which is to be even, and the rule is applicable only in case of logical doubt, when it is .5 which is to be rounded off.

EXERCISES

From Table IV find the values of the following functions.

1. cos 8° 13'.	*Ans.* .9898.	**2.** tan 19° 28'.
3. cot 24° 14'.	*Ans.* 2.2217.	**4.** sin 37° 31'.
5. tan 41° 56'.	*Ans.* .8983.	**6.** cot 10° 9'.
7. sin 48° 16'.	*Ans.* .7462.	**8.** cos 57° 57'.
9. sin 74° 31'.	*Ans.* .9637.	**10.** cos 64° 34'.
11. tan 45° 19'.	*Ans.* 1.0111.	**12.** cot 60° 55'.
13. sin 9° 35'.	*Ans.* .1664.	**14.** tan 27° 45'.

18. The angle corresponding to a given function. —

EXAMPLE 1. Given sin θ = .5225, find the value of θ. Looking in the column headed "Sine," we find the given entry on page 95, and write θ = 31° 30'.

EXAMPLE 2. Find θ if tan θ = 3.9136. This entry is found on page 93 in the column marked "Tangent" at the bottom. It corresponds to θ = 75° 40'.

EXAMPLE 3. Find θ if sin θ = .5531. This entry does not occur in the tables, but is between .5519 = sin 33° 30' and .5544 = sin 33° 40'. We can arrange the numbers as follows.

Angle	Sine	Difference
33° 30'	.5519	
θ	.5531	} 12 } 25
33° 40'	.5544	

Therefore sin θ is "twelve twenty-fifths of the way" from sin 33° 30' to sin 33° 40', and we conclude that θ is "twelve twenty-fifths of the way" from 33° 30' to 33° 40'. Using decimals we get 12/25 = .48 which we call .5. To 33° 30' we therefore add .5 $\times$ 10', and get θ = 33° 35'.

EXAMPLE 4. Find θ, given cos θ = .5164. This number appears between the entries for 58° 50' and 59° 0'. The tabular difference is 25; our difference is 75 − 64 = 11. The proportional part is 11/25, which we call .4, and the angle is θ = 58° 54'.

EXERCISES

From Table IV find an angle corresponding to each of the following functions, giving its value correctly to the nearest minute: (Answers are given after Example **28**.)

1. $\sin \theta = .0669.$	**2.** $\sin \theta = .6338.$	**3.** $\cos \theta = .9781.$
4. $\cos \theta = .9276.$	**5.** $\tan \theta = .1974.$	**6.** $\tan \theta = .6128.$
7. $\cot \theta = 1.3190.$	**8.** $\sin \theta = .9001.$	**9.** $\cos \theta = .5854.$
10. $\cos \theta = .2476.$	**11.** $\tan \theta = 1.6003.$	**12.** $\cot \theta = .3057.$
13. $\sin \theta = .5336.$	**14.** $\sin \theta = .1341.$	**15.** $\cos \theta = .9888.$
16. $\cos \theta = .8456.$	**17.** $\tan \theta = .5727.$	**18.** $\tan \theta = .8251.$
19. $\cot \theta = 1.5927.$	**20.** $\cot \theta = 2.8568.$	**21.** $\sin \theta = .8015.$
22. $\sin \theta = .8776.$	**23.** $\cos \theta = .6521.$	**24.** $\cos \theta = .0939.$
25. $\tan \theta = 1.5007.$	**26.** $\tan \theta = 11.943.$	**27.** $\cot \theta = .2573.$

28. Find the values of the other tabulated functions for each of the angles of Examples **1** to **27**.

Ans.	θ	$\sin \theta$	$\tan \theta$	$\cot \theta$	$\cos \theta$
1.	3° 50′	——	.0670	14.924	.9978.
3.	12° 0′	.2079	.2126	4.7046	——
13.	32° 15′	——	.6310	1.5849	.8458.
15.	8° 35′	.1492	.1510	6.6259	——
17.	29° 48′	.4970	——	1.7461	.8678.
19.	32° 7′	.5316	.6277	——	.8470.
21.	53° 16′	——	1.3400	.7463	.5981.
23.	49° 18′	.7581	1.1626	.8601	——
25.	56° 19′	.8321	——	.6665	.5546.
27.	75° 34′	.9684	3.8855	——	.2493.

19. A five-place table of trigonometric functions. — Table III is similar to Table IV, except that angles are given for every minute and the corresponding values of the functions are given to five places of decimals. It is proper, with this table, to interpolate to or from an angle expressed correctly to the nearest tenth of a minute.

EXAMPLE 1. Find sin 39° 41.3′. On page 87 of the tables, we find

$$\begin{array}{l} \sin 39°\ 41' = .63854 \\ \sin 39°\ 42' = .63877 \\ \hline \text{Tabular difference} = \quad 23 \end{array}$$

Then .3 × 23 = 6.9 which we call 7. We add this to sin 39° 41′, and so obtain sin 39° 41.3′ = .63861.

EXAMPLE 2. Find tan 62° 32.8′. The nearest entry is on page 81. The tabular difference is 14, .8 of which is 11.2. We find tan 62° 32.8′ = 1.9248.

EXAMPLE 3. Find θ, given cot θ = .61831. From page 83,

$$\begin{array}{ll} \cot 58°\ 16' = .61842 \\ \cot 58°\ 17' = .61801 \\ \hline \text{Tabular difference} = \quad 41. \end{array} \qquad \begin{array}{ll} \cot 58°\ 16' = .61842 \\ \cot \quad θ\ = .61831 \\ \hline \text{Our difference} = \quad 11. \end{array}$$

Proportional part = 11/41 or approximately .3. Therefore θ = 58° 16.3′.

EXAMPLE 4. Find θ, given cos θ = .96240. From page 75, the tabular difference = 8, our difference = 6. The proportional part is 6/8, which we round off to .8. Therefore θ = 15° 45.8′.

EXERCISES

Find from Table III the sine, cosine, tangent and cotangent of each of the following angles.

1. 14° 43′.	**2.** 7° 11′.	**3.** 51° 46′.
4. 69° 18′.	**5.** 44° 26′.	**6.** 45° 34′.
7. 31° 58.4′.	**8.** 11° 27.8′.	**9.** 58° 17.3′.
10. 74° 31.9′.	**11.** 77° 23.2′	**12.** 23° 0.6′.
13. 41° 0.2′.	**14.** 81° 40.3′.	**15.** 51° 16.6′.
16. 48° 18.8′.	**17.** 35° 55.5′.	**18.** 28° 8.5′.

Ans.	sin θ	tan θ	cot θ	cos θ
1.	.25404	.26266	3.8073	.96719.
3.	.78550	1.2693	.78786	.61887.
7.	.52953	.62422	1.6020	.84830.
9.	.85070	1.6184	.61789	.52564.
17.	.58672	.72454	1.3802	.80978.

In each of the following cases find θ (between 0° and 90°) correct to the nearest tenth of a minute, and find the values of the other tabulated functions.

19. $\sin \theta = .67666.$	**20.** $\sin \theta = .54000.$	**21.** $\cos \theta = .74002.$
22. $\cos \theta = .95337.$	**23.** $\tan \theta = .18895.$	**24.** $\tan \theta = .93906.$
25. $\cot \theta = 1.2145.$	**26.** $\cot \theta = 2.3201.$	**27.** $\sin \theta = .81412.$
28. $\sin \theta = .92287.$	**29.** $\cos \theta = .70360.$	**30.** $\cos \theta = .59342.$
31. $\tan \theta = 1.4559.$	**32.** $\tan \theta = 1.2002.$	**33.** $\cot \theta = .78269.$

34. $\sin \theta = .48881.$	**35.** $\sin \theta = .46521.$	**36.** $\sin \theta = .62083.$
37. $\sin \theta = .88791.$	**38.** $\sin \theta = .79629.$	**39.** $\cos \theta = .81356.$
40. $\cos \theta = .97314.$	**41.** $\cos \theta = .64137.$	**42.** $\cos \theta = .25286.$
43. $\tan \theta = .64137.$	**44.** $\tan \theta = .27933.$	**45.** $\tan \theta = 1.3860.$
46. $\tan \theta = 2.7844.$	**47.** $\tan \theta = 1.0008.$	**48.** $\cot \theta = 1.8249.$
49. $\cot \theta = 1.2398.$	**50.** $\cot \theta = .97452.$	**51.** $\cot \theta = .06689.$

Ans. **19.** 42° 35′.   **21.** 42° 16′.   **23.** 10° 42′.
    33. 51° 57′.   **35.** 27° 43.4′.   **39.** 35° 33.3′.
    43. 32° 40.5′.   **47.** 45° 1.3′.   **49.** 38° 53.4′.

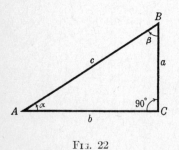

F I G. 22

20. The solution of a right triangle. — Besides its right angle, a right triangle possesses five *parts*, which are its two acute angles and its three sides. If two of these parts are known, at least one of them being a side, it is possible to determine the other three parts. The determination of the unknown parts constitutes a *solution* of the triangle.

For the solution of the right triangle ABC, we have the following formulas.

(1) $a^2 + b^2 = c^2,$ (2) $\alpha + \beta = 90°,$

(3) $\sin \alpha = \dfrac{a}{c} = \cos \beta,$ (4) $\cos \alpha = \dfrac{b}{c} = \sin \beta,$

$$(5) \quad \tan \alpha = \frac{a}{b} = \cot \beta \qquad\qquad (6) \quad \cot \alpha = \frac{b}{a} = \tan \beta.$$

In order to determine an unknown part, select and use one of the formulas which involves that part and no other unknown. As a check against gross errors draw the figure approximately to scale and compare the results with the figure. Methods of checking more closely will be explained in connection with the solutions of triangles by logarithms.

EXAMPLE 1. Solve the right triangle ABC, given

$$c = 21.33, \qquad \alpha = 32° 20'.$$

From formula (2), $\beta = 90° - 32° 20' = 57° 40'$.

From (3), $a = c \times \sin \alpha = 21.33 \times \sin 32° 20' = 21.33 \times .5348 = 11.41$.

From (4), $b = c \times \cos \alpha = 21.33 \times .8450 = 18.02$.

EXAMPLE 2. Solve the right triangle ABC, given

$$a = 10.2, \qquad b = 18.3.$$

From formula (5), $\tan \alpha = \dfrac{a}{b} = \dfrac{10.2}{18.3} = .5574.$

Therefore, by Table IV, $\alpha = 29° 8'$, $\beta = 90° - 29° 8' = 60° 52'$.

By formula (3), $c = \dfrac{a}{\sin \alpha} = \dfrac{10.2}{\sin 29° 8'} = \dfrac{10.2}{.4869} = 20.9.$

EXAMPLE 3. — A radio aërial is to be stretched from the corner of a house to the top of a pole 62 feet away. By sighting, it is observed that the wire will make an angle of 15° with the horizontal. How long must the wire be, if 8% be added to allow for sag and contraction?

In Figure 23, $b = 62$ feet, $\alpha = 15°$.

$$c = \frac{b}{\cos 15°} = \frac{62}{.9659} = 64.2 \text{ feet.}$$

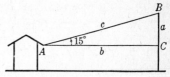

FIG. 23

Adding 8% or 5.1 feet to this, we get 69.3 feet as the length of the wire.

EXERCISES

In the following exercises give angles to the nearest minute. Solve the following right triangles, given:

1. $c = 16.4$, $\alpha = 24° 50'$.

                Ans. $a = 6.89$, $b = 14.88$, $\beta = 65° 10'$.

2. $c = 258$, $\alpha = 57° 30'$.

3. $c = 423.6$, $\alpha = 49° 27'$.

                Ans. $a = 321.85$, $b = 275.38$, $\beta = 40° 33'$.

4. $c = 60.24$, $\alpha = 28° 43'$.

5. $a = 24.6$, $b = 40.4$.

                Ans. $\alpha = 31° 20'$, $\beta = 58° 40'$, $c = 47.3$.

6. $a = 9.07$, $b = 5.63$.

7. $a = 6011$, $b = 8203$.

                Ans. $\alpha = 36° 14'$, $\beta = 53° 46'$, $c = 10170$.

8. $a = .8104$, $b = .5302$.

9. $a = 3.81$, $c = 5.07$.

                Ans. $\alpha = 48° 43'$, $\beta = 41° 17'$, $b = 3.35$.

10. $a = 511.2$, $c = 810.3$.

11. $b = .04318$, $c = .07004$.

                Ans. $\alpha = 51° 57'$, $\beta = 38° 3'$, $a = .05516$.

12. $b = 62.31$, $c = 100.44$.

13. $a = 25.3$, $\alpha = 38° 40'$.

                Ans. $\beta = 51° 20'$, $c = 40.49$, $b = 31.62$.

14. $a = .707$, $\alpha = 65° 22'$.

15. $a = 324.4$, $\beta = 21° 16'$.

                Ans. $\alpha = 68° 44'$, $c = 348.1$, $b = 126.3$.

16. $a = 4.021$, $\beta = 49° 9'$.

21. Angles of elevation and depression. — Suppose that an observer is at a point O, and a certain object is at a point P. The line OP is then called the *line of sight* from the observer to the object. Let OH be drawn horizontally in the vertical plane through OP.

Then the angle *HOP* which the line of sight makes with the horizontal is called the *angle of elevation* of the object *P* from *O* if *P* is higher than *O*, and it is called the *angle of depression* of *P* from *O*, if *P* is lower than *O*.

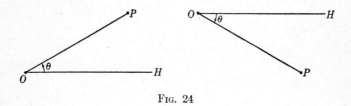

FIG. 24

EXERCISES

These exercises may be worked either with or without logarithms.

1. From a point on the ground 200 feet from the foot of a flagstaff, the angle of elevation of the top is 30°. How high is the flagstaff?

Ans. 115½ ft.

2. From a point 1150 feet from the foot of a cliff, the angle of elevation of the top is 20°. How high is the cliff?

3. If the angle of elevation of the sun is 30° how long a shadow will be cast on the ground by a man 6 feet tall? *Ans.* 10.4 ft.

4. If the angle of elevation of the sun is 60° how long a shadow will be cast on the ground by a spire 140 feet high?

5. Find the angle of elevation of the sun if an object 20 feet high casts a shadow 60 feet long. *Ans.* 18° 26′.

6. What is the angle of elevation of the sun if an object 40 feet high casts a shadow 60 feet long?

7. When the angle of elevation of the sun is 15° 1′, the shadow of the Great Pyramid reaches to a point about 1790 feet from the center of the square base. How high is the pyramid?

Ans. About 480 ft.

Historical note: One of the earliest uses of trigonometry was in determining the heights of the pyramids and other objects by measuring their shadows.

8. The angle of elevation of the sun is 60° and the shadow of a vertical post is 8.7 feet long. How high is the post?

9. The height of the Great Pyramid is about 480 feet and a side of the square base is about 760 feet. What are the angles of inclination of a face and of an edge? *Ans.* 51° 38′, 41° 46′

10. How high is a kite when the length of the string is 600 feet and its angle of elevation is 32°?

11. A ladder 36 feet long reaches from the ground to a window 33 feet high. How far from the wall is its foot, and what angle does it make with the horizontal? *Ans.* 14.4 ft., 66° 27′.

12. A guy wire is stretched from the top of a telephone pole 39 feet high to a stake on the ground 23 feet from the pole. Find the length of this wire and the angle which it makes with the pole.

13. From a lighthouse which stands 109.7 feet above the level of a lake, the angle of depression of a small object floating on the surface of the water is 19° 23′. Find the distance of the object from the base of the lighthouse. *Ans.* 311.8 ft.

14. A surveyor's instrument stands 4.7 feet above the ground and 187.3 feet from the foot of a vertical flagstaff. From the instrument the angle of elevation of the top of the flagstaff is 16° 42′. How high is the flagstaff?

15. A radio aërial is stretched from a point on a house 32.8 feet high to the top of a pole 51.4 feet high. The horizontal distance between the points is 63.7 feet. Find the angle which the aërial makes with the horizontal, and its length, if 0.4 foot be added to allow for contraction. *Ans.* 16° 17′, 66.7 ft.

16. A flagstaff stands on top of a tower. From a point on the level ground 221 feet from the base of the tower, the angle of elevation of the top of the flagstaff is 19° 15′, and the angle of elevation of the bottom of the flagstaff is 15° 40′. Find the height of the flagstaff.

17. From the window of an office building the angle of elevation of the top of a church steeple is 21° 35′ and the angle of depression of a point on the ground directly below the steeple is 32° 20′. The horizontal distance between window and church is 123 feet. How high is the steeple, and how far above the ground is the window?

Ans. 127 ft., 78 ft.

18. From the top of a lighthouse which stands 217 feet above the level of the sea, the angle of depression of the top of the mast of an anchored vessel is 23° 10′ and the angle of depression of a point on the vessel's waterline is 34° 35′. Find the height of the vessel and its distance from the base of the lighthouse.

19. A tower rises from the bank of a river. A man standing directly opposite on the other bank observes the angle of elevation of the top of the tower to be 58° 45′. He then goes back 102 feet from the river bank, and finds the angle of elevation of the top of the tower to be 26° 25′. Find the height of the tower and the width of the stream. *Ans.* 72.5 ft., 44 ft.

20. From a point on a horizontal plain the angle of elevation of a cross on top of a mountain is 21° 43′. After walking 1272 feet directly toward the mountain the observer finds the angle of elevation to be 26° 27′. How high is the mountain above the plain?

21. Two buoys are directly in line with a cliff which stands 282 feet above the water. Their angles of depression from the top of the cliff are 42° 25′ and 37° 15′. How far apart are the buoys and what are their horizontal distances from the cliff?

Ans. 62 ft., 371 ft., 309 ft.

22. Two buoys are anchored in line with a cliff and are 325 feet apart. At high tide the angles of depression from the top of the cliff are 38° 45′ and 27° 10′ respectively. At low tide the angles are 40° 20′ and 28° 30′. How high is the tide?

23. In order to find the distance from a boat dock, *A*, to an island, *B*, a line, *AC*, 1000 feet long, was measured along the shore in a direction at right angles to *AB*. The angle *ACB* was measured and found to be 63° 25′. What was the required distance? *Ans.* 1998 ft.

24. In Ex. **23** if there is a lighthouse 180 feet high at *C*, what is the angle *ADB* measured by an observer *D* at the top of the lighthouse?

25. A railroad track rises 1 foot for every 25 feet measured along the track. What angle does the track make with the horizontal? How many feet does it rise in a mile measured along the track? If it costs the road 1 cent to raise 330 tons of freight 1 foot (more than it does to move it on the level), what will this grade cost the road in moving 100,000 tons of freight 1 mile?

Ans. 2° 18′, 211.2 ft., $640.

26. In a certain department store there is an escalator or moving stairway which moves at the rate of 250 feet per minute and is inclined at 40° to the horizontal. How long will it take to carry a shopper from one floor to the next, the height of one story being 19 feet?

27. The minute hand of a certain clock is 4.5 inches long. At 10 minutes past 3 o'clock, the line joining the ends of the two hands is perpendicular to the hour hand. What is the length of the hour hand? *Ans.* 3.7 in.

28. Work Ex. **27**, taking the length of the minute hand as 5.4 inches and the time as 4 minutes before 10 o'clock.

29. At what time between 2 o'clock and 10 minutes past 2 will the line joining the ends of the hands of a clock be perpendicular to the hour hand, if the minute hand is 4.8 inches long and the hour hand is 3.1 inches long? *Ans.* 1.9 mins. past 2.

30. At what time between 11 and 11:10 will the hands be in the relative positions indicated in Ex. **29**, if the minute hand is 6.3 inches long, and the hour hand is 4.3 inches long?

31. In each step of a certain stairway the tread (or horizontal part) is 9 inches and the riser (or vertical part) is 8 inches. What angle does the banister make with the horizontal? *Ans.* 41° 38′.

32. If the tread of a stairway is 11 inches and if the banister makes an angle of 39° 27′, how high is the riser?

33. The radius of a circle is 20 inches. Find the length of a side of an inscribed regular pentagon (5-sided polygon). *Ans.* 23.51 in.

34. The radius of a circle is 20 inches. Find the perimeter of an inscribed regular octagon.

35. A side of an equilateral triangle is 20 inches. Find the radius of the inscribed circle. *Ans.* $r = 10/\sqrt{3} = 5.77$ in.

36. The area of an equilateral triangle is 300 square inches. Find the area of the inscribed circle.

37. Two boats are anchored 2500 feet apart. An airplane flies across the line joining them. Just as it does so its angle of elevation from one boat is 50° and its angle of elevation from the other is 60°. Find the height at which it was flying.   *Ans.*   1765 ft.

38. The angle of elevation of an approaching airplane from a landing field is 22°. The plane glides straight toward the landing field and arrives 90 seconds after it is first sighted. If its average speed during that time is 40 miles per hour, how high was it when first sighted?

39. A boat is anchored near a bridge. From a point on its deck 15 feet above the water, the angle of elevation of the top of the bridge is 39°, while the angle of depression of its image reflected in the water is 54°. Find the height of the bridge above the water and the distance of the boat from the bridge.   *Ans.*   Height 58 ft., dist. 53 ft.

40. An airplane is flying horizontally directly away from a station on the ground at the rate of 80 miles an hour. At a certain instant its angle of elevation from the station is 40°, and 30 seconds later its angle of elevation is 25°. Find the height at which it is flying.

CHAPTER III

LOGARITHMS

22. The uses of logarithms. — In solving triangles, and in many other problems, the work of numerical computation can be greatly lessened by the use of logarithms. We shall see that logarithms enable us to replace the processes of multiplication and division by the simpler ones of addition and subtraction, and to replace the taking of powers and roots by multiplication and division. *Logarithms*, we shall find, *are exponents*. For that reason in the next article we recall the fundamental laws of exponents.

23. Laws of exponents. — Let a be any positive number and x and y any two numbers. Then

I. $a^x \cdot a^y = a^{x+y}$.
EXAMPLE. $3^5 \cdot 3^2 = 3^7$.

II. $\dfrac{a^x}{a^y} = a^{x-y}$.
EXAMPLE. $3^5/3^2 = 3^3$.

III. $(a^x)^y = a^{xy}$.
EXAMPLE. $(3^5)^2 = 3^{10}$.

IV. $\sqrt[y]{a^x} = a^{\frac{x}{y}}$.
EXAMPLE. $\sqrt{3^5} = 3^{\frac{5}{2}}$.

V. $a^0 = 1$.
EXAMPLE. $3^0 = 1$.

VI. $a^{-x} = \dfrac{1}{a^x}$, and $\dfrac{1}{a^x} = a^{-x}$.

EXAMPLE. $\dfrac{1}{81} = \dfrac{1}{3^4} = 3^{-4}$.

36

VII. If a is any number greater than 1 and if y is positive, it is always possible to find a real exponent x such that

$$a^x = y.$$

But if y is negative no real value of x exists satisfying this relation.

24. Definition of logarithms. — If a, x, and y are three numbers such that

(1) $$a^x = y,$$

the exponent x is said to be the logarithm of y to the base a, which we write

(2) $$x = \log_a y.$$

The equations (1) and (2) are different ways of expressing the same relation among the three numbers a (the *base*), y (the *number*) and x (the *exponent* or *logarithm*). Equation (1) is in *exponential* form; while (2) says the same thing in *logarithmic* form.

Definition: The logarithm of a number to a given base is the exponent to which the base must be raised to yield the number. By VII, Article **23**, if a is greater than 1, any positive number has a logarithm to the base a, but a negative number has no real logarithm.

EXAMPLES. 1. Since $2^3 = 8$, $3 = \log_2 8$.

2. Since $3^{-4} = \frac{1}{81}$, $-4 = \log_3 (\frac{1}{81})$.

3. Since $\sqrt[3]{4} = 2^{\frac{2}{3}}$, $\frac{2}{3} = \log_2 (\sqrt[3]{4})$.

4. Since $a^1 = a$, $\log_a a = 1$.

5. Since $a^0 = 1$, $\log_a 1 = 0$.

ORAL EXERCISES

Change the following statements from exponential to logarithmic form.

1. $2^5 = 32$.   *Ans.* $\log_2 32 = 5$.   2. $3^2 = 9$.

3. $3^4 = 81$.   *Ans.* $\log_3 81 = 4$.   4. $5^3 = 125$.

5. $10^2 = 100$.   6. $10^4 = 10{,}000$.   7. $6^3 = 216$.

8. $\sqrt{4} = 2$.   *Ans.* $\log_4 2 = \frac{1}{2}$.   9. $\sqrt{9} = 3$.

10. $\sqrt[3]{27} = 3$.   11. $\sqrt[5]{32} = 2$.   12. $\sqrt{100} = 10$.

13. $2^{-2} = \frac{1}{4}$. *Ans.* $\log_2\left(\frac{1}{4}\right) = -2$. **14.** $3^{-1} = \frac{1}{3}$.

15. $10^{-2} = .01$. **16.** $10^{-1} = 0.1$. **17.** $10^{-3} = .001$.

18. $3^0 = 1$. **19.** $7^0 = 1$. **20.** $2^1 = 2$.

In each of the following examples, find the value of x.

21. $x = \log_2 16$. *Ans.* $x = 4$. **22.** $x = \log_6 36$.

23. $x = \log_{10} 100$. **24.** $x = \log_{10} .01$. **25.** $x = \log_9 81$.

26. $x = \log_4 8$.
    Ans. We have $4^x = 8$, or $2^{2x} = 2^3$. $\therefore$ $2x = 3$, $x = \frac{3}{2}$.

27. $x = \log_{27} 81$. **28.** $x = \log_{16} 2$. **29.** $x = \log_{36} 216$.

30. $x = \log_5\left(\dfrac{1}{\sqrt{125}}\right)$. *Ans.* $x = -\frac{3}{2}$. **31.** $x = \log_2 \dfrac{1}{\sqrt[3]{32}}$.

32. $\log_x 8 = 3$. *Ans.* $x = 2$. **33.** $\log_x 25 = 2$.

34. $\log_x 16 = \frac{4}{5}$.
    Ans. $x^{\frac{4}{5}} = 16$. $\therefore$ $x^{\frac{1}{5}} = \sqrt[4]{16} = 2$, $x = 2^5 = 32$.

35. $\log_x 81 = \frac{4}{3}$. **36.** $\log_x \left(\frac{27}{8}\right) = 3$. **37.** $\log_x \frac{1}{64} = -\frac{3}{2}$.

38. $\log_x .001 = -\frac{3}{2}$. **39.** $\log_x 256 = \frac{4}{3}$. **40.** $\log_x 25 = \frac{2}{3}$.

41. $\log_3 x = -5$. *Ans.* $x = \frac{1}{243}$. **42.** $\log_5 x = 3$.

43. $\log_{25} x = -\frac{3}{2}$. **44.** $\log_{10} x = 2$. **45.** $\log_4 x = \frac{5}{2}$.

46. $\log_a x = 0$. **47.** $\log_a x = 1$. **48.** $\log_a x = b$.

Show that

49. $a^{\log_a x} = x$. **50.** $\log_a (a^x) = x$. **51.** $\log_a\left(\dfrac{1}{a}\right) = -1$.

25. The fundamental theorems of logarithms. — Corresponding to the four laws of exponents we have the following four theorems.

I. *Multiplication.* — *The logarithm of the product of two numbers is equal to the sum of the logarithms of the two numbers:*

$$\log_a (M \cdot N) = \log_a M + \log_a N.$$

Proof. Let M and N be any two positive numbers, and let

$$x = \log_a M \quad \text{and} \quad y = \log_a N.$$

Then, from the definition of logarithms,

$$a^x = M \quad \text{and} \quad a^y = N.$$

Therefore, from I, Article **23**,
$$M \cdot N = a^x \cdot a^y = a^{x+y}.$$
Consequently
$$\log_a (M \cdot N) = x + y = \log_a M + \log_a N.$$

It is easily seen that the logarithm of the product of *any* number of factors is equal to the sum of their logarithms. This theorem enables us to replace the laborious process of multiplying two or more numbers, by the comparatively easy one of adding their logarithms.

II. *Division.* — *The logarithm of a quotient is equal to the logarithm of the dividend minus the logarithm of the divisor:*

$$\log_a\!\left(\frac{M}{N}\right) = \log_a M - \log_a N.$$

Proof. Using the same notation as before, we have

$$\frac{M}{N} = \frac{a^x}{a^y} = a^{x-y},$$

by Law II for exponents. This is equivalent to saying that

$$\log_a\!\left(\frac{M}{N}\right) = x - y = \log_a M - \log_a N,$$

as we wished to show.

This theorem permits us to substitute the simple process of subtraction for the more arduous one of division. By combining this theorem with the preceding one, we see that *the logarithm of any fraction is equal to the sum of the logarithms of the factors of the numerator minus the sum of the logarithms of the factors of the denominator.*

EXAMPLE.

$$\log_a\!\left(\frac{32 \times 12.7 \times 194}{17 \times 542}\right) = \log_a 32 + \log_a 12.7 + \log_a 194 - \log_a 17 - \log_a 542.$$

III. *Involution.* — *The logarithm of a power of a number is equal to the logarithm of the number multiplied by the exponent of the power:*

$$\log_a (M^n) = n \log_a M.$$

Proof. Let

$$x = \log_a M,$$

so that

$$a^x = M.$$

Then

$$M^n = (a^x)^n = a^{nx},$$

by Law III for exponents. Therefore, by the definition of the logarithm of a number,

$$\log_a (M^n) = nx = n \log_a M,$$

as we were to prove.

EXAMPLE. To find 17^{19}, we notice that $\log_{10} (17^{19}) = 19 \log_{10} 17$ which, as we shall see, is easily obtained.

IV. *Evolution. — The logarithm of a root of a number is equal to the logarithm of the number divided by the index of the root:*

$$\log_a (\sqrt[n]{M}) = \frac{\log_a M}{n}.$$

Proof. Since, by Law IV of exponents,

$$\sqrt[n]{M} = M^{\frac{1}{n}},$$

by the preceding theorem we have

$$\log_a (\sqrt[n]{M}) = \log_a (M^{\frac{1}{n}}) = \frac{1}{n} \log_a M,$$

as we wished to show.

EXAMPLE. To find $\sqrt[7]{247}$ directly is a difficult task, but we shall see that to find $\sqrt[7]{247}$ by logarithms is a simple matter, since

$$\log_{10} \sqrt[7]{247} = \tfrac{1}{7} \log_{10} 247.$$

EXERCISES

Given $\log_{10} 2 = 0.301$ and $\log_{10} 3 = 0.477$, find the following logarithms.

1. $\log_{10} 6$.	*Ans.*	0.778.	**2.** $\log_{10} \frac{3}{2}$.	
3. $\log_{10} \frac{2}{3}$.	*Ans.*	−0.176.	**4.** $\log_{10} 20$.	
5. $\log_{10} 10$.	*Ans.*	1.000.	**6.** $\log_{10} 1$.	
7. $\log_{10} 30$.	*Ans.*	1.477.	**8.** $\log_{10} 60$.	
9. $\log_{10} \frac{1}{2}$.	*Ans.*	−0.301.	**10.** $\log_{10} \frac{1}{3}$.	
11. $\log_{10} 2^2$.	*Ans.*	0.602.	**12.** $\log_{10} 3^2$.	
13. $\log_{10} 9$.	*Ans.*	0.954.	**14.** $\log_{10} 4$.	
15. $\log_{10} 12$.	*Ans.*	1.079.	**16.** $\log_{10} 18$.	
17. $\log_{10} 8$.	*Ans.*	0.903.	**18.** $\log_{10} 27$.	
19. $\log_{10} 40$.	*Ans.*	1.602.	**20.** $\log_{10} 180$.	
21. $\log_{10} 5$.	*Ans.*	0.699.	**22.** $\log_{10} \frac{1}{4}$.	
23. $\log_{10} \frac{1}{9}$.	*Ans.*	−0.954.	**24.** $\log_{10} 36$.	
25. $\log_{10} 48$.	*Ans.*	1.681.	**26.** $\log_{10} 72$.	
27. $\log_{10} 45$.	*Ans.*	1.653.	**28.** $\log_{10} 225$.	
29. $\log_{10} \sqrt[3]{2}$.	*Ans.*	0.100.	**30.** $\log_{10} \sqrt{3}$.	
31. $\log_{10} \sqrt[5]{3}$.	*Ans.*	0.095.	**32.** $\log_{10} \sqrt[4]{2}$.	
33. $\log_{10} \sqrt[17]{27}$.	*Ans.*	0.084.	**34.** $\log_{10} \sqrt[6]{6}$.	

26. Logarithms to the base 10. — In numerical computations the most useful base of logarithms is the number 10. Hereafter when we speak of the logarithm of a number without specifying the base, it is to be understood that the base of the logarithm is 10. And instead of writing $\log_{10} N$ we shall write merely $\log N$.

EXAMPLES.

$$\log 100 = 2, \qquad \log .1 = -1,$$
$$\log 10 \ \ = 1, \qquad \log .01 = -2.$$

27. Characteristic and mantissa. — Any number can be written as the sum of a whole number or integer and a fraction. These parts, of course, may be zero, or positive or negative. It is always possible, however, to take the fractional part of the number positive or zero.

EXAMPLES.

$$4.231 = .231 + 4.$$
$$0.462 = .462 + 0.$$
$$-0.563 = .437 - 1.$$
$$5 = 0 + 5.$$
$$-2.694 = .306 - 3.$$

For use in computation a logarithm is always written in this way as the sum of a whole (or "integral") number (positive, negative, or zero) and a fractional part (positive or zero). The integral part of a logarithm is called its *characteristic*, and its positive (or zero) fractional part is called its *mantissa*.

EXAMPLES.

Logarithm.		Characteristic.	Mantissa.
log 2 = 0.30103.		0.	.30103.
log 20 = 1.30103.		1.	.30103.
log .5 = −0.30103 = .69897 − 1.		−1.	.69897.
log 100 = 2.00000.		2.	.00000.
log .05 = −1.30103 = .69897 − 2.		−2.	.69897.

28. Significant digits. — The numbers 704200 and 0.07042 are said to have the same *sequence of significant digits*, 7042. The significant digits of a number are the figures to the right of which and to the left of which are no figures other than zeros.

In the next two paragraphs we shall make use of the following table and of the fact that *the logarithm of an integral power of* 10 *is a whole number*.

$$\log 1 = \log 10^0 = 0,$$

$$\log 10 = \log 10^1 = 1, \qquad \log .1 = \log 10^{-1} = -1,$$
$$\log 100 = \log 10^2 = 2, \qquad \log .01 = \log 10^{-2} = -2,$$
$$\log 1000 = \log 10^3 = 3, \qquad \log .001 = \log 10^{-3} = -3,$$
$$\text{etc.} \qquad\qquad\qquad \text{etc.}$$

29. The mantissa. — *Theorem. If two numbers have the same significant digits, their logarithms have the same mantissas.*

Proof. The larger of the two numbers may be obtained from the other by moving the decimal point to the right. This is equivalent to multiplying the number by an integral power of 10. By Theorem I, Article **25**, this has the effect of adding to the logarithm of the number, the logarithm of an integral power of 10, which, as we have seen, is a whole number. A change in the position of the decimal point in a number therefore changes the whole part of its logarithm or characteristic, but it does not change its fractional part or mantissa.

EXAMPLES. Given log 7.042 = 0.84770. Then

$$\log 70.42 \quad = \log 7.042 + \log 10 = 0.84770 + 1 = 1.84770.$$
$$\log 704.2 \quad = \log 7.042 + \log 100 = 0.84770 + 2 = 2.84770.$$
$$\log 0.7042 \quad = 7.042 - \log 10 = 0.84770 - 1.$$
$$\log 0.07042 = \log 7.042 - \log 100 = 0.84770 - 2.$$

ORAL EXERCISES

Given log 6.071 = 0.7833 and log 2.4 = 0.3802,

give the values of the following logarithms.

1. log 60.71. **2.** log 0.6071. **3.** log 607.1. **4.** log 24. **5.** log 240.
6. log 24000. **7.** log 0.06071. **8.** log 0.0006071. **9.** log 0.0024.

30. The characteristic. — We shall suppose that any number that we use in computation contains a decimal point; if it is not actually present, its presence is understood.

If a number has just one digit to the left of the decimal point (e.g., the number 7.21), the characteristic of its logarithm is zero. For the number (unless it be the number 1 itself, in which case its logarithm is zero) lies between 1 and 10. Therefore its logarithm is between log 1 = 0 and log 10 = 1, and has the characteristic 0.

Any positive number may be obtained from a number having one digit to the left of the decimal point by moving the decimal point a suitable number of places to the right or to the left. Each time that the decimal point is moved one place to the right the number is multiplied by 10, and log 10 = 1 is added to the characteristic. We can say, then, that if a number has two digits to the left of the decimal point (e.g., 72.1), the characteristic is 1; if there are three digits, the characteristic is 2; and if there are k digits to the left of the decimal point the characteristic is $(k - 1)$.

On the other hand, to move the decimal point one place to the left divides the number by 10 and reduces the characteristic of its logarithm by 1. It follows that if the decimal point immediately precedes the first significant digit (as in the number .721), the characteristic of the logarithm is −1; if the first significant digit is in the second place to the right of the decimal point (as in .0721), the characteristic is −2, etc.

Rule. If a number is greater than 1 and has k digits to the left of the decimal point, the characteristic of its logarithm is k − 1.

If a number is positive but less than 1, and if its first significant digit is in the kth place to the right of the decimal point, the characteristic of its logarithm is −k.

EXAMPLES. The characteristic of log 273.4 is 2; that of log 2.734 is 0; that of log 27.34 is 1; that of log 273400 is 5; that of log .2734 is −1; that of log .002734 is −3.

ORAL EXERCISES

What are the characteristics of the logarithms of the following numbers?

1. 5.76.　　2. 609.1.　　3. 2100.　　4. 23600.
5. .637.　　6. .78932.　　7. .042.　　8. .000632.

31. Notation. — Negative characteristics may be written in various ways. We may write

$$\log .08641 = .93656 - 2.$$

It would be incorrect to write this logarithm as −2.93656, for this would indicate that the mantissa is negative. Inasmuch, however, as −2 = 8 − 10, we may, *if we choose*, write

$$\log .08641 = 8.93656 - 10.$$

This method of writing negative characteristics in practice is the most convenient one, and will be used in this book. In a similar way we shall write

$$\log .8641 \quad = 9.93656 - 10,$$
$$\log .0008641 = 6.93656 - 10, \text{ etc.}$$

EXERCISES

ORAL EXERCISES

Given log 3.078 = 0.48827 and log 86.73 = 1.93817, find the following logarithms.

1. log 307.8.   *Ans.* 2.48827.   **2.** log 867.3.
3. log 8.673.   **4.** log 3078.   **5.** log 30.78.
6. log 307800. *Ans.* 5.48827.   **7.** log 30780.
8. log 8673000. **9.** log 86730.   **10.** log 8673.
11. log 0.8673. *Ans.* 9.93817 − 10.   **12.** log 0.08673.
13. log 0.3078. **14.** log 0.003078.   **15.** log 0.03078.

Given log 6.509 = 0.81351 and log 468.3 = 2.67052, find the value of N in each of the following cases.

16. log N = 2.81351.   **17.** log N = 0.67052.
18. log N = 1.81351.   **19.** log N = 5.81351.
20. log N = 8.67052.   **21.** log N = 8.67052 − 10.
22. log N = 9.81351 − 10.   **23.** log N = 6.67052 − 10.
24. log N = 8.81351 − 10.

WRITTEN EXERCISES

Given log 2 = 0.30103 and log 3 = 0.47712, find the number of places to the left of the decimal point or the position of the first significant figure for each of the following numbers.

25. 2^{35}. *Ans.* log 2^{35} = 35 log 2 = 35 × .30103 = 10.53605.

∴ There are 11 places to the left of the decimal point in 2^{35}.

26. 3^{24}.   **27.** 6^{15}.   *Ans.* 12 places.
28. $(1.5)^{27}$.   **29.** $(4\frac{1}{2})^{14}$.   *Ans.* 10 places.
30. $(20)^{12}$.   **31.** $(300)^{5}$.   *Ans.* 13 places.
32. $(0.2)^{11}$.   *Ans.* $\log (0.2)^{11} = 11 \log (0.2)$.

∴ $\log (0.2)^{11} = 11 \times (9.30103 - 10) = 102.31133 - 110 = 2.31133 - 10$.

∴ The first significant figure is in the 8th place to the right of the decimal point.

33. $(0.03)^{6}$.   *Ans.* 10th place.   **34.** $(0.06)^{7}$.

32. A table of logarithms. — Table I is a table of the mantissas of all whole numbers from 1 to 9999 correct to five decimal places.

The mantissa of the logarithm of *any* four-figure number can, therefore, be found in this table, since the mantissa depends only on the sequence of significant figures in the number and not on the position of the decimal point. This economy in the preparation and use of tables is one of the advantages gained by using 10 as the base of logarithms.

In seeking the logarithm of a number we look for the first three significant figures of the number in the column N at the left of the page. This gives the row in which the mantissa is to be found. The column is that in which the fourth figure of the number appears at the top of the page. The entry in the table gives only the last three figures of the mantissa. The first two figures, to save space, are printed only once, in the column headed 0 and at the left. Any entry is to have prefixed to it the last preceding pair of numbers at the left of the 0 column, unless it is marked with an asterisk, in which case the next following pair is to be used. The characteristic is determined by the position of the decimal point.

EXAMPLE 1. Find log 16.74. We find 167 in column N, page 3. In the column 4 we find the entry 376 without an asterisk. The mantissa is therefore .22376. The characteristic is 1. Therefore log 16.74 = 1.22376.

EXAMPLE 2. Find log .06763. On page 13, line 676, column 3, we find the entry *014. The mantissa is therefore .83014, and log .06763 = 8.83014 − 10.

33. The antilogarithm. — If $x = \log N$, N is said to be the *anti-logarithm* of x, $N = $ antilog x. In order to find the antilogarithm of a given logarithm we seek the given mantissa in the body of the table. The first three figures of the antilogarithm then appear in the same line in the column N, and the fourth figure appears at the top of the page. The decimal point is then placed by the value of the characteristic.

EXAMPLES. 1. Find x, given log $x = 2.84036$. We seek the mantissa .84036 in the body of the table. It is on page 13. The corresponding figures are 6924. Since the characteristic is 2, $x = 692.4$.

2. Find x, given log $x = 8.90157 - 10$. On page 15 we find $x = .07972$.

3. Find antilog 0.46045. *Ans.* 2.887.

EXERCISES
Find the logarithms of the following numbers.

1.	87130.	*Ans.*	4.94017.	**2.**	45.62.
3.	0.06209.	*Ans.*	8.79302 − 10.	**4.**	1.280.
5.	100.3.	*Ans.*	2.00130.	**6.**	.002615.
7.	.2457.	*Ans.*	9.39041 − 10.	**8.**	3637.
9.	.6166.	*Ans.*	9.79000 − 10.	**10.**	7.769.
11.	1.087.	*Ans.*	0.03623.	**12.**	632.8.

Find the antilogarithms of the following numbers.

13.	1.82406.	*Ans.*	66.69.	**14.**	2.94275.
15.	9.91955 − 10.	*Ans.*	0.8309.	**16.**	8.76916 − 10.
17.	4.83948.	*Ans.*	69100.	**18.**	7.63347 − 10.
19.	2.69011.	*Ans.*	489.9.	**20.**	3.82014.
21.	0.00087.	*Ans.*	1.002.	**22.**	9.99029 − 10.
23.	5.25018.	*Ans.*	177900.	**24.**	2.62003.

34. Interpolation. — The logarithm of a five-figure number can be found from the table by interpolation. (Article **17**.)

Before seeking the logarithm of any number of more than five significant figures, we will generally round it off to the nearest five-figure number, for our tables are not designed to give greater accuracy than this.

EXAMPLE 1. Find log 37.826. On page 7 of the tables we find

$$\begin{aligned} \log 37.82 &= 1.57772 \\ \log 37.83 &= 1.57784 \end{aligned}$$

Tabular difference = 12.

Therefore, in the last place we add .6 × 12 or 7 to log 37.82, getting log 37.826 = 1.57779.

The work of interpolation is made easier, however, by the tables of proportional parts which are at the right of each page. The numbers above the short columns are the tabular differences for the page. The nine numbers in a column are, in order, .1, .2, .3, etc. of the number above the column. Thus, on page 5, we see that .7 of the tabular difference 17 is 11.9.

EXAMPLE 2. Find log 152.47. On page 3 we find log 152.4 = 2.18298 and log 152.5 = 2.18327, with tabular difference 29. In the proportional parts column for 29, we find .7 × 29 = 20.3. Therefore log 152.47 = 2.18318.

EXAMPLE 3. Find log .010535.
From page 2, tabular difference = 41.
Proportional part = .5 × 41 = 20.5.

If this is rounded off to 21 the result is even, and

$$\log .010535 = 8.02264 - 10.$$

EXAMPLE 4. Find x, given log x = 1.34935.
From page 4, tabular difference = 19.

In the table of proportional parts for 19, we seek the nearest number to our difference, which is (35 − 28) or 7. We find 7.6, which corresponds to .4. Therefore x = 22.354.

EXERCISES

Find the logarithms of the following numbers.

1. 33.587.	*Ans.* 1.52617.	**2.** 114.34.	
3. 1.6307.	*Ans.* 0.21237.	**4.** 4.8606.	
5. 26354.	*Ans.* 4.42085.	**6.** 3.1667.	
7. 53.399.	*Ans.* 1.72753.	**8.** 334.98.	
9. .038096.	*Ans.* 8.58088 − 10.	**10.** .11295.	
11. .11197.	*Ans.* 9.04910 − 10.	**12.** .025795.	

Find the antilogarithms of the following numbers.

13. 1.57708.   *Ans.* 37.764.   **14.** 2.54089.
15. 9.18314 − 10.   *Ans.* .15246.   **16.** 7.09821 −10.
17. 3.21733.   *Ans.* 1649.4.   **18.** 1.11378.
19. 8.13008 − 10.   *Ans.* .013492.   **20.** 2.04347.
21. 3.09216.   *Ans.* 1236.4.·   **22.** 0.21103.
23. 0.20131.   *Ans.* 1.5897.   **24.** 1.15204.

35. Computation by logarithms. — In any problem of computation, before looking up logarithms one should make a blank outline for all of the work, indicating all of the operations. It is then possible to do the mechanical work without interruption, and thereby gain in speed and accuracy. Every part of the work, moreover, is labelled, which aids in later checking or examination.

EXAMPLE 1. Find the value of
$$x = 21.48 \times 306.4 \times .01206.$$

By Theorem I, Article **25**,
$$\log x = \log 21.48 + \log 306.4 + \log .01206.$$

The outline is as follows.

$$\begin{aligned}
\log 21.48 &= \\
\log 306.4 &= \\
\log .01206 &= \underline{\qquad\qquad\qquad} \ (+) \\
\log x &= \\
x &=
\end{aligned}$$

We can fill this out from the tables, getting

$$\begin{aligned}
\log 21.48 &= 1.33203 \\
\log 306.4 &= 2.48629 \\
\log .01206 &= \underline{8.08135 - 10} \ (+) \\
\log x &= 11.89967 - 10 \\
x &= 79.372
\end{aligned}$$

Here x is found as the antilogarithm of 1.89967.

EXAMPLE 2. Find the value of
$$x = \frac{38.614 \times 1.8263 \times 1.2345}{496.23 \times 0.26944}.$$

$$\begin{array}{rll}
\log 38.614 = & 1.58674 \\
\log 1.8263 = & 0.26157 \\
\log 1.2345 = & 0.09150 & (+) \\
\hline
\log \text{numerator} = & 11.93981 - 10 \\
\log \text{denominator} = & 2.12614 & (-) \\
\hline
\log x = & 9.81367 - 10 \\
x = & 0.65113.
\end{array}$$

$$\begin{array}{rl}
\log 496.23 = & 2.69568 \\
\log 0.26944 = & 9.43046 - 10 \ (+) \\
\hline
\log \text{denominator} = & 12.12614 - 10
\end{array}$$

It will be noticed that 10 was added to and subtracted from the logarithm of the numerator. This was done to avoid subtracting 2.12614 from a smaller number.

EXAMPLE 3. Find the value of

$$x = \sqrt[3]{\frac{28.693 \times (2.3614)^2}{89.325 \times 11.283}}.$$

By Article **25**, we have

$$\log x = \tfrac{1}{3}\,[\log 28.693 + 2 \log 2.3614 - \log 89.325 - \log 11.283].$$

The outline is:

$$\begin{array}{rll}
\log 2.3614 = & \\
& \times 2 \\
\hline
\log (2.3614)^2 = & \\
\log 28.693 = & \quad\quad (+) \\
\hline
\log \text{numerator} = & \\
\log \text{denominator} = & \quad\quad (-) \\
\hline
\log \text{radicand} = & \quad\quad (\div 3 \\
\log x = & \quad\quad \rightarrow x =
\end{array}$$

$$\begin{array}{rl}
\log 89.325 = & \\
\log 11.283 = & \quad\quad\quad (+) \\
\hline
\log \text{denominator} = &
\end{array}$$

This becomes:

$$\begin{array}{rll}
\log 2.3614 = & 0.37317 \\
& \times 2 \\
\hline
\log (2.3614)^2 = & 0.74634 \\
\log 28.693 = & 1.45778 & (+) \\
\hline
\log \text{numerator} = & 12.20412 - 10 \\
\log \text{denominator} = & 3.00340 & (-) \\
\hline
\log \text{radicand} = & 29.20072 - 30 \, (\div 3 \\
\log x = & 9.73357 - 10, \quad \rightarrow x = 0.54146.
\end{array}$$

$$\begin{array}{rl}
\log 89.325 = & 1.95098 \\
\log 11.283 = & 1.05242 \quad (+) \\
\hline
\log \text{denominator} = & 3.00340
\end{array}$$

Here, before dividing $9.20072 - 10$ by 3, which would have given the awkward number $(3.06691 - 3.33333)$, we added and subtracted 20, making the negative part 30. In general, *before dividing a negative logarithm we make its negative part an exact multiple of the divisor by adding and subtracting a suitable number.*

EXERCISES

Find by logarithms the value of each of the following numbers, correct to five significant figures.

1. 48.32×9876.   *Ans.* 477210.   2. 506.3×8.503.

3. $619.2 \times .04598$.   *Ans.* 28.471.   4. $23.79 \times .08395$.

5. $83.69 \div 7.631$.   *Ans.* 10.967.   6. $453.3 \div 6.029$.

7. $.9582 \div .03644$.   *Ans.* 26.295.   8. $.6307 \div .05824$.

9. $73.06 \div 84.11$.   *Ans.* .86862.   10. $3.086 \div 51.22$.

11. $.01699 \div .2525$.   *Ans.* .067287.   12. $.04404 \div .07329$.

13. $\dfrac{24.68 \times 93.21}{5.040 \times 11.63}$.   *Ans.* 39.246.   14. $\dfrac{54.23 \times 864.2}{918.2 \times 1.001}$.

15. $\dfrac{2.821 \times .06498}{54.26 \times .9801}$.   *Ans.* .0034469.   16. $\dfrac{30.41 \times 2.613}{6 \times 87.36}$.

17. $(1.623)^5$.   *Ans.* 11.262.   18. $(5.321)^6$.

19. $(.3647)^4$.   *Ans.* .017691.   20. $(.06319)^5$.

21. $\sqrt{47980}$.   *Ans.* 219.04.   22. $\sqrt{689700}$.

23. $\sqrt[3]{12.34}$.   *Ans.* 2.3108.   24. $\sqrt[3]{702.3}$.

25. $\sqrt[5]{1.251}$.   *Ans.* 1.0458.   26. $\sqrt[4]{119.6}$.

27. $\sqrt[3]{.03579}$.   *Ans.* .32955.   28. $\sqrt[3]{.6745}$.

29. $\sqrt[6]{.4444}$.   *Ans.* .87358.   30. $\sqrt[17]{.006254}$.

31. $\dfrac{3.142 \times (10.48)^2 \times 9.05}{72.93 \times \sqrt[3]{5.146}}$.   *Ans.* 24.803.   32. $\dfrac{(5.021)^3 \times 11.38}{\sqrt{36.37} \times \sqrt[4]{4.021}}$.

33. $\left(\dfrac{16.11 \times \sqrt{2.049}}{3.108 \times 10.74}\right)^5$.   *Ans.* .15738.   34. $\left(\dfrac{\sqrt{23.49} \times 6.01}{\sqrt{4568} \times 21.11}\right)^{12}$.

35. $\sqrt[3]{\dfrac{40.32 \times (.5114)^2}{16.91 \times 200.3}}$.   *Ans.* .14602.   36. $\sqrt[7]{\dfrac{.8543 \times 20.18}{69.69 \times 56.01}}$.

37. 24.638×11.483.   *Ans.* 282.91.   38. $.57693 \times 9.0468$.

39. $48.623 \div 1.4021$.   *Ans.* 34.678.   40. $.38497 \div 6.7604$.

41. $\dfrac{.57916 \times 1102.1}{407.23 \times (16.927)^2}$.   *Ans.* .0054704.   42. $\dfrac{(1.2616)^2 \times 11.982}{(3.1313)^5}$.

43. $\sqrt[3]{315.65}$.   *Ans.* 6.8088.   44. $\sqrt[3]{3156.5}$.

45. $\sqrt[3]{.015995}$.   *Ans.* .25196.   **46.** $\sqrt[3]{.0022795}$.

47. $\sqrt{\dfrac{105.23}{51.688 \times 11.963}}$.   *Ans.* .41254.   **48.** $\sqrt[3]{\dfrac{.098623 \times 11.003}{61.107}}$.

49. $(.026549)^{\frac{5}{3}}$.   *Ans.* .0023627.   **50.** $(.18896)^{\frac{4}{7}}$.

Find the values of the following expressions for the indicated values of the quantities involved. In Examples **51** to **54**, $k = 6.5579 \times 10^{-8}$.

51. $F = \dfrac{kmm'}{d^2}$, when $m = 5837$, $d = 24,378$, $m' = 11,432$.

$$\textit{Ans.} \quad F = 7.3635 \times 10^{-9}.$$

52. $F = \dfrac{kM}{r^2}$, when $M = 1372.5$, $r = 15.82$.

53. $F = \dfrac{2kM}{r}$, when $M = 4.87$, $r = 372.8$.

$$\textit{Ans.} \quad F = 1.7133 \times 10^{-9}.$$

54. $W = \dfrac{4kM^2}{7a}$, when $a = 24.76$, $M = 3789$.

55. $f = \dfrac{Mv^2}{R}$, when $M = 49.82$, $v = 5563$, $R = 17.94$.

$$\textit{Ans.} \quad f = 8.594 \times 10^7.$$

56. $T = 2\pi\sqrt{\dfrac{I}{Mgh}}$, when $g = 980.6$, $I = 53,933$, $h = 4.32$, $M = 278.4$.

57. $s = \frac{1}{2}gt^2$, when $g = 980.6$, $t = .8$.   *Ans.* $s = 313.79$.

58. $f = \dfrac{6\pi^2\gamma^2a^2b^2x}{(a^2+x^2)^{\frac{5}{2}}}$, when $a = 15.3$, $b = .873$, $x = 7.894$, $\gamma = .0376$.

59. $n = \dfrac{8\pi Mk^2l}{a^4\tau^2}$, when $\tau = 7$, $l = 200$, $M = 5247$, $k = 2.24$, $a = .762$.

$$\textit{Ans.} \quad n = 8010800.$$

60. $q = \dfrac{2\pi kt(V_a - V_b)}{2.3026\,(\log_{10} b - \log_{10} a)}$, when $t = 5$, $k = .97$, $a = 6$, $b = 9$, $V_a = 477$, $V_b = 382$.

Historical note: Logarithms were invented by the Scotchman, John Napier, Baron of Merchiston (1550–1617). He published a partial account of his discoveries in 1614. Merchiston Castle, now within the town of Edinburgh, at present houses a school for boys, the "dux" or head boy of which is said to be allowed the use of Napier's room as a study. The use of 10 as a base was suggested by the Englishman Briggs, a disciple of Napier. Briggs also gave the first tables of logarithms to the base 10.

★ **36. Cologarithms.** — *The cologarithm of a number is the logarithm of the reciprocal of the number:*

$$\operatorname{colog} x = \log\left(\frac{1}{x}\right) = -\log x.$$

EXAMPLE. $\operatorname{colog} 4.6723 = \log\left(\frac{1}{4.6723}\right) = -\log 4.6723 = -.66953.$

In order to write this with a positive mantissa we add and subtract 10, getting

$$\operatorname{colog} 4.6723 = (10 - .66953) - 10 = 9.33047 - 10.$$

By using the following rule we can make the necessary subtraction, and so write down the cologarithm, without first writing down the logarithm: *To subtract a number (less than 10) from 10, begin at the left and subtract each figure from 9 except the last, and subtract the last figure from 10.*

In computing a fraction it is often convenient to add the cologarithms of the factors of the denominator to the logarithms of the factors of the numerator, rather than to subtract the sum of their logarithms. In the later parts of this book solutions will be given without the use of cologarithms. It is suggested, however, that the student will frequently find it desirable to use cologarithms in the solutions of similar problems.

EXAMPLE 1. $\operatorname{colog} 274.61 = 7.56128 - 10.$

EXAMPLE 2. Find $\operatorname{colog} .076432$.
$$\begin{aligned}
\operatorname{colog} .076432 &= -\log(.076432)\\
&= -(8.88327 - 10) = 10 - 8.88327\\
&= 1.11673.
\end{aligned}$$

EXAMPLE 3. Find $N = \dfrac{27.468 \times 59.742}{3.8941 \times 47.631}.$

(a) *Solution without cologarithms.*

log 27.468 = 1.43883
log 59.742 = 1.77628 (+)
                3.21511
                2.26830 (−)

log N = 0.94681
N = 8.8472.

log 3.8941 = 0.59041
log 47.631 = 1.67789 (+)
←——————— 2.26830

(b) *Solution using cologarithms.*

log 27.468 =   1.43883
log 59.742 =   1.77628
colog 3.8941 = 9.40959 − 10
colog 47.631 = 8.32211 − 10 (+)
log N = 20.94681 − 20
N =   8.8472.

EXERCISES

Write the cologarithms of the following numbers, without first writing the logarithms.

1.	84.63.	*Ans.*	8.07248 − 10.	**2.**	96.87.
3.	581.3.	*Ans.*	7.23560 − 10.	**4.**	443.1.
5.	4.679.	*Ans.*	9.32985 − 10.	**6.**	8.319.
7.	0.04293.	*Ans.*	1.36724.	**8.**	0.004427.
9.	0.3634.	*Ans.*	0.43962.	**10.**	0.5757.
11.	21.683.	*Ans.*	8.66388 − 10.	**12.**	704.57.
13.	6.0278.	*Ans.*	9.21984 − 10.	**14.**	7.2486.
15.	356.97.	*Ans.*	7.44737 − 10.	**16.**	22.796.
17.	25.795.	*Ans.*	8.58846 − 10.	**18.**	1179.5.
19.	0.0046797.	*Ans.*	2.32978.	**20.**	0.088888.

Find the reciprocals of the following numbers, using cologarithms.

21.	78.463.	*Ans.*	0.012745	**22.**	532.67.
23.	1.3627.	*Ans.*	0.73383.	**24.**	2.4765.
25.	0.026798.	*Ans.*	37.316.	**26.**	0.0046193.

Find the values of the following numbers, using cologarithms.

27. $\dfrac{56.72 \times 1.362}{71.69 \times 0.3728}$.　　　*Ans.*　2.8905.

28. $\dfrac{397.4 \times 0.04625}{6.150 \times 1.703}$.

29. $\sqrt[3]{\dfrac{6.0783 \times .21667}{146.02 \times .087119}}$.　　*Ans.*　.46954

30. $\left(\dfrac{.028617 \times 23.346}{508.19 \times .11045}\right)^{\frac{3}{4}}$.

CHAPTER IV

THE RIGHT TRIANGLE

37. Logarithms of trigonometric functions. — In a right triangle, ABC, let us suppose that $a = 243.4$, $\alpha = 38° 42'$, and that we wish to find the hypotenuse, c. By Article **10**, we have

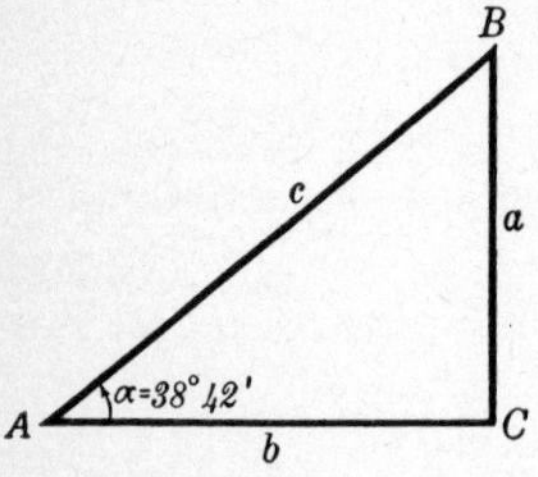

$$c = \frac{a}{\sin \alpha} = \frac{243.4}{\sin 38° 42'},$$

and, using Table III to find $\sin 38° 42'$, we get

$$c = \frac{243.4}{.62524}.$$

Fig. 25

We perform the division by logarithms:

$$\begin{aligned}
\log 243.4 &= \quad 12.38632 - 10 \\
\log .62524 &= \quad\ \ 9.79605 - 10 \quad (-) \\
\hline
\log c &= \quad\ \ 2.59027
\end{aligned}$$

$$c = 389.29 \text{ or } 389.3 \text{ to four places.}$$

It is unnecessary, however, first to look up $\sin \alpha$ and then its logarithm, if we use Table II, which gives the logarithms of the trigonometric functions directly.   On page 60, we find $\log \sin 38° 42' = 9.79605 - 10$.

The sine or cosine of any angle is less than 1.   So also is the tangent of any angle between 0° and 45° or the cotangent of any angle between 45° and 90°.   Consequently the logarithms of such functions are negative.   Therefore *the number* -10 *should be appended to any entry in the first, second or fourth principal column of Table II.* The cotangent of an angle less than 45° (or the tangent of an angle between 45° and 90°) is greater than 1; its logarithm is therefore positive, *and* −10 *should not be appended to any entry in the third principal column.*

Interpolation to the nearest tenth of a minute may be carried out by the methods already explained (Articles **17, 18, 19, 33**). Greater accuracy should not be sought in a five-place table. In Table II, the tabular differences are printed in the columns marked *d* for Log Sin and Log Cos, and in the column marked *cd* (common difference) for Log Tan and Log Cot.

EXAMPLE 1. Find log sin 8° 17.3′. On page 30, we find

$$\log \sin 8° 17′ = 9.15857 − 10,$$

with tabular difference 87 in the *d* column. From the table of proportional parts for 87, we find .3 × 87 = 26.1. Therefore log sin 8° 17.3′ = 9.15883 − 10.

EXAMPLE 2. Find log tan 84° 28.8′. On page 27, we find log tan 84° 28′ = 1.01378 with tabular difference 132. Since .8 × 132 = 105.6, log tan 84° 28.8′ = 1.01378 + .00106 = 1.01484.

EXAMPLE 3. Find θ, given log cos θ = 9.51797 − 10. On page 41, we find log cos 70° 45′ = 9.51811 − 10, with tabular difference 37. Our difference is 811 − 797 = 14. From the table of proportional parts for 37, we see that 14 corresponds most nearly to .4. Therefore θ = 70° 45.4′.

EXERCISES

Find

1. log sin 9° 38′.	*Ans.* 9.22361 − 10.	**2.** log sin 47° 46′.	
3. log cos 48° 49′.	*Ans.* 9.81854 − 10.	**4.** log cos 23° 15′.	
5. log tan 26° 22′.	*Ans.* 9.69520 − 10.	**6.** log tan 75° 43′.	
7. log cot 54° 28′.	*Ans.* 9.85380 − 10.	**8.** log cot 31° 24′.	
9. log sin 18° 18.7′.	*Ans.* 9.49719 − 10.	**10.** log sin 23° 44.8′.	
11. log sin 63° 52.4′.	*Ans.* 9.95319 − 10.	**12.** log sin 72° 31.6′.	
13. log cos 41° 12.5′.	*Ans.* 9.87640 − 10.	**14.** log cos 16° 52.5′.	
15. log cos 72° 19.4′.	*Ans.* 9.48236 − 10.	**16.** log cos 66° 16.8′.	
17. log tan 21° 39.8′.	*Ans.* 9.59902 − 10.	**18.** log tan 8° 14.6′.	
19. log tan 52° 22.6′.	*Ans.* 0.11309.	**20.** log tan 69° 43.5′.	
21. log cot 9° 28.7′.	*Ans.* 0.77740.	**22.** log cot 23° 18.9′.	
23. log cot 55° 51.5′.	*Ans.* 9.83130 − 10.	**24.** log cot 48° 32.4′.	

Find the value of θ, given:

25. log sin θ = 9.94773 − 10.   *Ans.* 62° 27′.

26. log sin θ = 9.52598 − 10.

27. log cos θ = 9.99822 − 10.   *Ans.* 5° 11′.

28. log cos θ = 9.82509 − 10.

29. log tan θ = 0.20562.   *Ans.* 58° 5′.

30. log tan θ = 9.88707 − 10.

31. log cot θ = 0.45610.   *Ans.* 19° 17′.

32. log cot θ = 8.67267 − 10.

33. log sin θ = 9.10909 − 10.   *Ans.* 7° 23.2′.

34. log sin θ = 9.26301 − 10.

35. log sin θ = 9.96227 − 10.   *Ans.* 66° 27.7′.

36. log sin θ = 9.87318 − 10.

37. log cos θ = 9.86514 − 10.   *Ans.* 42° 51.4′.

38. log cos θ = 9.96836 − 10.

39. log cos θ = 9.33724 − 10.   *Ans.* 77° 26.6′.

40. log cos θ = 8.97693 − 10.

41. log tan θ = 8.99302 − 10.   *Ans.* 5° 37.2′.

42. log tan θ = 9.23016 − 10.

43. log tan θ = 0.32141.   *Ans.* 64° 29.7′.

44. log tan θ = 0.50238.

45. log cot θ = 0.78560.   *Ans.* 9° 18.3′.

46. log cot θ = 0.33975.

47. log cot θ = 9.91833 − 10.   *Ans.* 50° 21.3′.

48. log cot θ = 9.57600 − 10.

49. Prove that the tabular difference for log tan θ must always be the same as for log cot θ, so that both may be entered in a table of "common differences."

*50. Find the cologarithms of the functions in Examples **1** to **24**.

In each case obtain the value of x, by logarithms.

51. $x = 74.62 \times \sin 16° 24′$.   *Ans.* 21.07.

52. $x = .05139 \times \tan 43° 16′$.

* This exercise is to be done only by those who have studied cologarithms.

53. $x = 524.1 \div \cos 58° 12'$.   *Ans.* 994.6.

54. $x = 63.24 \div \sin 67° 42'$.

55. $x = 568.49 \times \cot 14° 11.7'$.   *Ans.* 2247.4.

56. $x = .0046926 \times \tan 81° 14.2'$.

57. $x = 783.29 \div \cos 19° 23.7'$.   *Ans.* 830.42.

58. $x = 8.0036 \div \sin 20° 2.4'$.

59. $x = \sqrt{6.2309} \times \sin 29° 14.6'$.   *Ans.* 1.7447.

60. $x = \sqrt[3]{.53674} \times \cos 72° 11.7'$.

In each case find the value of θ by logarithms, given:

61. $\sin \theta = 14.763 \div 20.482$.   *Ans.* 46° 7.2′.

62. $\cos \theta = 2.4862 \div 5.3294$.

63. $\tan \theta = 42.365 \div 31.497$.   *Ans.* 53° 22.2′.

64. $\tan \theta = 8.6294 \div 11.636$.

65. $\cot \theta = 16.422 \div 13.115$.   *Ans.* 38° 36.7′.

66. $\cot \theta = .94625 \div 2.1441$.

38. The accuracy of a computed result. Errors due to inaccuracies in the data. — The results of most problems in applied mathematics which involve computation are liable to certain errors. Apart from sheer mistakes, which need not be tolerated, these errors are of two sorts: errors due to inaccuracies in the data and errors due to limitations of the tables used. In the very nature of things these errors cannot be eliminated, but one can see to it that the results be *sufficiently accurate for the purpose in view.*

The data of most problems are the result of observations or measurements. These measurements are made with greater or less accuracy, depending on the purposes for which they are made and the difficulties to be overcome. The number of significant figures in the data should correspond to the accuracy with which measurements have been made.

To say that the distance by railroad from Milwaukee to Boston is 1183 miles means that the distance has been measured so accurately that it can safely be said to be nearer to 1183 miles than to 1182 miles or 1184 miles, or, in other words, that the distance is between 1182.5 miles and 1183.5 miles. If the bore of an engine cylinder is given as 2.69 inches in diameter, then it is between 2.685 and 2.695; if it is given as 2.690 inches, then it is between 2.6895 inches and 2.6905 inches. In this connection we should notice that a zero placed at the end of a number sometimes indicates the degree of accuracy with which the number is given. There is, for example, a difference in implication in the numbers 27, 27.0, and 27.00. The first number presumably is accurate to the nearest unit and is given with "two-place" accuracy. The second is correct to the nearest tenth of a unit and has three-place accuracy. And the third has four-place accuracy.

Since the data of a problem are in general only approximate, results obtained from them by any process of computation will be only approximately correct. And the accuracy of the result will not exceed that of the data. For this reason the number of significant digits in a result should be rounded off so as not to exceed that of the data. Otherwise one would claim for the result an accuracy exceeding that of the data.

In applying this rule, one should keep in mind the geometrical or physical interpretation of a result. For example, if the two perpendicular sides of a right triangle are given as 6.41 feet and 8.62 feet, the hypotenuse may be computed to be 10.74 feet. It is proper to give the result in this form, though it contains one more significant figure than did the data, for the numbers all represent distances to the nearest hundredth of a foot. Only in rare cases, in such problems, will the last figure be incorrect.

Sometimes it is puzzling to know what degree of accuracy in one kind of unit corresponds to a certain accuracy in the other. In triangles it is proper to suppose that *four-place accuracy in the sides corresponds to accuracy to the nearest minute in the angles; five-place accuracy in the sides corresponds to accuracy to the nearest tenth of a minute in the angles.*

39. Errors due to the limitations of the tables. — Many problems in applied mathematics contain no errors in the data. This is true, for example, in most problems of compound interest, where the principal, rate, time, etc. are known exactly. But even in such problems results are subject to certain errors due to the use of tables. A logarithm or a sine is usually a never-ending decimal which can be given in a table only to a certain number of decimal places, that is, approximately but not exactly.

Five-place accuracy in results can usually be had by using five-place tables; four-place accuracy with four-place tables, etc., although errors may enter into the last place of the results. At any rate, one must not expect five-place accuracy when using four-place tables. On the other hand, to use five-place tables when two or three places would suffice involves unnecessary labor. But the use of tables having one more place than will be retained obviates unnecessary errors and, by doing away with interpolation, probably saves as much time as it wastes.

40. Logarithmic solution of the right triangle. —

EXAMPLE. Solve the right triangle ABC, given

$$a = 417.63, \quad b = 368.47.$$

We use the formulas

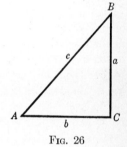

FIG. 26

$$\tan \alpha = \frac{a}{b}, \quad c = \frac{a}{\sin \alpha}, \quad \beta = 90° - \alpha.$$

$$\begin{aligned}
\log 417.63 &= 2.62079 \\
\log 368.47 &= 2.56640 \quad (-) \\
\log \tan \alpha &= .05439 \\
\alpha &= 48° 34.7' \\
\beta &= 90° - \alpha = 41° 25.3'.
\end{aligned}$$

$$\begin{aligned}
\log 417.63 &= 12.62079 - 10 \\
\log \sin \alpha &= 9.87498 - 10 \quad (-) \\
\log c &= 2.74581 \\
c &= 556.94.
\end{aligned}$$

Check: The formula

$$c^2 = a^2 + b^2$$

is not suitable, as it stands, for checking by logarithms. We can write it

$$a^2 = c^2 - b^2,$$

or

$$a^2 = (c + b)(c - b).$$

Therefore, as a check, we should find that

$$2 \log a = \log (c + b) + \log (c - b).$$

This is the best check for the solution of a right triangle by logarithms.
In the present example,

$$c + b = 925.41, \qquad \log (c + b) = 2.96634$$
$$c - b = 188.47, \qquad \log (c - b) = 2.27524 \quad (+)$$

$$\log [(c + b) (c - b)] = 5.24158.$$

And $\log a = 2.62079$,
so that $\log a^2 = 2 \log a = 5.24158$,

which, in this case, checks exactly.

EXERCISES

Using logarithms solve the right triangle for each of the following
sets of data. Check the solution.

1. $a = 27.46, c = 38.82$. *Ans.* $\alpha = 45° 1', \beta = 44° 59', b = 27.44$.
2. $a = 692.7, c = 1010.0$.
3. $b = 5046, c = 8423$. *Ans.* $\alpha = 53° 12', \beta = 36° 48', a = 6744$.
4. $b = 126.3, c = 142.5$.
5. $a = 81.48, b = 72.19$. *Ans.* $\alpha = 48° 28', \beta = 41° 32', c = 108.86$.
6. $a = 1246, b = 1583$.
7. $a = 14.92, \alpha = 65° 3'$. *Ans.* $\beta = 24° 57', b = 6.94, c = 16.46$.
8. $a = 106.6, \alpha = 17° 18'$.
9. $b = 1.927, \alpha = 40° 0'$. *Ans.* $\beta = 50° 0', a = 1.617, c = 2.516$.
10. $b = 0.7078, \alpha = 63° 21'$.
11. $a = 551.45, b = 490.13$.
    Ans. $\alpha = 48° 22.2', \beta = 41° 37.8', c = 737.78$.
12. $a = 12.138, b = 18.634$.
13. $c = 177.64, a = 161.48$.
    Ans. $\alpha = 65° 22.3', \beta = 24° 37.7', b = 74.028$.
14. $c = 0.70385, b = 0.52664$.
15. $c = 9.0024, b = 3.6512$.
    Ans. $\alpha = 66° 4.4', \beta = 23° 55.6', a = 8.2287$.
16. $c = 0.064493, a = 0.036254$.

17. $a = 83.577, \alpha = 71° 12.4'$.

> *Ans.* $\beta = 18° 47.6', b = 28.441, c = 88.282$.

18. $a = 5.9528, \beta = 24° 16.3'$.

19. $b = 0.81325, \alpha = 31° 31.7'$.

> *Ans.* $\beta = 58° 28.3', a = .49891, c = .95410$.

20. $b = 161.46, \beta = 38° 47.5'$.

21. $c = 38.506, \alpha = 49° 18.3'$.

> *Ans.* $\beta = 40° 41.7', a = 29.195, b = 25.107$.

22. $c = 798.05, \alpha = 68° 16.1'$.

23. $c = 8345.6, \beta = 58° 47.6'$.

> *Ans.* $\alpha = 31° 12.4', a = 4324.0, b = 7138.0$.

24. $c = 5.2869, \beta = 25° 31.0'$.

Solve the following oblique triangles, by dividing them into right triangles. Draw the figures.

25. $b = 243.4, \alpha = 31° 11', \beta = 47° 24'$.

(*Solution:* We draw the figure, and draw CD perpendicular to AB. Denote CD by h, AD by x, DB by y. We then use, in succession, the formulas:

$\gamma = 180° - (\alpha + \beta)$, $\quad x = b \cos \alpha$, $\quad h = b \sin \alpha$,
$\qquad y = h \cot \beta$, $\quad c = x + y$, $\quad a = h / \sin \beta$.

We find:

$\gamma = 101° 25'$, $\quad x = 208.23$, $\quad \log h = 2.10046$,
$\qquad y = 115.89$, $\quad c = 324.1$, $\quad a = 171.2$.

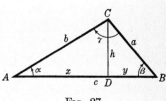

Fig. 27

The student should perform the computation.)

26. $b = 78.95, \alpha = 24° 46', \beta = 39° 57'$.

27. $a = 10.89, \alpha = 41° 17', \beta = 46° 52'$.

> *Ans.* $\gamma = 91° 51', b = 12.04, c = 16.50$.

28. $a = 479.4, \alpha = 26° 48', \beta = 50° 0'$.

29. $b = 71.39, \alpha = 42° 11', \beta = 116° 27'$.

> *Ans.* $\gamma = 21° 22', a = 53.54, c = 29.05$.

30. $b = 59.46, \alpha = 108° 52', \beta = 50° 16'$.

31. $b = 23.69$, $c = 30.47$, $\alpha = 31° 15'$.

$Ans.$ $\beta = 50° 16'$, $\gamma = 98° 29'$, $a = 15.98$.

32. $a = 60.04$, $c = 102.31$, $\beta = 47° 29'$.

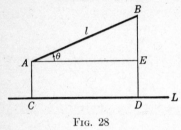

Fig. 28

★41. Projections. — If C and D are the feet of the perpendiculars drawn from points A and B, respectively, to the line L, CD is called the *projection* of AB on L. From the figure,

$$CD = AE = l \cos \theta.$$

EXERCISES

In each of the following examples find the projections of AB on a line which makes the angle θ with AB and on a line perpendicular to such a line.

1. $AB = 367.24$, $\theta = 27° 18.7'$.   *Ans.* 326.30, 168.50.

2. $AB = 982.36$, $\theta = 81° 47.4'$.

3. $AB = 4238.7$, $\theta = 60° 58.1'$.   *Ans.* 2057.0, 3706.1.

4. $AB = 1026.4$, $\theta = 48° 16.4'$.

In each of the following examples find the length of the line which makes the angle θ with a line L, and whose projection on L is AB.

5. $AB = 986.3$, $\theta = 41° 52.7'$.   *Ans.* 1324.7.

6. $AB = 1268.4$, $\theta = 68° 12.3'$.

7. $AB = 823.7$, $\theta = 79° 34.6'$.   *Ans.* 4552.8.

8. $AB = 6.261$, $\theta = 32° 46.9'$.

★42. Surveyors' terms. — *Inclination.* This is the angle which a line run on sloping ground makes with the horizontal. It is positive if the line rises in its forward direction and negative if it falls. In Figure 28, if AE is horizontal, θ is the inclination of AB.

Course of a line. This is the horizontal distance between the ends of the line.

In Figure 28, the course of AB is $AE = AB \cos \theta$. The course is the distance that appears on maps and descriptions of title to pieces of real estate.

Bearing of a line. This is the angle which the line makes with a north-south line.

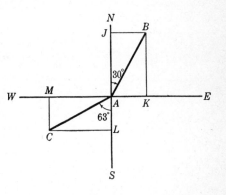

It is 0° if the line runs due north or south, 90° if it runs exactly east or west. In writing it, give first the letter N or S, then the angle of deviation from the north or south, then the letter E or W. In Figure 29 the bearing of AB is $N\ 30°\ E$; that of AC is $S\ 63°\ W$.

Fig. 29

Latitude of a course. This is the distance to the north (and then is positive) or to the south (and then is negative) which one goes in passing over the course.

In Figure 29, the latitude of AB is AJ. The latitude = length × cosine of bearing.

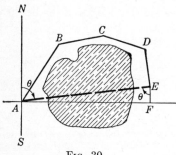

Fig. 30

Departure of a course. This is the distance to the east (and then is positive) or to the west (negative) which one goes while passing over the course.

In Figure 29, AK is the departure of course AB. The departure = length × sine of bearing.

The closing course. To avoid an obstacle which separates two points A and E, a surveyor measures the length and bearing of each part of a broken line, such as *ABCDE*. Then *AE* is the closing course of the broken line. Its latitude and departure are the algebraic sums of the latitudes and departures, respectively, of the partial courses.

Example 1. Find the course *AF* from the following data of lengths and inclinations.

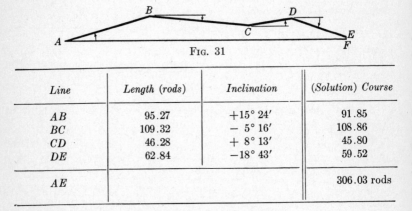

Fig. 31

Line	Length (rods)	Inclination	(Solution) Course
AB	95.27	+15° 24′	91.85
BC	109.32	− 5° 16′	108.86
CD	46.28	+ 8° 13′	45.80
DE	62.84	−18° 43′	59.52
AE			306.03 rods

For the course *AB* we have 95.27 cos 15° 24′ = 91.85.
The other items in the last column are found in a similar way.
Show that point *E* is 1.63 rods higher than *A*.

Example 2. Find the latitude, departure, length, and bearing of the closing course *AE* from the following data of lengths and bearings. (See Figure 30.) (Solution is in italics.)

Course	Length (rods)	Bearing	Latitude +	Latitude −	Departure +	Departure −
AB	147.62	N 33° 12.3′ E	*123.52*		*80.84*	
BC	101.46	N 79° 28.4′ E	*18.54*		*99.75*	
CD	96.24	S 72° 34.1′ E		*28.83*	*91.82*	
DE	81.56	S 8° 14.4′ E		*80.72*	*11.69*	
Total			*142.06*	*109.55*	*284.10*	
AE	*285.94*	N 83° 28.3′ E	*32.51*		*284.10*	

For the course AB, $147.62 \times \cos 33° 12.3' = 123.52$,

and $147.62 \times \sin 33° 12.3' = 80.84$.

The other latitudes and departures are found in a similar way.
The latitude of $AE = 142.06 - 109.55 = 32.51$.
The bearing, θ, of the closing course AE is found by taking (from Figure 30)

$$\cot \theta = \text{latitude/departure} = 32.51/284.10;$$

from which $\theta = 83° 28.3'$. And the length of AE is

$$l = \text{latitude}/\cos \theta = 32.51/\cos 83° 28.3' = 285.94.$$

EXERCISES

Some of these exercises are too long for work in the classroom, but are suitable for home work.

From each of the following sets of data find the horizontal course of the line and its net rise or fall. Draw the figure.

1.

Line	AB	BC	CD	DE	EF
Length (rods)	76.39	28.24	53.67	102.31	37.59
Inclination	$+11° 12'$	$-12° 43'$	$+9° 38'$	$-6° 51'$	$-14° 21'$

         Ans.   Course 293.40 rods; net fall 3.92 rods.

2.

Line	AB	BC	CD	DE
Length (rods)	83.21	62.62	100.30	41.20
Inclination	$-10° 16'$	$-7° 43'$	$+11° 54'$	$+5° 23'$

3.

Line	AB	BC	CD	DE
Length (ft.)	241.3	98.6	101.3	294.7
Inclination	−7° 12′	+6° 24′	−14° 14′	+18° 33′

Ans.   Course 715.0 ft.; net rise 49.6 ft.

4.

Line	AB	BC	CD	DE
Length (ft.)	143.7	91.3	114.5	83.7
Inclination	+6° 7′	+9° 24′	+5° 18′	−13° 39′

From each of the following sets of data find the latitude, departure, length, and bearing of the closing course.   Draw the figure.

5.

Course	AB	BC	CD	DE	EF
Length (ft.)	68.6	95.1	207.4	103.8	96.8
Bearing	N 7° 0′ W	N 15° 51′ E	N 84° 41′ E	S 5° 7′ E	S 49° 53′ W

Ans.   lat., +13.0; dep., +159.3; length, 159.8; N 85° 20′ E.

6.

Course	AB	BC	CD	DE
Length (ft.)	123.4	179.6	153.9	215.2
Bearing	N 73° 6′ E	N 22° 47′ E	N 84° 11′ E	S 54° 26′ E

From the following data find the latitude, departure, course, bearing, and net rise or fall of the closing course.

7.

Line	A B	BC	CD	DE	EF
Length (rods)	35.26	41.57	25.62	31.51	19.62
Inclination	+10° 14′	+6° 27′	−5° 10′	−8° 49′	−11° 37′
Bearing	S 61° 10′ E	N 81° 41′ E	N 28° 18′ E	N 32° 30′ W	N 10° 18′ E

Ans. Lat., 57.00; dep., 70.00; course, 90.27; bearing, N 50° 51′ E; net fall, 0.15 rods.

✶43. Forces and vectors. — In studying the forces that act on a body, it is convenient to think of them as vectors. A *vector* is a directed magnitude. Forces and velocities, for example, are vectors, since they have both magnitude and direction. A vector can be represented by a line segment whose length is proportional to the magnitude and whose direction is the direction of the vector. In Figure 32 the lines OP_1, OP_2, and OP_3 represent forces of three pounds, two pounds, and two and one-half pounds acting in the directions, N 55° E, N 25° W, and S 20° E.

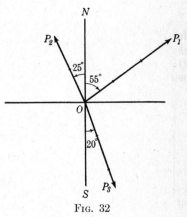

Fig. 32

If two or more forces act on a body at the same time, their combined effect is the same as would be that of a single force having a certain magnitude and direction. This single force is called the *sum* or *resultant* of the separate forces.

In a similar way, the velocity of a body may result from two or more elementary or component velocities. For example, if a man walks across the deck of a moving ship, his velocity relative to the ship combines with the velocity of the ship to give his velocity relative to the earth.

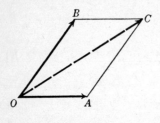

FIG. 33

If OA and OB represent two vectors, the sum or resultant of these vectors is represented both in direction and in magnitude by OC, the diagonal of the parallelogram of which OA and OB are adjacent sides.

It is a law of physics, proved both by experiment and theory, that *if two forces act on a body, they have the same effect as would their resultant acting alone.*

✴44. Components of a force. — If OC is the resultant of two forces, OA and OB, OA and OB are called *the components of OC in the directions OA and OB.* In particular, if the directions OA and OB are perpendicular to each other, and if OC makes the angle θ with OA,

$$OA = OC \cdot \cos \theta \quad \text{and} \quad OB = OC \cdot \sin \theta.$$

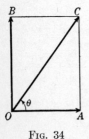

FIG. 34

EXAMPLE. Find the force necessary to push a ball which weighs 10 pounds up a plane inclined 20° to the horizontal.

The weight or force, OC, of ten pounds acts vertically downward. The component of this force OA, which is parallel to the inclined plane, and which the desired force must overcome, is

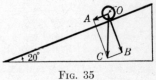

FIG. 35

$$OA = 10 \cos \angle AOC = 10 \cos 70° = 3.4 \text{ pounds.}$$

In order to roll the ball up hill it is therefore necessary to exert a force of 3.4 pounds in addition to the small force necessary to roll the ball on a level plane. The pressure of the ball against the plane is

$$OB = 10 \cos \angle BOC = 10 \cos 20° = 9.4 \text{ pounds.}$$

EXERCISES

1. A vertical force of 38.4 lbs. and a horizontal force of 17.6 lbs. act on a body. Find the magnitude and direction of their resultant.

Ans. 42.2 lbs., 65° 23′ from horizontal.

2. A body is acted on by a horizontal force of 98.3 lbs. and by a downward force of 173.6 lbs. Find the direction and magnitude of their resultant.

3. Find the horizontal and vertical components of a force of 987.6 lbs. inclined at 73° 25′ to the horizontal.

Ans. Horizontal, 281.9; vertical, 946.5.

4. Find the horizontal and vertical components of a force of 624.9 lbs. inclined at 21° 16′ to the horizontal.

5. A body is acted upon by a force of 706.3 lbs. in the direction N 53° 16′ E, and also by a force of 528.6 lbs. in the direction S 28° 39′ E. Find the east-west and north-south components, the direction and the magnitude of their resultant.

Ans. East, 819.5 lbs.; south 41.4; S 87° 6′ E; 820.5 lbs.

6. A body is acted upon by a force of 1263 lbs. in the direction N 42° 51′ E and by a force of 946 lbs. in the direction N 10° 18′ W. Find the east-west and north-south components, the direction, and the magnitude of the resultant.

7. A body is acted upon by a force of 1384 lbs. in the direction N 57° 12′ W, by a force of 1682 lbs., in the direction N 74° 46′ E, and by a force of 1964 lbs. in the direction S 6° 57′ W. Find the east-west and north-south components, the direction, and the magnitudes of their resultant.

Ans. East, 222 lbs.; south, 758 lbs.; S 16° 19′ E; 790 lbs.

8. A body is acted on by three forces having the following directions and magnitudes: 1006 lbs., N 17° 5′ E; 984 lbs., due east; 1382 lbs., S 31° 31′ W. Find the east-west and north-south components, the direction, and the magnitude of the resultant.

9. A body is acted on by a force of 18.63 lbs. in the direction N 28° 46′ E and by a force of 15.79 lbs. in the direction S 41° 28′ E. Find the magnitude and direction of a force which just counteracts them.   *Ans.* 19.93 lbs., S 76° 57′ W.

10. A certain force just counteracts the combined effect of a force of 213.6 lbs. in the direction $S\ 26°\ 29'\ E$ and a force of 187.7 lbs. in the direction $N\ 31°\ 11'\ W$. Find its magnitude and direction.

11. A ship travels due east making 20 miles per hour. A man walks directly across the deck at 4 miles per hour. Find his direction and velocity relative to the earth. *Ans.* $N\ 78°\ 41'\ E$; 20.4 mi./hr.

12. A duck which swims 5 miles per hour in still water swims directly across a current of 8 miles per hour. Find its actual velocity and direction.

13. An automobile is pulled by a cable up an inclined plane to the second floor of a repair shop. If the car weighs 2096 lbs. and the slope is $37°\ 45'$ from the horizontal, what is the tension in the cable?
Ans. 1283 lbs.

14. The approach to a bridge is inclined at $14°\ 25'$. What is the pressure against it due to the weight of a car which weighs 1895 lbs.?

15. How much more force is necessary to move a car weighing 2985 lbs. up a grade of $5°$ than to move one weighing 1985 lbs.?
Ans. 87.2 lbs. At a speed of 15 miles per hour this requires a difference in power of about 3.5 horse-power.

16. A mass of 387.46 lbs. rests on an inclined plane. A force of 238.18 lbs. is required to keep it from sliding down. What is the angle of inclination of the plane? Neglect friction.

17. A beam when horizontal can support 3847 lbs. What weight can it support if inclined at $28°\ 36'$? *Ans.* 4382 lbs.

18. A steel rafter which is inclined at $47°\ 16'$ supports a total weight of 4676 lbs. What is the end thrust or pressure of the rafter against the supporting girder?

19. A guy wire runs from the top of a telephone pole 38 ft. high to a point on the ground 23 ft. from the pole. The tension in the guy wire is 164 lbs. Find the horizontal component of this used in supporting the pole, and also the vertical component which adds to the downward thrust of the pole.
Ans. Horizontal, 84.9 lbs.; vertical, 140.3 lbs.

20. A cable is stretched from the top of a tower. At its point of attachment it makes an angle of $4°\ 2'$ with the horizontal. Its tension is 7846 lbs. Find its horizontal and vertical components.

21. A horizontal wire pulls with a force of 468 lbs. on the top of a pole 96 ft. high. Its pull is opposed by that of a guy wire attached to the ground at a point 44 ft. from the pole in the opposite direction. Find the tension in the guy wire if its pull just counteracts that of the horizontal wire. *Ans.* 1123 lbs.

22. A cable is supported by two steel towers. Its sag is such that at its point of support on one of the towers it makes an angle of 18° 19′ with the horizontal and its tension is 4980 lbs. Find its lateral pull and downward pressure on the tower.

23. A concrete pouring tower is 124 ft. high. Two guy wires run from its top to points on the ground which are on opposite sides of the tower, and are, respectively, 163 ft. and 71 ft. from the tower. The tension in the longer wire is 412 lbs. What is the tension in the shorter wire if it just overcomes the lateral pull of the longer one? What is the combined downward pull of the two wires on the tower?
Ans. Tension, 660 lbs.; downward pull, 822 lbs.

24. A boat is fast on a bar. The crew run out an anchor 64 ft. from the boat. It sinks to a depth of 18 ft. below the level of the deck. By winding the anchor cable on a capstan on the deck the crew hope to free the boat. If a horizontal pull of 1874 lbs. is required, what tension will be necessary in the cable?

CHAPTER V

RADIAN MEASURE

45. Definition of a radian. — In most problems involving the numerical values of the angles of a triangle, it is customary to express angles in terms of degrees and minutes. This is not the only system

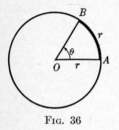

Fig. 36

of units for measuring angles, however, and for many purposes, notably in almost all problems involving the methods of calculus, it is best to express angles in terms of a different unit of angular measure called the radian.

Definition. A radian is an angle which, if its vertex is placed at the center of a circle, subtends on the circumference an arc equal to the radius of the circle.

In the figure, θ is equal to one radian, since the arc AB and the radius OA are equal. It is to be noticed that *a radian is an angle of fixed magnitude* and does not depend on the size of the circle at whose center it may happen to be placed, for the subtended arc is proportional to the radius.

46. Degrees and radians. — The circumference of any circle is equal to 2π times its radius. That is, the circumference contains 2π arcs each equal to the radius. Each such arc subtends at the center an angle of one radian, and the entire circumference subtends 2π radians. Therefore 360° equals 2π radians, or

(1) $$\pi \text{ radians } = 180°.$$

Consequently

(2) $$1 \text{ radian} = \frac{180}{\pi} = \frac{180}{3.1416} \text{ degrees,}$$

or

(3) $$1 \text{ radian} = 57.2958° = 57° \ 17.75'.$$

On the other hand

(4) $$1° = \frac{\pi}{180} \text{ radians} = .017453 \text{ radians.}$$

When no other unit of angular measure is indicated it is assumed that an angle is expressed in radian measure. For example, in writing $\theta = \pi/2$ we mean that θ is $\pi/2$ radians or $90°$.

EXERCISES

The following angles are given in radian measure. Express them in degrees.

1. $\pi/3$.	*Ans.*	$60°$.	2. 2π.	
3. $\pi/4$.	*Ans.*	$45°$.	4. $\pi/6$.	
5. $3\pi/2$.	*Ans.*	$270°$.	6. $2\pi/3$.	
7. $2\pi/5$.	*Ans.*	$72°$.	8. $7\pi/6$.	
9. $3\pi/4$.	*Ans.*	$135°$.	10. $11\pi/6$.	
11. $4\pi/3$.	*Ans.*	$240°$.	12. $5\pi/3$.	
13. $-5\pi/4$.	*Ans.*	$-225°$.	14. $-\pi/10$.	
15. $-\pi/2$.	*Ans.*	$-90°$.	16. -2π.	

Express in radian measure.

17. $36°$.	*Ans.*	$\pi/5$.	18. $90°$.	
19. $60°$.	*Ans.*	$\pi/3$.	20. $45°$.	
21. $330°$.	*Ans.*	$11\pi/6$.	22. $-210°$.	
23. $120°$.	*Ans.*	$2\pi/3$.	24. $240°$.	
25. $-135°$.	*Ans.*	$-3\pi/4$.	26. $150°$.	
27. $300°$.	*Ans.*	$5\pi/3$.	28. $270°$.	
29. $17°$.	*Ans.*	$.2967$.	30. $46°$.	
31. $-86° 30'$.	*Ans.*	-1.5097.	32. $113° 15'$.	
33. $24° 16'$.	*Ans.*	$.42353$.	34. $100° 38'$.	
35. $49° 48.7'$.	*Ans.*	$.86937$.	36. $62° 29.4'$.	

Give the values of the following functions.

37. $\sin \pi/6$.	*Ans.*	$1/2$.	38. $\cos \pi/3$.	
39. $\tan \pi/4$.	*Ans.*	1.	40. $\cot \pi/6$.	
41. $\cos 3\pi/4$.	*Ans.*	$-\frac{1}{2}\sqrt{2}$.	42. $\tan 5\pi/4$.	

Give in radian measure a value of θ less than 2π for each case:

43. $\sin\theta = \frac{1}{2}\sqrt{3}$.   *Ans.* $\pi/3$.   **44.** $\tan\theta = \frac{1}{3}\sqrt{3}$.

45. $\tan\theta = -1$.   *Ans.* $3\pi/4$.   **46.** $\sin\theta = 0$.

47. $\sec\theta = 2$.   *Ans.* $\pi/3$.   **48.** $\cot\theta = 1$.

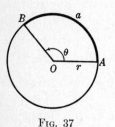

Fig. 37

47. Central angles and their subtended arcs. — If an angle equal to one radian is placed at the center of a circle of radius r, it subtends on the circumference an arc equal to r. Therefore a central angle equal to θ radians subtends on the circumference an arc whose length is equal to θr. If a denotes the length of the arc,

$$a = \theta r.$$

In this formula, we must remember, θ is *the number of radians* in the central angle. When we are given any two of the three numbers a, r, and θ, the formula may be used to find the third number.

EXAMPLE 1. On a circle of radius 9 inches, what arc will be subtended by a central angle of 36°? Here $r = 9$; the central angle is $36° = \pi/5$ radians, so that $\theta = \pi/5$. Therefore

$$a = \frac{\pi}{5} \cdot 9 = \frac{3.142 \times 9}{5} = 5.66 \text{ inches.}$$

EXAMPLE 2. On a circle 1 foot in diameter, what central angle will subtend an arc equal to 10 inches? If we use an inch as the unit of length, $r = 6$, $a = 10$, and

$$\theta = \frac{a}{r} = \frac{10}{6} = \frac{5}{3} \text{ radians} = \frac{5}{3} \times \frac{180°}{\pi} = 95° \, 30'.$$

EXAMPLE 3. What must be the radius of a wheel, on the rim of which an arc 16.1 inches long is subtended by a central angle of 25°? Here $\theta = 25\pi/180$, so that

$$r = \frac{a}{\theta} = \frac{16.1 \times 180}{25 \cdot \pi} = 36.9 \text{ inches.}$$

✶48. Linear and angular velocity. — If an object is moving uniformly, its *linear velocity* is its rate of motion; it is equal to the distance passed over in a certain time divided by the time, or to the number of units of distance passed over in one unit of time.

EXAMPLE. An object which travels steadily 20 yards in 5 seconds has a linear velocity equal to $20/5 = 4$ yards per second.

If an object turns uniformly, its *angular velocity* is its rate of turning; it is equal to the angle through which it turns in a certain time divided by the time, or to the number of units of angle through which the object turns in one unit of time.

EXAMPLES. An object which turns uniformly through 150° in 10 seconds has an angular velocity equal to $150/10 = 15$ degrees per second. An object which turns through 12 radians in 3 minutes has an angular velocity equal to 4 radians per minute.

If, in t units of time, an object turns through the angle θ, its angular velocity is

(1)
$$\alpha = \frac{\theta}{t}.$$

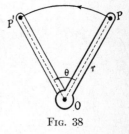

Suppose that an object revolve uniformly about the point O with the angular velocity α radians per second. Let us find the linear velocity of a point P which is on the object at the distance r from O. In one second the line OP turns through α radians, and the point P moves through an arc whose length is $r \cdot \alpha$. The linear velocity, v, of the point P is therefore

FIG. 38

(2)
$$v = r \cdot \alpha$$

units of length per second. From this and equation (1), we see that if OP turns uniformly through θ radians in t units of time, its linear velocity is

(3)
$$v = \frac{r \cdot \theta}{t}.$$

EXAMPLE 1. A pulley 1 foot in diameter makes 500 revolutions per minute. Find its angular velocity in radians per second and the speed of the belt which drives the pulley. *Solution:* In each revolution the pulley turns through 2π radians, so that in one minute it turns through $500 \times 2\pi$ radians. By equation (1) its angular velocity is therefore

$$\alpha = \frac{1000\,\pi}{60} = 52.36 \text{ radians per second.}$$

The speed of the belt is equal to the linear velocity of a point on the rim of the pulley. The radius of the pulley is $\frac{1}{2}$ foot, so that, by (2), the speed of the belt or pulley is

$$v = \tfrac{1}{2} \times 52.36 = 26.18 \text{ feet per second.}$$

EXERCISES

In the following exercises, r represents the radius of a circle, θ a central angle, and a the length of the subtended arc. In each case find the required number.

	r	θ	a	*Answer*
1.	10 in.	2 radians	required	20 in.
2.	3 ft.	8 radians	required	
3.	564.73 in.	$\pi/6$ radians	required	295.69 in.
4.	7046.9 ft.	$2\pi/3$ radians	required	
5.	40 ft.	required in radians	30 ft.	.75 radians
6.	21 ft.	required in radians	35 ft.	
7.	209.78 rods	required in radians	318.69 rods	1.5191 radians
8.	1243.6 ft.	required in radians	697.32 ft.	
9.	required	$\pi/2$ radians	600 ft.	382 ft.
10.	required	3 radians	627 ft.	
11.	1653.8 ft.	17°	required	490.7 ft.
12.	407.35 rods	46°	required	
13.	637.18 rods	required in degrees	214.79 rods	19° 18.8′
14.	427.6 ft.	required in degrees	516.5 ft.	
15.	required	38° 18.4′	776.4 ft.	1161.3 ft.
16.	required	29° 48′	1024.3 ft.	

17. A railroad curve is laid out on a circle of radius 723 feet. What is its length, if it subtends an angle of 23° 17′ at the center?

Ans. 293.8 ft.

18. A pendulum 37.46 inches long swings through an arc of 3.63 inches. Find the angle through which it swings, in degrees.

19. An automobile has tires 30.5 inches in diameter. (*a*) How many revolutions will a wheel make in one mile? (*b*) Through how many radians will the wheel turn in one mile?

       Ans. (*a*) 661.2 revs. (*b*) 4154.7 rads.

20. A pulley 18.7 inches in diameter is driven by a belt. (*a*) How far will the belt travel while the pulley makes 100 revolutions? (*b*) How far will it travel while the pulley turns through 6 radians?

21. What is the angular velocity of a wheel which makes 20 revolutions per second? *Ans.* 40π rads. per sec., or 7200 deg. per sec.

22. How many revolutions per minute are made by a wheel which turns with an angular velocity of 12 radians per second?

23. What is the linear velocity of a pulley 20 inches in diameter making 500 revolutions per minute? *Ans.* 43.63 ft. per sec.

24. What is the radius of a pulley if a belt traveling at the rate of 56 feet per second drives it at the rate of 360 revolutions per minute?

25. A wheel 29 inches in diameter is turning with an angular velocity of 6.4 radians per second. What is the linear velocity of a point on the rim? *Ans.* 7.7 ft. per sec.

26. The rim of a wheel 42 inches in diameter has a linear velocity of 18 feet per second. What is the angular velocity in radians per second? In degrees per second?

27. What is the radius of a wheel which has an angular velocity of 264 degrees per second when driven by a chain on the wheel which travels 140 feet per minute? *Ans.* 6.08 ins.

28. The minute hand of a clock is 6 inches long. How far does its end travel in 25 minutes?

29. An automobile has tires 32 inches in diameter. When the car travels 20 miles an hour how fast does a wheel turn on its axle in revolutions per second? What is its angular velocity in radians per second? Take $\pi = 22/7$. *Ans.* $3\frac{1}{2}$ r.p.s.; 22 radians per sec.

30. An airplane propellor makes 1975 revolutions per minute, and is 7 feet 9 inches from tip to tip. What is the linear velocity of its tip?

CHAPTER VI

PROPERTIES OF THE TRIGONOMETRIC FUNCTIONS

49. Related angles. — Our tables of trigonometric functions are formed only for positive acute angles. If we are to use them to find the functions of other angles, we must therefore be able to express the functions of any angle in terms of the functions of an acute angle. This we may do by the use of a *related angle*. If θ is any angle, we shall call the related angle of θ the positive acute angle which, when added to or subtracted from θ, gives an angle coterminal with either 180° or 360°.

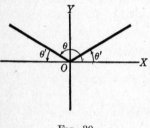

Fig. 39

EXAMPLES. In the figure, θ' is the related angle of θ. The related angle of 216° is 36°, since 216° − 36° = 180°. The related angle of 336° is 24°, since 336° + 24° = 360°.

EXERCISES

For each of the following angles find the related angle.

1. 98°	*Ans.* 82°.	**2.**	164°.
3. 200°.	*Ans.* 20°.	**4.**	252°.
5. 295°.	*Ans.* 65°.	**6.**	340°.
7. −476°.	*Ans.* 64°.	**8.**	848°.
9. −112°.	*Ans.* 68°.	**10.**	−17°.

50. A standard construction. — In the following paragraphs, when any two angles θ and θ' are considered we shall suppose that (1) θ and θ' are in standard position on a set of coördinate axes; (2) P is some

80

conveniently chosen point on the terminal side of θ; (3) (x, y) and r are the coördinates and radius vector of P; (4) P' is the point on the terminal side of θ' which is *at the same distance, $r' = r$, from the origin* as is P; (5) (x', y') are the coördinates of P'; (6) M and M', respectively, are the feet of the perpendiculars drawn from P and P' to the x-axis.

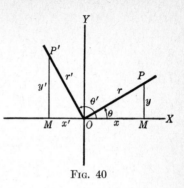

Fig. 40

EXERCISES

Draw the figure for this standard construction for each of the following cases:

1. $\theta = 60°$, $\theta' = 150°$.   2. $\theta = 30°$, $\theta' = -30°$.
3. $\theta = 210°$, $\theta' = -210°$.   4. $\theta = 150°$, $\theta' = \theta + 90°$.
5. $\theta = 240°$, $\theta' = \theta - 180°$.   6. $\theta = 240°$, $\theta' = \theta - 270°$.

In each of the following cases show that the triangles OMP and $OM'P'$ are equal, when θ is an acute angle.

7. $\theta' = -\theta$.   8. $\theta' = 180° - \theta$.
9. $\theta' = \theta + 180°$.   10. $\theta' = 360° - \theta$.

In the following cases show that triangles OMP and $OM'P'$ are equal for all values of θ. Draw the figure for at least two values of θ taken in different quadrants.

11. $\theta' = -\theta$.   12. $\theta' = \theta + 90°$.   13. $\theta' = \theta + 180°$.
14. $\theta' = \theta + 270°$.   15. $\theta' =$ the related angle of θ.

51. Functions of related angles. — *Theorem: Any trigonometric function of an angle is numerically equal to the same function of the related angle.* To prove this, let θ be any angle (shown in second, third and fourth quadrants in Figure 41). Denote by θ' its related

angle, and make the standard construction of Article **50**. The right
triangles OMP and $OM'P'$ are then equal (Example 15, Article **50**),
and their parts correspond so that r and r', x and x', y and y' are

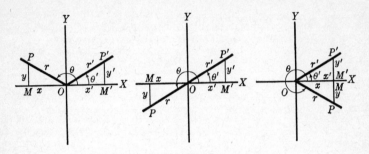

FIG. 41

numerically equal (that is, equal except perhaps for sign).   Consequently

$$\frac{y}{r} \text{ and } \frac{y'}{r'}, \qquad \frac{x}{r} \text{ and } \frac{x'}{r'}, \qquad \frac{y}{x} \text{ and } \frac{y'}{x'},$$

$$\frac{x}{y} \text{ and } \frac{x'}{y'}, \qquad \frac{r}{x} \text{ and } \frac{r'}{x'}, \qquad \frac{r}{y} \text{ and } \frac{r'}{y'}$$

are numerically equal.   Therefore

$\sin \theta$ and $\sin \theta'$,	$\cos \theta$ and $\cos \theta'$,	$\tan \theta$ and $\tan \theta'$,
$\cot \theta$ and $\cot \theta'$,	$\sec \theta$ and $\sec \theta'$,	$\csc \theta$ and $\csc \theta'$

are numerically equal.   Any trigonometric function of an angle is
numerically equal to the same function of the related angle.   The
sign of a given function of θ can be determined by the quadrant in
which θ terminates.

If θ is an angle between 90° and 180°, we can write it as $(180° - \alpha)$
where α is the related angle of θ.   If θ is between 180° and 270°,
$\theta = 180° + \alpha$; and if θ is between 270° and 360°, $\theta = 360° - \alpha$,
where, in each case, α is the related angle of θ.   We can therefore
say that *if α is any acute angle, any function of the angle $(180° - \alpha)$*

or of the angle (180° + α) *or of the angle* (360° − α) *is numerically equal to the same function of* α.   Later on in this chapter it will be shown that this statement is true when α is *any* angle.

EXAMPLE 1.   Express the sine and cotangent of 147° 35′ as functions of an acute angle.   The related angle is 32° 25′.   Since 147° 35′ is in the second quadrant, its sine is positive and its cotangent is negative.   Therefore

$$\sin 147° \, 35′ = \sin 32° \, 25′,$$
$$\cot 147° \, 35′ = -\cot 32° \, 25′.$$

EXAMPLE 2.   Find the sine and cosine of 163° 12′.   The related angle is 16° 48′.   The desired numbers are numerically equal to sin 16° 48′ = .28903 and cos 16° 48′ = .95732.   Since 163° 12′ is in the second quadrant, its sine is positive and its cosine is negative.   Therefore sin 163° 12′ = .28903, and cos 163° 12′ = −.95732.

EXAMPLE 3.   Find the sine and tangent of 258° 23′.   The related angle is 78° 23′.   Since 258° 23′ is in the third quadrant, its sine is negative and its tangent is positive.   Therefore

$$\sin 258° \, 23′ = -\sin 78° \, 23′ = -.97952,$$
$$\tan 258° \, 23′ = \tan 78° \, 23′ = 4.8644.$$

EXAMPLE 4.   By logarithms find the value of

$$x = 47.61 \times \cos 212° \, 16′.$$

We have

$$x = 47.61 \times (-\cos 32° \, 16′) = -47.61 \times \cos 32° \, 16′.$$

Negative numbers have no real logarithms.   We shall therefore first compute the value of

$$47.61 \times \cos 32° \, 16′,$$

and then prefix the negative sign.

$$\log 47.61 = 1.67770$$
$$\underline{\log \cos 32° \, 16′ = 9.92715 - 10}$$
$$1.60485$$

$$-x = 40.26, \qquad x = -40.26.$$

EXERCISES

Without using tables, find the values of the trigonometric functions of the following angles.

1. 120°.	**2.** 135°.	**3.** −30°.
4. −45°.	**5.** 210°.	**6.** 240°.
7. −150°.	**8.** −120°.	**9.** 225°.
10. 315°.	**11.** 300°.	**12.** −180°.
13. 480°.	**14.** 660°.	**15.** 570°.
16. 780°.	**17.** −405°.	**18.** −495°.

Using the five-place tables, find the values of the following functions.

19. sin 114° 26′.	*Ans.* .91044.	**20.** cos 172° 51′.
21. tan 197° 14′.	*Ans.* .31019.	**22.** cot 256° 18′.
23. cos 538° 46′.	*Ans.* −.99977.	**24.** sin 324° 19′.
25. cot 462° 12′.	*Ans.* −.21621.	**26.** tan 283° 11′.
27. sin 211° 53′.	*Ans.* −.52819.	**28.** tan 654° 17′.
29. cos (−100° 12′).	*Ans.* −.17708.	**30.** cot (−267° 54′).
31. cot 131° 16.9′.	*Ans.* −.87796.	**32.** sin (−124° 28.3′).
33. tan 169° 13.7′.	*Ans.* −.19025.	**34.** cos 101° 15.6′.

Find the values of the following numbers by logarithms.

35. 28.36 × sin 124° 42′.	*Ans.*	23.32.
36. 11.32 × cos 301° 12′.		
37. 304.7 × tan 227° 33′.	*Ans.*	333.1.
38. 294.6 × cot 254° 48′.		
39. 103.6 × cos 147° 16′.	*Ans.*	−87.15.
40. 7203 × tan 129° 29′.		
41. 6.048 × cot 298° 24′.	*Ans.*	−3.270.
42. .05679 × sin 342° 24′.		
43. 17.632 × cos 212° 13.4′.	*Ans.*	−14.916.
44. 399.536 ÷ cos 186° 42.3′.		
45. 41.763 × csc 304° 17′.	*Ans.*	−50.544.
46. 501.43 × sec 501° 43′.		

52. Functions of $(-\theta)$. — Let θ be any angle, and let $\theta' = -\theta$. Make the standard construction of Article **50**. The triangles OMP and $OM'P'$ are equal (Example 11, Article **50**). Therefore points P and P' are symmetrically placed on opposite sides of the x-axis, and $x' = x$ and $y' = -y$. Consequently

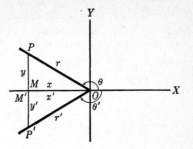

Fig. 42

$$\sin(-\theta) = \frac{y'}{r'} = \frac{-y}{r} = -\sin\theta, \qquad \cos(-\theta) = \frac{x'}{r'} = \frac{x}{r} = \cos\theta,$$

$$\tan(-\theta) = \frac{y'}{x'} = -\frac{y}{x} = -\tan\theta, \qquad \cot(-\theta) = \frac{x'}{y'} = \frac{x}{-y} = -\cot\theta,$$

$$\sec(-\theta) = \frac{r'}{x'} = \frac{r}{x} = \sec\theta, \qquad \csc(-\theta) = \frac{r'}{y'} = \frac{r}{-y} = -\csc\theta.$$

These results can be expressed as follows: *Changing the sign of an angle without changing its numerical value, leaves the cosine and secant of the angle unchanged, but reverses the signs of all the other functions without changing their numerical values.*

We sometimes say that an expression which is not changed in any way when the sign of the variable is reversed is an *even function* of the variable. Thus any *even* power of x is an even function of x, since x^2, x^4, x^6, etc., are unchanged if x is replaced by $(-x)$. Hence the name even function. Likewise, a function such as x, x^3, x^5 or any odd power of x, which reverses its sign but is unchanged in numerical value when the sign of the variable is changed, is called an *odd function* of the variable. We can say, then, that $\cos\theta$ and $\sec\theta$ are even functions of θ, and all the other trigonometric functions are odd functions of θ.

If θ is any angle, $360° - \theta$ is coterminal with $(-\theta)$. The functions of $(360° - \theta)$ are therefore numerically equal to the same functions of θ.

★**53. Functions of $(\theta + 90°)$.** — Let θ be any angle, and let $\theta' = \theta + 90°$. Make the standard construction of Article **50**.

The angle θ may be in any quadrant and the figure is drawn for each quadrant. The right triangles OMP and $OM'P'$ are equal (Example

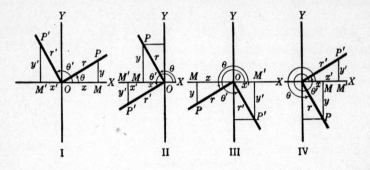

Fig. 43

12, Article **50**), the horizontal side of one being equal to the vertical side of the other. Taking account of the signs, we have, *for all four figures:*

$$x' = -y, \qquad y' = x, \qquad r' = r.$$

Therefore, by the definitions of the trigonometric functions,

$$\sin \theta' = \frac{y'}{r'} = \frac{x}{r} = \cos \theta, \qquad \cos \theta' = \frac{x'}{r'} = \frac{-y}{r} = -\sin \theta,$$

$$\tan \theta' = \frac{y'}{x'} = \frac{x}{-y} = -\cot \theta, \qquad \cot \theta' = \frac{x'}{y'} = \frac{-y}{x} = -\tan \theta,$$

$$\sec \theta' = \frac{r'}{x'} = \frac{r}{-y} = -\csc \theta, \qquad \csc \theta' = \frac{r'}{y'} = \frac{r}{x} = \sec \theta,$$

or

$$\sin (\theta + 90°) = \cos \theta, \qquad \cos (\theta + 90°) = -\sin \theta,$$
$$\tan (\theta + 90°) = -\cot \theta, \qquad \cot (\theta + 90°) = -\tan \theta,$$
$$\sec (\theta + 90°) = -\csc \theta, \qquad \csc (\theta + 90°) = \sec \theta.$$

These and similar formulas should always be translated by the student into words, as, for example:

If two angles differ by 90°, the sine of the larger angle is equal to the cosine of the smaller angle; the cosine of the larger is equal to the negative of the sine of the smaller, etc.

★ **54. Functions of $(\theta - 90°)$.** — If, in the results of the preceding paragraph, we indicate the *larger* angle by θ, the smaller one will be $(\theta - 90°)$, and we have

$$\sin (\theta - 90°) = -\cos \theta, \qquad \cos (\theta - 90°) = \sin \theta,$$
$$\tan (\theta - 90°) = -\cot \theta, \qquad \cot (\theta - 90°) = -\tan \theta,$$
$$\sec (\theta - 90°) = \csc \theta, \qquad \csc (\theta - 90°) = -\sec \theta.$$

Combining these results with those for the functions of $(-\theta)$, since $(90° - \theta)$ is the negative of $(\theta - 90°)$, we have

$$\sin (90° - \theta) = \cos \theta, \qquad \cos (90° - \theta) = \sin \theta,$$
$$\tan (90° - \theta) = \cot \theta, \qquad \cot (90° - \theta) = \tan \theta,$$
$$\sec (90° - \theta) = \csc \theta, \qquad \csc (90° - \theta) = \sec \theta.$$

★ **55. Functions of $(\theta \pm 180°)$.** — The functions of $(\theta + 180°)$ can be expressed in terms of the functions of θ by adding 90° to $(\theta + 90°)$ and applying the results of Article **53** twice. Thus, we may write

$$\sin (\theta + 180°) = \sin [(\theta + 90°) + 90°] = \cos (\theta + 90°) = -\sin \theta.$$

We obtain the formulas

$$\sin (\theta + 180°) = -\sin \theta, \qquad \cos (\theta + 180°) = -\cos \theta,$$
$$\tan (\theta + 180°) = \tan \theta, \qquad \cot (\theta + 180°) = \cot \theta,$$
$$\sec (\theta + 180°) = -\sec \theta, \qquad \csc (\theta + 180°) = -\csc \theta.$$

The functions of $(\theta - 180°)$ are the same as those of $(\theta + 180°)$ since these two angles have the same terminal sides. Since $(180° - \theta)$ is the negative of $(\theta - 180°)$, its functions are numerically the same as the same functions of θ.

EXERCISE: Write out formulas for $\sin (180° - \theta)$, $\cos (180° - \theta)$, etc., in terms of the functions of θ.

★56. Functions of (θ ± 270°). — The functions of $(\theta + 270°)$ may be expressed in terms of the functions of θ by combining the results of Articles **53** and **55**. Thus,

$$\sin(\theta + 270°) = \sin[(\theta + 180°) + 90°] = \cos(\theta + 180°) = -\cos\theta.$$

We can thus obtain definite formulas which hold for all values of θ. It is best to remember, however, merely the fact that any function of $(\theta \pm 270°)$ is numerically the same as the cofunction of θ, the algebraic sign being determined by the quadrant in which the angle terminates.

EXERCISE: Write formulas for the functions of $(\theta + 270°)$, $(\theta - 270°)$ and $(270° - \theta)$ in terms of the functions of θ.

★57. Summary. — Any function of $(-\theta)$, $(\theta + 180°)$, $(\theta - 180°)$, $(180° - \theta)$, or of $(360° - \theta)$ is numerically equal to the same function of θ. Any function of $(\theta + 90°)$, $(\theta + 270°)$, $(90° - \theta)$, $(\theta - 270°)$, or $(270° - \theta)$ is numerically equal to the cofunction of θ. The algebraic sign to be used in the formula connecting a function of any one of these angles with the same function or cofunction of θ will be the same whether θ is in the first or in some other quadrant. To determine the algebraic sign, then, assume that θ is in the first quadrant, and construct the given angle. From the figure determine whether the required function is plus or minus the function or cofunction of θ.

We need not consider especially such angles as $\theta + 630°$, since the functions of this angle are the same as the functions of the coterminal angle $(\theta + 630°) - 360° = \theta + 270°$, which has been considered above.

EXAMPLE 1. Express $\cos(540° + \theta)$ as a function of θ. We write $\cos(540° + \theta) = \cos(180° + \theta)$. This is *numerically* equal to $\cos\theta$. To determine whether it has the same sign as $\cos\theta$ or the opposite sign, we see that *if* θ is in the first quadrant (so that $\cos\theta$ is positive), $(\theta + 180°)$ is in the third quadrant, so that its cosine is negative. Therefore

$$\cos(\theta + 540°) = -\cos\theta,$$

for all values of θ.

EXAMPLE 2. Express tan $(7\pi/2 - \theta)$ as a function of θ. We have

$$\tan\left(\frac{7\pi}{2} - \theta\right) = \tan\left[\left(\frac{7\pi}{2} - \theta\right) - 2\pi\right] = \tan\left(\frac{3\pi}{2} - \theta\right).$$

Numerically this is equal to cot θ, since $3\pi/2$ radians equals 270°. If θ is in the first quadrant, $(3\pi/2 - \theta)$ is in the third quadrant. Therefore its tangent is positive, and

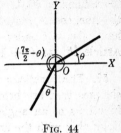

$$\tan (7\pi/2 - \theta) = \cot \theta$$

for all values of θ.

Fig. 44

EXERCISES

Express each of the following functions as a function of θ.

1. sin $(270° + \theta)$.   *Ans.* $-\cos \theta$.   **2.** cos $(\theta - 270°)$.
3. cos $(540° + \theta)$.   *Ans.* $-\cos \theta$.   **4.** tan $(\theta + 180°)$.
5. tan $(810° + \theta)$.   *Ans.* $-\cot \theta$.   **6.** cot $(450° + \theta)$.
7. cot $(\theta - 630°)$.   *Ans.* $-\tan \theta$.   **8.** sin $(1080° + \theta)$.
9. tan $(540° + \theta)$.   *Ans.* $\tan \theta$.   **10.** cos $(720° - \theta)$.
11. sin $(810° - \theta)$.   *Ans.* $\cos \theta$.   **12.** tan $(900° - \theta)$.
13. csc $(900° - \theta)$.   *Ans.* $\csc \theta$.   **14.** sin $(630° - \theta)$.
15. cos $(\pi + \theta)$.   *Ans.* $-\cos \theta$.   **16.** tan $(3\pi/2 + \theta)$.
17. cot $(4\pi - \theta)$.   *Ans.* $-\cot \theta$.   **18.** sec $(5\pi/2 + \theta)$.
19. csc $(9\pi/2 + \theta)$.   *Ans.* $\sec \theta$.   **20.** tan $(7\pi/2 - \theta)$.

58. Periodic functions. — We have seen that if an angle is increased by 360° or 2π radians, the value of the sine of the angle is unchanged. That is, if θ is any angle,

$$\sin (\theta + 2\pi) = \sin \theta.$$

The values of the sine of an angle thus recur *periodically*, the period of recurrence being 2π.

An expression in θ which, for every value of θ, is unchanged when θ is increased by p, is said to be a *periodic function of θ with period p*. The values assumed by the function in any interval of length p will be taken on in any other interval of the same length.

The trigonometric functions are all periodic functions of period 2π radians or 360°. This is the smallest or fundamental period for the sine, cosine, secant and cosecant. But the tangent and cotangent have also a smaller period equal to π radians or 180°. For, by Article **55**, tan $(\theta + 180°) = \tan \theta$, for all values of θ.

59. The functions of a variable angle. — We shall now study the changes that are brought about in the values of the trigonometric functions of an angle by changes in the value of the angle itself. Beginning with the angle zero, we shall let the angle increase gradually. Its functions will then vary in value, each function in its own way. We need to let the angle vary only from 0° to 360°, for other angles lead to no new positions of the terminal side (the angle being taken in standard position) and therefore to no new values of the trigonometric functions.

60. The variation of the sine and cosine. — Let θ be any angle, in standard position. Then $\sin \theta = y/r$ and $\cos \theta = x/r$, where x, y, and r are the coördinates and radius vector of any point P on the

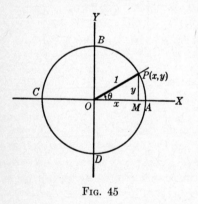

FIG. 45

terminal side of θ. For convenience take P so that r is always equal to 1. Then, as θ varies, the point P moves along the circle drawn about the origin as center with one unit as radius.

Since $r = 1$,

$$\sin \theta = \frac{y}{r} = \frac{y}{1} = y,$$

and

$$\cos \theta = \frac{x}{r} = \frac{x}{1} = x.$$

That is, $\sin \theta$ is a number equal to the number of units in the length of y, due regard being had to sign. For example, when θ has a certain value equal to about 37°, point P on the circle has coördinates (4/5, 3/5). Since the length of y is 3/5 of a unit, $\sin \theta = 3/5$. Similarly, since $x = 4/5$, $\cos \theta = 4/5$.

If θ starts at $0°$ and increases to $90°$, P starts at A, and moves along the circle to B, so that $\sin \theta$ (or y) starts at 0 and increases to 1.   And $\cos \theta$ (or x) starts at 1, and decreases to 0.   In fact:

When θ increases	P moves	sin θ (or y)	cos θ (or x)
from 0° to 90°	from A to B	increases from 0 to 1,	decreases from 1 to 0;
from 90° to 180°	from B to C	decreases from 1 to 0,	decreases from 0 to −1;
from 180° to 270°	from C to D	decreases from 0 to −1,	increases from −1 to 0;
from 270° to 360°	from D to A	increases from −1 to 0,	increases from 0 to 1.

61. The variation of the tangent and cotangent. — In studying the function $\tan \theta = y/x$, we keep x numerically equal to 1.   For angles in the first and fourth quadrants, P then lies on the line AP (the tangent at A to the unit circle, whence the name "tangent").   Therefore

$$\tan \theta = \frac{y}{x} = \frac{y}{1} = y.$$

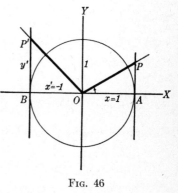

If θ is in the second or third quadrant, P lies on BP', and

$$\tan \theta = \frac{y}{x} = \frac{y}{-1} = -y.$$

Fig. 46

When $\theta = 0°$, P is at A, $y = 0$, and therefore $\tan 0° = 0$.   As θ increases, P moves up the line AP, and y increases.   Therefore $\tan \theta$ increases, and continues to increase so long as θ is increasing while still less than $90°$.   As θ draws near to $90°$, P moves very far up on the line AP, and y or $\tan x$ increases without limit.   If θ is exactly $90°$, the point P will be somewhere on the y-axis, and, whatever the value of y may be, the value of x is zero.   Therefore, since y/x or $y/0$ has no meaning because division by zero is impossible, the angle $90°$ has no tangent.   Or, as we say, *the tangent of $90°$ is not defined.*

However, when θ is nearly 90°, the point P is very far up on the line AP, and $y = \tan \theta$ is very large. In fact, by taking θ less than 90° but near enough to 90°, we can evidently take P as high as we wish, that is, make $\tan \theta$ as great as we desire. We may write $\tan 90° = \infty$, which may be read "the tangent of 90° is infinite," but it must be remembered that *this is merely an abbreviation for the statement:* "90° has no tangent; by taking θ less than 90° but sufficiently close to 90° we can make $\tan \theta$ as large as we wish." This is a statement that the student should remember verbatim.

For angles in the second quadrant, $x = -1$, and $\tan \theta = -y$. As θ increases from 90° to 180°, y decreases to 0 after passing through all positive values, and therefore $\tan \theta$ is negative and increases through all negative values to 0.

The student should study for himself the variation in $\tan \theta$ as θ increases from 180° to 360° and compare the results with the table of Article **62**.

Cot θ. The variation of $\cot \theta$ should be traced from the fact that $\cot \theta = 1/\tan \theta$. Since $\tan \theta$ increases continuously, $\cot \theta$ decreases. When $\tan \theta$ becomes infinite, $\cot \theta$ becomes zero, and when $\tan \theta$ approaches zero, $\cot \theta$ becomes infinite.

62. The variation of the secant and cosecant. — *Sec θ.* We think of $\sec \theta$ as the reciprocal of $\cos \theta$; $\sec \theta = 1/\cos \theta$. When either of these functions increases the other decreases.

If θ increases from 0° to 90°, $\cos \theta$ starts at 1 and decreases. Therefore $\sec \theta$ starts at 1 and increases. Now $\cos 90° = 0$, and therefore $\sec 90°$ is not defined. By taking θ sufficiently close to 90° we can make $\sec \theta$ as large as we wish. Using the notation in the same sense as for the tangent, we can write $\sec 90° = \infty$. *The student should repeat the entire phrase of which this is an abbreviation.*

When θ varies from 90° to 180°, $\cos \theta$ decreases from 0 to -1, and $\sec \theta$ increases up to -1 after passing through values which are negative but numerically very large. The student should trace the variation of $\sec \theta$ as θ increases from 180° to 360° and compare the results with the table on page 93.

Csc θ. It is left to the student to trace the variation of csc θ, recalling that csc θ = 1/sin θ.

The foregoing results may be summarized as follows:

Quadrant	I		II		III		IV	
Variation	*From*	*To*	*From*	*To*	*From*	*To*	*From*	*To*
θ	0	90°	90°	180°	180°	270°	270°	360°
sin θ	0	1	1	0	0	−1	−1	0
cos θ	1	0	0	−1	−1	0	0	1
tan θ	0	∞	−∞	0	0	∞	−∞	0
cot θ	∞	0	0	−∞	∞	0	0	−∞
sec θ	1	∞	−∞	−1	−1	−∞	∞	1
csc θ	∞	1	1	∞	−∞	−1	−1	−∞

We should notice particularly that the sine and cosine never exceed 1 in numerical value; the tangent and cotangent may assume any value; the secant and cosecant take on no values numerically less than 1. *In the first quadrant* the sine, tangent, and secant increase when the angle increases, but their cofunctions, the cosine, cotangent, and cosecant decrease.

EXERCISES

Using Figure 3, make a table of the values of the sine, cosine, tangent, and cotangent for multiples of 20° from 0° to 360°.

63. The graph of $y = \sin x$. — In the following discussion, x will be used to denote the value of an angle and y to denote the value of the sine of that angle. They are no longer the coördinates of a point on the terminal side of some angle. Let us draw a set of coördinate axes. Distances on the x-scale now measure angles, and distances on the y-scale will represent values of the sine. Corresponding to any value of the angle x we can determine (from a table or otherwise) the value of $y = \sin x$, and plot the point whose coördinates are these values of x and y. The whole set of points that can be obtained in this way form a smooth curve which is the graph of the function $y = \sin x$.

The choice of scale, to a certain extent, is arbitrary. But *in graphing the trigonometric functions we shall always assume that x is expressed in radian measure*, so that *the same distance which represents the number 1 on the vertical scale represents one radian on the horizontal scale*.

In applications of the graphs, particularly in the calculus, the use of any other scale leads to very awkward forms and complicated formulas. Since π is approximately equal to 3.14, the vertical distance representing the number 1 is slightly less than one-third of the horizontal distance representing π radians.

We can predict the general appearance of the curve from the results summarized in Article 62. From any table of sines we can obtain as many points as we wish for values of x from $x = 0$ to $x = 2\pi$. Since $y = \sin x$ is periodic with period 2π, the curve obtained for the interval from 0 to 2π will be reproduced in the intervals 2π to 4π, -2π to 0, 4π to 6π, etc., and may be continued as far as we like to the right or left. Figure 47 is obtained by plotting the points from the following table.

x	0	$\dfrac{\pi}{6}$	$\dfrac{\pi}{3}$	$\dfrac{\pi}{2}$	$\dfrac{2\pi}{3}$	$\dfrac{5\pi}{6}$	π	$\dfrac{7\pi}{6}$	$\dfrac{4\pi}{3}$	$\dfrac{3\pi}{2}$	$\dfrac{5\pi}{3}$	$\dfrac{11\pi}{6}$	2π
$y = \sin x$	0	.50	.87	1	.87	.50	0	$-.50$	$-.87$	-1	$-.87$	$-.50$	0

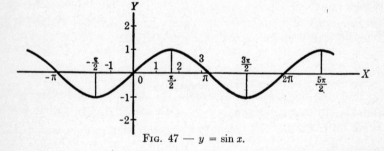

Fig. 47 — $y = \sin x$.

The student should learn to draw a hasty sketch of this graph from memory.

★**64. Another construction.** — The graph of $y = \sin x$ may be drawn in the following way without using a table. Take any convenient point, C, on the x-axis. With C as center, draw a circle with radius one unit. Let x be any number, and with its vertex at C lay off from the x-axis the angle ACP equal to x radians. The arc AP which it subtends is in length equal to x units (Article **47**), and $\sin x$ is equal to the number of units in the height MP (Article **60**). Lay

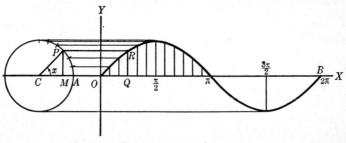

FIG. 48 — $y = \sin x$.

off the distance OQ equal to the length of the arc AP (which is equal to x). Vertically through Q draw QR equal to MP (which is equal to $\sin x$). The point R is therefore in the graph of $y = \sin x$, since its abscissa is x and its ordinate is y. We can find as many such points as we wish. In order to find points P and Q that correspond, so that OQ equals arc AP we can lay off the distance OB equal to 2π (which equals the circumference of our circle), and then divide the circumference and OB into some convenient number of equal parts. P and Q will then be corresponding points of division.

EXERCISES

1. Draw the graph of $y = \cos x$ by one of the above methods, and also by using the graph of $y = \sin x$ and the fact that $\cos x = \sin (x + \pi/2)$.

★**2.** An engine piston is connected by a rod to a flywheel which turns with uniform speed. Show how the position of the piston can be represented by means of a trigonometric function.

65. The graph of $y = \tan x$. — The most characteristic features of the graph are: (1) the curve always slopes upward toward the right; (2) the function becomes positively infinite as x tends toward any odd multiple of $\pi/2$ from the left, and negatively infinite as x tends toward such a value from the right; (3) the graph crosses the x-axis when x is any multiple of π; (4) the function has the period π, so that there are two complete patterns of the function in any interval of length 2π. A very few plotted points will now suffice to determine the figure. The student should learn to sketch the figure quickly from memory.

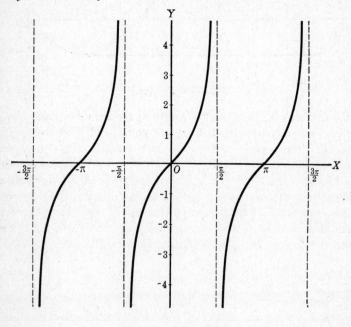

Fig. 49 — $y = \tan x$.

Graph the function $y = \cot x$.   Use the fact that this function is the reciprocal of $\tan x$, so that when one function becomes infinite the other becomes zero, and the graph of $y = \cot x$ slopes downward to the right.

★66. **The graph of $y = \csc x$.** — The graph of this function can be obtained from that of $y = \sin x$ of which it is the reciprocal.   When $\sin x = \pm1$, $\csc x$ has the same value.   When x is equal to any multiple of π, $\sin x = 0$, and $\csc x$ becomes infinite.

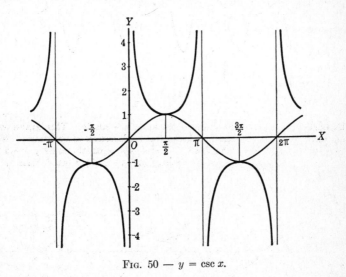

Fig. 50 — $y = \csc x$.

EXERCISE

Graph the function $y = \sec x$.

★67. **The graphs of certain related functions. —**

EXAMPLE 1.   Graph the function $y = 3 \sin 2x$.   This graph can be drawn very easily by considering the graph of $y = \sin x$.   While x varies from 0 to π, $2x$

varies from 0 to 2π. Therefore in the interval from $x = 0$ to $x = \pi$, sin $2x$ goes through the same set of values that sin x takes on in the entire interval from $x = 0$ to $x = 2\pi$. And, $y = 3 \sin 2x$ varies between the limits 3 and -3. The graphs of $y = \sin x$ and $y = 3 \sin 2x$ are shown together in Figure 51.

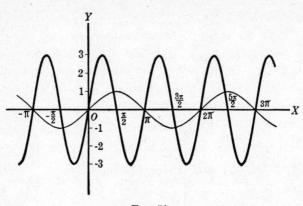

FIG. 51

EXAMPLE 2. Graph the function $y = \sin x + \sin 2x$. This graph can be made most easily by the method known as composition of ordinates. We first draw, on the same axes, the graphs of the two separate terms $y = \sin x$ and $y = \sin 2x$. Then, the height of the graph of $y = \sin x + \sin 2x$ can be found

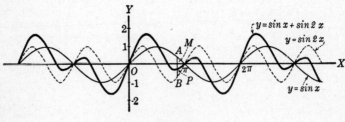

FIG. 52

for any value of x by adding the heights of the other two curves. Of course we must take the sign into account. Thus, to get the point P of Figure 52 we must measure the distance MB downward from the point A, since MB, which represents the value of sin $2x$, is negative at this point.

EXAMPLE 3. Graph the function $y = x + \sin x$. Graph the two functions $y = x$, which is represented by a straight line, and $y = \sin x$. The desired graph is then obtained as in the preceding example, by the composition of ordinates.

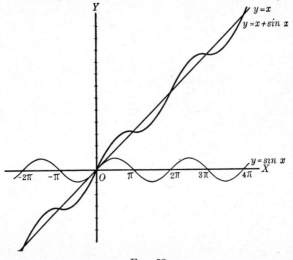

FIG. 53

Note: It may be objected here that x stands for a number in the first term of the function, and for an angle in the second term. As a matter of fact, however, *x represents a number in each term.* When we graph $y = \sin x$, we really assume that y is a function of the *number x.* *By the sine of the number x, we mean the sine of the angle the number of radians in which is equal to x.* Similar definitions hold for the other trigonometric functions of a number.

EXERCISES

Graph the following functions in the interval from $x = -2\pi$ to $x = 2\pi$.

1. $y = \sin 3x$.
2. $y = 2 \sin 4x$.
3. $y = \cos 2x$.
4. $y = -\cos 3x$.
5. $y = \csc 2x$.
6. $y = \sec 2x$.
7. $y = \sin x - \sin 2x$.
8. $y = \sin x + \cos x$.

9. $y = \sin x + \frac{1}{3}\sin 3x + \frac{1}{5}\sin 5x.$ **10.** $y = 2\sin x - \sin 2x + \frac{2}{3}\sin 3x.$

11. $y = \cos x + \cos 2x.$ **12.** $y = \cos x + \frac{1}{9}\cos 3x.$

13. $y = \tan x + \cot x.$ **14.** $y = x - \sin x.$

15. $y = 2x + \sin 2x.$ **16.** $y = \tan x + \sin x.$

CHAPTER VII

THE FUNDAMENTAL RELATIONS

68. The fundamental relations. — Using the notation of Article **8**, if θ is any angle,

(a) $\sin \theta = \dfrac{y}{r}$,　　　(b) $\cos \theta = \dfrac{x}{r}$,　　　(c) $\tan \theta = \dfrac{y}{x}$,

(d) $\cot \theta = \dfrac{x}{y}$,　　　(e) $\sec \theta = \dfrac{r}{x}$,　　　(f) $\csc \theta = \dfrac{r}{y}$.

Moreover, since x, y, and r are numerically equal to the sides of a right triangle, we have

$$\text{(g)} \quad x^2 + y^2 = r^2.$$

From these seven equations we obtain eight *fundamental relations* or *fundamental identities* that always connect the functions of an angle. Three of these, which we may call the *reciprocal relations*, we have already proved and used repeatedly. They are:

(1) $$\csc \theta = \frac{1}{\sin \theta},$$

(2) $$\sec \theta = \frac{1}{\cos \theta},$$

(3) $$\cot \theta = \frac{1}{\tan \theta}.$$

To prove the first of these, for example, by equations (a) and (b) we have

$$\csc \theta = \frac{r}{y} = \frac{1}{\dfrac{y}{r}} = \frac{1}{\sin \theta}.$$

101

Two others, the *ratio relations*, are obtained with almost equal ease:

(4) $$\frac{\sin \theta}{\cos \theta} = \tan \theta,$$

(5) $$\frac{\cos \theta}{\sin \theta} = \cot \theta.$$

To get (4), we use equations (a), (b), (c), writing

$$\frac{\sin \theta}{\cos \theta} = \frac{\dfrac{y}{r}}{\dfrac{x}{r}} = \frac{y}{x} = \tan \theta.$$

The remaining three fundamental relations, or *squares relations*, are:

(6) $$\sin^2 \theta + \cos^2 \theta = 1,$$
(7) $$\tan^2 \theta + 1 = \sec^2 \theta,$$
(8) $$\cot^2 \theta + 1 = \csc^2 \theta.$$

They are obtained by dividing equation (g) by r^2 to get (6), by x^2 to get (7), and by y^2 to get (8). Thus, on dividing equation (g) by r^2 we have

$$\frac{x^2}{r^2} + \frac{y^2}{r^2} = 1,$$

which, by (a) and (b), is

$$\cos^2 \theta + \sin^2 \theta = 1.$$

The student should memorize the fundamental identities at once, and learn, also, to recognize them in modified forms. The relation (6), for example, is often useful in one of the forms

$$\sin \theta = \pm \sqrt{1 - \cos^2 \theta} \quad \text{or} \quad \cos \theta = \pm \sqrt{1 - \sin^2 \theta},$$

for, in such a form, it gives us the value of the sine or the cosine when the other is known.

EXAMPLE 1. Given that x is an angle in the second quadrant, and that $\sin x = 5/13$, find the other functions of x. From (6) we have

$$\cos x = \pm \sqrt{1 - \sin^2 x} = \pm \sqrt{1 - \tfrac{25}{169}} = \pm \tfrac{12}{13}.$$

However, since x is in the second quadrant, the cosine is negative, and $\cos x$ $= -12/13$. From (4),

$$\tan x = \frac{\sin x}{\cos x} = \frac{\frac{5}{13}}{-\frac{12}{13}} = -\frac{5}{12}.$$

The relations (1), (2), and (3) then give

$$\csc x = 13/5, \qquad \sec x = -13/12, \qquad \cot x = -12/5.$$

This is an *algebraic* method of finding the values of the other functions when one of them is known. In an earlier chapter (Article 9) we solved the same problem geometrically.

EXAMPLE 2.   Given that ϕ is an angle in the fourth quadrant and that $\tan \phi$ $= -3$, find the other functions of ϕ. By relation (7) we have

$$\sec \phi = \sqrt{1 + \tan^2 \phi} = \sqrt{1 + 9} = \sqrt{10}.$$

Then, by (2), $\cos \phi = \dfrac{1}{\sqrt{10}} = \frac{1}{10} \sqrt{10}$; and by (3), $\cot \phi = -\frac{1}{3}$.

To find $\sin \phi$, we use (4), taking it in the form

$$\sin \phi = \tan \phi \cdot \cos \phi = -3 \cdot \tfrac{1}{10} \sqrt{10} = -\tfrac{3}{10} \sqrt{10},$$

and

$$\csc \phi = \frac{1}{\sin \phi} = -\tfrac{1}{3} \sqrt{10}.$$

EXERCISES

1. Prove the relations (5), (7), and (8).

2. State each of the fundamental relations in words.

From equations (1) to (8), obtain the following relations.

3. $\sin x \csc x = 1.$ **4.** $\tan x \cot x = 1.$

5. $\sin x = \pm \sqrt{1 - \cos^2 x}.$ **6.** $\csc x = \pm \sqrt{\cot^2 x + 1}.$

7. $\cot x = \pm \sqrt{\csc^2 x - 1}.$ **8.** $\tan x = \dfrac{\sec x}{\csc x}.$

9. $\cos x = \dfrac{\sin x}{\tan x}$.   **10.** $\cos x = \sin x \cot x$.

11. $\sin x = \dfrac{\tan x}{\pm\sqrt{1 + \tan^2 x}}$.   **12.** $\cos x = \dfrac{\cot x}{\pm\sqrt{1 + \cot^2 x}}$.

In the following examples use the fundamental relations to obtain all the functions not given.

13. $\sin \alpha = -3/5$, α in third quadrant.
Ans. $\cos \alpha = -4/5$, $\tan \alpha = 3/4$, $\cot \alpha = 4/3$, $\sec \alpha = -5/4$, $\csc \alpha = -5/3$.

14. $\cos \alpha = 5/6$, α in fourth quadrant.

15. $\tan x = -5/7$, x in fourth quadrant.
Ans. $\sin x = -\frac{5}{74}\sqrt{74}$, $\cos x = \frac{7}{74}\sqrt{74}$, $\cot x = -\frac{7}{5}$, $\sec x = \frac{1}{7}\sqrt{74}$, $\csc x = -\frac{1}{5}\sqrt{74}$.

16. $\sec z = 3$, z in first quadrant.

17. $\cot \phi = -\frac{1}{4}$, ϕ in second quadrant.
Ans. $\sin \phi = \frac{4}{17}\sqrt{17}$, $\cos \phi = -\frac{1}{17}\sqrt{17}$, $\tan \phi = -4$, $\sec \phi = -\sqrt{17}$, $\csc \phi = \frac{1}{4}\sqrt{17}$.

18. $\csc x = 8/5$, x in first quadrant.

In the following examples assume that x is an angle in the first quadrant.

19. Find algebraically the value of $(\sec^2 x - 1)\cot x$, given $\tan x = 3$.   *Ans.* 3.

20. Find algebraically the value of $(\sin^2 x - \cos^2 x)\csc x$, given $\sin x = 1/2$.

21. Find the value of $(\tan^2 x + \cot^2 x)(\sec^2 x + \csc^2 x)$, given $\tan x = 2$.   *Ans.* 425/16.

22. Find the value of $(1 - \csc^2 x)\tan x$, given $\sin x = 1/3$.

23. Find the value of $\cot^2 x - \sin^2 x + \tan^2 x - \cos^2 x$, given $\cos x = 1/3$.   *Ans.* 57/8.

24. Find the value of $\dfrac{1 - \sin x \cos x}{1 + \sin x \cos x}$, given $\tan x = 2$.

25. Express each of the other functions of x in terms of $\sin x$.

Ans. $\sqrt{1 - \sin^2 x}, \dfrac{\sin x}{\sqrt{1 - \sin^2 x}}, \dfrac{\sqrt{1 - \sin^2 x}}{\sin x}, \dfrac{1}{\sqrt{1 - \sin^2 x}}, \dfrac{1}{\sin x}$.

26. Express each of the other functions of x in terms of (1) the cosine, (2) the tangent, (3) the secant of x.

Reduce the following expressions to equivalent expressions involving only $\sin x$.

27. $\sin x \tan x$.

28. $\dfrac{\cot x}{\csc x}$.

29. $\sec^2 x + \csc^2 x$.

30. $\tan^2 x + \cot^2 x$.

31. $\sec x (1 - \tan x)$.

32. $\dfrac{\cot x - 1}{\csc^2 x}$.

33. $\cos x \tan x$.

34. $\dfrac{\sec x - \tan x}{\csc x - \cot x}$.

35. $\dfrac{\cos x - \cot x}{\tan x - \csc x}$.

36. $\sin x \cot x$.

37. $\tan x + \cot x$.

38. $(\tan x - 1)(\cot x - 1)$.

39. $\sec x \csc x$.

40. $(\tan x - \sec x)(\tan x + \sec x)$.

Reduce the following expressions to expressions containing only $\tan x$.

41. $\csc^2 x - \sec^2 x$.

42. $\cos^2 x + 1$.

43. $\cot x \sec^2 x$.

44. $\cot x \sin x + \cos x \tan x$.

Find the value of each of the following expressions.

45. $\cos \theta \csc^2 \theta$, when $\sin \theta = \frac{2}{3}$.　　　*Ans.* $\pm \frac{3}{4} \sqrt{5}$.

46. $\dfrac{\sin x \cos x}{2 \csc^2 x - 1}$, when $\tan x \doteq 3$.

47. $\dfrac{\sin^2 y}{(\tan^2 y + 1) \cos y}$, when $\cos y = \frac{3}{5}$.　　　*Ans.* $\frac{48}{125}$.

48. $\dfrac{\cot y}{\sec y \sqrt{\tan^2 y + 2}}$, when $\cos y = \frac{4}{5}$.

69. Identities and equations. — An *identity* is a statement of equality which is true for all values of the quantities involved. Thus the algebraic statement

$$x^2 - 2\,xy + y^2 = (x - y)^2$$

is an identity, because it is true for all values of x and y. The statement

$$\sin^2 x + \cos^2 x = 1$$

is a trigonometric identity, because it is true for any value of the angle x.

A *conditional equation* (or, for simplicity, an *equation*) is a statement of equality which is true only for certain particular values or sets of values of the quantities involved. Thus,

$$x^2 - 5\,x + 6 = 0$$

is a conditional equation, because it is untrue for most values of x, but is true only for $x = 2$ and $x = 3$. The trigonometric equation

$$\sin x = \cos x$$

is conditional, because it is true only for $x = \pi/4$, $x = 5\pi/4$, and for values of x coterminal with these.

The implication of an identity is merely that of a simple declarative sentence. It states that the quantity on the left-hand side is, for all values of the letters, equal to the quantity on the right-hand side, and the one quantity can always be reduced to or replace the other.

The implication of an equation, on the other hand, is that of a question. When we write $x^2 - 5x + 6 = 0$, we imply the question: For what values of x is this statement true? The solution of an equation, whether it be trigonometric or of some other form, consists in finding all of the values of the letters for which the equation is satisfied.

70. Trigonometric identities. — It is frequently necessary to be able to change a trigonometric expression from one form into another form which is identically equal to it, but which is more convenient or suitable for the purpose in view. Sometimes these reductions are difficult to make. The most practicable method of learning how to make them is to practice in verifying or proving the truth of given trigonometric identities.

With this end in view, when a student is asked to prove an identity he should strive by one or more changes to transform one side of the identity into the form of the other side *which should be left unchanged.* If no other way can be found for proving the identity, the method may be suggested by expressing all of the functions in terms of sines and cosines, which may be done by means of the fundamental relations.

No general rule can be given for proving identities. Practice is the best teacher, and thorough familiarity with the fundamental relations the best tool. We must always keep in mind not only the expression which we are trying to modify but also the form to which we wish to reduce it so as to select the useful transformation and avoid mere futile fumbling. In general it is better to work upon the more complicated side of the identity and to try to simplify it to the form of the other side.

EXAMPLE 1. Prove the identity

$$\sin x = \frac{\tan x}{\sec x}.$$

The right-hand side is the more complicated, and we will therefore work with it, expressing it in terms of $\sin x$ and $\cos x$. We have

$$\frac{\tan x}{\sec x} = \frac{\dfrac{\sin x}{\cos x}}{\dfrac{1}{\cos x}} = \frac{\sin x}{\cos x} \cdot \frac{\cos x}{1} = \sin x,$$

which proves the identity.

EXAMPLE 2. Prove the identity

$$\tan^2 x - \sin^2 x = \sin^2 x \cdot \tan^2 x.$$

We shall modify the left-hand side, and write

$$\tan^2 x - \sin^2 x = \frac{\sin^2 x}{\cos^2 x} - \sin^2 x,$$

$$= \sin^2 x \left(\frac{1}{\cos^2 x} - 1 \right),$$

$$= \sin^2 x \ (\sec^2 x - 1),$$

$$= \sin^2 x \cdot \tan^2 x,$$

as we wished to show. Another method is to transform the right-hand side, as follows

$$\sin^2 x \cdot \tan^2 x = (1 - \cos^2 x) \tan^2 x$$

$$= \tan^2 x - \tan^2 x \cdot \cos^2 x$$

$$= \tan^2 x - \frac{\sin^2 x}{\cos^2 x} \cdot \cos^2 x$$

$$= \tan^2 x - \sin^2 x.$$

EXERCISES

Prove the following identities.

1. $\tan x = \pm \dfrac{\sqrt{1 - \cos^2 x}}{\cos x}.$

2. $\dfrac{\sec^2 x}{\sin^2 x} = \csc^2 x + \sec^2 x.$

3. $(\sin x + \cos x) \ (\sec x - \csc x) = \tan x - \cot x.$

4. $\dfrac{\sin x}{1 + \cos x} + \dfrac{1 + \cos x}{\sin x} = 2 \csc x.$

5. $\csc^2 x \ (1 - \cos^2 x) = 1.$

6. $2 \sin x + \tan x = \dfrac{2 + \sec x}{\csc x}.$

7. $\dfrac{\tan x + \cot x}{\tan x - \cot x} = \dfrac{\tan^2 x + 1}{\tan^2 x - 1}.$

8. $\dfrac{\sec x - \cos x}{\sec x + \cos x} = \dfrac{\sec^2 x - 1}{\sec^2 x + 1}.$

9. $\sin x \tan x = \sec x - \cos x.$

10. $\sin^3 x + \cos^3 x = (\sin x + \cos x) \ (1 - \sin x \cos x).$

11. $\tan x + \cot x = \sec x \csc x.$

12. $\sin^2 x \sec^2 x = \sec^2 x - 1.$

13. $\cos^2 x \csc^2 x = \csc^2 x - 1.$

14. $1 - \cos\theta = \dfrac{\sin^2\theta}{1 + \cos\theta}.$

15. $(1 + \cos x)(\csc x - \cot x) = \sin x.$

16. $\dfrac{1 + \tan\theta}{\sec\theta} = \sin\theta + \cos\theta.$

17. $\dfrac{1 - \cot\theta}{1 + \cot\theta} = \dfrac{\tan\theta - 1}{\tan\theta + 1}.$

18. $\dfrac{\sec\theta - 1}{\sec\theta + 1} = \dfrac{1 - \cos\theta}{1 + \cos\theta}.$

19. $\dfrac{1 + \tan^2\alpha}{1 + \cot^2\alpha} = \dfrac{\sin^2\alpha}{\cos^2\alpha}.$

20. $\sqrt{\dfrac{1 - \cos\alpha}{1 + \cos\alpha}} = \csc\alpha - \cot\alpha.$

21. $\csc^2 x + \cot^2 x = \csc^4 x - \cot^4 x.$

22. $\dfrac{\sin x}{\sec x} = \dfrac{1}{\tan x + \cot x}.$

23. $\dfrac{\sin y}{\tan y} = \dfrac{1}{\sec y}.$

24. $(1 - \cos y)(1 + \cos y) = \sin^2 y.$

25. $(\csc x - \cot x)(\csc x + \cot x) = 1.$

26. $\dfrac{\tan^2 x}{\sin^2 x} - \dfrac{\sin^2 x}{\cos^2 x} = 1.$

27. $\sin^2 y \cot^2 y + \cos^2 y \tan^2 y = 1.$

28. $\cos^2 y = \dfrac{\cot^2 y}{1 + \cot^2 y}.$

29. $\csc y - \sin y = \sin y \cot^2 y.$

30. $\dfrac{\sin^2\theta}{(1 - \cos\theta)^2} = \dfrac{(1 + \cos\theta)^2}{\sin^2\theta}.$

31. $\cot x + \cot y = \cot x \cot y (\tan x + \tan y).$

32. $(\sec x - \tan x)(\sec x + \tan x) = 1.$

33. $(\sin\alpha\cos\beta + \cos\alpha\sin\beta)^2 + (\cos\alpha\cos\beta - \sin\alpha\sin\beta)^2 = 1.$

34. $(\sin x\cos y - \cos x\sin y)^2 + (\cos x\cos y + \sin x\sin y)^2 = 1.$

35. $(\cos^2 x - \sin^2 x)^2 + 4 \sin^2 x \cos^2 x = 1.$

36. $\dfrac{\tan x + \tan y}{1 - \tan x \tan y} \cdot \dfrac{\cot x \cot y - 1}{\cot x + \cot y} = 1.$

71. Trigonometric equations. — A solution of a trigonometric equation consists in finding all the angles which satisfy the equation. It is enough to give the values which satisfy the equation and lie between 0 and 2π ($0°$ and $360°$).

Usually we solve the equation for one or more trigonometric functions of the angle, and then find the corresponding values of the angle. A solution is partly a matter of algebra and partly a matter of trigonometry. The following suggestions apply to the *algebraic* part: Sometimes after arranging the equation so that we have a certain expression set equal to zero, we find that the expression can be factored. Then set each factor equal to zero and solve the simpler equations that result.

EXAMPLE 1. Solve the following equation for values of x from $0°$ to $360°$.

$$\sin^2 x = \sin x.$$

Transposing and factoring, we get

$$\sin^2 x - \sin x = 0, \quad \text{or} \quad \sin x (\sin x - 1) = 0.$$

We must now set *each* of the factors equal to zero. For if either factor is equal to zero the equation holds true. We get

$$\sin x = 0 \quad \text{and} \quad \sin x - 1 = 0 \quad \text{or} \quad \sin x = 1.$$

The values of x from $0°$ to $360°$ for which $\sin x - 0$ arc $0°, 180°, 360°$. The only value of x in this range for which $\sin x = 1$ is $90°$. The roots of the equation are therefore $0°, 90°, 180°, 360°$.

In the course of the algebraic work if we have occasion to take the square root of both sides of the equation or to divide by a factor, we must take care not to throw away any roots.

EXAMPLE 2. In solving the equation

$$\sin^2 x = 1,$$

we must not only take $\sin x = 1$, giving $x = 90°$, but also $\sin x = -1$, giving $x = 270°$.

And in the equation

$$\sin^2 x = \sin x \cos x$$

ıf we divide by $\sin x$, getting

$$\sin x = \cos x,$$

we must also write $\sin x = 0$, since the given equation is satisfied if $\sin x = 0$.

On the other hand, if we square both sides of an equation (to get rid of radicals perhaps) or if we multiply it by a factor (in order to clear the equation of fractions), we must remember that we may have introduced factors that will lead to extraneous roots, that is, to values of the unknown that satisfy the derived equation but not the original given equation.   The best test is to substitute the supposed roots in the given equation and reject any of them that fail to satisfy it.

On the side of trigonometry, if several functions of an angle are involved in the equation, it is suggested that all of the functions be expressed in terms of a single function by algebraic or geometric methods, and that while this is being done the use of radicals be avoided when possible.   The methods are illustrated in the following examples.

EXAMPLE 3.   Solve the equation

$$\cos^2 x + \sin x = 1$$

for values of x from $0°$ to $360°$.

Transposing the first term, we get

$$\sin x = 1 - \cos^2 x,$$

or

$$\sin x = \sin^2 x,$$

which is the equation of Example 1.

EXAMPLE 4.   Solve the equation

$$\cos x = -\sin x$$

for values of x from $0°$ to $360°$.

Divide both sides by cos x, getting

$$1 = -\frac{\sin x}{\cos x}, \quad \text{or} \quad \tan x = -1.$$

The values of x between $0°$ and $360°$ which satisfy this equation are $x = 135°$ and $x = 315°$. These results satisfy the given equation since

$$\cos 135° = -\tfrac{1}{2}\sqrt{2} = -\sin 135°,$$

and

$$\cos 315° = \tfrac{1}{2}\sqrt{2} = -\sin 315°.$$

Another method is to change the functions to sines, writing

$$\sqrt{1 - \sin^2 x} = -\sin x.$$

Squaring, we get

$$1 - \sin^2 x = \sin^2 x,$$

or

$$2 \sin^2 x = 1 \quad \text{and} \quad \sin^2 x = \tfrac{1}{2},$$

or

$$\sin x = \pm\tfrac{1}{2}\sqrt{2}.$$

The angles for which this is satisfied are $x = 45°, 135°, 225°, 315°$. But on substituting in the original equation, we see that $45°$ and $225°$ do not satisfy, since $\sin 45° = \cos 45°$ and $\sin 225° = \cos 225°$. When we squared both sides of the equation we lost track of the signs, and introduced extraneous roots.

EXAMPLE 5. Solve the equation

$$\sqrt{3} \tan x \sec x - 2 = \sec x - 2\sqrt{3} \tan x$$

for values of x from $0°$ to $360°$.

We can write this in the form

$$\sqrt{3} \tan x (\sec x + 2) = \sec x + 2,$$

or

$$(\sqrt{3} \tan x - 1)(\sec x + 2) = 0.$$

Setting each factor equal to zero, we get

$$\sqrt{3} \tan x - 1 = 0, \quad \text{so that} \quad \tan x = 1/\sqrt{3}, \quad \text{and} \quad x = 30° \text{ or } 210°,$$

and

$$\sec x + 2 = 0, \quad \text{so that} \quad \sec x = -2, \quad \text{and} \quad x = 120° \text{ or } 240°.$$

The student should substitute these results, and see that they satisfy the given equation.

EXAMPLE 6. Solve the equation

$$\sec^2 x \, (1 + \cos x \tan x) = 2.$$

Expressing all of the functions in terms of sines and cosines, we get

$$\frac{1}{\cos^2 x}\left(1 + \cos x \frac{\sin x}{\cos x}\right) = 2$$

or

$$1 + \sin x = 2 \cos^2 x.$$

Using only sines, we get

$$1 + \sin x = 2 \, (1 - \sin^2 x)$$

or

$$2 \sin^2 x + \sin x - 1 = 0.$$

We factor this, writing

$$(2 \sin x - 1) \, (\sin x + 1) = 0.$$

This gives

$$2 \sin x - 1 = 0, \quad \text{or} \quad \sin x = \tfrac{1}{2}, \quad \text{so that} \quad x = 30° \text{ or } 150°,$$

and

$$\sin x + 1 = 0, \quad \text{or} \quad \sin x = -1, \quad \text{so that} \quad x = 270°.$$

The results $x = 30°$ and $x = 150°$ satisfy the equation, but we must reject 270°, for the original equation involves tan x and sec x, and tan 270° and sec 270° do not exist. We introduced the extraneous result when we multiplied both sides of the equation by $\cos^2 x$, which is zero when $x = 270°$.

EXERCISES

Solve the following equations for positive (or zero) angles less than 360°.

1. $\sin^2 \theta = \tfrac{1}{4}$.   *Ans.* 30°, 150°, 210°, 330°.
2. $\cos^2 \theta = \tfrac{1}{4}$.
3. $\tan^2 \theta = 1$.   *Ans.* 45°, 135°, 225°, 315°.
4. $\sec^2 \theta = 1$.
5. $(\sin \theta + 1) \, (2 \cos \theta - 1) = 0$.   *Ans.* 60°, 270°, 300°.
6. $(2 \cos \theta + \sqrt{3}) \, (\sqrt{2} \sin \theta - 1) = 0$.
7. $(\tan^2 x - 3) \, (\csc x - 2) = 0$.

Ans.   30°, 60°, 120°, 150°, 240°, 300°.

8. $(\cot x + 1)(3 \sec^2 x - 4) = 0.$

9. $\sqrt{2} \tan \theta \sin \theta - \tan \theta = 0.$ *Ans.* $0°, 45°, 135°, 180°, 360°.$

10. $2 \sec \theta \sin \theta - \sec \theta = 0.$

11. $2 \tan^2 \theta - \sec^2 \theta = 0.$ *Ans.* $45°, 135°, 225°, 315°.$

12. $(4 \cos^2 \theta - 3) \csc^2 \theta = 0.$

13. $1 - \sin x = \sqrt{3} \cos x.$ *Ans.* $90°, 330°.$

14. $1 + \cos x + \sqrt{3} \sin x = 0.$

15. $\csc x - 1 = \cot x.$ *Ans.* $90°.$

16. $\cos x - \sin x = 1.$

17. $2 \sin^2 x + \sin x - 1 = 0.$ *Ans.* $30°, 150°, 270°.$

18. $2 \sin^2 x = \cos x + 1.$

19. $\csc^2 x - \cot x = 1.$ *Ans.* $45°, 90°, 225°, 270°.$

20. $\sec^2 x = 1 - \sqrt{3} \tan x.$

21. $\tan^2 x + 3 \csc^2 x = 7.$

Ans. $45°, 60°, 120°, 135°, 225°, 240°, 300°, 315°.$

22. $3 \cot^2 x + \sec^2 x = 5.$

23. $2 \cot x + \cos x \cot x = 2 \cot x \sin^2 x.$

Ans. $90°, 120°, 240°, 270°.$

24. $2 \sin \theta \tan \theta = 2 \cos \theta.$

25. $(2 \sin^2 x - 1)(\sin x - 3) = 0.$ *Ans.* $45°, 135°, 225°, 315°.$

26. $(\sqrt{2} \cos x - 2)(\cos^2 x - 4) = 0.$

27. $\sqrt{3} \tan x - 1 = \sec x.$ *Ans.* $60°, 180°.$

28. $5(\csc x - 1) = 2 \cos x \cot x.$

29. $\tan x + \sqrt{3} \cot x = \sqrt{3} + 1.$ *Ans.* $45°, 225°, 60°, 240°.$

30. $4 \csc^2 x - 7 \cot^2 x = 3.$

Prove the following identities.

31. $\tan x \sec x = \sin^3 x \sec^2 x + \sin x.$

32. $\cot x \csc x = \dfrac{1}{\sec x - \cos x}.$

33. $\tan^2 x - \sin^2 x = \sin^4 x \sec^2 x.$

34. $\dfrac{1 + \cos x}{1 - \cos x} = 1 + \dfrac{2 \cos x (1 + \cos x)}{\sin^2 x}.$

35. $\dfrac{\cos x}{1 + \sin x} + \dfrac{1 + \sin x}{\cos x} = 2 \sec x.$

36. $\sin^4 x - \cos^4 x = 1 - 2 \cos^2 x.$

37. $\sin^4 x + \cos^4 x = 1 - 2 \sin^2 x \cos^2 x.$

38. $(1 - \sin x)(\sec x + \tan x) = \cos x.$

39. $(\tan \theta + \cot \theta)^2 = \sec^2 \theta + \csc^2 \theta.$

40. $(1 - \tan \theta)(1 - \cot \theta) = 2 - \sec \theta \csc \theta.$

41. $\cos \alpha \csc^2 \alpha \tan \alpha - \sin \alpha = \cos^2 \alpha \csc \alpha.$

42. $\dfrac{\tan \alpha - \sin \alpha}{\sin^3 \alpha} = \dfrac{\sec \alpha}{1 + \cos \alpha}.$

43. $\dfrac{\cot \alpha - \tan \alpha}{\cos \alpha - \sin \alpha} = \dfrac{\cos \alpha + \sin \alpha}{\cos \alpha \sin \alpha}.$

44. $\sqrt{\dfrac{1 - \sin \alpha}{1 + \sin \alpha}} = \sec \alpha - \tan \alpha.$

45. $\dfrac{\sin \theta}{\cot \theta} + \dfrac{\cos \theta}{\tan \theta} = (1 - \sin \theta \cos \theta)(\sec \theta + \csc \theta).$

46. $\dfrac{\tan x - \tan y}{\sec x + \sec y} = \dfrac{\sec x - \sec y}{\tan x + \tan y}.$

47. $\dfrac{\cot x + \cot y}{\csc x - \csc y} = \dfrac{\csc x + \csc y}{\cot x - \cot y}.$

In the following examples reduce the left-hand side to the form of the right-hand side.

48. $\tan x + x \sec^2 x - \sin x \sec x - x = x \tan^2 x.$

49. $\dfrac{a \sin x \cos x - b \sin x \cos x}{a \sin^2 x + b \cos^2 x} = \dfrac{(a - b) \tan x}{a \tan^2 x + b}.$

50. $\sec^m x - \sec^{m-2} x = \sec^{m-2} x \tan^2 x.$

51. $6 \tan^2 x \sec^3 x + 2 \tan^4 x \sec x + \sec^3 x + \tan^2 x \sec x - \sec x$
$= 8 \tan^2 x \sec^3 x.$

52. $\sec^2 x (\tan x - 3 \cot x) + \tan x (\sec^2 x + 3 \csc^2 x)$
$= 2 \sec^2 x \tan x.$

53. $\dfrac{a (a \cos x - b \sin x)}{a \sin x + b \cos x} + b = \dfrac{a^2 + b^2}{a \tan x + b}.$

54. $\sec^6 x = (\tan^2 x + 1)^2 \sec^2 x.$

55. $\csc^4 x = (\cot^2 x + 1) \csc^2 x.$

CHAPTER VIII

FUNCTIONS OF TWO ANGLES

72. Sin (α + β) and cos (α + β). — The sine of an angle which is the sum of two angles is not, in general, equal to the sum of the sines of the two angles.

A single example is enough to show this. Let $\alpha = 30°$ and $\beta = 60°$. Then

$$\sin \alpha + \sin \beta = \sin 30° + \sin 60° = \tfrac{1}{2} + \tfrac{1}{2}\sqrt{3} = \tfrac{1}{2}(1 + \sqrt{3}).$$

But this is not equal to

$$\sin (\alpha + \beta) = \sin (30° + 60°) = \sin 90° = 1.$$

We proceed now to obtain formulas for the sine and the cosine of the sum of two angles in terms of the functions of the separate angles; that is, for $\sin (\alpha + \beta)$ and $\cos (\alpha + \beta)$ in terms of the functions of α and β. For the present we shall prove the formulas only for the case in which α and β are positive, acute angles, and in Article **73** will prove that the same formulas are true for all values of α and β whatsoever.

Suppose, then, that α and β are any two positive, acute angles. Then $(\alpha + \beta)$ is less than 180°. Place the angle α in standard position with reference to a system of coördinate axes. Place the angle β with its vertex at the origin and its initial side, OQ, on the terminal side of α. The angle $(\alpha + \beta)$ is then also in standard position. Let P be any convenient point on the terminal side of $(\alpha + \beta)$. From P draw the line PQ perpendicular to the common side of α and β. Draw PA and QB perpendicular to the x-axis, and draw QC perpendicular to AP. Then the angle CPQ is equal to α, since its sides are respectively perpendicular to the sides of α.

From the right triangle BOQ, we see that

(1) $BQ = OQ \cdot \sin \alpha,$ and   (2) $OB = OQ \cdot \cos \alpha.$

From the right triangle PCQ, we find that

(3) $CQ = QP \cdot \sin \alpha$ and   (4) $CP = QP \cdot \cos \alpha.$

And from the right triangle OQP, we obtain

(5) $\dfrac{QP}{OP} = \sin \beta$ and   (6) $\dfrac{OQ}{OP} = \cos \beta.$

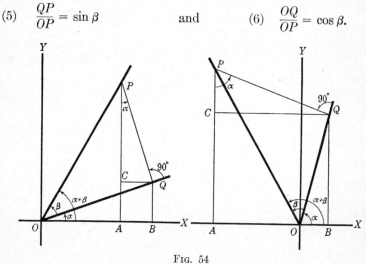

FIG. 54

From the definition of the sine of an angle we have

$$\sin (\alpha + \beta) = \frac{AP}{OP} = \frac{AC + CP}{OP} = \frac{AC}{OP} + \frac{CP}{OP} = \frac{BQ}{OP} + \frac{CP}{OP}.$$

From (1) and (4) this yields

$$\sin (\alpha + \beta) = \frac{OQ}{OP} \sin \alpha + \frac{QP}{OP} \cos \alpha.$$

Then, applying (5) and (6), we get the desired formula:

I. $\sin (\alpha + \beta) = \sin \alpha \cos \beta + \cos \alpha \sin \beta.$

Likewise, by the definition of the cosine of an angle,

$$\cos (\alpha + \beta) = \frac{OA}{OP} = \frac{OB - AB}{OP} = \frac{OB}{OP} - \frac{AB}{OP} = \frac{OB}{OP} - \frac{CQ}{OP}.$$

By the use of (2) and (3) and then of (5) and (6) we get

$$\cos(\alpha + \beta) = \frac{OQ}{OP}\cos\alpha - \frac{QP}{OP}\sin\alpha,$$

and, finally,

II. $\cos(\alpha + \beta) = \cos\alpha\cos\beta - \sin\alpha\sin\beta.$

These two laws may be stated as follows:

The sine of the sum of two angles is equal to the sine of one of the angles multiplied by the cosine of the second, plus the cosine of the first angle times the sine of the second.

The cosine of the sum of two angles is equal to the product of the cosines of the two angles minus the product of their sines.

It is important that the student learn these laws and all of the others in this chapter and be able to express them either in formulas or in words.

EXAMPLE. Given $\sin 30° = \frac{1}{2}$, $\cos 30° = \frac{1}{2}\sqrt{3}$, $\sin 45° = \cos 45° = \frac{1}{2}\sqrt{2}$, find $\sin 75°$ and $\cos 75°$.

$$\sin 75° = \sin(30° + 45°) = \sin 30° \cos 45° + \cos 30° \sin 45°.$$
$$= \tfrac{1}{2}\cdot\tfrac{1}{2}\sqrt{2} + \tfrac{1}{2}\sqrt{3}\cdot\tfrac{1}{2}\sqrt{2} = \tfrac{1}{4}\sqrt{2}\,(1+\sqrt{3})$$
$$= \frac{1.414 \times 2.732}{4} = .966.$$

$$\cos 75° = \cos(30° + 45°) = \cos 30° \cos 45° - \sin 30° \sin 45°$$
$$= \tfrac{1}{2}\sqrt{3}\cdot\tfrac{1}{2}\sqrt{2} - \tfrac{1}{2}\cdot\tfrac{1}{2}\sqrt{2} = \tfrac{1}{4}\sqrt{2}\,(\sqrt{3}-1)$$
$$= \frac{1.414 \times .732}{4} = .259.$$

★73. **Extension of addition formulas to all angles.** — We have proved formulas I and II of Article **72** if α and β are any two *acute* angles. We wish to prove that they are true for all values of α and β.

I. We shall first show* that *if α and β are any two angles* (acute or not) *for which these formulas hold, the formulas are still true if either α or β is either increased or decreased by* 90°. In particular, suppose

---

* The reader who is familiar with the process of proof by mathematical induction will recognize this as an example of that process.

that α is increased by 90°.   Assume, then, that α and β are any two angles such that

(1) $\sin(\alpha + \beta) = \sin\alpha\cos\beta + \cos\alpha\sin\beta,$

(2) $\cos(\alpha + \beta) = \cos\alpha\cos\beta - \sin\alpha\sin\beta,$

and, on this hypothesis, let us try to prove that

(3) $\sin(\alpha' + \beta) = \sin\alpha'\cos\beta + \cos\alpha'\sin\beta,$

(4) $\cos(\alpha' + \beta) = \cos\alpha'\cos\beta - \sin\alpha'\sin\beta,$

where $\alpha' = \alpha + 90°.$

We have

(5) $\sin(\alpha' + \beta) = \sin(\alpha + \beta + 90°) = \cos(\alpha + \beta)$ (Article **53**.)

$= \cos\alpha\cos\beta - \sin\alpha\sin\beta,$ by equation (2).

But $\cos\alpha = \cos(\alpha' - 90°) = \sin\alpha',$

and $\sin\alpha = \sin(\alpha' - 90°) = -\cos\alpha'.$ (Article **54**.)

Consequently, from (5),

(6) $\sin(\alpha' + \beta) = \sin\alpha'\cos\beta + \cos\alpha'\sin\beta,$

which is equation (3).   In a similar way,

$\cos(\alpha' + \beta) = \cos(\alpha + \beta + 90°) = -\sin(\alpha + \beta)$
$= -[\sin\alpha\cos\beta + \cos\alpha\sin\beta]$ by equation (1),
$= -[-\cos\alpha'\cos\beta + \sin\alpha'\sin\beta],$

which gives equation (4).

It is left to the student to prove that if (1) and (2) are true, then (3) and (4) must be true, where

$$\alpha' = \alpha - 90°,$$

and also to show, by Article **53**, that equations (1) and (2) are true when either α or β instead of being actually acute is equal to 90°.

II.   Now suppose that α' and β' are any two angles whatsoever. We can then find two angles, α and β, either acute or right angles, such that α' can be obtained from α by adding or subtracting 90° a certain number of times and β' can be obtained from β by adding or subtracting 90° a certain number of times.   Therefore, if the formulas (1) and (2) hold for this α and β, the formulas must also hold for α' and β'.   For, holding β fast, we can replace α by α' by making successive additions or subtractions of 90°, and after each such change the formulas will still be true.   Then β, in a similar way, can be replaced by β'.

But the formulas (1) and (2) are true for α and β since α and β are acute or right angles.   Therefore the formulas are true for α' and β', that is, for any angles.

74. Tan $(\alpha + \beta)$ and cot $(\alpha + \beta)$. — By means of I and II, we can write

$$\tan (\alpha + \beta) = \frac{\sin (\alpha + \beta)}{\cos (\alpha + \beta)} = \frac{\sin \alpha \cos \beta + \cos \alpha \sin \beta}{\cos \alpha \cos \beta - \sin \alpha \sin \beta}.$$

Dividing numerator and denominator of this fraction by $\cos \alpha \cos \beta$, we get

$$\tan (\alpha + \beta) = \frac{\dfrac{\sin \alpha}{\cos \alpha} + \dfrac{\sin \beta}{\cos \beta}}{1 - \dfrac{\sin \alpha}{\cos \alpha} \cdot \dfrac{\sin \beta}{\cos \beta}},$$

or

III. $$\tan (\alpha + \beta) = \frac{\tan \alpha + \tan \beta}{1 - \tan \alpha \tan \beta};$$

the tangent of the sum of two angles is equal to the sum of the tangents of the angles divided by 1 minus the product of their tangents.

It is left to the student to prove the formula

IV. $$\cot (\alpha + \beta) = \frac{\cot \alpha \cot \beta - 1}{\cot \alpha + \cot \beta}.$$

EXAMPLE.

$$\tan 75° = \tan (45° + 30°) = \frac{\tan 45° + \tan 30°}{1 - \tan 45° \tan 30°}$$

$$= \frac{1 + \dfrac{1}{\sqrt{3}}}{1 - \dfrac{1}{\sqrt{3}}} = \frac{\sqrt{3} + 1}{\sqrt{3} - 1} = \frac{(\sqrt{3} + 1)\,(\sqrt{3} + 1)}{(\sqrt{3} - 1)\,(\sqrt{3} + 1)}$$

$$= \frac{4 + 2\sqrt{3}}{3 - 1} = 2 + \sqrt{3} = 3.73.$$

75. Functions of (α − β). — Since the formulas for functions of $(\alpha + \beta)$ are true for all values of α and β, we may replace β by $-\beta$. Since $\cos(-\beta) = \cos \beta$, while $\sin(-\beta) = -\sin \beta$, $\tan(-\beta) = -\tan \beta$, and $\cot(-\beta) = -\cot \beta$, the terms in formulas I, II, III, and IV which contain $\sin \alpha$, $\tan \alpha$, or $\cot \alpha$ will be reversed in sign, while the other terms will remain unchanged.   We get

V. $\sin (\alpha - \beta) = \sin \alpha \cos \beta - \cos \alpha \sin \beta.$

VI. $\cos (\alpha - \beta) = \cos \alpha \cos \beta + \sin \alpha \sin \beta.$

VII. $\tan (\alpha - \beta) = \dfrac{\tan \alpha - \tan \beta}{1 + \tan \alpha \tan \beta}.$

VIII. $\cot (\alpha - \beta) = \dfrac{\cot \alpha \cot \beta + 1}{\cot \beta - \cot \alpha}.$

EXAMPLE.

$$\sin 15° = \sin (45° - 30°)$$
$$= \sin 45° \cos 30° - \cos 45° \sin 30°$$
$$= \tfrac{1}{2}\sqrt{2} \cdot \tfrac{1}{2}\sqrt{3} - \tfrac{1}{2}\sqrt{2} \cdot \tfrac{1}{2} = \tfrac{1}{4}\sqrt{2}\,(\sqrt{3} - 1) = .259.$$

$$\cos 15° = \cos (45° - 30°)$$
$$= \cos 45° \cos 30° + \sin 45° \sin 30°$$
$$= \tfrac{1}{2}\sqrt{2} \cdot \tfrac{1}{2}\sqrt{3} + \tfrac{1}{2}\sqrt{2} \cdot \tfrac{1}{2} = \tfrac{1}{4}\sqrt{2}\,(\sqrt{3} + 1) = .966.$$

$$\tan 15° = \frac{\tan 45° - \tan 30°}{1 + \tan 45° \tan 30°}$$

$$= \frac{1 - \dfrac{1}{\sqrt{3}}}{1 + \dfrac{1}{\sqrt{3}}} = \frac{\sqrt{3} - 1}{\sqrt{3} + 1} = \frac{(\sqrt{3} - 1)^2}{3 - 1} = 2 - \sqrt{3} = .268.$$

EXERCISES

Suppose that α and β are two positive acute angles. Find the sine, cosine, and tangent of $(\alpha + \beta)$ and $(\alpha - \beta)$, under each of the following suppositions.

1. $\sin \alpha = 2/3$, $\cos \beta = 3/5$.

Solution: We first find the other functions of α and β. By either algebraic or geometric methods we find $\cos \alpha = \sqrt{5}/3$; $\tan \alpha = 2/\sqrt{5} = \frac{2}{5} \sqrt{5}$.

$$\sin \beta = 4/5; \qquad \tan \beta = 4/3.$$

Then

$$\sin (\alpha + \beta) = \frac{2}{3} \cdot \frac{3}{5} + \frac{\sqrt{5}}{3} \cdot \frac{4}{5} = \frac{2}{15} (3 + 2 \sqrt{5}).$$

$$\sin (\alpha - \beta) = \frac{2}{3} \cdot \frac{3}{5} - \frac{\sqrt{5}}{3} \cdot \frac{4}{5} = \frac{2}{15} (3 - 2 \sqrt{5}).$$

$$\cos (\alpha + \beta) = \frac{\sqrt{5}}{3} \cdot \frac{3}{5} - \frac{2}{3} \cdot \frac{4}{5} = \frac{1}{15} (3 \sqrt{5} - 8).$$

$$\cos (\alpha - \beta) = \frac{\sqrt{5}}{3} \cdot \frac{3}{5} + \frac{2}{3} \cdot \frac{4}{5} = \frac{1}{15} (3 \sqrt{5} + 8).$$

$$\tan (\alpha + \beta) = \frac{\dfrac{2}{\sqrt{5}} + \dfrac{4}{3}}{1 - \dfrac{2}{\sqrt{5}} \cdot \dfrac{4}{3}} = \frac{6 + 4 \sqrt{5}}{3 \sqrt{5} - 8} = -\tfrac{1}{19} (108 + 50 \sqrt{5}),$$

a result obtainable from the values of $\sin (\alpha + \beta)$ and $\cos (\alpha + \beta)$ already found.

$$\tan (\alpha - \beta) = \frac{6 - 4 \sqrt{5}}{3 \sqrt{5} + 8} = \tfrac{1}{19} (108 - 50 \sqrt{5}).$$

2. $\sin \alpha = 4/5$, $\cos \beta = 5/13$.

3. $\tan \alpha = 2$, $\cot \beta = 3/2$.

Ans. $\sin (\alpha + \beta) = \tfrac{8}{65} \sqrt{65}$, $\sin (\alpha - \beta) = \tfrac{4}{65} \sqrt{65}$,

$\cos (\alpha + \beta) = -\tfrac{1}{65} \sqrt{65}$, $\cos (\alpha - \beta) = \tfrac{7}{65} \sqrt{65}$,

$\tan (\alpha + \beta) = -8$, $\tan (\alpha - \beta) = \tfrac{4}{7}$.

4. $\tan \alpha = 3$, $\sec \beta = 2$.

5. Find $\sin \alpha$, $\cos \alpha$, $\tan \alpha$, given that $\cos (\alpha + \beta) = 3/4$ and $\sin \beta = 1/3$, and that all the angles are acute.

Ans. $\sin \alpha = \frac{1}{12} (\sqrt{56} - 3)$, $\cos \alpha = \frac{1}{12} (3 \sqrt{8} + \sqrt{7})$,
$\tan \alpha = \frac{1}{65} (27 \sqrt{7} - 16 \sqrt{8})$.

6. Find $\sin \alpha$, $\cos \alpha$, $\tan \alpha$, given that $\cos (\alpha - \beta) = 3/4$ and $\sin \beta = 1/4$, and that all the angles are acute.

Assuming that α and β are acute, in what quadrant does $(\alpha + \beta)$ lie in each of the following cases?

7. $\sin \alpha = 3/4$, $\sin \beta = 2/3$.   *Ans.*   Second.
8. $\sin \alpha = 2/3$, $\sin \beta = 2/3$.
9. $\cos \alpha = 2/3$, $\cos \beta = 1/2$.   *Ans.*   Second.
10. $\cos \alpha = 1/2$, $\sin \beta = 3/5$.
11. Find $\sin 120°$ from functions of $30°$ and $90°$.
12. Find $\cos 150°$ from functions of $180°$ and $30°$.
13. Show that

$$\sin (\alpha + \beta + \gamma) = \sin [(\alpha + \beta) + \gamma]$$
$$= \sin \alpha \cos \beta \cos \gamma + \cos \alpha \sin \beta \cos \gamma$$
$$+ \cos \alpha \cos \beta \sin \gamma - \sin \alpha \sin \beta \sin \gamma.$$

14. Show that

$$\cos (\alpha + \beta + \gamma) = \cos \alpha \cos \beta \cos \gamma - \sin \alpha \cos \beta \sin \gamma$$
$$- \cos \alpha \sin \beta \sin \gamma - \sin \alpha \sin \beta \cos \gamma.$$

15. Show that

$$\tan (\alpha + \beta + \gamma) = \frac{\tan \alpha + \tan \beta + \tan \gamma - \tan \alpha \tan \beta \tan \gamma}{1 - \tan \alpha \tan \beta - \tan \beta \tan \gamma - \tan \gamma \tan \alpha}.$$

Find the values of the following expressions.

16. $\sin (30° + \alpha)$.

17. $\cos (\alpha + 45°)$.   *Ans.* $\frac{1}{2} \sqrt{2} (\cos \alpha - \sin \alpha)$.

18. $\tan (\alpha + 60°)$.

Show that

19. $\cos(x + 30°) - \cos(x - 30°) = -\sin x$.

20. $\cos(x + 45°) + \cos(x - 45°) = \sqrt{2}\cos x$.

21. $\sin(x + 60°) + \sin(x - 60°) = \sin x$.

22. $\sin(x + 30°) + \cos(x + 60°) = \cos x$.

23. $\cos(\alpha + \beta)\cos(\alpha - \beta) + \sin(\alpha + \beta)\sin(\alpha - \beta) = 1 - 2\sin^2\beta$.

24. $\cos(\alpha + \beta)\cos(\alpha - \beta) - \sin(\alpha + \beta)\sin(\alpha - \beta) = 2\cos^2\alpha - 1$.

25. $\tan(\alpha + 45°) + \cot(\alpha - 45°) = 0$.

26. $\dfrac{\tan(45° + \alpha)}{\tan(45° - \alpha)} = \dfrac{(1 + \tan\alpha)^2}{(1 - \tan\alpha)^2}$.

27. $\cos(x + y)\cos y - \cos(x + z)\cos z$
$\qquad = \sin(x + z)\sin z - \sin(x + y)\sin y$.

28. $\sin(x + y)\cos y + \cos(x + z)\sin z$
$\qquad = \sin(x + z)\cos z + \cos(x + y)\sin y$.

76. Functions of twice an angle. — If we replace β by α in Formulas I, II, III, and IV, $(\alpha + \beta)$ becomes equal to 2α, and we have

IX. $\qquad\qquad \sin 2\alpha = 2\sin\alpha\cos\alpha$.

X. $\qquad\qquad \cos 2\alpha = \cos^2\alpha - \sin^2\alpha$
$\qquad\qquad\qquad\quad = 1 - 2\sin^2\alpha$
$\qquad\qquad\qquad\quad = 2\cos^2\alpha - 1$.

XI. $\qquad\qquad \tan 2\alpha = \dfrac{2\tan\alpha}{1 - \tan^2\alpha}$.

XII. $\qquad\qquad \cot 2\alpha = \dfrac{\cot^2\alpha - 1}{2\cot\alpha}$.

We have three forms for $\cos 2\alpha$ obtained by setting

$$\cos 2\alpha = \cos^2\alpha - \sin^2\alpha = (1 - \sin^2\alpha) - \sin^2\alpha = 1 - 2\sin^2\alpha,$$

and

$$\cos 2\alpha = \cos^2\alpha - \sin^2\alpha = \cos^2\alpha - (1 - \cos^2\alpha) = 2\cos^2\alpha - 1.$$

The formulas should be expressed in words, as, for example, *the cosine of twice an angle is equal to the square of the cosine of the angle minus the square of the sine of the angle; or to 1 minus twice the square of the sine of the angle; or to twice the square of the cosine of the angle minus 1.*

EXAMPLE. Verify the formulas for the case $\alpha = 30°$.

By IX, $\sin 60° = \sin (2 \times 30°) = 2 \sin 30° \times \cos 30°$
$$= 2 \times \tfrac{1}{2} \times \tfrac{1}{2} \sqrt{3} = \tfrac{1}{2} \sqrt{3}.$$

$$\cos 60° = \cos (2 \times 30°) = \cos^2 30° - \sin^2 30° = \tfrac{3}{4} - \tfrac{1}{4} = \tfrac{1}{2}.$$

$$\tan 60° = \tan (2 \times 30°) = \frac{2 \tan 30°}{1 - \tan^2 30°} = \frac{\dfrac{2}{\sqrt{3}}}{1 - \dfrac{1}{3}} = \frac{\dfrac{2}{\sqrt{3}}}{\dfrac{2}{3}} = \sqrt{3}.$$

$$\cot 60° = \cot (2 \times 30°) = \frac{\cot^2 30° - 1}{2 \cot 30°} = \frac{3 - 1}{2 \sqrt{3}} = \tfrac{1}{3} \sqrt{3}.$$

77. Functions of half an angle. — From the results of the preceding article we obtain formulas for the functions of half an angle in terms of the functions of the whole angle. Since, by Article **76**, the cosine of twice an angle is equal to 1 minus twice the square of the sine of the angle, by taking $\alpha/2$ as "the angle" and α as "twice the angle," we have

$$\cos \alpha = 1 - 2 \sin^2 \frac{\alpha}{2}.$$

Therefore

$$2 \sin^2 \frac{\alpha}{2} = 1 - \cos \alpha,$$

and

XIII. $$\sin \frac{\alpha}{2} = \pm \sqrt{\frac{1 - \cos \alpha}{2}}.$$

Likewise from the third form for the cosine of twice an angle,

$$\cos \alpha = 2 \cos^2 \frac{\alpha}{2} - 1,$$

and

XIV. $$\cos \frac{\alpha}{2} = \pm \sqrt{\frac{1 + \cos \alpha}{2}}.$$

On dividing XIII by XIV, we find

XV. $$\tan\frac{\alpha}{2} = \pm\sqrt{\frac{1-\cos\alpha}{1+\cos\alpha}}.$$

XVI. $$\cot\frac{\alpha}{2} = \pm\sqrt{\frac{1+\cos\alpha}{1-\cos\alpha}}.$$

The student should state these relations in words.

EXAMPLE 1. Verify these formulas for the angle $\alpha = 60°$. Now $\alpha/2 = 30°$, and

$$\sin 30° = \sin\frac{60°}{2} = \sqrt{\frac{1-\cos 60°}{2}} = \sqrt{\frac{1-\frac{1}{2}}{2}} = \sqrt{\tfrac{1}{4}} = \tfrac{1}{2},$$

$$\cos 30° = \sqrt{\frac{1+\cos 60°}{2}} = \sqrt{\frac{1+\frac{1}{2}}{2}} = \sqrt{\tfrac{3}{4}} = \tfrac{1}{2}\sqrt{3},$$

$$\tan 30° = \sqrt{\frac{1-\cos 60°}{1+\cos 60°}} = \sqrt{\frac{1-\frac{1}{2}}{1+\frac{1}{2}}} = \sqrt{\tfrac{1}{3}} = \tfrac{1}{3}\sqrt{3}.$$

EXAMPLE 2. Prove the identity

$$\sin 3x = 3\sin x - 4\sin^3 x.$$

We can write

$$\begin{aligned}
\sin 3x &= \sin(2x+x)\\
&= \sin 2x\cos x + \cos 2x\sin x \quad \text{(By I)}\\
&= (2\sin x\cos x)\cos x + (1-2\sin^2 x)\sin x \quad \text{(By IX and X)}\\
&= 2\sin x\cos^2 x + \sin x - 2\sin^3 x\\
&= 2\sin x(1-\sin^2 x) + \sin x - 2\sin^3 x\\
&= 3\sin x - 4\sin^3 x,
\end{aligned}$$

as we wished to show.

EXAMPLE 3. Prove the identity

$$\tan^2\alpha = 4\sin^2\alpha\csc^2 2\alpha - 1.$$

The right-hand side is the more complicated, so we simplify it. The chief difficulty is that the identity contains functions of two different angles, α and 2α. When functions of two angles are present in an equation, we usually try to reduce them to functions of one angle. In this example we express $\csc^2 2\alpha$ in terms of functions of α. We write

$$\begin{aligned}
4\sin^2\alpha\csc^2 2\alpha - 1 &= \frac{4\sin^2\alpha}{\sin^2 2\alpha} - 1\\
&= \frac{4\sin^2\alpha}{(2\sin\alpha\cos\alpha)^2} - 1\\
&= \frac{1}{\cos^2\alpha} - 1 = \sec^2\alpha - 1 = \tan^2\alpha.
\end{aligned}$$

EXERCISES

Find the values of the following functions without using the tables.

1. sin 90°, from functions of 45°.
2. tan 120°, from functions of 60°.
3. sin 22½°.   *Ans.* $\frac{1}{2}\sqrt{2 - \sqrt{2}} = .38.$
4. cos 22½°.
5. tan 15°.   *Ans.* $2 - \sqrt{3} = .268.$
6. sin 15°.
7. sin 67½°.   *Ans.* $\frac{1}{2}\sqrt{2 + \sqrt{2}} = .924.$
8. cos 67½°.

Prove the following identities.

9. $\cos 3x = 4\cos^3 x - 3\cos x.$
10. $4\sin^2 x \cos^2 x = 1 - \cos^2 2x.$
11. $\cos^2 x = \sin^2 x + \cos 2x.$
12. $\cos 4x = 1 - 8\sin^2 x \cos^2 x.$
13. $\sec 2x = \dfrac{1}{2\cos^2 x - 1}.$
14. $\sec 2x = \dfrac{\sec^2 x}{2 - \sec^2 x}.$
15. $\sec 2x = \dfrac{\csc^2 x}{\csc^2 x - 2}.$
16. $2\csc 2x = \sec x \csc x.$
17. $2\cot 2x = 2\cos x \csc x - \sec x \csc x.$
18. $\cos^4 x - \sin^4 x = \cos 2x.$
19. $1 - \sin 2x = (\sin x - \cos x)^2.$
20. $\dfrac{1 - \sin 2x}{\cos 2x} = \dfrac{1 - \tan x}{1 + \tan x}.$
21. $\dfrac{1 + \tan^2 x}{1 - \tan^2 x} = \sec 2x.$
22. $\cos 5x \cos x - \sin 5x \sin x = \cos 6x.$
23. $\cos 2x \cos x + \sin 2x \sin x = \cos x.$
24. $\dfrac{\cos 3x}{\sin x} + \dfrac{\sin 3x}{\cos x} = 2\cot 2x.$

25. $\dfrac{\cos 3x}{\sin x} - \dfrac{\sin 3x}{\cos x} = 4 \cot 4x \cos 2x.$

26. $\dfrac{1 + \tan x}{1 - \tan x} = \sec 2x + \tan 2x.$

27. $\dfrac{2 \cot x}{1 + \cot^2 x} = \sin 2x.$

28. $\dfrac{\sec x - 1}{\sec x + 1} = \sec^2 \dfrac{x}{2} - 1.$

29. $\dfrac{\sec x + 1}{\sec x - 1} = \csc^2 \dfrac{x}{2} - 1.$

30. $\tan 2x = \tan x \,(1 + \sec 2x).$

31. $\csc x = \frac{1}{2}\left(\tan \dfrac{x}{2} + \cot \dfrac{x}{2}\right).$

32. $\sec^2 \dfrac{x}{2} = \dfrac{2 \tan x}{\tan x + \sin x}.$

33. $\dfrac{\sin 3x}{\sin x} - \dfrac{\cos 3x}{\cos x} = 2.$

34. $2 \cot 2x = \cot x - \tan x.$

35. $\dfrac{1 - \cos 2x}{\sin 2x} = \tan x.$

36. $\dfrac{\sec 2x - 1}{\sec 2x + 1} = \tan^2 x.$

37. $\csc x - \cot x = \tan \dfrac{x}{2}.$

38. $\dfrac{\sin x}{1 + \cos x} = \tan \dfrac{x}{2}.$

39. $\sin 2x = 2 \sin^3 x \cos x + 2 \sin x \cos^3 x.$

40. $4 \,(\sin^6 x + \cos^6 x) = 4 - 3 \sin^2 2x.$

78. Product formulas. — From the formulas

$$\text{I. } \quad \sin (\alpha + \beta) = \sin \alpha \cos \beta + \cos \alpha \sin \beta,$$
$$\text{II. } \quad \cos (\alpha + \beta) = \cos \alpha \cos \beta - \sin \alpha \sin \beta,$$
$$\text{V. } \quad \sin (\alpha - \beta) = \sin \alpha \cos \beta - \cos \alpha \sin \beta,$$
$$\text{VI. } \quad \cos (\alpha - \beta) = \cos \alpha \cos \beta + \sin \alpha \sin \beta,$$

we get

$$(1) \quad \cos (\alpha + \beta) - \cos (\alpha - \beta) = -2 \sin \alpha \sin \beta,$$
$$(2) \quad \cos (\alpha + \beta) + \cos (\alpha - \beta) = 2 \cos \alpha \cos \beta,$$
$$(3) \quad \sin (\alpha + \beta) + \sin (\alpha - \beta) = 2 \sin \alpha \cos \beta,$$
$$(4) \quad \sin (\alpha + \beta) - \sin (\alpha - \beta) = 2 \cos \alpha \sin \beta.$$

From equations (1), (2), and (3) we obtain the *product formulas:*

XVII. $\quad \sin \alpha \sin \beta = \frac{1}{2} [\cos (\alpha - \beta) - \cos (\alpha + \beta)],$

XVIII. $\quad \cos \alpha \cos \beta = \frac{1}{2} [\cos (\alpha + \beta) + \cos (\alpha - \beta)],$

XIX. $\quad \sin \alpha \cos \beta = \frac{1}{2} [\sin (\alpha + \beta) + \sin (\alpha - \beta)].$

For the purposes of this book the formulas of this Article are less important than those of Article **79**, and they may be omitted. In other fields of mathematics they are important.

These formulas should be stated in words. Thus, for XVII, we can say: *The product of the sines of two angles is equal to one-half the difference of the cosine of the difference of the angles and the cosine of the sum of the angles.*

EXAMPLE. Verify these formulas in the case $\alpha = 30°$, $\beta = 60°$.
By XIII,
$$\sin 30° \sin 60° = \frac{1}{2} [\cos (-30°) - \cos 90°] \quad \text{or} \quad \frac{1}{2} \cdot \frac{1}{2} \sqrt{3} = \frac{1}{2} [\frac{1}{2} \sqrt{3} - 0];$$

by XIV,
$$\cos 30° \cos 60° = \frac{1}{2} [\cos 90° + \cos (-30°)] \quad \text{or} \quad \frac{1}{2} \sqrt{3} \cdot \frac{1}{2} = \frac{1}{2} [0 + \frac{1}{2} \sqrt{3}];$$

by XV,
$$\sin 30° \cos 60° = \frac{1}{2} [\sin 90° + \sin (-30°)] \quad \text{or} \quad \frac{1}{2} \cdot \frac{1}{2} = \frac{1}{2} [1 - \frac{1}{2}].$$

79. Sums of functions. — In order to obtain formulas for the sum or difference of the sines or cosines of two angles, in equations (1) to (4) of Article **78**, we will set

$$\alpha + \beta = x$$
$$\alpha - \beta = y.$$

Adding these two equations, we get $2\alpha = x + y$, and on subtracting, $2\beta = x - y$. Therefore

$$\alpha = \tfrac{1}{2}(x + y), \quad \beta = \tfrac{1}{2}(x - y).$$

Using these values in equations (3), (4), (2), (1), we get:

   XX. $\sin x + \sin y = 2 \sin \tfrac{1}{2}(x + y) \cos \tfrac{1}{2}(x - y).$

   XXI. $\sin x - \sin y = 2 \cos \tfrac{1}{2}(x + y) \sin \tfrac{1}{2}(x - y).$

   XXII. $\cos x + \cos y = 2 \cos \tfrac{1}{2}(x + y) \cos \tfrac{1}{2}(x - y).$

   XXIII. $\cos x - \cos y = -2 \sin \tfrac{1}{2}(x + y) \sin \tfrac{1}{2}(x - y).$

The formulas should be stated in words. Thus, for **XX**: *The sum of the sines of two angles is equal to twice the sine of half the sum of the angles times the cosine of half the difference of the angles.*

EXAMPLE 1. Prove the identity

$$2 \sin 3z \cos 7z + \sin 4z = \sin 10z.$$

From XIX, using $\alpha = 3z$, $\beta = 7z$, we have

$$\sin 3z \cos 7z = \tfrac{1}{2}[\sin 10z + \sin (-4z)].$$

Therefore

$$2 \sin 3z \cos 7z + \sin 4z = \sin 10z - \sin 4z + \sin 4z = \sin 10z.$$

EXAMPLE 2. Prove the identity

$$\frac{\sin 7z + \sin 3z}{\cos 7z + \cos 3z} = \tan 5z.$$

Applying XX and XXII to numerator and denominator of the left-hand side, we find

$$\frac{\sin 7z + \sin 3z}{\cos 7z + \cos 3z} = \frac{2 \sin \tfrac{1}{2}(7z + 3z) \cos \tfrac{1}{2}(7z - 3z)}{2 \cos \tfrac{1}{2}(7z + 3z) \cos \tfrac{1}{2}(7z - 3z)}$$

$$= \frac{2 \sin 5z \cos 2z}{2 \cos 5z \cos 2z} = \frac{\sin 5z}{\cos 5z} = \tan 5z.$$

EXAMPLE 3. Solve the equation

$$\sin 2x + \sqrt{2} \cos x = 0$$

for all values of x from $0°$ to $360°$.

We reduce this so that it will contain only the single angle x:

$$2 \sin x \cos x + \sqrt{2} \cos x = 0$$

or

$$\cos x \, (2 \sin x + \sqrt{2}) = 0.$$

Hence

$$\cos x = 0, \quad \text{so that} \quad x = 90° \text{ or } 270°, \quad \text{and}$$
$$2 \sin x + \sqrt{2} = 0 \quad \text{or} \quad \sin x = -\tfrac{1}{2} \sqrt{2}, \quad \text{so that} \quad x = 225° \text{ or } 315°.$$

These four values of x satisfy the original equation.

EXAMPLE 4. Solve the equation

$$\sin 3x + \sin 2x + \sin x = 0$$

for all values of x from 0° to 360°.

We write the equation

$$(\sin 3x + \sin x) + \sin 2x = 0,$$

and apply formula XX, getting

$$2 \sin 2x \cos x + \sin 2x = 0$$

or $\qquad\qquad\qquad \sin 2x \, (2 \cos x + 1) = 0.$

Hence $\qquad\qquad 2 \cos x + 1 = 0 \quad \text{or} \quad \cos x = -1/2,$

which gives $x = 120°$ and $x = 240°$.

Also $\qquad\qquad\qquad\qquad \sin 2x = 0.$

In order to get all of the values of x which satisfy this equation and which lie between 0° and 360°, we must find all of the values of $2x$ which satisfy the equation and lie between 0° and 720°. They are

$$2x = 0°, 180°, 360°, 540°, 720°,$$

so that

$$x = 0°, 90°, 180°, 270°, 360°.$$

The complete solution therefore is

$$x = 0°, 90°, 120°, 180°, 240°, 270°, 360°.$$

EXERCISES

Express the following products as sums or differences of two functions.

1. $2 \sin 7\alpha \sin 3\alpha$.   *Ans.* $\cos 4\alpha - \cos 10\alpha$.

2. $2 \sin 2\alpha \sin \alpha$.

3. $2 \cos \dfrac{5\alpha}{2} \cos \dfrac{\alpha}{2}$.   *Ans.* $\cos 3\alpha + \cos 2\alpha$.

4. $2 \cos (x + y) \cos (x - y)$.

5. $2 \sin (180° + \alpha) \cos (180° - \alpha)$.

       Ans. $\sin 2\alpha + \sin 360° = \sin 2\alpha$.

6. $\sin \dfrac{2x}{3} \cos \dfrac{x}{3}$.

Express each of the following quantities as a single term.

7. $\sin x + \sin (x + y)$.   *Ans.* $2 \sin \left(x + \dfrac{y}{2}\right) \cos \dfrac{y}{2}$.

8. $\sin 5x + \sin x$.

9. $\cos 5x + \cos 3x$.   *Ans.* $2 \cos 4x \cos x$.

10. $\cos (a + b) + \cos (a - b)$.

11. $\sin 3x - \sin x$.   *Ans.* $2 \sin x \cos 2x$.

12. $\cos 4x - \cos 2x$.

Prove the following identities.

13. $\dfrac{\cos 3x - \cos x}{\cos 3x + \cos x} = -\tan 2x \tan x$.

14. $\dfrac{\sin 5x - \sin 3x}{\sin 5x + \sin 3x} = \tan x \cot 4x$.

15. $\dfrac{\cos 3x - \cos 5x}{\sin 3x + \sin 5x} = \tan x$.

16. $\dfrac{\cos 3x + \cos x}{\sin 3x + \sin x} = \cot 2x$.

17. $\dfrac{\cos 3x - \cos x}{\sin 3x - \sin x} = \dfrac{2 \tan x}{\tan^2 x - 1}$.

18. $\sin (45° + x) - \sin (45° - x) = \sqrt{2} \sin x$.

19. $\cos(45° + x) - \cos(45° - x) = -\sqrt{2}\sin x$.

20. $\sin\frac{1}{2}(x+y)\cos\frac{1}{2}(x-y) + \cos\frac{1}{2}(x+y)\sin\frac{1}{2}(x-y) = \sin x$.

21. $\sin 5x + \sin 3x = 8\sin x\cos^2 x\cos 2x$.

22. $\cos 6x - \cos 2x = -16\sin^2 x\cos^2 x(2\cos^2 x - 1)$.

23. $\cot 4x + \tan x = \dfrac{2\cos 3x}{\sin 5x + \sin 3x}$.

24. $1 + \tan 2x\cot 3x = \dfrac{2\sin 5x}{\sin x + \sin 5x}$.

25. $\cot x + \cot 2x = \dfrac{2\sin 3x}{\cos x - \cos 3x}$.

26. $1 + \tan 3x\tan 4x = \dfrac{2\cos x}{\cos 7x + \cos x}$.

27. $\dfrac{\cos 2A + \cos A + 1}{\sin 2A + \sin A} = \cot A$.

28. $\dfrac{\sin A + \cos 2A - 1}{\cos A - \sin 2A} = \tan A$.

29. $\dfrac{1 + \sin x - \cos x}{1 + \sin x + \cos x} = \tan\dfrac{x}{2}$.

30. $\sin 2x + \sin 4x + \sin 6x = 4\cos x\cos 2x\sin 3x$.

31. $\cos 2x + \cos 4x + \cos 6x = 4\cos x\cos 2x\cos 3x - 1$.

32. $\dfrac{\cos 2x + \cos 7x}{\cos 3x + \cos 6x} + \dfrac{\cos 6x - \cos x}{\cos 5x - \cos 2x} = \dfrac{2\sin 4x}{\sin 3x}$.

33. $\dfrac{\sin 10x + \sin 6x}{\sin 12x + \sin 4x} - \dfrac{\sin 5x - \sin x}{\sin 7x + \sin x} = \dfrac{2\sin 2x}{\sin 8x}$.

34. $\dfrac{\cos 6x + \cos 12x}{\sin 14x - \sin 4x} + \dfrac{\sin 7x - \sin x}{\cos 9x + \cos x} = \dfrac{2\cos 2x}{\sin 10x}$.

35. $\dfrac{\sin x + \sin 2x + \sin 3x}{\cos x + \cos 2x + \cos 3x} = \tan 2x$.

36. $\sin^2 3x - \sin^2 x = 2\sin^2 2x\cos 2x$.

37. $\dfrac{\sin(x+3y) + \sin(3x+y)}{\sin 2x + \sin 2y} = 2\cos(x+y)$.

38. $\dfrac{\cos(x+3y) - \cos(3x+y)}{\cos 2x - \cos 2y} = -2\cos(x+y)$.

Solve the following equations for all values of x from $0°$ to $360°$.

39. $\sin 2x = \sin x$.   *Ans.* $0°, 60°, 180°, 300°, 360°$.
40. $\sin 2x = \cos x$.
41. $\cos 2x = \cos x$.   *Ans.* $0°, 120°, 240°, 360°$.
42. $\cos 2x = \sin x$.
43. $\tan 2x + \tan x = 0$.   *Ans.* $0°, 60°, 120°, 180°, 240°, 300°, 360°$.
44. $\tan 2x = \tan x$.
45. $\sin 2x + \sin x = 0$.   *Ans.* $0°, 120°, 180°, 240°, 360°$.
46. $\sin 2x + \cos x = 0$.
47. $\cos 2x + \cos x = 0$.   *Ans.* $60°, 180°, 300°$.
48. $\cos 2x + \sin x = 0$.
49. $\cos 4x + \sin 2x = 0$.   *Ans.* $45°, 105°, 165°, 225°, 285°, 345°$.
50. $\sin 4x + \sin 2x = 0$.

51. $\sin \dfrac{x}{2} + \cos x = 1$.   *Ans.* $0°, 60°, 300°, 360°$.

52. $\cos \dfrac{x}{2} - \cos x = 1$.

53. $\tan \dfrac{x}{2} + \cos x = 1$.   *Ans.* $0°, 90°, 360°$.

54. $\cot \dfrac{x}{2} - \cos x = 1$.

55. $\sin \dfrac{x}{2} - \cos x = 1$.   *Ans.* $102° \ 39.8', 257° \ 20.2'$.

56. $2 \tan x = 2 - \sec^2 x$.
57. $\sin 3x + \sin x = \cos x$.   *Ans.* $15°, 75°, 90°, 195°, 255°, 270°$.
58. $\cos 3x - \cos x = \sin x$.
59. $2 \sin 3x + 2 \sin x = \tan x$.   *Ans.* $0°, 60°, 180°, 300°, 360°$.
60. $\sin 3x + \sin x = \cot x \cos x$.
61. $\tan x - \cot x = \cot 2x$.   *Ans.* $45°, 135°, 225°, 315°$.
62. $(2 \cos 2x + 1)(\sin 3x - 3) = 0$.
63. $\tan 3x - \tan x = \sec 3x$.   *Ans.* No solutions.
64. $\sin 5x + \sin x = \cos 2x$.
65. $\sin 5x - \sin x + \cos 4x + \cos 2x = 0$.
                    Ans. $30°, 90°, 150°, 210°, 270°, 330°$.

66. $\cos 5x - \cos 3x + 2 \sin x = 0$.

67. $\sin 5x + 2 \cos x + \sin 3x = 0$.

Ans. $67\frac{1}{2}°$, $90°$, $157\frac{1}{2}°$, $247\frac{1}{2}°$, $270°$, $337\frac{1}{2}°$.

68. $\cos 5x - \cos 3x + \sin x = 0$.

69. $\tan 3x + \tan x = 0$. *Ans.* $0°, 45°, 135°, 180°, 225°, 315°, 360°$.

70. $\sin x + \sin 3x + \sin 5x = 0$.

71. $\cos x + \cos 2x + \cos 3x = 0$.

Ans. $45°$, $120°$, $135°$, $225°$, $240°$, $315°$.

72. $\cos x + \cos 3x + \cos 5x = 0$.

Prove the following relations on the assumption that A and B are complementary angles.

73. $\sin (A - B) = \cos 2B$.

74. $\cos (A - B) = \sin 2A = \sin 2B$.

75. $\tan (A - B) = \cot 2B$.

Prove the following relations on the assumption that $A + B + C = 180°$.

76. $\sin A + \sin B + \sin C = 4 \cos \dfrac{A}{2} \cos \dfrac{B}{2} \cos \dfrac{C}{2}$.

[*Solution:*

$$(\sin A + \sin B) + \sin C = 2 \sin \frac{A+B}{2} \cos \frac{A-B}{2} + \sin C$$

$$= 2 \sin \frac{A+B}{2} \cos \frac{A-B}{2} + 2 \sin \frac{C}{2} \cos \frac{C}{2}.$$

Since $\dfrac{A + B}{2} + \dfrac{C}{2} = 90°$, $\sin \dfrac{A + B}{2} = \cos \dfrac{C}{2}$. Therefore

$$\sin A + \sin B + \sin C = 2 \cos \frac{C}{2} \left(\cos \frac{A - B}{2} + \sin \frac{C}{2} \right)$$

$$= 2 \cos \frac{C}{2} \left(\cos \frac{A - B}{2} + \cos \frac{A + B}{2} \right)$$

$$= 2 \cos \frac{C}{2} \left(2 \cos \frac{A}{2} \cos \frac{B}{2} \right) = 4 \cos \frac{A}{2} \cos \frac{B}{2} \cos \frac{C}{2}.]$$

77. $\cos A + \cos B + \cos C = 1 + 4\sin\dfrac{A}{2}\sin\dfrac{B}{2}\sin\dfrac{C}{2}.$

78. $\tan A + \tan B + \tan C = \tan A \tan B \tan C.$
[*Suggestion:* $\tan C = -\tan(A+B)$.]

79. $\sin A + \sin B - \sin C = 4\sin\dfrac{A}{2}\sin\dfrac{B}{2}\cos\dfrac{C}{2}.$

Prove the following identities.

80. $\cos\alpha\tan(\theta-\alpha) + \sin\alpha = \dfrac{\sin\theta}{\cos(\theta-\alpha)}.$

81. $\dfrac{\sec^2\left(ax - \dfrac{\pi}{4}\right)}{\tan\left(ax - \dfrac{\pi}{4}\right)} = -2\sec 2ax.$

82. $\sin^2 4x \cos^4 3x \cos 4x - \sin^3 4x \cos^3 3x \sin 3x$
$$= \sin^2 4x \cos^3 3x \cos 7x.$$

83. $\csc^3 x + \cot^2 x \csc x + \dfrac{\sec^2\dfrac{x}{2}}{2\tan\dfrac{x}{2}} = 2\csc^3 x.$

84. $\dfrac{\cos\frac12(\theta-\alpha)\sin\frac12(\theta+\alpha) - \cos\frac12(\theta+\alpha)\sin\frac12(\theta-\alpha)}{2\sin\frac12(\theta-\alpha)\sin\frac12(\theta+\alpha)} = \dfrac{\sin\alpha}{\cos\alpha-\cos\theta}.$

85. $\cos\left(2x - \dfrac{\pi}{4}\right)\sin\left(2x + \dfrac{\pi}{4}\right) - \cos\left(2x + \dfrac{\pi}{4}\right)\sin\left(2x - \dfrac{\pi}{4}\right) = 1.$

86. $\dfrac{\sec^2\dfrac{x}{2}}{2\left(\tan\dfrac{x}{2} - 2\right)\left(2\tan\dfrac{x}{2} - 1\right)} = \dfrac{1}{4 - 5\sin x}.$

87. $\sin^4 x = \tfrac14\left[1 - 2\cos 2x + \dfrac{1+\cos 4x}{2}\right].$

88. $\cos^4 x = \tfrac14\left[1 + 2\cos 2x + \dfrac{1+\cos 4x}{2}\right].$

89. $\sin^2 x \cos^2 x = \tfrac18(1 - \cos 4x).$

90. $\sin^4 x \cos^4 x = \tfrac{1}{64}\left(1 - 2\cos 4x + \dfrac{1+\cos 8x}{2}\right).$

CHAPTER IX

THE OBLIQUE TRIANGLE

80. The parts of a triangle. — The six *parts* of a triangle are its three sides and three angles. We shall commonly denote the vertices as A, B, C, the angles at the vertices as α, β, γ and the respectively opposite sides as a, b, c. If three parts are given, at least one of which is a side, it is possible to determine the other three parts except in one ambiguous case which will be described later. This determination of the unknown parts is the *solution* of the triangle.

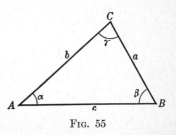

Fig. 55

In the paragraphs that follow we obtain certain laws or relations that exist among the parts of any triangle. One of these laws is already familiar to us. It is that *the sum of the angles of any triangle is equal to* 180°.

$$\alpha + \beta + \gamma = 180°.$$

This enables us to find one angle of a triangle if the other two angles are known.

The method of solution of a triangle depends on which set of three parts is given. The possible cases are as follows. We may be given:

   I. One side and two angles.
  II. Two sides and the angle opposite one of them.
 III. Two sides and the included angle.
 IV. Three sides.

81. The law of cosines. — The law of cosines is as follows: *In any triangle the square of any side is equal to the sum of the squares of the*

137

other two sides minus twice the product of those sides times the cosine of the included angle. As an equation this takes one of the forms

$$a^2 = b^2 + c^2 - 2\,bc\cos\alpha.$$
$$b^2 = c^2 + a^2 - 2\,ca\cos\beta.$$
$$c^2 = a^2 + b^2 - 2\,ab\cos\gamma.$$

Proof. In any given triangle, let a be any side. From an ad-

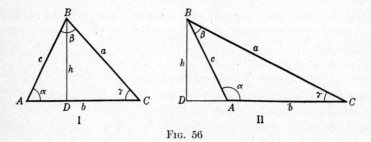

Fig. 56

jacent vertex, B, drop the perpendicular BD to AC or to AC produced. If α is acute, the figure is like Figure 56 I. If α is obtuse, the figure is like II.* Let h denote the length of $\overline{BD}$.

In either figure, in the right triangle CDB,

$$a^2 = h^2 + \overline{CD}^2.$$

In I, $\qquad \overline{DC} = b - \overline{AD} = b - c\cos\alpha,$

since $\qquad \overline{AD} = c\cos\alpha.$

In II, $\qquad \overline{DC} = b + \overline{DA} = b - c\cos\alpha,$

since $\qquad \overline{DA} = -c\cos\alpha.$

In either figure, $h = c\sin\alpha$. Therefore

$$\begin{aligned}
a^2 &= c^2\sin^2\alpha + (b - c\cos\alpha)^2 \\
&= c^2\sin^2\alpha + b^2 - 2\,bc\cos\alpha + c^2\cos^2\alpha \\
&= b^2 + c^2(\sin^2\alpha + \cos^2\alpha) - 2\,bc\cos\alpha,
\end{aligned}$$

---

* If α is acute and γ is obtuse, D falls on AC produced, but the equations are the same as for Figure I. If α is a right angle, $\cos\alpha = 0$, and the law of cosines becomes $a^2 = b^2 + c^2$, which is known to be true since a, b, and c are the sides of a right triangle.

which gives the result

$$a^2 = b^2 + c^2 - 2\,bc \cos \alpha.$$

This proves the law of cosines for all sides, since a was any side.

82. Applications of the law of cosines. — Besides its use in the solution of triangles, the law of cosines has many applications in other fields of geometry — more applications probably than the other laws which we are to develop. Its use in solving triangles is limited, however, because it does not lend itself to logarithmic computation. For, since the three terms are to be added, it is impossible to combine them by means of logarithms. In examples in which the numbers are small and easy to handle without logarithms and when two sides are given together with the included angle, the law of cosines may be used to advantage in finding the third side. And if three sides are given, the law of cosines may be used to find the angles.

EXAMPLE 1. Given $b = 4$, $c = 3$, $\alpha = 60°$, find a. From the formula,

$$a^2 = 4^2 + 3^2 - 2 \times 4 \times 3 \times \tfrac{1}{2} = 13.$$
$$a = \sqrt{13} = 3.6.$$

EXAMPLE 2. Given $a = 6$, $b = 5$, $c = 4$, find β. We use the law of cosines in the form

$$b^2 = a^2 + c^2 - 2ac \cos \beta$$

or

$$\cos \beta = \frac{a^2 + c^2 - b^2}{2ac} = \frac{36 + 16 - 25}{2 \times 6 \times 4} = \frac{9}{16} = .56.$$

From a table of cosines, we find $\beta = 56°$ to the nearest degree.

EXERCISES

1. Given $a = 5$, $c = 3$, $\beta = 45°$, find b. *Ans.* 3.6.

2. Given $a = 7$, $b = 5$, $\gamma = 30°$, find c.

3. Given $a = 4$, $b = 2$, $c = 3$, find α. *Ans.* $104\frac{1}{2}°$.

4. Given $a = 5$, $b = 3$, $c = 6$, find β.

5. Given $b = 12$, $c = 8$, $\alpha = 44°$, find a. *Ans.* 8.4.

6. Given $a = 7$, $c = 9$, $\beta = 61°$, find b.

7. Given $b = 10$, $c = 15$, $\alpha = 112°$, find a.   *Ans.* 20.9.

8. Given $a = 8$, $b = 6$, $\gamma = 138°$, find c.

9. An observer is 200 feet from one end of a pond and 300 feet from the other. He observes the angle subtended by the pond and finds it to be 120°. Find the length of the pond.   *Ans.* 436 ft.

10. A body is acted upon by a force of 90 lbs. and by another force of 75 lbs. which makes an angle of 55° with the first force. Find the magnitude of the resultant force.

11. Sound travels at the rate of about 1100 feet per second. From a hill near a lake, the angle subtended by the line joining two boats on the lake is 15°. A pistol shot fired at the top of the hill is heard 1 second later in the nearer boat and 1⅜ seconds after firing in the further boat. How far apart are the boats?   *Ans.* 753 ft.

83. The law of sines. — *In any triangle the sides are proportional to the sines of the respectively opposite angles.*

$$\frac{a}{\sin \alpha} = \frac{b}{\sin \beta} = \frac{c}{\sin \gamma}.$$

The law may be proved in the following manner.

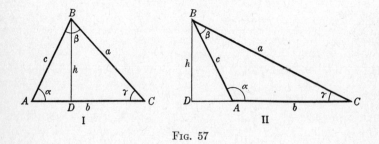

Fig. 57

Given any triangle, ABC, draw the figure just as in Article **81.** There are two cases, one in which α and γ are both acute angles, as in I; the other in which either α or γ is obtuse. In this case, for definiteness, suppose that α is the obtuse angle, as in II.

In either figure,

$$h = a \sin \gamma,$$

as we may see from the right triangle DCB.

From the right triangle ADB we find that $h = c \sin \angle DAB$. In I, $\angle DAB = \alpha$. In II, $\angle DAB$ is the supplement of α. In either case, $\sin \angle DAB = \sin \alpha$. Therefore

$$h = c \sin \alpha.$$

Equating the two values of h, we have

$$a \sin \gamma = c \sin \alpha.$$

Therefore

$$\frac{a}{\sin \alpha} = \frac{c}{\sin \gamma} \, .$$

This shows that any two sides are proportional to the sines of the opposite angles, so that

$$\frac{a}{\sin \alpha} = \frac{b}{\sin \beta} = \frac{c}{\sin \gamma} \, .$$

84. Applications of the law of sines. — The law of sines lends itself readily to logarithmic work, since it involves only ratios and products. It may be used in solving a triangle whenever the given parts include a side and the opposite angle. Moreover the law of sines may be used in completing or in checking solutions undertaken by other laws. In general, any solution should be checked by some method involving the use of other formulas than those used in the original solution, and, of course, all of the parts not given. Until we have obtained other formulas we shall postpone logarithmic checks.

There are two cases of triangle problems in which the given parts include a side and the opposite angle, Case I of Article **80**, which we will now consider, and Case II, which will be discussed in the next article.

CASE I. *Given one side and two angles.* — Knowing two angles, we can find the third angle from the relation

$$\alpha + \beta + \gamma = 180°.$$

Suppose, for definiteness, that we are given side a; it remains to find b and c. This we can do since, by the law of sines,

$$b = \frac{a}{\sin \alpha} \cdot \sin \beta \quad \text{and} \quad c = \frac{a}{\sin \alpha} \cdot \sin \gamma.$$

Since $a/\sin \alpha$ appears in each expression, in solving by logarithms, one first obtains

$$\log (a/\sin \alpha) = \log a - \log \sin \alpha$$

before adding $\log \sin \beta$ or $\log \sin \gamma$.

Before beginning the solution it is always well to make a sketch approximately to scale.

EXAMPLE 1. Solve the triangle, given $\beta = 30°$, $\gamma = 45°$, $b = 6$.

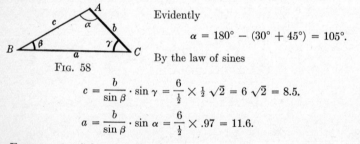

FIG. 58

Evidently

$$\alpha = 180° - (30° + 45°) = 105°.$$

By the law of sines

$$c = \frac{b}{\sin \beta} \cdot \sin \gamma = \frac{6}{\frac{1}{2}} \times \frac{1}{2} \sqrt{2} = 6 \sqrt{2} = 8.5.$$

$$a = \frac{b}{\sin \beta} \cdot \sin \alpha = \frac{6}{\frac{1}{2}} \times .97 = 11.6.$$

EXAMPLE 2. Solve the triangle, given $a = 54.87$, $\beta = 43° 26'$, $\gamma = 58° 19'$. We first find

$$\alpha = 180° - (\beta + \gamma) = 180° - 101° 45' = 78° 15'.$$

By the law of sines

$$b = \frac{a}{\sin \alpha} \cdot \sin \beta = \frac{54.87}{\sin 78° 15'} \cdot \sin 43° 26',$$

$$c = \frac{54.87}{\sin 78° 15'} \cdot \sin 58° 19'.$$

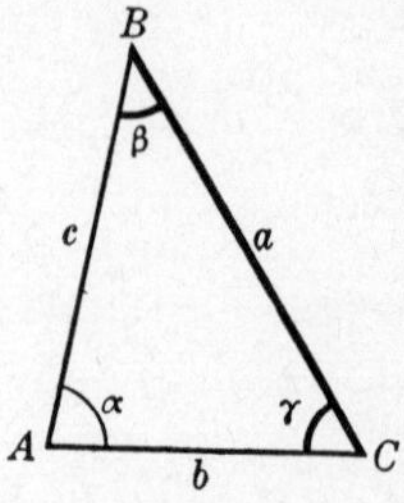

We arrange the work as follows:

FIG. 59

log 54.87 =
log sin 78° 15' = _____ (−)
log (a/sin α) =
log sin 43° 26' = _____ (+)
   log b =
    b =

       log (a/sin α) =
      log sin 58° 19' = _____ (+)
         log c =
          c =

On filling in the blank spaces, we get

log 54.87 = 1.73933
log sin 78° 15' = 9.99080 − 10 (−)
log (a/sin α) = 1.74853
log sin 43° 26' = 9.83728 − 10 (+)
   log b = 1.58581
    b = 38.53

    log (a/sin α) = 1.74853
   log sin 58° 19' = 9.92991 − 10 (+)
      log c = 1.67844
       c = 47.69

EXAMPLE 3. Solve the triangle ABC, given $b = 3$, $c = 2$, $\alpha = 60°$. This is Case III, two sides and the included angle being given. By the law of cosines

$$a^2 = 9 + 4 - 2 \times 3 \times 2 \times \tfrac{1}{2} = 7,$$
$$a = \sqrt{7} = 2.65.$$

By the law of sines

$$\sin \beta = \frac{\sin \alpha}{a} \cdot b = \frac{.866}{2.65} \times 3 = .980$$

and

$$\sin \gamma = \frac{\sin \alpha}{a} \cdot c = .653.$$

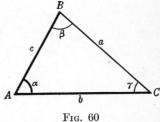

FIG. 60

Therefore

$$\beta = 79°, \quad \gamma = 41° \text{ to the nearest degree.}$$

We can check by the law of cosines, writing

$$\cos \beta = \frac{a^2 + c^2 - b^2}{2ac} = \frac{7 + 4 - 9}{2(2.65)2} = .189, \quad \beta = 79°,$$

and

$$\cos \gamma = \frac{a^2 + b^2 - c^2}{2ab} = \frac{7 + 9 - 4}{2(2.65)3} = .754, \quad \gamma = 41°.$$

EXERCISES

Solve the following triangles without logarithms.

1. Given $a = 10$, $\beta = 45°$, $\gamma = 60°$.

Ans. $\alpha = 75°$, $b = 7.3$, $c = 8.9$.

2. Given $a = 8$, $\beta = 30°$, $\gamma = 56°$.

3. Given $b = 5$, $\beta = 42°$, $\gamma = 28°$.

Ans. $\alpha = 110°$, $a = 7.0$, $c = 3.5$.

4. Given $c = 11$, $\alpha = 39°$, $\gamma = 53°$.

5. Given $a = 4$, $b = 6$, $\gamma = 60°$.

Ans. $c = 5.3$, $\alpha = 40° 50'$, $\beta = 79° 10'$.

6. Given $b = 20$, $c = 30$, $\alpha = 40°$.

Solve the following triangles, using logarithms.

7. Given $b = 27.36$, $\beta = 24° 18'$, $\gamma = 32° 24'$.

Ans. $\alpha = 123° 18'$, $a = 55.57$, $c = 35.63$.

8. Given $c = 541.7$, $\alpha = 62° 43'$, $\gamma = 48° 17'$.

9. Given $a = 6425$, $\beta = 73° 29'$, $\gamma = 36° 52'$.

Ans. $\alpha = 69° 39'$, $b = 6570$, $c = 4111$.

10. Given $a = 102.3$, $\alpha = 16° 16'$, $\gamma = 38° 42'$.

11. Given $c = 14.327$, $\beta = 68° 22.7'$, $\gamma = 29° 26.3'$.

Ans. $\alpha = 82° 11.0'$, $b = 27.100$, $a = 28.880$.

12. Given $b = 624.38$, $\alpha = 79° 23.5'$, $\beta = 33° 44.8'$.

13. Given $a = 4327.4$, $\alpha = 36° 16.8'$, $\beta = 42° 24.6'$.

Ans. $\gamma = 101° 18.6'$, $b = 4932.1$, $c = 7171.0$.

14. Given $c = 602.49$, $\beta = 43° 16'$, $\gamma = 111° 18'$.

15. Two points, A and B, are on opposite sides of a stream. In order to find AB, a point C is taken on the same side of the stream as A and 1000.0 feet from A. By measurement $\angle CAB = 33° 27'$, $\angle ACB = 47° 32'$. Find AB. *Ans.* 746.9 ft.

16. A body is acted upon by a force of 973 lbs. and by a force of unknown magnitude which makes an angle of 49° 10' with the direction of the first force. The resultant force can be measured and is found to be 1268 lbs. Find the magnitude of the second force and the angle which it makes with the resultant force.

85. The ambiguous case. — Case II, in which we are given two sides and the angle opposite one of them, is called the *ambiguous case*, because the conditions are sometimes not sufficient to determine the triangle uniquely. Suppose, for definiteness, that we are given the sides a and b and the angle α.

From these data we attempt to draw the triangle. We first draw $\overline{AC} = b$. From AC we lay off the angle α getting the direction AD in which the side c is to lie. Not knowing c, we cannot yet fix the point B

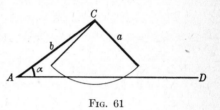

FIG. 61

on AD. With C as center we now draw an arc of a circle of radius a. The third vertex, B, can be taken where this arc meets the line AD.

In case the given a is less than b, there are three possibilities:

(i) If a is just equal to the perpendicular line from C to AD, the point B is at the foot of this perpendicular, and can occupy no other position. The triangle is a right triangle, and $\sin \beta = 1$. By the law of sines

$$\sin \beta = \frac{b \sin \alpha}{a},$$

so that this case occurs whenever $b \sin \alpha / a = 1$.

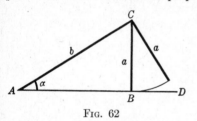

FIG. 62

(ii) If a is longer than the perpendicular line from C to AD, the arc intersects the line AD in two points, B and B', each of which is the vertex of a triangle which satisfies the given conditions. Because the triangle is not determined uniquely,

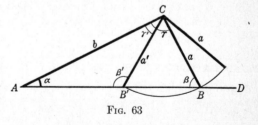

FIG. 63

this is referred to as the ambiguous case, in the strict sense of the term, though the same name is given to the whole group of cases in which two sides and the angle opposite one of them are given. For a complete solution, it is necessary to solve both triangles ABC and $AB'C$, though in a practical problem it is usually evident with which triangle we must deal.

In this case a is longer, for a given b and α, than in the preceding case, so that $b \sin \alpha / a$ is less than 1. This, of course, was to be expected since, when β is not a right angle,

$$\sin \beta = \frac{b \sin \alpha}{a} \text{ is less than 1.}$$

(iii) The third case occurs when a is shorter than the perpendicular line from C to AD. In this case no triangle exists satisfying the

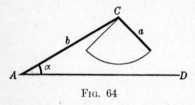

FIG. 64

given conditions. For a given b and α, a is smaller than for the case (i), so that $b \sin \alpha / a$ is greater than 1. This indicates the impossibility of satisfying the given conditions, since for no value of β is $\sin \beta$ greater than 1.

(iv) There remains the case in which a is greater than or equal to b. In this case the triangle always exists and is uniquely determined. For the arc cuts the line AD in two points B and B' which lie on opposite sides of A, if a is greater than b. And, of the two triangles ABC and $AB'C$, one contains the given angle α; the other contains the supplement of α but not α itself. If a is just equal to b,

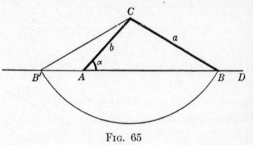

FIG. 65

B' falls at A, and only one triangle is possible. The triangle in this case is isosceles.

We can say then that:

(i) if a is less than b, and if $b \sin \alpha / a = 1$, the triangle exists, is unique, and is a right triangle;

(ii) if a is less than b, and if $b \sin \alpha / a$ is less than 1, there exist two triangles satisfying the conditions.

(iii) if a is less than b, and if $b \sin \alpha / a$ is greater than 1, no triangle exists satisfying the conditions.

(iv) if a is greater than or equal to b, just one triangle exists satis, fying the given conditions.

In the solution by logarithms, when a is less than b,

(i) if $\log (b \sin \alpha / a) = 0$, one right triangle exists;

(ii) if $\log (b \sin \alpha / a)$ is negative, two triangles exist;

(iii) if $\log (b \sin \alpha / a)$ is positive, no triangle exists.

EXAMPLE 1. Solve the triangle ABC, given

$$a = 6, \quad b = 8, \quad \alpha = 30°.$$

By the law of sines

$$\sin \beta = \frac{\sin \alpha}{a} \cdot b$$

$$= \frac{1}{2 \times 6} \times 8 = \frac{2}{3} = .667,$$

which gives

$$\beta = 42°,$$
$$\beta' = 180° - 42° = 138°.$$

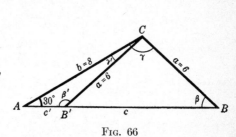

FIG. 66

Then

$$\gamma = 180° - (30° + 42°) = 108°, \ \gamma' = 180° - (30° + 138°) = 12°$$

and

$$c = \frac{a}{\sin \alpha} \cdot \sin \gamma = 2 \times 6 \times .95 = 11.4,$$

$$c' = \frac{a}{\sin \alpha} \cdot \sin \gamma' = 2 \times 6 \times .21 = 2.5.$$

EXAMPLE 2. Solve the triangle ABC, given

$$a = 4, \quad b = 8, \quad \alpha = 30°.$$

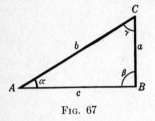

FIG. 67

By the law of sines,

$$\sin \beta = \frac{\sin \alpha}{a} \cdot b = \frac{1}{2 \times 4} \times 8 = 1,$$

so that $\beta = 90°$,

and the triangle is unique. Evidently

$$\gamma = 60°,$$

and

$$c = b \cos \alpha = .866 \times 8 = 6.9.$$

EXAMPLE 3. Solve the triangle ABC, given

$$a = 3, \quad b = 8, \quad \alpha = 30°.$$

By the law of sines

$$\sin \beta = \frac{\sin \alpha}{a} \cdot b = \frac{1}{2 \times 3} \times 8 = \frac{4}{3}.$$

Since this is greater than 1, the triangle is impossible.

EXAMPLE 4. Solve the triangle ABC, given

$$\begin{aligned} a &= 21.34, \\ b &= 27.56, \\ \alpha &= 34° \ 26', \end{aligned}$$

$$\sin \beta = \frac{\sin \alpha}{a} \cdot b.$$

$$\begin{aligned} \log \sin \alpha &= 9.75239 - 10 \\ \log a &= 1.32919 \quad (-) \\ \hline \log\left(\frac{\sin \alpha}{a}\right) &= 8.42320 - 10 \\ \log b &= 1.44028 \quad (+) \\ \hline \log \sin \beta &= 9.86348 - 10 \end{aligned}$$

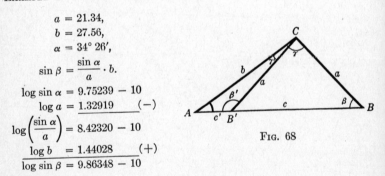

FIG. 68

Since this logarithm is negative, and since a is less than b, we see that two triangles exist satisfying the given conditions. Call them ABC and $AB'C'$.

In the triangle ABC, from the value of log sin β, we find $\beta = 46°\ 54'$.

$$\gamma = 180° - (\alpha + \beta) = 180° - 81°\ 20' = 98°\ 40'.$$

$$c = \frac{a}{\sin \alpha} \sin \gamma.$$

$$\log \sin \gamma = \log \sin 81°\ 20' = 9.99501 - 10$$

$$\log \left(\frac{\sin \alpha}{a}\right) = \underline{8.42320 - 10} \quad (-)$$

$$\log c = 1.57181$$

$$c = 37.31.$$

For the triangle $AB'C'$, since $B'CB$ is isosceles,

$$\beta' = 180° - \beta = 133°\ 6'.$$

$$\gamma' = 180° - (\alpha + \beta') = 12°\ 28'.$$

$$\log \sin \gamma' = 9.33420 - 10$$

$$\log \left(\frac{\sin \alpha}{a}\right) = \underline{8.42320 - 10} \quad (-)$$

$$\log c' = 0.91100$$

$$c' = 8.15.$$

EXAMPLE 5. Solve the triangle ABC, given

$$a = 5.632$$
$$b = 7.254$$
$$\alpha = 64°\ 18'.$$

As in the preceding example, we seek

$$\sin \beta = \frac{\sin \alpha}{a} \cdot b$$

$$\log \sin \alpha = 9.95476 - 10$$

$$\log a = \underline{0.75066} \quad\quad (-)$$

$$\log \left(\frac{\sin \alpha}{a}\right) = 9.20410 - 10$$

$$\log b = \underline{0.86058} \quad\quad (+)$$

$$0.06468$$

Since this logarithm is positive, no triangle exists which satisfies the given conditions, and we need proceed no further.

EXAMPLE 6. Solve the triangle ABC, given

$$a = 97.636$$
$$c = 64.680$$
$$\gamma = 41°\ 29.3'.$$

We use the relation

$$\sin \alpha = \frac{\sin \gamma}{c} \cdot a.$$

$$\begin{aligned}
\log \sin \gamma &= 9.82116 - 10 \\
\log c &= 1.81077 \quad (-) \\
\hline
&8.01039 - 10 \\
\log a &= 1.98961 \\
\hline
\log \sin \alpha &= 10.00000 - 10.
\end{aligned}$$

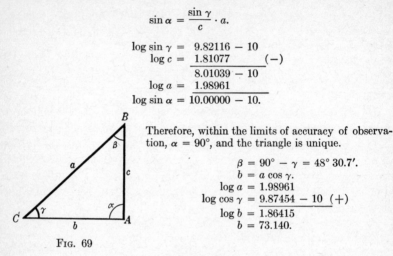

Therefore, within the limits of accuracy of observation, $\alpha = 90°$, and the triangle is unique.

$$\begin{aligned}
\beta &= 90° - \gamma = 48° \, 30.7'. \\
b &= a \cos \gamma. \\
\log a &= 1.98961 \\
\log \cos \gamma &= 9.87454 - 10 \quad (+) \\
\hline
\log b &= 1.86415 \\
b &= 73.140.
\end{aligned}$$

Fig. 69

EXERCISES

Find the number of possible triangles for each of the following sets of data, and complete the solution of all possible triangles. Solve Examples **1** to **4** without logarithms.

1. $a = 8, \alpha = 34°, b = 12.$

> *Ans.* $\beta = 57°, \gamma = 89°, c = 14.3;$
> $\beta' = 123°, \gamma' = 23°, c' = 5.6.$

2. $c = 10, \gamma = 49°, a = 12.$

3. $b = 9, \beta = 24°, c = 9.$ *Ans.* $\gamma = 24°, \alpha = 132°, a = 16.4.$

4. $a = 21, \alpha = 35°, c = 21.$

5. $a = 65.6, \alpha = 64°, c = 73.0.$

> *Ans.* $\gamma = 90°, \beta = 26°, b = 32.0.$

6. $b = 96.0, c = 46.5, \gamma = 29°.$

7. $a = 12, b = 14, \beta = 38°.$

> *Ans.* $\alpha = 31° \, 50', \gamma = 110° \, 10', c = 21.3.$

8. $b = 13, c = 20, \gamma = 53°.$

9. $b = 68.479, \gamma = 72° \, 12.3', c = 41.623.$ *Ans.* Impossible.

10. $a = 246.35$, $\alpha = 65° 46.7'$, $c = 289.58$.

11. $b = 7073.2$, $\beta = 59° 27.8'$, $c = 7836.5$.

$Ans.$ $\gamma = 72° 36.2'$, $\alpha = 47° 56.0'$, $a = 6096.4$;
$\gamma' = 107° 23.8'$, $\alpha' = 13° 8.4'$, $a' = 1866.9$.

12. $a = 918.29$, $b = 746.63$, $\beta = 32° 19.4'$.

13. $a = 976.34$, $b = 602.57$, $\alpha = 109° 44.6'$.

$Ans.$ $\beta = 35° 30.8'$, $\gamma = 34° 44.6'$, $c = 591.17$.

14. $a = 421.83$, $c = 617.68$, $\gamma = 131° 34.7'$.

15. In a children's playground a toboggan slide is 28 feet long and makes an angle of 39° with the ground. Its top is reached by a ladder 18 feet long. How steep is the ladder? $Ans.$ 78°.

16. In a studio the north side of the roof is of glass. It is 18 feet from eaves to ridge and makes an angle of 68° with the horizontal. The south side of the roof is 31 feet from eaves to ridge. How wide is the studio?

86. The law of tangents. — *In any triangle the difference between two sides is to their sum as the tangent of one-half of the difference between the opposite angles is to the tangent of one-half of the sum of those angles:*

$$\frac{a - b}{a + b} = \frac{\tan \frac{1}{2} (\alpha - \beta)}{\tan \frac{1}{2} (\alpha + \beta)},$$

$$\frac{b - c}{b + c} = \frac{\tan \frac{1}{2} (\beta - \gamma)}{\tan \frac{1}{2} (\beta + \gamma)},$$

$$\frac{c - a}{c + a} = \frac{\tan \frac{1}{2} (\gamma - \alpha)}{\tan \frac{1}{2} (\gamma + \alpha)}.$$

Proof. In the triangle ABC, let a and b be any two sides and α and β the respectively opposite angles. By the law of sines

$$\frac{a}{b} = \frac{\sin \alpha}{\sin \beta}.$$

Therefore

$$\frac{a}{b} - 1 = \frac{\sin \alpha}{\sin \beta} - 1, \quad \text{and} \quad \frac{a}{b} + 1 = \frac{\sin \alpha}{\sin \beta} + 1.$$

Consequently

$$\frac{a - b}{b} = \frac{\sin \alpha - \sin \beta}{\sin \beta},$$

and

$$\frac{a + b}{b} = \frac{\sin \alpha + \sin \beta}{\sin \beta}.$$

Dividing the first of these two equations by the second, we get

$$\frac{a - b}{a + b} = \frac{\sin \alpha - \sin \beta}{\sin \alpha + \sin \beta}.$$

Therefore, by formulas XX and XXI of Chapter VIII,

$$\frac{a - b}{a + b} = \frac{2 \sin \frac{1}{2} (\alpha - \beta) \cos \frac{1}{2} (\alpha + \beta)}{2 \sin \frac{1}{2} (\alpha + \beta) \cos \frac{1}{2} (\alpha - \beta)}$$

$$= \frac{\dfrac{\sin \frac{1}{2} (\alpha - \beta)}{\cos \frac{1}{2} (\alpha - \beta)}}{\dfrac{\sin \frac{1}{2} (\alpha + \beta)}{\cos \frac{1}{2} (\alpha + \beta)}},$$

and

$$\frac{a - b}{a + b} = \frac{\tan \frac{1}{2} (\alpha - \beta)}{\tan \frac{1}{2} (\alpha + \beta)}.$$

Since a and b are any two sides, this establishes the law.

87. Applications of the law of tangents. — The law of tangents may be used to solve a triangle when two sides and the included angle are given. It is usually preferable to the law of cosines, for it is well adapted to logarithmic computation. Suppose that a and b and the included angle γ are given. If a is greater than b, we use the law of tangents in the form:

$$\tan \tfrac{1}{2} (\alpha - \beta) = \frac{a - b}{a + b} \tan \tfrac{1}{2} (\alpha + \beta).$$

Since a and b are given, $(a - b)$ and $(a + b)$ can be found. Since $\gamma = 180° - (\alpha + \beta)$, $\frac{1}{2} (\alpha + \beta) = 90° - \frac{1}{2}\gamma$ may be found. This enables us to find $\frac{1}{2}(\alpha - \beta)$ by the law of tangents. Having $\frac{1}{2}(\alpha + \beta)$ and $\frac{1}{2}(\alpha - \beta)$, by addition we find α, and by subtraction we find β. We then solve for c by the law of sines, and check by the same law.

EXAMPLE 1. Solve the triangle ABC, given

$$a = 564.7$$
$$b = 387.2$$
$$\gamma = 48° \, 28'.$$

Solution:

$$a = 564.7$$
$$b = 387.2$$
$$a - b = 177.5$$
$$a + b = 951.9$$
$$\tfrac{1}{2}(\alpha + \beta) = 90° - \tfrac{1}{2}\gamma = 90° - 24° \, 14' = 65° \, 46'.$$

$$\tan \tfrac{1}{2}(\alpha - \beta) = \frac{a - b}{a + b} \tan \tfrac{1}{2}(\alpha + \beta)$$

$$\begin{aligned}
\log(a - b) &= 12.24920 - 10 \\
\log(a + b) &= \underline{2.97859 \qquad (-)} \\
&\ \ 9.27061 - 10 \\
\log \tan \tfrac{1}{2}(\alpha + \beta) &= \underline{0.34667 \qquad (+)} \\
\log \tan \tfrac{1}{2}(\alpha - \beta) &= 9.61728 - 10
\end{aligned}$$

Therefore $\qquad \tfrac{1}{2}(\alpha - \beta) = 22° \, 30'.$
But $\qquad\qquad \tfrac{1}{2}(\alpha + \beta) = 65° \, 46'.$
Adding, we get $\qquad \alpha = 88° \, 16'.$
Subtracting, $\qquad\quad \beta = 43° \, 16'.$
To find c, we set

$$c = \frac{a}{\sin \alpha} \cdot \sin \gamma.$$

Check:

$$c = \frac{b}{\sin \beta} \sin \gamma$$

$$\begin{aligned}
\log a &= 12.75182 - 10 \\
\log \sin \alpha &= \underline{9.99980 - 10 \,(-)} \\
&\ \ 2.75202 \\
\log \sin \gamma &= \underline{9.87423 - 10 \,(+)} \\
\log c &= 2.62625 \\
c &= 422.9.
\end{aligned}$$

$$\begin{aligned}
\log b &= 12.58794 - 10 \\
\log \sin \beta &= \underline{9.83594 - 10 \ (-)} \\
&\ \ 2.75200 \\
\log \sin \gamma &= \underline{9.87423 - 10 \ (+)} \\
&\ \ 2.62623 \\
c &= 422.9.
\end{aligned}$$

The results should check within five figures if carried to five digits, and within two figures if carried to four digits, unless the angles are very close to 90° or 0°, in which case, due to the slow variation of the functions, the check may not be so good.

EXAMPLE 2. Solve the triangle ABC, given

$$a = 68.46$$
$$\gamma = 91° 38'$$
$$\beta = 54° 46',$$

and check the solution.

We first write $\alpha = 180° - (\beta + \gamma) = 33° 36'$,

$$b = \frac{a}{\sin \alpha} \cdot \sin \beta, \qquad\qquad c = \frac{a}{\sin \alpha} \cdot \sin \gamma.$$

$$\log a = 11.83544 - 10$$
$$\log \sin \alpha = \underline{\ 9.74303 - 10\ } (-)$$

$\log \dfrac{a}{\sin \alpha} = 2.09241$	$\log \dfrac{a}{\sin \alpha} = 2.09241$
$\log \sin \beta = \underline{\ 9.91212 - 10\ } (+)$	$\log \sin \gamma = \underline{9.99982 - 10} (+)$
$\log b = 2.00453$	$\log c = 2.09223$
$b = 101.05$	$c = 123.66.$

Check:
$$\frac{\tan \tfrac{1}{2} (\gamma - \beta)}{\tan \tfrac{1}{2} (\gamma + \beta)} = \frac{c - b}{c + b}.$$

$$c - b = \ \ 22.61 \qquad\qquad \gamma + \beta = 146° 24', \tfrac{1}{2} (\gamma + \beta) = 73° 12'$$
$$c + b = 224.71 \qquad\qquad \gamma - \beta = \ \ 36° 52', \tfrac{1}{2} (\gamma - \beta) = 18° 26'$$

$$\log (c - b) = \ 11.35430 - 10 \qquad\qquad \log \tan 18° 26' = 9.52284 - 10$$
$$\log (c + b) = \underline{\ \ \ 2.35162\ \ } (-) \qquad\qquad \log \tan 73° 12' = \underline{0.52011} \qquad (-)$$
$$\qquad\qquad\ \ 9.00268 - 10 \qquad\quad \text{checking with} \qquad\quad 9.00273 - 10$$

EXERCISES

Solve the following triangles, and check.

1. $a = 28,$ *Ans.* $\alpha = 53° 30',$ **2.** $b = 48,$
     $b = 34,$ $\beta = 77° 30',$ $c = 39,$
     $\gamma = 49°.$ $c = 26.3.$ $\alpha = 84°.$

3. $b = 879,$ *Ans.* $\beta = 116° 20',$ **4.** $a = 312,$
     $c = 498,$ $\gamma = 30° 30',$ $c = 1293,$
     $\alpha = 33° 10'.$ $a = 537.$ $\beta = 124° 40'.$

5. $a = 5968,$ *Ans.* $b = 4501,$ **6.** $a = 62.37,$
     $c = 7034,$ $\alpha = 57° 24',$ $b = 81.42,$
     $\beta = 39° 27'.$ $\gamma = 83° 9'.$ $\gamma = 59° 38'.$

7. $a = 536.8$,   *Ans.* $\alpha = 15° 48.4'$.
$b = 1124.4$, $\beta = 34° 47.0'$,
$\gamma = 129° 24.6'$. $c = 1522.8$.

8. $b = 691.4$,
$c = 1263.8$,
$\alpha = 104° 39.4'$.

9. $\alpha = 64° 26.3'$,   *Ans.* $\gamma = 76° 38.8'$,
$\beta = 38° 54.9'$, $b = 4349.6$,
$a = 6246.7$. $c = 6737.0$.

10. $\beta = 42° 35.3'$,
$\gamma = 29° 53.8'$,
$a = 7983.4$.

11. $b = 32698$,   *Ans.* $\beta = 55° 45.1'$,
$c = 28463$, $\gamma = 46° 1.1'$,
$\alpha = 78° 13.8'$. $a = 38725$.

12. $a = 5674.3$,
$b = 7327.9$,
$\gamma = 68° 49.3'$.

13. $b = 6842.3$,   *Ans.* $\alpha = 74° 47.9'$,
$c = 8967.7$, $\beta = 42° 37.7'$,
$\gamma = 62° 34.4'$. $a = 9749.8$.

14. $a = 594.03$,
$b = 521.74$,
$\beta = 58° 16.7'$.

15. To find the distance between two points A and B at opposite ends of a lake, a third point is chosen 256.7 rods from one and 178.4 rods from the other. At this point the angle subtended by the line AB is $57° 32'$. Find the distance AB.   *Ans.* 220.4 rods.

16. A body is subject to a force of 873.4 pounds and to a second force of 561.8 pounds acting in a direction at $71° 24'$ from the direction of the first force. Find the magnitude and direction of the resultant force.

88. Half-angle formulas. — When three sides of a triangle are given, the angles may be found by using the law of cosines. But this method is convenient only if the numbers are easily handled without logarithms. Starting with the law of cosines, we now obtain formulas in terms of the sides of the triangle for the functions of $\alpha/2$, $\beta/2$, $\gamma/2$, that is, of angles which are half as large as the angles of the triangle.

By formula XIII, Chapter VIII,

(1) $$\sin \frac{\alpha}{2} = \sqrt{\frac{1 - \cos \alpha}{2}}.$$

If α is any one of the angles of a triangle, by the law of cosines

$$a^2 = b^2 + c^2 - 2bc \cos \alpha,$$

so that

$$\cos \alpha = \frac{b^2 + c^2 - a^2}{2bc}.$$

Therefore

$$\sin^2 \frac{\alpha}{2} = \tfrac{1}{2}(1 - \cos \alpha) = \tfrac{1}{2}\left(1 - \frac{b^2 + c^2 - a^2}{2bc}\right)$$

$$= \frac{a^2 - b^2 + 2bc - c^2}{4bc}$$

$$= \frac{a^2 - (b - c)^2}{4bc}.$$

We can factor this, getting

(2) $$\sin^2 \frac{\alpha}{2} = \frac{(a - b + c)}{2} \cdot \frac{(a + b - c)}{2bc}.$$

The formulas become more symmetrical, if we denote by s *one-half* of the perimeter of the triangle, or

(3) $$s = \frac{a + b + c}{2}.$$

This gives

$$s - a = \frac{a + b + c}{2} - a = \frac{b + c - a}{2},$$

and

(4) $$s - a = \frac{b + c - a}{2}, \; s - b = \frac{a - b + c}{2}, \; s - c = \frac{a + b - c}{2}.$$

Substituting in equation (2), we obtain

$$\sin^2 \frac{\alpha}{2} = \frac{(s - b)(s - c)}{bc}.$$

Finally

$$\sin \frac{\alpha}{2} = \sqrt{\frac{(s - b)(s - c)}{bc}}.$$

Likewise

$$\sin\frac{\beta}{2} = \sqrt{\frac{(s-a)\,(s-c)}{ac}}, \qquad \sin\frac{\gamma}{2} = \sqrt{\frac{(s-a)\,(s-b)}{ab}}.$$

In a similar way, we write

$$\cos^2\frac{\alpha}{2} = \tfrac{1}{2}\,(1+\cos\alpha) = \tfrac{1}{2}\left(1 + \frac{b^2+c^2-a^2}{2bc}\right)$$

$$= \frac{(b^2+2bc+c^2)-a^2}{4bc}$$

$$= \frac{(b+c-a)}{2}\cdot\frac{(a+b+c)}{2bc}$$

$$= \frac{s(s-a)}{bc}.$$

Therefore

$$\cos\frac{\alpha}{2} = \sqrt{\frac{s(s-a)}{bc}}, \quad \cos\frac{\beta}{2} = \sqrt{\frac{s(s-b)}{ac}}, \quad \cos\frac{\gamma}{2} = \sqrt{\frac{s(s-c)}{ab}}.$$

In all cases the radicals are positive since they represent sines and cosines of acute angles.

89. The tangent of the half-angle. — Division of $\sin(\alpha/2)$ by $\cos(\alpha/2)$ gives

(1) $\qquad \tan\frac{\alpha}{2} = \sqrt{\frac{(s-b)\,(s-c)}{s(s-a)}} = \sqrt{\frac{(s-a)\,(s-b)\,(s-c)}{s(s-a)^2}},$

or

(2) $\qquad \tan\frac{\alpha}{2} = \frac{1}{s-a}\sqrt{\frac{(s-a)\,(s-b)\,(s-c)}{s}}.$

To simplify this expression, set

(3) $\qquad r = \sqrt{\frac{(s-a)(s-b)(s-c)}{s}}.$

In Article **91** it will be shown that r is equal to the radius of the circle which can be inscribed in the triangle. For the present we need only think of r as a symbol for the expression in equation (3). We then get

$$(4) \qquad \tan\frac{\alpha}{2} = \frac{r}{s-a}; \qquad \tan\frac{\beta}{2} = \frac{r}{s-b}; \qquad \tan\frac{\gamma}{2} = \frac{r}{s-c}.$$

90. Applications of the half-angle formulas. — These formulas are used for finding the angles of a triangle when all of the sides are given. If only one of the angles is desired, the sine or cosine formula is satisfactory unless the angle is very large or very small. The tangent formulas are suitable in all cases. And if one wishes to find all of the angles it is always best to use the tangent formulas, since log r may be computed once for all. The method also furnishes a convenient check for other solutions.

EXAMPLE 1. Solve the triangle ABC, given

$$\begin{aligned} a &= 49.63 \\ b &= 57.98 \\ c &= 36.11 \\ \hline \end{aligned}$$

Adding, $2s = 143.72.$

$$s = 71.86 \qquad\qquad r = \sqrt{\frac{(s-a)(s-b)(s-c)}{s}}$$

$$\begin{aligned} s - a &= 22.23 \\ s - b &= 13.88 \\ s - c &= 35.75 \\ \hline \end{aligned}$$

Add $\overline{3s - (a+b+c)} = 71.86 = s$

(This addition gives a check,
since we should have

$$3s - (a+b+c) = 3s - 2s = s.)$$

$\log(s-a) =$	1.34694
$\log(s-b) =$	1.14239
$\log(s-c) =$	$1.55328 \quad (+)$
	4.04261
$\log s =$	$1.85649 \quad (-)$
$\log r^2 =$	$2.18612 \quad (\div 2$
$\log r =$	1.09306

$$\tan\frac{\alpha}{2} = \frac{r}{s-a}, \qquad\qquad \tan\frac{\beta}{2} = \frac{r}{s-b},$$

$$\begin{aligned} \log r &= 11.09306 - 10 \\ \log(s-a) &= \underline{1.34694} \quad (-) \\ \log\tan\frac{\alpha}{2} &= 9.74612 - 10, \end{aligned} \qquad \begin{aligned} \log r &= 11.09306 - 10 \\ \log(s-b) &= \underline{1.14239} \quad (-) \\ \log\tan\frac{\beta}{2} &= 9.95067 - 10, \end{aligned}$$

$$\frac{\alpha}{2} = 29°\,8', \qquad\qquad\qquad \frac{\beta}{2} = 41°\,45',$$

$$\tan\frac{\gamma}{2} = \frac{r}{s-c}$$

$$\begin{aligned}
\log r &= 11.09306 - 10 \\
\log (s-c) &= \underline{\ \ 1.55328\ \ } \quad (-) \\
\log \tan\frac{\gamma}{2} &= \ \ 9.53978 - 10
\end{aligned}$$

$$\frac{\gamma}{2} = 19°\ 7'.$$

Therefore

$$\begin{aligned}
\alpha &= \ 58°\ 16' \\
\beta &= \ 83°\ 30' \\
\gamma &= \ \underline{38°\ 14'} \\
\alpha + \beta + \gamma &= \ 180°\ 0', \text{ which checks.}
\end{aligned}$$

EXAMPLE 2. In the triangle ABC find β only, given

$$\begin{aligned}
a &= \ \ 82.16 \\
b &= \ \ 70.67 \\
c &= \ \ \underline{48.25} \\
2s &= 201.08, \quad s = 100.54.
\end{aligned}$$

Adding,

$$\sin\frac{\beta}{2} = \sqrt{\frac{(s-a)(s-c)}{ac}}.$$

$$s - a = 18.38 \qquad\qquad s - c = 52.29.$$

$$\begin{aligned}
\log (s-a) &= 1.26435 & \log a &= 1.91466 \\
\log (s-c) &= \underline{1.71842}\ (+) & \log c &= \underline{1.68350}\ (+) \\
&\ \ 12.98277 - 10 & \log (ac) &= 3.59816 \\
\log (ac) &= \underline{\ 3.59816}\ (-) \\
\div\ 2&)\overline{19.38461 - 20}
\end{aligned}$$

$$\log\sin\frac{\beta}{2} = \ 9.69230 - 10, \qquad \frac{\beta}{2} = 29°\ 29.8', \qquad \beta = 59°\ 0'.$$

EXERCISES

Solve the following triangles, and check.

1. $a = 6$,   *Ans.* $\alpha = 46°\ 40'$,
   $b = 8$, $\beta = 104°\ 20'$,
   $c = 4$. $\gamma = 29°\ 0'$.

2. $a = 11$,
   $b = 6$,
   $c = 9$.

3. $a = 14$,   *Ans.* $\alpha = 55°\ 20'$,
   $b = 17$, $\beta = 92°\ 40'$,
   $c = 9$. $\gamma = 32°\ 0'$.

4. $a = 120$,
   $b = 90$,
   $c = 150$.

5. $a = 1694,$ *Ans.* $\alpha = 34° 47',$ 6. $a = 37.62,$
   $b = 2043,$ $\beta = 43° 30',$ $b = 29.87,$
   $c = 2907.$ $\gamma = 101° 44'.$ $c = 49.51.$

7. $a = 7439.5,$ *Ans.* $\alpha = 54° 33.0',$ 8. $a = 576.49,$
   $b = 9062.4,$ $\beta = 82° 54.6',$ $b = 921.26,$
   $c = 6174.3.$ $\gamma = 42° 32.4'.$ $c = 502.98.$

9. $a = 67.274,$ *Ans.* $\alpha = 117° 0.2',$ 10. $a = 743.26,$
   $b = 38.665,$ $\beta = 30° 48.2',$ $b = 597.49,$
   $c = 40.229.$ $\gamma = 32° 11.8'.$ $c = 203.51.$

11. A body is acted on by a force of 723.4 pounds and by a second force of 529.5 pounds. The resultant force is 633.7 pounds. Find the angles that the second force and the resultant make with the first force. *Ans.* 121° 40′, 45° 20′.

12. Three forces of 269.8 pounds, 103.5 pounds, and 184.7 pounds act in such directions that they are in equilibrium. Draw a figure showing the directions of the forces, and find the angles between them to the nearest minute.

91. The area of a triangle. — Let S denote the area of the triangle ABC, and h its altitude from B.

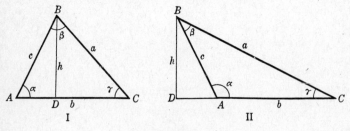

Fig. 70

Then $S = \frac{1}{2}bh$ and $h = c \sin \alpha.$

Therefore $S = \frac{1}{2}bc \sin \alpha,$ or *the area of a triangle is equal to one-half the product of two sides times the sine of the included angle.*

$$S = \tfrac{1}{2}bc \sin \alpha, \qquad S = \tfrac{1}{2}ca \sin \beta, \qquad S = \tfrac{1}{2}ab \sin \gamma.$$

From this we can obtain another formula by using the law of sines:

$$c = \frac{b \sin \gamma}{\sin \beta}.$$

Then

$$S = \tfrac{1}{2}bc \sin \alpha = \frac{b^2 \sin \gamma \sin \alpha}{2 \sin \beta} = \frac{b^2 \sin \alpha \sin \gamma}{2 \sin (\alpha + \gamma)},$$

since $\sin \beta = \sin [180° - (\alpha + \gamma)] = \sin (\alpha + \gamma).$

That is, *the area of a triangle is equal to one-half the square of any side times the product of the sines of the adjacent angles divided by the sine of the sum of those angles.*

$$S = \frac{a^2 \sin \beta \sin \gamma}{2 \sin (\beta + \gamma)}, \quad S = \frac{b^2 \sin \alpha \sin \gamma}{2 \sin (\alpha + \gamma)}, \quad S = \frac{c^2 \sin \alpha \sin \beta}{2 \sin (\alpha + \beta)}.$$

Still another formula can be found to express the area in terms of the sides. In the formula

$$S = \tfrac{1}{2}bc \sin \alpha,$$

set $$\sin \alpha = 2 \sin \frac{\alpha}{2} \cos \frac{\alpha}{2}.$$

From Article **88,**

$$\sin \frac{\alpha}{2} = \sqrt{\frac{(s - b)\,(s - c)}{bc}}, \quad \cos \frac{\alpha}{2} = \sqrt{\frac{s(s - a)}{bc}}.$$

Therefore,

$$S = \sqrt{s(s - a)\,(s - b)\,(s - c)}.$$

Therefore, also

$$S = sr,$$

where r has the meaning given to it in Article **89:**

$$r = \sqrt{\frac{(s - a)\,(s - b)\,(s - c)}{s}}.$$

Now draw the inscribed circle of the triangle, and divide the triangle into three triangles by joining the vertices to the center of the circle.   The area of one of the

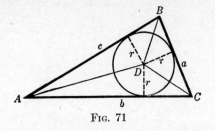

FIG. 71

triangles is equal to the radius times one-half the base, so that

$$S = s \times \text{(the radius of the inscribed circle)}.$$

This shows that r, as used in Article **89**, is equal to the radius of the inscribed circle.

EXAMPLE 1.   Find the area of the triangle ABC, given

$$a = 9.015, \quad b = 10.234, \quad \gamma = 54° 16'.$$

Set $S = \tfrac{1}{2} ab \sin \gamma.$

$$
\begin{aligned}
\log a &= \quad 0.95497 \\
\log b &= \quad 1.01005 \\
\log \sin \gamma &= \quad 9.90942 - 10 \; (+) \\
\hline
\log 2S &= \quad 1.87444 \\
2S &= 74.893 \\
S &= 37.446.
\end{aligned}
$$

EXAMPLE 2.   Find the area of the triangle ABC, given

$$c = 14.32, \quad \alpha = 74° 18', \quad \beta = 51° 42'.$$

Set $S = \dfrac{c^2 \sin \alpha \sin \beta}{2 \sin (\alpha + \beta)}.$ $\alpha + \beta = 126° 0'.$

$$
\begin{aligned}
\log c &= \quad 1.15594 \\
\log c &= \quad 1.15594 \\
\log \sin \alpha &= \quad 9.98349 - 10 \\
\log \sin \beta &= \quad 9.89475 - 10 \; (+) \\
\hline
&\quad 12.19012 - 10 \\
\log \sin (\alpha + \beta) &= \quad 9.90796 - 10 \; (-) \\
\hline
\log 2S &= \quad 2.28216 \\
2S &= 191.50 \\
S &= \quad 95.75.
\end{aligned}
$$

EXAMPLE 3.   Find the area of the triangle ABC, given

$$a = 68.44, \quad b = 79.83, \quad c = 52.79.$$

Set $\qquad\qquad S = \sqrt{s(s - a)(s - b)(s - c)}.$

$2s = 201.06$		
$s = 100.53$	$\log s = 2.00230$	
$s - a = 32.09$	$\log (s - a) = 1.50637$	
$s - b = 20.70$	$\log (s - b) = 1.31597$	
$s - c = 47.74$	$\log (s - c) = 1.67888$	$(+)$
Add $\qquad s = 100.53$	$\div\ 2)\overline{6.50352}$	
	$\log S = \overline{3.25176}$	
	$S = 1785.5.$	

EXERCISES

Find the areas of the following triangles.   Work Examples **1 to 6** without logarithms.

1. $a = 7,$
$b = 6,$
$\gamma = 30°.$
Ans. 10.5.

2. $a = 12,$
$c = 8,$
$\beta = 60°.$

3. $\alpha = 30°,$
$\beta = 45°,$
$c = 20.$
Ans. 73.2.

4. $\beta = 40°,$
$\gamma = 120°,$
$a = 10.$

5. $a = 6,$
$b = 9,$
$c = 5.$
Ans. 14.14.

6. $a = 13,$
$b = 7,$
$c = 8.$

7. $a = 869.4,$
$b = 733.8,$
$\gamma = 56° 27'.$
Ans. 265,850.

8. $b = 21.48,$
$c = 38.69,$
$\alpha = 111° 24'.$

9. $b = 62.97,$
$c = 41.32,$
$\beta = 28° 19'.$
Ans. 942.9.

10. $a = 468.3,$
$c = 372.9,$
$\alpha = 41° 49'.$

11. $a = 743.2,$
$\alpha = 81° 18',$
$\beta = 62° 47'.$
Ans. 145,750.

12. $c = 429.7,$
$\alpha = 73° 11',$
$\beta = 55° 29'.$

13. $a = 629.7,$
$b = 308.4,$
$c = 411.2.$
Ans. 54,092.

14. $a = 18.17,$
$b = 3.24,$
$c = 16.85.$

15. Find the area of the circle inscribed in the triangle the lengths of whose sides are 62.31, 20.43, 48.96. *Ans.* 129.56.

16. Find the area of the circle inscribed in the triangle the lengths of whose sides are 40.58, 31.69, 24.82.

EXERCISES AND APPLICATIONS

Solve the following triangles, find their areas, and check the solutions.

1. $a = 698.43$,   *Ans.* $\alpha = 41° 39.4'$,   **2.** $b = 24.839$,
    $\beta = 113° 27.4'$, $b = 963.94$, $\beta = 72° 44.7'$,
    $\gamma = 24° 53.2'$. $c = 442.19$, $\gamma = 68° 17.2'$.
                          $S = 141660$.

3. $\gamma = 28° 16.4'$, $b = 563.49$, $c = 384.17$.
   Ans.
    $\alpha = 107° 43.1'$, $\beta = 44° 0.5'$, $a = 772.58$, $S = 103100$;
    $\alpha' = 15° 44.1'$, $\beta' = 135° 59.5'$, $a' = 219.94$, $S' = 29356$.

4. $a = 423.61$, $c = 593.72$, $\alpha = 41° 17.4'$.

5. $a = 302.54$,   *Ans.* $\alpha = 13° 13.5'$,   **6.** $b = 11.49$,
    $c = 893.68$, $\gamma = 42° 30.1'$, $c = 204.16$,
    $\beta = 124° 16.5'$. $b = 1092.8$, $\alpha = 19° 24.7'$.
                      $S = 111710$.

7. $a = 561.62$,   *Ans.* $\alpha = 68° 54.6'$,   **8.** $a = 748.87$,
    $b = 238.49$, $\beta = 23° 20.4'$, $b = 501.46$,
    $c = 601.47$. $\gamma = 87° 44.8'$, $c = 295.21$.
                     $S = 66917$.

9. A level road leads directly away from a cliff. From the top of the cliff the angle of depression of a milestone on the road is 6° 18', and the angle of depression of the next nearer milestone is 57° 29'. Find the height of the cliff. *Ans.* 627 ft.

10. An enemy battery is on a hill above a plain. Its angle of elevation from a certain point in the plain is 8° 48'. From a point

823 feet nearer its angle of elevation is 13° 19′. How high is the battery above the plain?

11. An airplane is flying horizontally over a guiding line of boats which are anchored 2000 feet apart. As it approaches, its angle of elevation is observed simultaneously at two neighboring boats. At the nearer one it is 24°; at the other it is 18°. At what elevation is the plane flying (to the nearest 100 feet)? *Ans.* 2400 ft.

12. A farmhouse is separated by a grove from a road which runs straight east and west. It is visible, however, from two points on the road which are westward from the grove and 754 feet apart. From one of these points the house is 41° 20′ north of the road, and from the other it is 23° 40′ north of the road. How far is the farmhouse from the road?

13. A flagpole stands on a hill which is inclined at 18° to the horizontal. From a point 250 feet down the hill the angle of elevation of the top of the pole is 27°. How high is the flagpole? *Ans.* 44 ft.

14. A flagpole 36.6 feet high stands on a hill which has a slope of 16°. How long will its shadow be if, when the shadow extends directly down the hill, the altitude of the sun is 32°?

15. A lighthouse stands on a rock at a certain distance from a straight shore. It throws a beam of light which revolves uniformly. One-half second after illuminating the nearest point of the shore the beam reaches a point 400 feet along the shore, and one-half second later still, it reaches a point 600 feet still further along the shore. How far is the lighthouse from the shore, and how long does it take the light to make one revolution?

Ans. 895 ft., 7.5 secs.

16. A statue 12 feet high stands on a pedestal 9 feet high. How far from the pedestal is a point on the ground where the statue and pedestal subtend equal angles?

17. A line 620 feet long is drawn along one bank of a river. The angles which it makes with the lines of sight drawn to a point on the other bank are 47° 20′ and 63° 40′ respectively. How wide is the river? *Ans.* 438 ft.

18. A balloon floats directly above the line joining two points on the ground. The two points are one mile apart. From one of them the angle of elevation of the balloon is 22° 10′, and from the other its angle of elevation is 29° 40′. Find the height of the balloon.

19. A tower 109 feet high stands on a cliff beside a river. From a point on the other side of the river and directly across from the tower the angle of elevation of the top of the tower is 38° 30′, and that of the bottom of the tower is 26° 30′. Find the width of the river.

Ans. 367 ft.

20. A northbound ship steams past a lighthouse. At a certain instant the bow of the vessel is 36° north of east and its stern is 27° north of east from the light. How far is the light from the path of the ship, if the ship's length is known to be 564 feet?

21. From a point 3.6 miles from one end of a lake, and 5.4 miles from the other end, the angle subtended by the lake is 104°. How long is the lake? *Ans.* 7.2 miles.

22. Two ends on a football team start from points on the line 25 yards apart and run down the field under a kick. They run directly toward the man who catches the ball and reach him just as he catches it, 5.5 seconds after they start. One can run 100 yards in 12 seconds, the other in 11 seconds. How far beyond the line of scrimmage did the ball go, and at what angle did the runners converge?

23. A and B are points on two islands. In order to find the distance AB from the shore, two points, C and D, are taken on shore 879 feet apart, and the angles at C and D are measured and found to be $\angle ACB = 79° 34′$, $\angle ACD = 24° 42′$, $\angle ADB = 82° 14′$, $\angle BDC = 38° 21′$. Find AB. *Ans.* 1464 ft.

24. Two points, A and B, which are 3100 feet apart, are directly below the line of flight of an airplane. At a certain instant when the plane is above the line AB its angle of elevation at A is 79° 20′, and its angle of elevation at B is 18° 50′. Just 15 seconds later, while it is still above AB, its angle of elevation at A is 21° 10′, and its angle of elevation at B is 49° 40′. What is its speed in miles per hour?

25. Surveyors establish five points, A, B, C, D, E. AB is measured and found to be 1698 feet. The bearings of the various lines are taken and found to be as follows.

AB: $S\ 26°\ 40'\ W$, CB: $N\ 73°\ 0'\ W$, DE: $S\ 21°\ 30'\ E$.
AC: $S\ 34°\ 30'\ E$, CD: $N\ 39°\ 50'\ E$,
AD: $N\ 83°\ 20'\ E$, CE: $N\ 82°\ 40'\ E$,

Find the length of DE. $Ans.$ 2422 ft.

26. The course of a boat race is marked by five buoys, A, B, C, D, E. The first leg, AB, is 1010 feet long, and has the bearing $N\ 72°\ 40'\ W$. The bearings of the other legs are BC, $N\ 27°\ 50'\ E$; CD, $N\ 73°\ 40'\ E$; DE, $S\ 47°\ 20'\ E$; EA, $S\ 58°\ 10'\ W$. The bearing of C from A is $N\ 34°\ 10'\ W$, and that of D from A is $N\ 38°\ 10'\ E$. Find the length of the entire course.

27. Find the diameter of the largest circular circus tent that can be placed on a triangular lot whose sides are 73 feet, 64 feet and 85 feet in length. $Ans.$ 41 ft.

28. A triangle is inscribed in a circle. Two of its sides are 123.9 cm. and 156.4 cm. in length, while the arc of which the third side is the chord is one-seventh of the circumference of the circle. Find the length of the third side and all of the angles.

29. A filling station is built on a triangular lot having a frontage of 175 feet on Main Street and 110 feet on First Avenue, which streets intersect obliquely. The rear line of the lot is 230 feet long. By how much will the area of the lot be increased if land is purchased so that the First Avenue frontage is increased to 200 feet, the Main Street frontage remaining unchanged? $Ans.$ 7595 sq. ft.

30. A triangular lot has frontages of 78 feet and 94 feet and a rear line 69 feet long. If the 78 feet frontage is increased to 109 feet how much more will it cost to fence the new lot than it did to fence the old one, the cost of fencing being 45 cents a running foot?

31. A and B are points on opposite sides of a pond. The broken line $ACDB$ is run around the end of the pond, and it is found that $AC = 978$ feet, $CD = 1424$ feet, $DB = 2111$ feet, while $\angle CAD = 37°\ 44'$ and $\angle CBD = 29°\ 18'$. Find AB. $Ans.$ 2672 ft.

32. We wish to find the distance between two points, A and B, which are hidden from each other. A straight line is run from B to a point C and continued to a point D from which A is visible.

By measurement $BC = 432$ yards, $CD = 587$ yards, $\angle BCA = 98° 20'$, $\angle BDA = 69° 40'$.   Find AB.

33. When the elevation of the sun is such that a vertical rod 10 feet long casts a horizontal shadow 16 feet long, how long a shadow will be cast by a pole 24 feet long tipped 10° from the vertical away from the sun?   *Ans.* 42 ft.

34. When a vertical rod 10 feet long casts a horizontal shadow 18 feet long, how long is a flagpole which, if tipped 12° from the vertical toward the sun, will cast a shadow 40 feet long?

35. A tower stands at a point A on an island.   It is desired to find its height and its distance from a point B on the mainland.   A point C is taken on the mainland 312 feet from B.   The horizontal angles ABC and ACB are found to be 79° 42' and 70° 28', while the angle of elevation of the top of the tower from B is 20° 38'.   Find the height of the tower and the distance AB.   *Ans.*   223 ft., 591 ft.

36. Work Ex. **35**, using $BC = 408$ feet, $ABC = 67° 23'$, $ACB = 59° 12'$, the angle of elevation $= 18° 16'$.

37. From the balcony of a fraternity house a flagpole 11 feet long leans forward so that its top is 9 feet farther forward than its foot. From a point on the ground directly in front of the pole, the angle of elevation of the top of the pole is 28° 11' and that of the foot of the pole is 19° 24'.   Find the height of the balcony and its horizontal distance from the point of observation.   *Ans.*   21.4 ft., 60.7 ft.

38. At the top of a hill which slopes 17° 34' from the horizontal, stands a pole 49.3 feet long, which is tipped 9° 15' from the vertical toward the bottom of the hill.   From the bottom of the hill the angle of elevation of the top of the pole is 21° 29'.   Find the height of the hill.

39. A tower of a power transmission line is 102 feet high.   It stands on top of a hill.   From a point 634 feet down the hill from the tower the angle subtended by the tower is 8° 47'.   How steep is the hill?   *Ans.*   9° 34'.

40. The Eiffel Tower is 300 meters high.   The top of the Arch of Triumph is 54 meters higher than the base of the tower.   From the top of the arch the tower subtends an angle of 10° 10'.   Find the horizontal distance from the arch to the tower.

41. An airplane is flying in a straight, horizontal line at the rate of 120 miles per hour. A person directly below the path of the plane observes it just after it has passed overhead. Its angle of elevation is 82° 30′. One minute later its angle of elevation is 20° 20′. At what height is it flying? *Ans.* 4114 ft.

42. Work Ex. **41**, using the two angles of elevation 74° 20′ and 34° 15′, and assuming that between the times of the two observations the plane passes directly over the observer.

43. A battleship is anchored off a straight shore which runs due north and south. There are two observing stations on the shore 3 miles apart. From one the bearing of the battleship is N 38° 20′ E; and its bearing from the other is N 61° 30′ E. How far is the ship from the shore? *Ans.* 4.16 miles.

44. Work Ex. **43**, making the bearings N 78° 40′ E and S 74° 10′ E.

45. A battleship which is steaming steadily along a straight course is observed simultaneously from two stations, one of which is 3 miles due north of the other. At one instant its bearings from the two stations are N 36° 40′ E and N 17° 30′ E. Twelve minutes later its bearings from the stations are S 68° 10′ E and N 57° 40′ E. Find the speed of the battleship. *Ans.* 17.9 miles per hour.

46. Work Ex. **45**, using the bearings N 42° 40′ E and N 21° 20′ E at the first, and S 58° 30′ E and N 78° 10′ E at the second observation.

47. A torpedo boat enforcing a blockade is 11 miles N 62° W from an enemy port. A vessel sails from the port in the direction S 22° W at the rate of 14 miles per hour. At what rate and in what direction should the torpedo boat steam in order to overtake the vessel 8 miles from port? *Ans.* S 23° 57′ E, 22.6 miles per hour.

48. Two boys wish to find the distance from a point A on the shore to a point B on an island, but have no instruments for measuring angles. They choose a point C on shore 438 feet from A, and prolong BA to D and BC to E. By measurement $AD = 498$ feet, $AE = 833$ feet, $CE = 524$ feet, $CD = 679$ feet. Find AB.

49. In any triangle, prove that
$$\frac{a+b}{c} = \frac{\cos\frac{1}{2}(\alpha - \beta)}{\sin\frac{1}{2}\gamma}.$$

Suggestion: Extend AC to D, making AD equal to $(a + b)$. Apply the sine law to triangle ABD, and note that

$$\beta + \tfrac{1}{2}\gamma = \beta + \tfrac{1}{2}\,(180^\circ - \alpha - \beta) = 90^\circ + \tfrac{1}{2}\,(\beta - \alpha).$$

Note: This formula may be used conveniently to check any solution, since it involves all of the parts and is suitable for logarithmic work.

50. In any triangle, prove that

$$\frac{a - b}{c} = \frac{\sin \tfrac{1}{2}\,(\alpha - \beta)}{\cos \tfrac{1}{2}\gamma}.$$

51. By the formulas of Ex. **49** and Ex. **50** prove the law of tangents.

52. Use the formulas of Ex. **49** and Ex. **50** to check the solutions of the triangles of Ex. **1** to Ex. **8**.

53. A ladder leans against a building and makes an angle of 42° 30′ with the horizontal. When its foot is moved 16 feet nearer the building it makes an angle of 72° 10′ with the horizontal. How much higher does it reach in the second position than in the first?

Ans.   10 ft., 3 ins.

54. A ladder leans against a house, and makes an angle of 37° 12′ with the horizontal. When its foot is moved 10.4 feet nearer the house it makes an angle of 78° 33′ with the horizontal. Find the length of the ladder.

55. In the roof of an athletic field house three steel girders, 27.4 feet, 39.6 feet, and 50.5 feet, in length, are to be riveted into a triangle. The rivet holes must be made so as to allow the girders to meet at what angles?   *Ans.*   32° 39′, 51° 14′, 96° 7′.

56. The sides of a triangle are 16.53 meters, 11.49 meters, and 21.37 meters in length. Find the area of the inscribed circle.

57. The sides of a triangle are 9.58 meters, 12.21 meters, and 15.35 meters. Find the radius of the circumscribed circle.

Ans.   7.68 meters.

58. The sides of a triangle are 21.47, 32.68, 47.11. Find the area of the circumscribed circle.

59. Show that the radius of the circle circumscribed about a triangle whose sides are a, b, c, is

$$R = \frac{abc}{4 \sqrt{s(s-a)(s-b)(s-c)}}.$$

60. Show that the product of the sides of a triangle is equal to twice the perimeter of the triangle multiplied by the radii of the inscribed and circumscribed circles.

61. Surveyors are running a straight line AB, which is stopped by an obstacle at B. In order to prolong the line beyond the obstacle, at B they turn 49° 17′ to the right and measure 334.6 feet to a point C. They then turn 78° 43′ to the left, and measure a certain distance until they reach the prolongation of AB at a point D. What must this distance CD be, and what is the length of the gap BD?

Ans.   516.1 ft., 667.7 ft.

62. Work Ex. **61**, making $BC = 521.7$ feet, $ABC = 124°\ 12′$, and $BCD = 63°\ 18′$.

63. Without instruments for measuring angles, it is desired to find the distance between two points, A and B, which are separated by an obstacle. A third point, C, is taken 269 feet from A and 362 feet from B. A point D is taken on AC 104 feet from C, and E is taken on BC 93 feet from C. By measurement $DE = 121$ feet. Find AB.   *Ans.* $393\frac{1}{2}$ ft.

64. Work Ex. **63**, taking C 184 feet from A and 274 feet from B. Let $DC = 67$ feet, $EC = 58$ feet, and $DE = 84$ feet.

65. In mapping a lake, it is desired to find the distance between two points A and B on two islands. There is only one point, C, on the mainland from which both A and B are visible. A point D from which A is visible is chosen, and the line DC is continued past C to a point E from which B is visible. By measurement, $DCA = 48°\ 10′$, $CDA = 74°\ 40′$, $BCE = 58°\ 10′$, $BEC = 80°\ 20′$, $DC = 643$ feet, $CE = 897$ feet. Find AB and the angle that AB makes with the direction DC.   *Ans.*   1394 ft., 43° 30′.

66. Work Ex. **65**, using the following measurements. $DCA = 28°\ 50′$, $CDA = 98°\ 0′$, $BCE = 112°\ 20′$, $BEC = 54°\ 40′$, $DC = 746$ feet, $CE = 564$ feet.

CHAPTER X

THE INVERSE TRIGONOMETRIC FUNCTIONS

92. Inverse functions. — The equation

$$y = \log_a x$$

enables us to find the value of y when the value of x is known; that is, it *expresses y as a function of x.* But it also enables us to find x when the value of y is known, since it is equivalent to the equation

$$x = a^y.$$

It therefore *expresses x as a function of y.* When two variables, x and y, are connected by some law which enables us to express y as one function of x and x as some (in general different) function of y, those two functions are said to be *inverse functions,* each of the other. Thus, the logarithmic function is the inverse of the exponential function, since the equations

$$y = \log_a x \quad \text{and} \quad x = a^y$$

express the same relation between x and y.

93. The inverse trigonometric functions. — If x and y are related by the equation

$$y = \sin x,$$

y is a certain function (namely the sine function) of x, and x is a certain function (the inverse of the sine function) of y.

Definition: If y is the sine of x, we say that x is the *inverse sine* of y. There are two common notations for this:

$$x = \arcsin y \quad \text{and} \quad x = \sin^{-1} y.$$

172

The student should be familiar with both of these notations, for he may meet with either. Here we shall use the form $x = \arcsin y$.

Evidently if $y = \sin x$ (or if $x = \arcsin y$, which means the same thing), x is *an angle whose sine is* y. The equation $x = \arcsin y$ may be read in any of the following ways: x is equal to the *inverse sine* of y, or to the *arc-sine* of y, or to the *anti-sine* of y. But better than any of these, for the present, is the phrase: x is equal to *an angle whose sine is* y, for this reading carries its own definition.

The student should frame analogous definitions for arccos y, arctan y, arccot y, arcsec y, and arccsc y.

94. Values for which the inverse trigonometric functions are defined. — Since the sine function takes on only the values from -1 to 1, the inverse sine function, arcsin x, is defined only for values of x from $x = -1$ to $x = 1$. For example, arcsin 2 is not defined since there is no angle whose sine is 2. On the other hand, arctan x is defined for all values of x, since the tangent assumes all values.

Exercise. Write the values of x for which each of the trigonometric functions of x is defined.

Example 1. Find arcsin $\frac{1}{2}$. Here we wish to find "an angle whose sine is $\frac{1}{2}$." Since $\sin \frac{\pi}{6} = \frac{1}{2}$, $\arcsin \frac{1}{2} = \frac{\pi}{6}$.

Example 2. Find arctan (-1). Since $\tan \frac{3\pi}{4} = -1$, $\arctan (-1) = \frac{3\pi}{4}$.

Example 3. Find arcsin $(\frac{1}{2} \sqrt{3}) + \arctan (1/\sqrt{3})$. An angle whose sine is $\frac{1}{2} \sqrt{3}$ is $\pi/3$; an angle whose tangent is $(1/\sqrt{3})$ is $\pi/6$. Therefore

$$\arcsin (\tfrac{1}{2} \sqrt{3}) + \arctan \frac{1}{\sqrt{3}} = \frac{\pi}{3} + \frac{\pi}{6} = \frac{\pi}{2}.$$

Example 4. Show that $\arctan x = \operatorname{arccot} (1/x)$. If we let

$$y = \arctan x,$$

then, by definition,

$$x = \tan y.$$

Therefore

$$\cot y = 1/x.$$

Consequently

$$\operatorname{arccot} (1/x) = y = \arctan x.$$

EXAMPLE 5. Show that $\arcsin x = \arccos \sqrt{1 - x^2}$.

Set

$$\theta = \arcsin x,$$

so that

$$x = \sin \theta.$$

Then

$$\cos \theta = \sqrt{1 - \sin^2 \theta} = \sqrt{1 - x^2},$$

and

$$\arccos \sqrt{1 - x^2} = \theta = \arcsin x.$$

EXAMPLE 6. Show that $\arcsin x + \arccos x = \pi/2$.

Note: As will be seen in Article **95** this sum has many different values. We are to prove here that, no matter what allowable value is assigned to x there is *one* value of the sum which is equal to $\pi/2$. A similar remark applies to Example 3, above.

Whatever the value of θ, we know that if we set

$$\phi = \frac{\pi}{2} - \theta,$$

then $\cos \phi = \sin \theta$. If we now take $\theta = \arcsin x$, we shall have

$$x = \sin \theta = \cos \phi,$$

so that $\phi = \arccos x$. But since $\theta + \phi = \pi/2$,

$$\arcsin x + \arccos x = \pi/2.$$

Suggestion: In a problem involving inverse trigonometric functions, if no other solution occurs to you, substitute some letter, just as θ, ϕ, and y were substituted in these examples, for each of the inverse functions involved. The problem may then usually be restated in terms of the trigonometric functions instead of their inverses.

EXERCISES

Find the values of the following numbers.

1. $\arcsin 1$.   *Ans.* $\pi/2$.   **2.** $\arccos(-1)$.

3. $\operatorname{arcsec} 2$.   *Ans.* $\pi/3$.   **4.** $\operatorname{arccot} \sqrt{3}$.

5. $\arcsin(-1)$.   *Ans.* $-\pi/2$.   **6.** $\operatorname{arccsc} \dfrac{2}{\sqrt{3}}$.

7. $\arctan 0$.   *Ans.* 0.   **8.** $\operatorname{arccot} 0$.

9. $\arccos \dfrac{\sqrt{3}}{2}$.   *Ans.* $\pi/6$.   **10.** $\arctan 1$.

11. arcsin (sin y).   *Ans.* y.

12. arctan (tan x).

13. sin (arcsin x).   *Ans.* x.

14. cos (arccos y).

15. cos (arcsin x).   *Ans.* $\sqrt{1 - x^2}$.

16. sin (arccos z).

17. tan (arcsec x).   *Ans.* $\sqrt{x^2 - 1}$.

18. sec (arctan x).

19. cot (arctan x).   *Ans.* $1/x$.

20. csc (arcsin x).

95. Multiple values of the functions. — Since there are many angles whose sine is equal to $\frac{1}{2}$, it is evident that arcsin $\frac{1}{2}$ is not defined uniquely. It may have any one of the values $\pi/6$, $5\pi/6$, $-7\pi/6$, $-11\pi/6$, $13\pi/6$, etc. And, in general, if α is a value of arcsin x, so is $(\pi - \alpha)$, and so is any angle obtained from α or $(\pi - \alpha)$ by adding or subtracting any multiple of 2π. We say that the inverse trigonometric functions are *multiple-valued functions*, since, corresponding to any value of the variable, for which they are defined at all, there are many values of each function.

96. Principal values. — To avoid confusion, out of the infinitely many values of an inverse trigonometric function we select one, which is called the *principal value* of the function. For a given x, the principal value of an inverse trigonometric function of x is the value which is numerically the smallest; but if a positive and a negative value are numerically equal but smaller than any other, then the positive value is the principal one.

The principal values of arcsin x, arctan x, arccot x and arccsc x range in value from $-\pi/2$ to $\pi/2$, while the principal value of arccos x and arcsec x ranges from 0 to π.

Thus the principal value of

$$\text{arcsin } \tfrac{1}{2} = \frac{\pi}{6},$$

for $\pi/6$ is numerically the smallest value of the function. And the principal value of

$$\text{arccos } \tfrac{1}{2} = \frac{\pi}{3},$$

for, though $\pi/3$ and $-\pi/3$ are two values which are numerically equal, preference is to be given to the positive value.

When we write an inverse trigonometric function *we shall*, from now on, *suppose that it stands for its principal value*, unless there is reason to suppose otherwise.

EXERCISES

Write the principal value of each of the following quantities.

1. $\arcsin\left(-\frac{1}{2}\right)$.   *Ans.* $-\pi/6$.   **2.** $\arccos\left(-\frac{1}{2}\sqrt{3}\right)$.

3. $\arctan(-1)$.   *Ans.* $-\pi/4$.   **4.** $\text{arccot}(-1)$.

5. $\arccos 0$.   *Ans.* $\pi/2$.   **6.** $\arcsin 1$.

7. $\text{arcsec}(-1)$.   *Ans.* π.   **8.** $\text{arcsec}(-2)$.

9. $\text{arccot}\, 1$.   *Ans.* $\pi/4$.   **10.** $\arctan 0$.

11. $\text{arccsc}(-2)$.   *Ans.* $-\pi/6$.   **12.** $\text{arccsc}(-1)$.

Write the value of each of the following expressions.

13. $\sin \arcsin(-1)$.   *Ans.* -1.   **14.** $\cos \arccos \frac{1}{2}$.

15. $\cos \arcsin\left(-\frac{1}{2}\right)$.   *Ans.* $\frac{1}{2}\sqrt{3}$.   **16.** $\tan \arcsin\left(-\frac{1}{2}\right)$.

17. $\tan \arcsin\left(-\frac{1}{2}\sqrt{3}\right)$.   *Ans.* $-\sqrt{3}$.   **18.** $\cot \arccos\left(-\frac{1}{2}\right)$.

19. $\tan \arccos\left(-\frac{1}{2}\right)$.   *Ans.* $-\sqrt{3}$.   **20.** $\sec \arcsin\left(-\frac{1}{2}\right)$.

21. $\sec \arcsin\left(-\frac{1}{2}\sqrt{2}\right)$.   *Ans.* $\sqrt{2}$.   **22.** $\csc \arctan 1$.

23. $\sin \arctan(-1)$.   *Ans.* $-\frac{1}{2}\sqrt{2}$.   **24.** $\sin \arccos\left(-\frac{1}{2}\sqrt{3}\right)$.

25. $\arcsin(\sin 45°)$.   *Ans.* $45°$.   **26.** $\arccos(\cos 112°)$.

27. $\arcsin(\sin 120°)$.   *Ans.* $60°$.   **28.** $\arccos(\cos 210°)$.

29. $\arctan(\sin 90°)$.   *Ans.* $45°$.   **30.** $\text{arccot}(\sin 270°)$.

                                             Ans. 1.

31. $\sin(\arcsin x + \arccos x)$.

32. $\sin(\arccos x - \arcsin x)$.

33. $\sin(\arcsin x + \arcsin y)$.

              Ans. $x\sqrt{1-y^2} + y\sqrt{1-x^2}$.

34. $\cos(\arcsin x + \arcsin y)$.

35. $\sin(\arcsin x + \arccos y)$.

              Ans. $xy + \sqrt{(1-x^2)(1-y^2)}$.

36. $\cos(\arcsin x - \arccos y)$.

37. $\sin(2\arcsin x)$.

              Ans. $2x\sqrt{1-x^2}$.

38. $\cos(2\arcsin x)$.

39. $\sin(3\arcsin x)$.

              Ans. $3x - 4x^3$.

40. $\cos(3\arccos x)$.

41. $\sin(4\arcsin x)$.

        Ans. $\sqrt{1-x^2}\,(4x - 8x^3)$.

42. $\cos(4\arccos x)$.

43. tan (2 arctan x).   *Ans.* $2x/(1 - x^2)$.

44. tan (arctan x − arctan y).

45. arctan$\left(\dfrac{2 \tan x}{1 - \tan^2 x}\right)$.   *Ans.* $2x$.

46. arcsin (2 sin x cos x).

47. arccos$\sqrt{\dfrac{1 + \cos x}{2}}$.   *Ans.* $x/2$.

48. arccos (2 cos^2 x − 1).

★**97. Graphs of the inverse trigonometric functions.** — Since the equations

$$x = \sin y \quad \text{and} \quad y = \arcsin x$$

express exactly the same relation between x and y, the graph of the function

$$y = \arcsin x$$

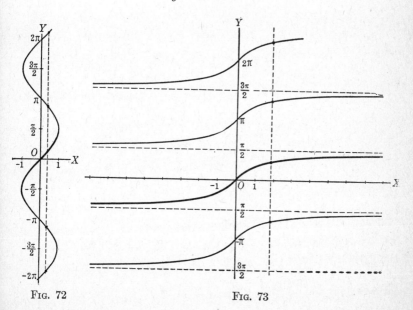

FIG. 72   FIG. 73

is precisely the same as the graph of

$$y = \sin x$$

except that the x and y axes are interchanged with respect to the curve. The graph is shown in Figure 72. The intersections of the curve with any vertical line give the values of the arcsine for the corresponding value of x. The principal values lie on the heavy line. The graph of the function

$$y = \arctan x$$

is shown in Figure 73. The principal values lie on the heavy line.

EXERCISE: Sketch the graphs of the other inverse trigonometric functions, indicating the principal values with a heavy line.

EXAMPLE 1. Prove the identity

$$3 \arcsin x = \arcsin (3x - 4x^3).$$

Set $\theta = \arcsin x$, so that $\sin \theta = x$. Then, since

$$\sin 3\theta = 3 \sin \theta - 4 \sin^3 \theta,$$

for any angle θ,

$$3 \arcsin x = 3\theta = \arcsin (3 \sin \theta - 4 \sin^3 \theta)$$
$$= \arcsin (3x - 4x^3).$$

EXAMPLE 2. Solve for x the equation

$$\arcsin x + \arcsin 2x = 90°.$$

Let $\theta = \arcsin x$ and $\phi = \arcsin 2x$, and take the sine of each side of the equation. We get

$$\sin (\theta + \phi) = 1 \quad \text{or} \quad \sin \theta \cos \phi + \cos \theta \sin \phi = 1.$$

But $\sin \theta = x$, $\cos \theta = \sqrt{1 - x^2}$, $\sin \phi = 2x$, $\cos \phi = \sqrt{1 - 4x^2}$. Therefore

(1) $$x\sqrt{1 - 4x^2} + 2x\sqrt{1 - x^2} = 1.$$

After squaring and collecting terms we reduce this to the equation

(2) $$5x^2 - 1 = 0.$$

Therefore $$x = \pm\tfrac{1}{5} \sqrt{5} = \pm.4472.$$

However $-\tfrac{1}{5} \sqrt{5}$ does not satisfy equation (1), so we retain only the value $x = .4472$.

To check this result we find from a table of sines that

$$\text{arcsin } x = \text{arcsin } (.4472) = 26° \, 34',$$
$$\text{arcsin } 2x = \text{arcsin } (.8944) = 63° \, 26'.$$

Therefore, if $x = .4472$,

$$\text{arcsin } x + \text{arcsin } 2x = 90°.$$

EXERCISES

Prove the following identities.

1. $2 \arcsin x = \arccos (1 - 2x^2)$.

2. $2 \operatorname{arccot} x = \arctan \dfrac{2x}{x^2 - 1}$.

3. $2 \arccos x = \operatorname{arcsec} \dfrac{1}{2x^2 - 1}$.

4. $2 \arccos x = \operatorname{arccsc} \dfrac{1}{2x\sqrt{1 - x^2}}$.

5. $\arctan x + \arctan y = \arctan \dfrac{x + y}{1 - xy}$.

6. $\arcsin x + \arcsin y + \arcsin z$
$= \arcsin \left[x\sqrt{(1 - y^2)(1 - z^2)} + y\sqrt{(1 - z^2)(1 - x^2)} \right.$
$\left. + z\sqrt{(1 - x^2)(1 - y^2)} - xyz \right].$

7. $\arccos x + \arccos y + \arccos z$
$= \arccos \left[xyz - x\sqrt{(1 - y^2)(1 - z^2)} - y\sqrt{(1 - z^2)(1 - x^2)} \right.$
$\left. - z\sqrt{(1 - x^2)(1 - y^2)} \right].$

8. $\arcsin x + \arcsin y + \arcsin z$
$= \arccos \left[\sqrt{(1 - x^2)(1 - y^2)(1 - z^2)} - xy\sqrt{1 - z^2} \right.$
$\left. - yz\sqrt{1 - x^2} - zx\sqrt{1 - y^2} \right].$

Solve the following equations for x.

9. $\arctan 2x = \pi/4 - \arctan x$.   *Ans.* .2808.

10. $\arcsin 2x = \pi/4 - \arcsin x$.

11. $\arccos (2x^2 - 1) = 2 \arccos \frac{1}{2}$.   *Ans.* .5.

12. $\arccos (1 - 2x^2) = 2 \arcsin \frac{3}{4}$.

13. $\arcsin x = \pi/2 - \arctan x$.   *Ans.* .786.

14. $\arccos x = \pi/2 - \arctan x$.

CHAPTER XI

DE MOIVRE'S THEOREM AND SERIES EXPANSIONS

★98. Polar coördinates. — The position of a point in a plane is determined if its rectangular coördinates (x, y) are known. An alternative method of stating the position of a point is to give its *polar coördinates.* These are r, which is the length of the line drawn

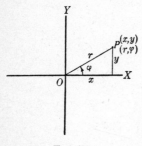

FIG. 74

from the origin or *pole* to the point, and ϕ, which is the angle that this line makes with the x-axis or *polar axis.* The coördinates are written (r, ϕ); r is called the *radius vector* of the point; ϕ is called its *vectorial angle.* The radius vector is expressed in any convenient unit of length, and the vectorial angle is commonly expressed in radians, though degrees may be used. The distance r, if positive, is measured from the pole along the terminal line of the angle ϕ. If r is negative, it is to be measured in the opposite direction, that is, from the origin or pole but along the line made by extending the terminal side of ϕ through the pole.

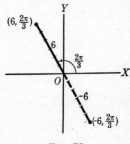

FIG. 75

In the figure, the points $(6, 2\pi/3)$ and $(-6, 2\pi/3)$ are shown.

If (x, y) and (r, ϕ) are respectively the rectangular and the polar coördinates of the same point, we clearly have the following relations, by which to convert from one system to the other,

180

$$x = r \cos \phi, \qquad r = \sqrt{x^2 + y^2},$$

$$y = r \sin \phi, \qquad \phi = \text{arc tan} \frac{y}{x}.$$

EXAMPLE 1. Find polar coördinates of the point whose rectangular coördinates are $(1, \sqrt{3})$. For this point

$$r = \sqrt{1 + 3} = 2,$$

$$\phi = \arctan \frac{\sqrt{3}}{1} = \frac{\pi}{3}.$$

The required coördinates are therefore $(2, \pi/3)$.

EXAMPLE 2. Find the rectangular coördinates of the point whose polar coördinates are $(5, 4\pi/3)$. We have

$$x = r \cos \phi = 5 \cos \frac{4\pi}{3} = 5 \left(-\tfrac{1}{2}\right) = -\tfrac{5}{2},$$

$$y = r \sin \phi = 5 \sin \frac{4\pi}{3} = 5 \left(-\tfrac{1}{2} \sqrt{3}\right) = -\tfrac{5}{2} \sqrt{3}.$$

The required coördinates are $(-\tfrac{5}{2}, -\tfrac{5}{2} \sqrt{3})$.

It should be particularly noted that, while each point has just one set of rectangular coördinates, there are infinitely many sets of polar coördinates for each point. For there are infinitely many values of arctan (y/x), and consequently infinitely many values of ϕ, differing by multiples of 2π. Thus, in Example 1, above, the coördinates may be taken as $(2, \pi/6 \pm 2n\pi)$ where n is any integer.

To plot the point (r, ϕ), first lay off the angle ϕ from the polar axis, and then, along the terminal side of ϕ, measure off the distance r from the pole (or the distance $-r$, along the terminal side extended through the pole, if r is negative).

EXERCISES

Plot the points having the following polar coördinates and find their rectangular coördinates.

1. $(3, \pi/2)$.   *Ans.* $(0, 3)$.   **2.** $(4, \pi)$.

3. $(4, 0)$.   *Ans.* $(4, 0)$.   **4.** $(2, -4\pi)$.

5. $(5, 7\pi/6)$.   *Ans.* $(-5\sqrt{3}/2, -5/2)$.   **6.** $(4, 5\pi/3)$.
7. $(1, -9\pi/2)$.   *Ans.* $(0, -1)$.   **8.** $(0, 6\pi)$.
9. $(0, 4)$.   *Ans.* $(0, 0)$.   **10.** $(5, 0)$.
11. $(3, 1/2)$.   *Ans.* $(2.63, 1.44)$.   **12.** $(4, -2/3)$.
13. $(-4, \pi/2)$.   *Ans.* $(0, -4)$.   **14.** $(-2, \pi)$.
15. $(-2, \pi/6)$.   *Ans.* $(-\sqrt{3}, -1)$.   **16.** $(-3, 3\pi/4)$.
17. $(-4, 4\pi/3)$.   *Ans.* $(2, 2\sqrt{3})$.   **18.** $(-6, 11\pi/6)$.

For the following points the rectangular coördinates are given. Find one set of polar coördinates for each point, and plot the point.

19. $(0, 6)$.   *Ans.* $(6, \pi/2)$.   **20.** $(7, 0)$.
21. $(-3, 0)$.   *Ans.* $(3, \pi)$.   **22.** $(0, -4)$.
23. $(2, 3)$.   *Ans.* $(\sqrt{13}, \arctan \frac{3}{2})$.   **24.** $(4, 1)$.
25. $(-12, 5)$.   *Ans.* $(13, \arctan \frac{-5}{12})$.   **26.** $(3, -4)$.
27. $(0, 0)$.   *Ans.* $(0, \phi)$.   **28.** $(\pi, \pi/2)$.

★99. Complex numbers. — We shall use the letter i to denote the imaginary number, $i = \sqrt{-1}$. We then have

$$i^2 = -1, \ i^3 = -i, \ i^4 = 1, \ i^5 = i, \ i^6 = -1, \text{ etc.}$$

If a and b are two real numbers, $a + bi$ is called a *complex number*, of which a is the *real part* and bi is the *imaginary part*. Complex numbers are treated algebraically according to the following rules: Let $a + bi$ and $c + di$ be two complex numbers. Then

I. If $a + bi = c + di$, $a = c$ and $b = d$; or, *if two complex numbers are equal, their real parts are equal and their imaginary parts are equal.*

II. $(a + bi) + (c + di) = (a + c) + i(b + d)$.

III. $(a + bi) (c + di) = (ac - bd) + i(bc + ad)$.

IV. $\dfrac{a + bi}{c + di} = \dfrac{(a + bi) (c - di)}{(c + di) (c - di)} = \dfrac{(ac + bd) + i(bc - ad)}{c^2 + d^2}$.

These rules are best applied by operating with i as though it were a real number and, in the end, replacing i^2 by -1.

✸100. Graphical representation of complex numbers. — The complex number $x + iy$ may be represented graphically by the point (x, y). Thus, the point whose rectangular coördinates are $(3, -7)$ represents the complex number $3 - 7i$. Suppose that (r, ϕ) are the polar coördinates of the point (x, y). Then

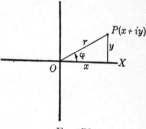

$$r = \sqrt{x^2 + y^2}$$

is said to be the *modulus* or *absolute value* of the complex number $(x + iy)$. This may also be written

Fig. 76

$$r = |x + iy|.$$

And

$$\phi = \arctan \frac{y}{x}$$

is called the *amplitude* or *angle* of the number $(x + iy)$.

Since $x = r \cos \phi$ and $y = r \sin \phi$, we can write

$$x + iy = r (\cos \phi + i \sin \phi).$$

Still another way of representing the complex number $(x + iy)$ is to picture it as the *vector OP* (Article **43**). It is not essential, in this case, that the vector extend from the point O. Provided that it has the length r and makes with OX an angle ϕ, a vector represents the number $r (\cos \phi + i \sin \phi)$, no matter what its initial point.

EXERCISES

Find the modulus and amplitude of each of the following complex numbers. Represent each number graphically as a point and also as a vector.

1. $3 + 4i$. *Ans.* $r = 5, \phi = \arctan \frac{4}{3}$.   **2.** $4 - 3i$.

3. i.   *Ans.* $r = 1, \phi = \pi/2 \pm 2n\pi$.   **4.** $-4i$.

5. $5 - 3i$. *Ans.* $r = \sqrt{34}, \phi = \arctan \left(-\frac{3}{5}\right)$.   **6.** $-7 + 8i$.

7. -2.   *Ans.* $r = 2, \phi = \pi \pm 2n\pi$.   **8.** $1 + i$.

Given the following pairs of values of r and ϕ, write the corresponding complex numbers. Draw the figure.

9. $r = 4, \phi = \pi/6.$ *Ans.* $2\sqrt{3} + 2i.$ **10.** $r = 8, \phi = 3\pi/4.$

11. $r = 7, \phi = 3\pi/2.$ *Ans.* $-7i.$ **12.** $r = 4, \phi = -\pi.$

13. $r = 13, \phi = \arctan(5/12).$ *Ans.* $12 + 5i.$

14. $r = 34, \phi = \arctan(-8/15).$

15. $r = 4, \phi = 2.$ *Ans.* $4(\cos 2 + i \sin 2).$ **16.** $r = 6, \phi = 0.$

★**101. Multiplication of complex numbers.** — Let z_1 and z_2 be any two complex numbers, say,

$$z_1 = r_1(\cos \phi_1 + i \sin \phi_1),$$
$$z_2 = r_2(\cos \phi_2 + i \sin \phi_2).$$

By Article **99**, Rule III, their product is

$$\begin{aligned} z_1 z_2 &= r_1(\cos \phi_1 + i \sin \phi_1) \cdot r_2(\cos \phi_2 + i \sin \phi_2) \\ &= r_1 r_2 [(\cos \phi_1 \cos \phi_2 - \sin \phi_1 \sin \phi_2) + i(\sin \phi_1 \cos \phi_2 + \cos \phi_1 \sin \phi_2)] \\ &= r_1 r_2 [\cos(\phi_1 + \phi_2) + i \sin(\phi_1 + \phi_2)]. \end{aligned}$$

This is a complex number whose modulus is $r_1 r_2$ and whose amplitude is $(\phi_1 + \phi_2)$. Therefore *the product of two complex numbers is a number whose modulus is the product of the moduli of the two factors and whose amplitude is the sum of the amplitudes of the two factors.*

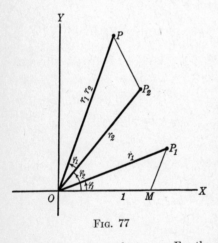

Fig. 77

The product may be constructed in the following way. Let P_1 and P_2 be the points representing z_1 and z_2. Let M be the point 1. Then construct the triangle OP_2P similar to OMP_1. The point P then represents the product z_1z_2. For the angle P_2OP is equal to angle MOP_1

and therefore to ϕ_1, so that angle MOP is equal to $(\phi_1 + \phi_2)$. And, from the similarity of the triangles,

$$\frac{\overline{OP}}{\overline{OP_1}} = \frac{\overline{OP_2}}{\overline{OM}}.$$

Therefore, since $OM = 1$,

$$\overline{OP} = \overline{OP_1} \cdot \overline{OP_2} = r_1 \cdot r_2.$$

Applying the law of multiplication to n factors, we find:

$$[r_1(\cos \phi_1 + i \sin \phi_1)] [r_2(\cos \phi_2 + i \sin \phi_2)] \cdot \cdots \cdot [r_n(\cos \phi_n + i \sin \phi_n)]$$
$$= r_1 r_2 \cdot \cdots \cdot r_n [\cos (\phi_1 + \phi_2 + \cdots + \phi_n) + i \sin (\phi_1 + \phi_2 + \cdots + \phi_n)].$$

★**102. De Moivre's Theorem.** — If we set each of the n factors of the preceding formula equal to $r (\cos \phi + i \sin \phi)$, it becomes

$$[r (\cos \phi + i \sin \phi)]^n = r^n (\cos n\phi + i \sin n\phi).$$

In particular, if $r = 1$,

$$(\cos \phi + i \sin \phi)^n = \cos n\phi + i \sin n\phi.$$

This is known as *De Moivre's Theorem*.

We have proved De Moivre's Theorem in case n is any positive integer. We shall now prove that it is true if n is any rational number, positive or negative, integral or fractional.

In case n is a negative integer, set $n = -m$ where m is a positive integer. Then

$$(\cos \phi + i \sin \phi)^n = (\cos \phi + i \sin \phi)^{-m}$$
$$= \frac{1}{(\cos \phi + i \sin \phi)^m} = \frac{1}{\cos m\phi + i \sin m\phi}$$
$$= \frac{\cos m\phi - i \sin m\phi}{\cos^2 m\phi + \sin^2 m\phi} = \cos m\phi - i \sin m\phi$$
$$= \cos (-m\phi) + i \sin (-m\phi) = \cos n\phi + i \sin n\phi.$$

If n is a rational fraction, say $n = p/q$,

$$(\cos \phi + i \sin \phi)^n = (\cos \phi + i \sin \phi)^{\frac{p}{q}}.$$

This is equal to some complex number. Set

$$(\cos \phi + i \sin \phi)^{\frac{p}{q}} = \rho (\cos \theta + i \sin \theta).$$

Take the qth power of each side. Since q is an integer,

$$(\cos \phi + i \sin \phi)^p = \rho^q (\cos q\theta + i \sin q\theta)$$

and

$$\cos p\phi + i \sin p\phi = \rho^q (\cos q\theta + i \sin q\theta).$$

Equating real and imaginary parts, we see that $\rho = 1$, and

$$q\theta = p\phi \pm 2k\pi,$$

so that

$$\theta = \frac{p}{q} \phi \pm \frac{2k\pi}{q}.$$

There are q sets of values of $\cos \theta$ and $\sin \theta$, corresponding to $k = 0, 1, 2 \ldots$, $q - 1$; and there are therefore q values of

$$(\cos \phi + i \sin \phi)^{\frac{p}{q}}.$$

Taking $k = 0$, we get $\theta = p\phi/q$, and

$$(\cos \phi + i \sin \phi)^{\frac{p}{q}} = \cos \frac{p}{q} \phi + i \sin \frac{p}{q} \phi,$$

as we wished to show.

★103. **The roots of a complex number.** — By a method similar to that just used, we shall now prove that, if k is any positive integer, any complex number (other than zero) has exactly k distinct kth roots. Let the number be

$$z = r (\cos \phi + i \sin \phi), \text{ where } r \neq 0.$$

We wish to show that z has k distinct kth roots. We shall try to determine values of ρ and θ so that the number $w = \rho (\cos \theta + i \sin \theta)$ shall be a kth root of z; that is, so that

$$w^k = \rho^k (\cos \theta + i \sin \theta)^k = r (\cos \phi + i \sin \phi).$$

By De Moivre's theorem, this is equivalent to

$$w^k = \rho^k (\cos k\theta + i \sin k\theta) = r (\cos \phi + i \sin \phi).$$

Separating reals and imaginaries, we have

(1) $$\rho^k \cos k\theta = r \cos \phi,$$

(2) $$\rho^k \sin k\theta = r \sin \phi.$$

Squaring and adding, we get

$$\rho^{2k}(\cos^2 k\theta + \sin^2 k\theta) = r^2(\cos^2 \phi + \sin^2 \phi),$$

so that $\rho^{2k} = r^2$ or $\rho = \sqrt[k]{r}$. This is the unique positive kth root of the positive number r. From equations (1) and (2) we then have $\cos k\theta = \cos \phi$ and $\sin k\theta = \sin \phi$. These equations are satisfied if $k\theta$ has any one of the following values:

$$k\theta = \phi, \phi + 2\pi, \phi + 4\pi, \cdots, \phi + 2(k-1)\pi.$$

or

$$\theta = \frac{\phi}{k}, \frac{\phi}{k} + \frac{2\pi}{k}, \frac{\phi}{k} + \frac{4\pi}{k}, \cdots, \frac{\phi}{k} + \frac{2(k-1)\pi}{k}.$$

Moreover, these values of θ yield distinct values of w:

$$w_1 = \sqrt[k]{r}\left(\cos\frac{\phi}{k} + i\sin\frac{\phi}{k}\right),$$

$$w_2 = \sqrt[k]{r}\left[\cos\left(\frac{\phi}{k} + \frac{2\pi}{k}\right) + i\sin\left(\frac{\phi}{k} + \frac{2\pi}{k}\right)\right],$$

· · · · · · · · · · · ·

$$w_k = \sqrt[k]{r}\left[\cos\left(\frac{\phi}{k} + \frac{2\pi(k-1)}{k}\right) + i\sin\left(\frac{\phi}{k} + \frac{2\pi(k-1)}{k}\right)\right].$$

On expanding the kth power of any one of these numbers by De Moivre's theorem, we see that it yields

$$z = r(\cos\phi + i\sin\phi).$$

So these k distinct roots exist. There are no other roots; for example, if we should take $k\theta = \phi + 2k\pi$, or

$$\theta = \frac{\phi}{k} + 2\pi,$$

this would merely duplicate the value of w_1. The amplitude of w_1 is ϕ/k. The roots $w_1, w_2, \ldots, w_k$ are equally spaced on a circle

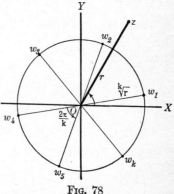

Fig. 78

of radius $\sqrt[k]{r}$ drawn about the origin, the difference between successive amplitudes being $2\pi/k$.

EXAMPLE 1. Find the three cube roots of unity. (Cube roots of 1.) Here

$$r (\cos \phi + i \sin \phi) = 1,$$

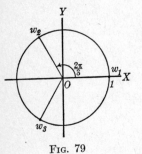

FIG. 79

so that $r = 1$ and $\phi = 0$. Then $\sqrt[3]{r} = 1$, the three values of θ are 0, $2\pi/3$, and $4\pi/3$, and the three roots are

$$w_1 = (\cos 0 + i \sin 0) = 1,$$

$$w_2 = \left(\cos \frac{2\pi}{3} + i \sin \frac{2\pi}{3}\right) = -\frac{1}{2} + \frac{i}{2} \sqrt{3},$$

$$w_3 = \left(\cos \frac{4\pi}{3} + i \sin \frac{4\pi}{3}\right) = -\frac{1}{2} - \frac{i}{2} \sqrt{3}.$$

EXAMPLE 2. Find the fifth roots of $z = 1 + i$. Writing this in polar form, we get

$$z = \sqrt{2} \left(\cos \frac{\pi}{4} + i \sin \frac{\pi}{4}\right),$$

so that $r = \sqrt{2}$ and $\phi = \pi/4$. Then $\sqrt[5]{r} = \sqrt[10]{2} = 1.07$. The five values of θ are

$$\frac{\pi}{20}, \frac{\pi}{20} + \frac{2\pi}{5}, \frac{\pi}{20} + \frac{4\pi}{5}, \frac{\pi}{20} + \frac{6\pi}{5}, \frac{\pi}{20} + \frac{8\pi}{5}.$$

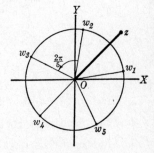

FIG. 80

The roots are

$$w_1 = \sqrt[10]{2} \left(\cos \frac{\pi}{20} + i \sin \frac{\pi}{20}\right) = 1.06 + .167\, i.$$

$$w_2 = \sqrt[10]{2} \left(\cos \frac{9\pi}{20} + i \sin \frac{9\pi}{20}\right) = .167 + 1.06\, i.$$

$$w_3 = \sqrt[10]{2} \left(\cos \frac{17\pi}{20} + i \sin \frac{17\pi}{20}\right) = -.953 + .486\, i.$$

$$w_4 = \sqrt[10]{2}\left(\cos\frac{25\pi}{20} + i\sin\frac{25\pi}{20}\right) = -.756 - .756\,i.$$

$$w_5 = \sqrt[10]{2}\left(\cos\frac{33\pi}{20} + i\sin\frac{33\pi}{20}\right) = .486 - .953\,i.$$

EXAMPLE 3.   Find the value of

$$z = \frac{625}{(3 - 4i)^4},$$

stating the results correctly to four significant figures.

We can take

$$z = 625\,(3 - 4i)^{-4} = 625\,[5\,(\cos\phi + i\sin\phi)]^{-4},$$

where $\phi = -\arccos 3/5 = -53° 7.8'$.

Therefore, by De Moivre's theorem,

$$z = \frac{625}{5^4}\,[\cos(-4\phi) + i\sin(-4\phi)]$$

$$= \cos 212° 31.2' - i\sin 212° 31.2'$$

$$= -.84321 + .53759\,i.$$

EXERCISES

1. Find the fourth roots of 5.   *Ans.* $\sqrt[4]{5}, \sqrt[4]{5}i, -\sqrt[4]{5}, -\sqrt[4]{5}i$.

2. Find the sixth roots of 27.

3. Find the fifth roots of 32.

   Ans. $2, .618 \pm 1.902\,i, -1.618 \pm 1.176\,i$.

4. Find the seventh roots of 4.

5. Find the cube roots of $2 - i$.

Ans. $(1.2921 - .2013i), (-.4717 + 1.2196i), (-.8204 - 1.0183i)$.

6. Find the fifth roots of $(-3 + 4i)$.

7. Find the value of $(2 - 6i)^6$ and plot the point which represents it.   *Ans.* $(22526 - 59904i)$.

8. Find the value of $(-3 + 2i)^5$, and plot the point which represents it.

9. Find the value of $\dfrac{1000}{(-8 - 6i)^3}$.   *Ans.* $.352 + .936i$.

10. Find the value of $\dfrac{4913}{(-8 + 15i)^3}$.

★104. Definition of the number *e*. — Let us compute the value of the number

$$S_n = \left(1 + \frac{1}{n}\right)^n$$

for various integral values of n. We have

$$S_1 = (1 + 1)^1 = 2,$$
$$S_2 = (1 + \tfrac{1}{2})^2 = \tfrac{9}{4} = 2.25,$$
$$S_3 = (1 + \tfrac{1}{3})^3 = \tfrac{64}{27} = 2.37,$$
$$S_4 = (1 + \tfrac{1}{4})^4 = \tfrac{625}{256} = 2.44,$$
$$S_{10} = (1 + \tfrac{1}{10})^{10} = 2.59,$$
$$S_{100} = (1 + \tfrac{1}{100})^{100} = 2.70,$$
$$S_{1000} = 2.716.$$

It will be noticed that when n increases, the value of S_n increases. But S_n does not increase indefinitely. In fact it can be shown that, as n increases indefinitely, the value of S_n approaches a limit; that is, there is a certain number the difference between which and S_n becomes (and remains) as small as we wish, if the value of n is taken sufficiently large. This limit we denote by the letter e, so that

$$e = \lim_{n=\infty} \left(1 + \frac{1}{n}\right)^n.$$

This is read: e is the limit as n becomes infinite of $\left(1 + \dfrac{1}{n}\right)^n$. This number e is very important in higher mathematics. To six significant figures its value is $e = 2.71828$.

★ **105. A series expression for e^x.** — The quantity e^x is a function of x which may be defined in the following way. Evidently

$$e^x = [\lim_{n=\infty} S_n]^x = \left[\lim_{n=\infty} \left(1 + \frac{1}{n} \right)^n \right]^x .$$

It can be shown that this is equal to

$$e^x = \lim_{n=\infty} \left[\left(1 + \frac{1}{n} \right)^{nx} \right],$$

and by expanding the expression in brackets by the binomial theorem and then taking the limit, we can reduce this to

$$e^x = 1 + x + \frac{x^2}{2!} + \frac{x^3}{3!} + \frac{x^4}{4!} + \cdots ,$$

where $2! = 1 \cdot 2$, $3! = 1 \cdot 2 \cdot 3$, $4! = 1 \cdot 2 \cdot 3 \cdot 4$, etc. It is shown in calculus that if the sum of the first n terms of this series be formed for any given value of x, this sum really approaches as a limit (or "converges to") the corresponding value of e^x when the number of terms, n, increases without limit.

EXAMPLE. From this series we can compute to any desired number of places the value of e^x for any value of x. Let us, for example, take $x = 1$, and so compute the value of e:

$$e = 1 + 1 + \frac{1}{2!} + \frac{1}{3!} + \cdots .$$

$$1 = 1.$$
$$1 = 1.$$
$$1/2! = 0.5$$
$$1/3! = 0.166667$$
$$1/4! = 0.041667$$
$$1/5! = 0.008333$$
$$1/6! = 0.001389$$
$$1/7! = 0.000198$$
$$1/8! = 0.000025$$
$$1/9! = 0.000003$$

Sum $= 2.718282$; $e = 2.71828$ to six figures.

EXERCISE

Compute, from the series, the value of e^2 to 4 decimal places, and the value of $\sqrt{e}$ to 6 decimal places.

★106. Computation of sines and cosines by series. — In a course in calculus the following series developments are obtained for sin x and cos x:

$$\sin x = x - \frac{x^3}{3!} + \frac{x^5}{5!} - \frac{x^7}{7!} + \cdots,$$

$$\cos x = 1 - \frac{x^2}{2!} + \frac{x^4}{4!} - \frac{x^6}{6!} + \cdots.$$

These series give the correct values of the sine and cosine for any value of x. When substituting we must express x in radians. Assuming these expressions, we can at once note many of the properties of the functions. For example, sin x is an odd function, since in its expansion only odd powers of x occur, and, if x changes sign, every term changes sign. In a similar way we see that cos x is an even function. Also, if x is numerically small, sin x is very nearly equal to x, since for small values of x the higher powers of x are very small indeed, so that all terms after the first are very small.

The series are useful in forming tables of the trigonometric functions, for the series converge rapidly for small values of x; that is, only a few terms are necessary to give the value of the function with considerable accuracy.

EXAMPLE. Compute sin 10° and cos 10° to five significant figures. We write

$$10° = \frac{180°}{18} = \frac{\pi}{18} \text{ radians} = .174533 \text{ radians},$$

so that $x = .174533$. Therefore

$$\sin 10° = .174533 - \frac{(.174533)^3}{6} + \frac{(.174533)^5}{120} - \cdots$$

$$= .174533 - .000876 + .000001 - \cdots$$

$$= .17365.$$

$$\cos 10° = 1 - \frac{(.174533)^2}{2} + \frac{(.174533)^4}{24} - \frac{(.174533)^6}{720} + \cdots$$
$$= 1 - .015230 + .000039 + \cdots$$
$$= .98481.$$

From these values we can easily compute others, as, for example,

$$\sin 20° = 2 \sin 10° \cos 10° = 2 \times .17365 \times .98481 = .34202.$$

EXERCISES

Compute the sine and cosine of each of the following angles to five figures, and verify the results by means of a table.

1. 2°.   **2.** 7° 30'.   **3.** 15°.   **4.** 5°.

✱ **107. Relations between trigonometric and exponential functions.** — In Articles **105** and **106** we have had the following expansions:

(1) $$e^x = 1 + x + \frac{x^2}{2!} + \frac{x^3}{3!} + \frac{x^4}{4!} + \cdots,$$

(2) $$\sin x = x - \frac{x^3}{3!} + \frac{x^5}{5!} - \frac{x^7}{7!} + \cdots,$$

(3) $$\cos x = 1 - \frac{x^2}{2!} + \frac{x^4}{4!} - \frac{x^6}{6!} + \cdots.$$

These series are valid for both real and complex values of x; that is, they give the correct values of the functions for real values of x, and may be used to define the functions for complex values of x. In place of x in (1) let us substitute the imaginary number xi, where $i = \sqrt{-1}$, and separate the real and imaginary terms.

$$e^{xi} = 1 + xi + \frac{x^2 i^2}{2!} + \frac{x^3 i^3}{3!} + \frac{x^4 i^4}{4!} + \cdots$$

or

$$e^{xi} = 1 - \frac{x^2}{2!} + \frac{x^4}{4!} - \frac{x^6}{6!} + \cdots$$
$$+ i\left(x - \frac{x^3}{3!} + \frac{x^5}{5!} - \frac{x^7}{7!} + \cdots\right).$$

Therefore, by (2) and (3),

$$(4) \qquad e^{xi} = \cos x + i \sin x.$$

We see from this that the modulus of e^{xi} is equal to 1, and the amplitude of e^{xi} is equal to x for any real value of x. Evidently

$$e^{x+iy} = e^x \cdot e^{yi} = e^x (\cos y + i \sin y),$$

so that the absolute value of e^{x+iy} is equal to e^x and the amplitude is the coefficient of the imaginary part of the exponent, or y.

From the equation

$$e^{xi} = \cos x + i \sin x,$$

we get

$$e^{-xi} = \cos x - i \sin x,$$

by substituting $-x$ for x. If we subtract the second of these equations from the first, we find

$$e^{xi} - e^{-xi} = 2i \sin x$$

or

$$(5) \qquad \sin x = \frac{e^{xi} - e^{-xi}}{2i}.$$

After adding the equations, we see that

$$(6) \qquad \cos x = \frac{e^{xi} + e^{-xi}}{2}.$$

From these equations it is possible to prove many trigonometric relations. For example, let us show that

$$\sin^2 x + \cos^2 x = 1.$$

From (4) and (5),

$$\sin^2 x + \cos^2 x = \frac{e^{2xi} - 2 + e^{-2xi}}{4i^2} + \frac{e^{2xi} + 2 + e^{-2xi}}{4}$$

$$= \frac{e^{2xi} - 2 + e^{-2xi}}{-4} + \frac{e^{2xi} + 2 + e^{-2xi}}{4} = 1.$$

EXERCISES

1. Show that $\sin^2 x + \cos^2 x = 1$ by multiplying the expressions for e^{xi} and e^{-xi}.

By means of equations (5) and (6) prove the following relations.

2. $\sin 2x = 2 \sin x \cos x$.

3. $\cos 2x = \cos^2 x - \sin^2 x$.

4. $\sin (x + y) = \sin x \cos y + \cos x \sin y$.

5. $\cos (x + y) = \cos x \cos y - \sin x \sin y$.

6. $\sin x + \sin y = 2 \sin \frac{1}{2} (x + y) \cos \frac{1}{2} (x - y)$.

7. $\cos x - \cos y = -2 \sin \frac{1}{2} (x + y) \sin \frac{1}{2} (x - y)$.

★**108. Computation of logarithms by series.** — Either by starting with the expansion of Article **105** or by working entirely by the methods of calculus, it is possible to find the following series:

$$(1) \qquad \log_e (1 + x) = x - \frac{x^2}{2} + \frac{x^3}{3} - \frac{x^4}{4} + \cdots .$$

In this logarithm the base is the number e defined in Article **104**, and the series gives the correct value of the logarithm for any real value of x between -1 and 1.

Substituting $-x$ for x in this series, we get

$$(2) \qquad \log_e (1 - x) = -x - \frac{x^2}{2} - \frac{x^3}{3} - \frac{x^4}{4} - \cdots .$$

Subtracting this from the series for $\log_e (1 + x)$, we get

$$(3) \qquad \log_e \left(\frac{1 + x}{1 - x}\right) = \log_e (1 + x) - \log_e (1 - x)$$

$$= 2\left(x + \frac{x^3}{3} + \frac{x^5}{5} + \cdots\right).$$

This series is more useful than the series (1) for computing logarithms, because it converges much more rapidly. That is, fewer terms are required to give a satisfactory result with (3) than with (1).

EXAMPLE 1. Compute $\log_e 2$.

Here let us set

$$\frac{1+x}{1-x} = 2,$$

which we can solve for x, getting $x = 1/3$. Then

$$\log_e 2 = \log_e \left(\frac{1+\frac{1}{3}}{1-\frac{1}{3}}\right) = 2\left(\frac{1}{3} + \frac{(\frac{1}{3})^3}{3} + \frac{(\frac{1}{3})^5}{5} + \cdots\right).$$

$$
\begin{aligned}
\tfrac{1}{3} &= .333333 \\
(\tfrac{1}{3})^3/3 &= .012345 \\
(\tfrac{1}{3})^5/5 &= .000823 \\
(\tfrac{1}{3})^7/7 &= .000065 \\
\underline{(\tfrac{1}{3})^9/9} &= \underline{.000006} \\
\tfrac{1}{2}\log_e 2 &= .34657 \\
\log_e 2 &= .6931.
\end{aligned}
$$

Series (3) can be written so as to give us $\log_e (n + 1)$ when $\log_e n$ is known. Set

$$\frac{n+1}{n} = \frac{1+x}{1-x}.$$

or

$$n + 1 - nx - x = n + nx,$$

from which we get

$$x = \frac{1}{2n+1}.$$

Using this value of x in (3), we get

$$\log_e \left(\frac{n+1}{n}\right) = 2\left[\frac{1}{(2n+1)} + \frac{1}{3(2n+1)^3} + \frac{1}{5(2n+1)^5} + \cdots\right]$$

and

(4) $\log_e (n + 1)$
$$= \log_e n + 2\left[\frac{1}{(2n+1)} + \frac{1}{3(2n+1)^3} + \frac{1}{5(2n+1)^5} + \cdots\right].$$

EXAMPLE 2.   Find $\log_e 3$, given $\log_e 2 = .69315$.
From (4), using $n = 2$, we get

$$\log_e 3 = \log_e 2 + 2\left(\frac{1}{5} + \frac{1}{3.5^3} + \frac{1}{5.5^5} + \cdots\right)$$
$$= .69315 + 2(.2 + .002667 + .000064 + \cdots)$$
$$= 1.09861.$$

EXAMPLE 3.   Find $\log_e 10$, given $\log_e 3 = 1.09861$.
We can write

$$\log_e 10 = \log_e (9 + 1).$$

We can find $\log_e 9 = \log_e 3^2 = 2 \times 1.09861$, and in (4) take $n = 9$.   Then

$$\log_e 10 = 2 \times 1.09861 + 2\left(\frac{1}{19} + \frac{1}{3.19^3} + \frac{1}{5.19^5} + \cdots\right)$$
$$= 2.19722 + 2(.052632 + .000051 + \cdots)$$
$$= 2.30259.$$

★109. **Formation of logarithmic tables.** — By using series (3) and (4) of Article **108**, we can form tables of logarithms to the base e. From these it is possible to form tables of logarithms to the base 10 by means of the relation

$$\log_{10} M = \frac{\log_e M}{\log_e 10}.$$

To prove this relation, set

$$x = \log_{10} M, \quad y = \log_e M,$$

so that

$$10^x = M, \qquad e^y = M.$$

Therefore

$$10^x = e^y$$

and

$$e^{\frac{y}{x}} = 10.$$

Therefore $\log_e 10 = \dfrac{y}{x}$, by the definition of logarithms,

or $x = \dfrac{y}{\log_e 10}.$

This gives the formula

$$\log_{10} M = \frac{\log_e M}{\log_e 10}.$$

Using the value $\log_e 10 = 2.30259$, which we computed in Article **108**, we get

$$\log_{10} M = \frac{\log_e M}{2.30259} = .43429 \log_e M.$$

EXAMPLE. Find $\log_{10} 2$, given $\log_e 2 = .69315$.
We have

$$\log_{10} 2 = .43429 \times .69315 = .30103.$$

EXERCISES

Compute the logarithms to the bases e and 10 of the integers from 1 to 20 to five places, and verify by means of a table.

LOGARITHMIC AND
TRIGONOMETRIC TABLES

CONTENTS

TABLE I

COMMON LOGARITHMS OF NUMBERS

TO

FIVE DECIMAL PLACES

1 — 100

N.	Log	N.	Log	N.	Log	N.	Log	N.	Log
1	0.00 000	21	1.32 222	41	1.61 278	61	1.78 533	81	1.90 849
2	0.30 103	22	1.34 242	42	1.62 325	62	1.79 239	82	1.91 381
3	0.47 712	23	1.36 173	43	1.63 347	63	1.79 934	83	1.91 908
4	0.60 206	24	1.38 021	44	1.64 345	64	1.80 618	84	1.92 428
5	0.69 897	25	1.39 794	45	1.65 321	65	1.81 291	85	1.92 942
6	0.77 815	26	1.41 497	46	1.66 276	66	1.81 954	86	1.93 450
7	0.84 510	27	1.43 136	47	1.67 210	67	1.82 607	87	1.93 952
8	0.90 309	28	1.44 716	48	1.68 124	68	1.83 251	88	1.94 448
9	0.95 424	29	1.46 240	49	1.69 020	69	1.83 885	89	1.94 939
10	1.00 000	30	1.47 712	50	1.69 897	70	1.84 510	90	1.95 424
11	1.04 139	31	1.49 136	51	1.70 757	71	1.85 126	91	1.95 904
12	1.07 918	32	1.50 515	52	1.71 600	72	1.85 733	92	1.96 379
13	1.11 394	33	1.51 851	53	1.72 428	73	1.86 332	93	1.96 848
14	1.14 613	34	1.53 148	54	1.73 239	74	1.86 923	94	1.97 313
15	1.17 609	35	1.54 407	55	1.74 036	75	1.87 506	95	1.97.772
16	1.20 412	36	1.55 630	56	1.74 819	76	1.88 081	96	1.98 227
17	1.23 045	37	1.56 820	57	1.75 587	77	1.88 649	97	1.98 677
18	1.25 527	38	1.57 978	58	1.76 343	78	1.89 209	98	1.99 123
19	1.27 875	39	1.59 106	59	1.77 085	79	1.89 763	99	1.99 564
20	1.30 103	40	1.60 206	60	1.77 815	80	1.90 309	100	2.00 000
N.	Log	N.	Log	N.	Log	N.	Log	N.	Log

N.	0	1	2	3	4	5	6	7	8	9
100	00 000	043	087	130	173	217	260	303	346	389
01	432	475	518	561	604	647	689	732	775	817
02	860	903	945	988	*030	*072	*115	*157	*199	*242
03	01 284	326	368	410	452	494	536	578	620	662
04	703	745	787	828	870	912	953	995	*036	*078
05	02 119	160	202	243	284	325	366	407	449	490
06	531	572	612	653	694	735	776	816	857	898
07	938	979	*019	*060	*100	*141	*181	*222	*262	*302
08	03 342	383	423	463	503	543	583	623	663	703
09	743	782	822	862	902	941	981	*021	*060	*100
110	04 139	179	218	258	297	336	376	415	454	493
11	532	571	610	650	689	727	766	805	844	883
12	922	961	999	*038	*077	*115	*154	*192	*231	*269
13	05 308	346	385	423	461	500	538	576	614	652
14	690	729	767	805	843	881	918	956	994	*032
15	06 070	108	145	183	221	258	296	333	371	408
16	446	483	521	558	595	633	670	707	744	781
17	819	856	893	930	967	*004	*041	*078	*115	*151
18	07 188	225	262	298	335	372	408	445	482	518
19	555	591	628	664	700	737	773	809	846	882
120	918	954	990	*027	*063	*099	*135	*171	*207	*243
21	08 279	314	350	386	422	458	493	529	565	600
22	636	672	707	743	778	814	849	884	920	955
23	991	*026	*061	*096	*132	*167	*202	*237	*272	*307
24	09 342	377	412	447	482	517	552	587	621	656
25	691	726	760	795	830	864	899	934	968	*003
26	10 037	072	106	140	175	209	243	278	312	346
27	380	415	449	483	517	551	585	619	653	687
28	721	755	789	823	857	890	924	958	992	*025
29	11 059	093	126	160	193	227	261	294	327	361
130	394	428	461	494	528	561	594	628	661	694
31	727	760	793	826	860	893	926	959	992	*024
32	12 057	090	123	156	189	222	254	287	320	352
33	385	418	450	483	516	548	581	613	646	678
34	710	743	775	808	840	872	905	937	969	*001
35	13 033	066	098	130	162	194	226	258	290	322
36	354	386	418	450	481	513	545	577	609	640
37	672	704	735	767	799	830	862	893	925	956
38	988	*019	*051	*082	*114	*145	*176	*208	*239	*270
39	14 301	333	364	395	426	457	489	520	551	582
140	613	644	675	706	737	768	799	829	860	891
41	922	953	983	*014	*045	*076	*106	*137	*168	*198
42	15 229	259	290	320	351	381	412	442	473	503
43	534	564	594	625	655	685	715	746	776	806
44	836	866	897	927	957	987	*017	*047	*077	*107
45	16 137	167	197	227	256	286	316	346	376	406
46	435	465	495	524	554	584	613	643	673	702
47	732	761	791	820	850	879	909	938	967	997
48	17 026	056	085	114	143	173	202	231	260	289
49	319	348	377	406	435	464	493	522	551	580
150	609	638	667	696	725	754	782	811	840	869
N.	0	1	2	3	4	5	6	7	8	9

Prop. Parts

	44	43	42
1	4.4	4.3	4.2
2	8.8	8.6	8.4
3	13.2	12.9	12.6
4	17.6	17.2	16.8
5	22.0	21.5	21.0
6	26.4	25.8	25.2
7	30.8	30.1	29.4
8	35.2	34.4	33.6
9	39.6	38.7	37.8

	41	40	39
1	4.1	4.0	3.9
2	8.2	8.0	7.8
3	12.3	12.0	11.7
4	16.4	16.0	15.6
5	20.5	20.0	19.5
6	24.6	24.0	23.4
7	28.7	28.0	27.3
8	32.8	32.0	31.2
9	36.9	36.0	35.1

	38	37	36
1	3.8	3.7	3.6
2	7.6	7.4	7.2
3	11.4	11.1	10.8
4	15.2	14.8	14.4
5	19.0	18.5	18.0
6	22.8	22.2	21.6
7	26.6	25.9	25.2
8	30.4	29.6	28.8
9	34.2	33.3	32.4

	35	34	33
1	3.5	3.4	3.3
2	7.0	6.8	6.6
3	10.5	10.2	9.9
4	14.0	13.6	13.2
5	17.5	17.0	16.5
6	21.0	20.4	19.8
7	24.5	23.8	23.1
8	28.0	27.2	26.4
9	31.5	30.6	29.7

	32	31	30
1	3.2	3.1	3.0
2	6.4	6.2	6.0
3	9.6	9.3	9.0
4	12.8	12.4	12.0
5	16.0	15.5	15.0
6	19.2	18.6	18.0
7	22.4	21.7	21.0
8	25.6	24.8	24.0
9	28.8	27.9	27.0

$\log \sqrt{2} = .150515$

N.	0	1	2	3	4	5	6	7	8	9
150	17 609	638	667	696	725	754	782	811	840	869
51	898	926	955	984	*013	*041	*070	*099	*127	*156
52	18 184	213	241	270	298	327	355	384	412	441
53	469	498	526	554	583	611	639	667	696	724
54	752	780	808	837	865	893	921	949	977	*005
55	19 033	061	089	117	145	173	201	229	257	285
56	312	340	368	396	424	451	479	507	535	562
57	590	618	645	673	700	728	756	783	811	838
58	866	893	921	948	976	*003	*030	*058	*085	*112
59	20 140	167	194	222	249	276	303	330	358	385
160	412	439	466	493	520	548	575	602	629	656
61	683	710	737	763	790	817	844	871	898	925
62	952	978	*005	*032	*059	*085	*112	*139	*165	*192
63	21 219	245	272	299	325	352	378	405	431	458
64	484	511	537	564	590	617	643	669	696	722
65	748	775	801	827	854	880	906	932	958	985
66	22 011	037	063	089	115	141	167	194	220	246
67	272	298	324	350	376	401	427	453	479	505
68	531	557	583	608	634]	660	686	712	737	763
69	789	814	840	866	891	917	943	968	994	*019
170	23 045	070	096	121	147	172	198	223	249	274
71	300	325	350	376	401	426	452	477	502	528
72	553	578	603	629	654	679	704	729	754	779
73	805	830	855	880	905	930	955	980	*005	*030
74	24 055	080	105	130	155	180	204	229	254	279
75	304	329	353	378	403	428	452	477	502	527
76	551	576	601	625	650	674	699	724	748	773
77	797	822	846	871	895	920	944	969	993	*018
78	25 042	066	091	115	139	164	188	212	237	261
79	285	310	334	358	382	406	431	455	479	503
180	527	551	575	600	624	648	672	696	720	744
81	768	792	816	840	864	888	912	935	959	983
82	26 007	031	055	079	102	126	150	174	198	221
83	245	269	293	316	340	364	387	411	435	458
84	482	505	529	553	576	600	623	647	670	694
85	717	741	764	788	811	834	858	881	905	928
86	951	975	998	*021	*045	*068	*091	*114	*138	*161
87	27 184	207	231	254	277	300	323	346	370	393
88	416	439	462	485	508	531	554	577	600	623
89	646	669	692	715	738	761	784	807	830	852
190	875	898	921	944	967	989	*012	*035	*058	*081
91	28 103	126	149	171	194	217	240	262	285	307
92	330	353	375	398	421	443	466	488	511	533
93	556	578	601	623	646	668	691	713	735	758
94	780	803	825	847	870	892	914	937	959	981
95	29 003	026	048	070	092	115	137	159	181	203
96	226	248	270	292	314	336	358	380	403	425
97	447	469	491	513	535	557	579	601	623	645
98	667	688	710	732	754	776	798	820	842	863
99	885	907	929	951	973	994	*016	*038	*060	*081
200	30 103	125	146	168	190	211	233	255	276	298
N.	0	1	2	3	4	5	6	7	8	9

Prop. Parts

	29	28
1	2.9	2.8
2	5.8	5.6
3	8.7	8.4
4	11.6	11.2
5	14.5	14.0
6	17.4	16.8
7	20.3	19.6
8	23.2	22.4
9	26.1	25.2

	27	26
1	2.7	2.6
2	5.4	5.2
3	8.1	7.8
4	10.8	10.4
5	13.5	13.0
6	16.2	15.6
7	18.9	18.2
8	21.6	20.8
9	24.3	23.4

$\log\sqrt{3}=.238561$

	25	24
1	2.5	2.4
2	5.0	4.8
3	7.5	7.2
4	10.0	9.6
5	12.5	12.0
6	15.0	14.4
7	17.5	16.8
8	20.0	19.2
9	22.5	21.6

	23	22
1	2.3	2.2
2	4.6	4.4
3	6.9	6.6
4	9.2	8.8
5	11.5	11.0
6	13.8	13.2
7	16.1	15.4
8	18.4	17.6
9	20.7	19.8

	21
1	2.1
2	4.2
3	6.3
4	8.4
5	10.5
6	12.6
7	14.7
8	16.8
9	18.9

N.	0	1	2	3	4	5	6	7	8	9
200	30 103	125	146	168	190	211	233	255	276	298
01	320	341	363	384	406	428	449	471	492	514
02	535	557	578	600	621	643	664	685	707	728
03	750	771	792	814	835	856	878	899	920	942
04	963	984	*006	*027	*048	*069	*091	*112	*133	*154
05	31 175	197	218	239	260	281	302	323	345	366
06	387	408	429	450	471	492	513	534	555	576
07	597	618	639	660	681	702	723	744	765	785
08	806	827	848	869	890	911	931	952	973	994
09	32 015	035	056	077	098	118	139	160	181	201
210	222	243	263	284	305	325	346	366	387	408
11	428	449	469	490	510	531	552	572	593	613
12	634	654	675	695	715	736	756	777	797	818
13	838	858	879	899	919	940	960	980	*001	*021
14	33 041	062	082	102	122	143	163	183	203	224
15	244	264	284	304	325	345	365	385	405	425
16	445	465	486	506	526	546	566	586	606	626
17	646	666	686	706	726	746	766	786	806	826
18	846	866	885	905	925	945	965	985	*005	*025
19	34 044	064	084	104	124	143	163	183	203	223
220	242	262	282	301	321	341	361	380	400	420
21	439	459	479	498	518	537	557	577	596	616
22	635	655	674	694	713	733	753	772	792	811
23	830	850	869	889	908	928	947	967	986	*005
24	35 025	044	064	083	102	122	141	160	180	199
25	218	238	257	276	295	315	334	353	372	392
26	411	430	449	468	488	507	526	545	564	583
27	603	622	641	660	679	698	717	736	755	774
28	793	813	832	851	870	889	908	927	946	965
29	984	*003	*021	*040	*059	*078	*097	*116	*135	*154
230	36 173	192	211	229	248	267	286	305	324	342
31	361	380	399	418	436	455	474	493	511	530
32	549	568	586	605	624	642	661	680	698	717
33	736	754	773	791	810	829	847	866	884	903
34	922	940	959	977	996	*014	*033	*051	*070	*088
35	37 107	125	144	162	181	199	218	236	254	273
36	291	310	328	346	365	383	401	420	438	457
37	475	493	511	530	548	566	585	603	621	639
38	658	676	694	712	731	749	767	785	803	822
39	840	858	876	894	912	931	949	967	985	*003
240	38 021	039	057	075	093	112	130	148	166	184
41	202	220	238	256	274	292	310	328	346	364
42	382	399	417	435	453	471	489	507	525	543
43	561	578	596	614	632	650	668	686	703	721
44	739	757	775	792	810	828	846	863	881	899
45	917	934	952	970	987	*005	*023	*041	*058	*076
46	39 094	111	129	146	164	182	199	217	235	252
47	270	287	305	322	340	358	375	393	410	428
48	445	463	480	498	515	533	550	568	585	602
49	620	637	655	672	690	707	724	742	759	777
250	794	811	829	846	863	881	898	915	933	950
N.	0	1	2	3	4	5	6	7	8	9

Prop. Parts

	22	21
1	2.2	2.1
2	4.4	4.2
3	6.6	6.3
4	8.8	8.4
5	11.0	10.5
6	13.2	12.6
7	15.4	14.7
8	17.6	16.8
9	19.8	18.9

	20	19
1	2.0	1.9
2	4.0	3.8
3	6.0	5.7
4	8.0	7.6
5	10.0	9.5
6	12.0	11.4
7	14.0	13.3
8	16.0	15.2
9	18.0	17.1

	18	17
1	1.8	1.7
2	3.6	3.4
3	5.4	5.1
4	7.2	6.8
5	9.0	8.5
6	10.8	10.2
7	12.6	11.9
8	14.4	13.6
9	16.2	15.3

N.	0	1	2	3	4	5	6	7	8	9
250	39 794	811	829	846	863	881	898	915	933	950
51	967	985	*002	*019	*037	*054	*071	*088	*106	*123
52	40 140	157	175	192	209	226	243	261	278	295
53	312	329	346	364	381	398	415	432	449	466
54	483	500	518	535	552	569	586	603	620	637
55	654	671	688	705	722	739	756	773	790	807
56	824	841	858	875	892	909	926	943	960	976
57	993	*010	*027	*044	*061	*078	*095	*111	*128	*145
58	41 162	179	196	212	229	246	263	280	296	313
59	330	347	363	380	397	414	430	447	464	481
260	497	514	531	547	564	581	597	614	631	647
61	664	681	697	714	731	747	764	780	797	814
62	830	847	863	880	896	913	929	946	963	979
63	996	*012	*029	*045	*062	*078	*095	*111	*127	*144
64	42 160	177	193	210	226	243	259	275	292	308
65	325	341	357	374	390	406	423	439	455	472
66	488	504	521	537	553	570	586	602	619	635
67	651	667	684	700	716	732	749	765	781	797
68	813	830	846	862	878	894	911	927	943	959
69	975	991	*008	*024	*040	*056	*072	*088	*104	*120
270	43 136	152	169	185	201	217	233	249	265	281
71	297	313	329	345	361	377	393	409	425	441
72	457	473	489	505	521	537	553	569	584	600
73	616	632	648	664	680	696	712	727	743	759
74	775	791	807	823	838	854	870	886	902	917
75	933	949	965	981	996	*012	*028	*044	*059	*075
76	44 091	107	122	138	154	170	185	201	217	232
77	248	264	279	295	311	326	342	358	373	389
78	404	420	436	451	467	483	498	514	529	545
79	560	576	592	607	623	638	654	669	685	700
280	716	731	747	762	778	793	809	824	840	855
81	871	886	902	917	932	948	963	979	994	*010
82	45 025	040	056	071	086	102	117	133	148	163
83	179	194	209	225	240	255	271	286	301	317
84	332	347	362	378	393	408	423	439	454	469
85	484	500	515	530	545	561	576	591	606	621
86	637	652	667	682	697	712	728	743	758	773
87	788	803	818	834	849	864	879	894	909	924
88	939	954	969	984	*000	*015	*030	*045	*060	*075
89	46 090	105	120	135	150	165	180	195	210	225
290	240	255	270	285	300	315	330	345	359	374
91	389	404	419	434	449	464	479	494	509	523
92	538	553	568	583	598	613	627	642	657	672
93	687	702	716	731	746	761	776	790	805	820
94	835	850	864	879	894	909	923	938	953	967
95	982	997	*012	*026	*041	*056	*070	*085	*100	*114
96	47 129	144	159	173	188	202	217	232	246	261
97	276	290	305	319	334	349	363	378	392	407
98	422	436	451	465	480	494	509	524	538	553
99	567	582	596	611	625	640	654	669	683	698
300	712	727	741	756	770	784	799	813	828	842
N.	0	1	2	3	4	5	6	7	8	9

Prop. Parts

	18	17
1	1.8	1.7
2	3.6	3.4
3	5.4	5.1
4	7.2	6.8
5	9.0	8.5
6	10.8	10.2
7	12.6	11.9
8	14.4	13.6
9	16.2	15.3

$M = \log_{10} e = \log_{10} 2.71828\ldots = .43429$

	16	15
1	1.6	1.5
2	3.2	3.0
3	4.8	4.5
4	6.4	6.0
5	8.0	7.5
6	9.6	9.0
7	11.2	10.5
8	12.8	12.0
9	14.4	13.5

	14
1	1.4
2	2.8
3	4.2
4	5.6
5	7.0
6	8.4
7	9.8
8	11.2
9	12.6

N.	0	1	2	3	4	5	6	7	8	9
300	47 712	727	741	756	770	784	799	813	828	842
01	857	871	885	900	914	929	943	958	972	986
02	48 001	015	029	044	058	073	087	101	116	130
03	144	159	173	187	202	216	230	244	259	273
04	287	302	316	330	344	359	373	387	401	416
05	430	444	458	473	487	501	515	530	544	558
06	572	586	601	615	629	643	657	671	686	700
07	714	728	742	756	770	785	799	813	827	841
08	855	869	883	897	911	926	940	954	968	982
09	996	*010	*024	*038	*052	*066	*080	*094	*108	*122
310	49 136	150	164	178	192	206	220	234	248	262
11	276	290	304	318	332	346	360	374	388	402
12	415	429	443	457	471	485	499	513	527	541
13	554	568	582	596	610	624	638	651	665	679
14	693	707	721	734	748	762	776	790	803	817
15	831	845	859	872	886	900	914	927	941	955
16	969	982	996	*010	*024	*037	*051	*065	*079	*092
17	50 106	120	133	147	161	174	188	202	215	229
18	243	256	270	284	297	311	325	338	352	365
19	379	393	406	420	433	447	461	474	488	501
320	515	529	542	556	569	583	596	610	623	637
21	651	664	678	691	705	718	732	745	759	772
22	786	799	813	826	840	853	866	880	893	907
23	920	934	947	961	974	987	*001	*014	*028	*041
24	51 055	068	081	095	108	121	135	148	162	175
25	188	202	215	228	242	255	268	282	295	308
26	322	335	348	362	375	388	402	415	428	441
27	455	468	481	495	508	521	534	548	561	574
28	587	601	614	627	640	654	667	680	693	706
29	720	733	746	759	772	786	799	812	825	838
330	851	865	878	891	904	917	930	943	957	970
31	983	996	*009	*022	*035	*048	*061	*075	*088	*101
32	52 114	127	140	153	166	179	192	205	218	231
33	244	257	270	284	297	310	323	336	349	362
34	375	388	401	414	427	440	453	466	479	492
35	504	517	530	543	556	569	582	595	608	621
36	634	647	660	673	686	699	711	724	737	750
37	763	776	789	802	815	827	840	853	866	879
38	892	905	917	930	943	956	969	982	994	*007
39	53 020	033	046	058	071	084	097	110	122	135
340	148	161	173	186	199	212	224	237	250	263
41	275	288	301	314	326	339	352	364	377	390
42	403	415	428	441	453	466	479	491	504	517
43	529	542	555	567	580	593	605	618	631	643
44	656	668	681	694	706	719	732	744	757	769
45	782	794	807	820	832	845	857	870	882	895
46	908	920	933	945	958	970	983	995	*008	*020
47	54 033	045	058	070	083	095	108	120	133	145
48	158	170	183	195	208	220	233	245	258	270
49	283	295	307	320	332	345	357	370	382	394
350	407	419	432	444	456	469	481	494	506	518
N.	0	1	2	3	4	5	6	7	8	9

Prop. Parts

	15	14
1	1.5	1.4
2	3.0	2.8
3	4.5	4.2
4	6.0	5.6
5	7.5	7.0
6	9.0	8.4
7	10.5	9.8
8	12.0	11.2
9	13.5	12.6

	13	12
1	1.3	1.2
2	2.6	2.4
3	3.9	3.6
4	5.2	4.8
5	6.5	6.0
6	7.8	7.2
7	9.1	8.4
8	10.4	9.6
9	11.7	10.8

N.	0	1	2	3	4	5	6	7	8	9	Prop. Parts	
350	54 407	419	432	444	456	469	481	494	506	518		
51	531	543	555	568	580	593	605	617	630	642		
52	654	667	679	691	704	716	728	741	753	765		
53	777	790	802	814	827	839	851	864	876	888		
54	900	913	925	937	949	962	974	986	998	*011		
55	55 023	035	047	060	072	084	096	108	121	133		
56	145	157	169	182	194	206	218	230	242	255		
57	267	279	291	303	315	328	340	352	364	376		
58	388	400	413	425	437	449	461	473	485	497		
59	509	522	534	546	558	570	582	594	606	618		
360	630	642	654	666	678	691	703	715	727	739		
											13	**12**
61	751	763	775	787	799	811	823	835	847	859		
62	871	883	895	907	919	931	943	955	967	979		
63	991	*003	*015	*027	*038	*050	*062	*074	*086	*098	1 1.3	1.2
64	56 110	122	134	146	158	170	182	194	205	217	2 2.6	2.4
											3 3.9	3.6
65	229	241	253	265	277	289	301	312	324	336	4 5.2	4.8
											5 6.5	6.0
66	348	360	372	384	396	407	419	431	443	455	6 7.8	7.2
67	467	478	490	502	514	526	538	549	561	573	7 9.1	8.4
68	585	597	608	620	632	644	656	667	679	691	8 10.4	9.6
69	703	714	726	738	750	761	773	785	797	808	9 11.7	10.8
370	820	832	844	855	867	879	891	902	914	926		
71	937	949	961	972	984	996	*008	*019	*031	*043		
72	57 054	066	078	089	101	113	124	136	148	159		
73	171	183	194	206	217	229	241	252	264	276		
74	287	299	310	322	334	345	357	368	380	392		
75	403	415	426	438	449	461	473	,484	496	507		
76	519	530	542	553	565	576	588	600	611	623		
77	634	646	657	669	680	692	703	715	726	738		
78	749	761	772	784	795	807	818	830	841	852		
79	864	875	887	898	910	921	933	944	955	967		
380	978	990	*001	*013	*024	*035	*047	*058	*070	*081		
											11	**10**
81	58 092	104	115	127	138	149	161	172	184	195		
82	206	218	229	240	252	263	274	286	297	309		
83	320	331	343	354	365	377	388	399	410	422	1 1.1	1.0
84	433	444	456	467	478	490	501	512	524	535	2 2.2	2.0
											3 3.3	3.0
85	546	557	569	580	591	602	614	625	636	647	4 4.4	4.0
											5 5.5	5.0
86	659	670	681	692	704	715	726	737	749	760	6 6.6	6.0
87	771	782	794	805	816	827	838	850	861	872	7 7.7	7.0
88	883	894	906	917	928	939	950	961	973	984	8 8.8	8.0
89	995	*006	*017	*028	*040	*051	*062	*073	*084	*095	9 9.9	9.0
390	59 106	118	129	140	151	162	173	184	195	207		
91	218	229	240	251	262	273	284	295	306	318		
92	329	340	351	362	373	384	395	406	417	428		
93	439	450	461	472	483	494	506	517	528	539		
94	550	561	572	583	594	605	616	627	638	649		
95	660	671	682	693	704	715	726	737	748	759		
96	770	780	791	802	813	824	835	846	857	868		
97	879	890	901	912	923	934	945	956	966	977		
98	988	999	*010	*021	*032	*043	*054	*065	*076	*086		
99	60 097	108	119	130	141	152	163	173	184	195		
400	206	217	228	239	249	260	271	282	293	304		
N.	0	1	2	3	4	5	6	7	8	9	Prop. Parts	

N.	0	1	2	3	4	5	6	7	8	9	Prop. Parts
400	60 206	217	228	239	249	260	271	282	293	304	
01	314	325	336	347	358	369	379	390	401	412	
02	423	433	444	455	466	477	487	498	509	520	
03	531	541	552	563	574	584	595	606	617	627	
04	638	649	660	670	681	692	703	713	724	735	
05	746	756	767	778	788	799	810	821	831	842	
06	853	863	874	885	895	906	917	927	938	949	
07	959	970	981	991	*002	*013	*023	*034	*045	*055	
08	61 066	077	087	098	109	119	130	140	151	162	
09	172	183	194	204	215	225	236	247	257	268	
410	278	289	300	310	321	331	342	352	363	374	

		11	10
	1	1.1	1.0
	2	2.2	2.0
	3	3.3	3.0
	4	4.4	4.0
	5	5.5	5.0
	6	6.6	6.0
	7	7.7	7.0
	8	8.8	8.0
	9	9.9	9.0

N.	0	1	2	3	4	5	6	7	8	9
11	384	395	405	416	426	437	448	458	469	479
12	490	500	511	521	532	542	553	563	574	584
13	595	606	616	627	637	648	658	669	679	690
14	700	711	721	731	742	752	763	773	784	794
15	805	815	826	836	847	857	868	878	888	899
16	909	920	930	941	951	962	972	982	993	*003
17	62 014	024	034	045	055	066	076	086	097	107
18	118	128	138	149	159	170	180	190	201	211
19	221	232	242	252	263	273	284	294	304	315
420	325	335	346	356	366	377	387	397	408	418
21	428	439	449	459	469	480	490	500	511	521
22	531	542	552	562	572	583	593	603	613	624
23	634	644	655	665	675	685	696	706	716	726
24	737	747	757	767	778	788	798	808	818	829
25	839	849	859	870	880	890	900	910	921	931
26	941	951	961	972	982	992	*002	*012	*022	*033
27	63 043	053	063	073	083	094	104	114	124	134
28	144	155	165	175	185	195	205	215	225	236
29	246	256	266	276	286	296	306	317	327	337
430	347	357	367	377	387	397	407	417	428	438
31	448	458	468	478	488	498	508	518	528	538
32	548	558	568	579	589	599	609	619	629	639
33	649	659	669	679	689	699	709	719	729	739
34	749	759	769	779	789	799	809	819	829	839
35	849	859	869	879	889	899	909	919	929	939
36	949	959	969	979	988	998	*008	*018	*028	*038
37	64 048	058	068	078	088	098	108	118	128	137
38	147	157	167	177	187	197	207	217	227	237
39	246	256	266	276	286	296	306	316	326	335
440	345	355	365	375	385	395	404	414	424	434

		9
	1	0.9
	2	1.8
	3	2.7
	4	3.6
	5	4.5
	6	5.4
	7	6.3
	8	7.2
	9	8.1

N.	0	1	2	3	4	5	6	7	8	9	Prop. Parts
41	444	454	464	473	483	493	503	513	523	532	
42	542	552	562	572	582	591	601	611	621	631	
43	640	650	660	670	680	689	699	709	719	729	
44	738	748	758	768	777	787	797	807	816	826	
45	836	846	856	865	875	885	895	904	914	924	
46	933	943	953	963	972	982	992	*002	*011	*021	
47	65 031	040	050	060	070	079	089	099	108	118	
48	128	137	147	157	167	176	186	196	205	215	
49	225	234	244	254	263	273	283	292	302	312	
450	321	331	341	350	360	369	379	389	398	408	
N.	0	1	2	3	4	5	6	7	8	9	Prop. Parts

N.	0	1	2	3	4	5	6	7	8	9
450	65 321	331	341	350	360	369	379	389	398	408
51	418	427	437	447	456	466	475	485	495	504
52	514	523	533	543	552	562	571	581	591	600
53	610	619	629	639	648	658	667	677	686	696
54	706	715	725	734	744	753	763	772	782	792
55	801	811	820	830	839	849	858	868	877	887
56	896	906	.916	925	935	944	954	963	973	982
57	992	*001	*011	*020	*030	*039	*049	*058	*068	*077
58	66 087	096	106	115	124	134	143	153	162	172
59	181	191	200	210	219	229	238	247	257	266
460	276	285	295	304	314	323	332	342	351	361
61	370	380	389	398	408	417	427	436	445	455
62	464	474	483	492	502	511	521	530	539	549
63	558	567	577	586	596	605	614	624	633	642
64	652	661	671	680	689	699	708	717	727	736
65	745	755	764	773	783	792	801	811	820	829
66	839	848	857	867	876	885	894	904	913	922
67	932	941	950	960	969	978	987	997	*006	*015
68	67 025	034	043	052	062	071	080	089	099	108
69	117	127	136	145	154	164	173	182	191	201
470	210	219	228	237	247	256	265	274	284	293
71	302	311	321	330	339	348	357	367	376	385
72	394	403	413	422	431	440	449	459	468	477
73	486	495	504	514	523	532	541	550	560	569
74	578	587	596	605	614	624	633	642	651	660
75	669	679	688	697	706	715	724	733	742	752
76	761	770	779	788	797	806	815	825	834	843
77	852	861	870	879	888	897	906	916	925	934
78	943	952	961	970	979	988	997	*006	*015	*024
79	68 034	043	052	061	070	079	088	097	106	115
480	124	133	142	151	160	169	178	187	196	205
81	215	224	233	242	251	260	269	278	287	296
82	305	314	323	332	341	350	359	368	377	386
83	395	404	413	422	431	440	449	458	467	476
84	485	494	502	511	520	529	538	547	556	565
85	574	583	592	601	610	619	628	637	646	655
86	664	673	681	690	699	708	717	726	735	744
87	753	762	771	780	789	797	806	815	824	833
88	842	851	860	869	878	886	895	904	913	922
89	931	940	949	958	966	975	984	993	*002	*011
490	69 020	028	037	046	055	064	073	082	090	099
91	108	117	126	135	144	152	161	170	179	188
92	197	205	214	223	232	241	249	258	267	276
93	285	294	302	311	320	329	338	346	355	364
94	373	381	390	399	408	417	425	434	443	452
95	461	469	478	487	496	504	513	522	531	539
96	548	557	566	574	583	592	601	609	618	627
97	636	644	653	662	671	679	688	697	705	714
98	723	732	740	749	758	767	775	784	793	801
99	810	819	827	836	845	854	862	871	880	888
500		897	906	914	923	932	940	949	958	966	975
N.	0	1	2	3	4	5	6	7	8	9

Prop. Parts

	10	9
1	1.0	0.9
2	2.0	1.8
3	3.0	2.7
4	4.0	3.6
5	5.0	4.5
6	6.0	5.4
7	7.0	6.3
8	8.0	7.2
9	9.0	8.1

	8
1	0.8
2	1.6
3	2.4
4	3.2
5	4.0
6	4.8
7	5.6
8	6.4
9	7.2

N.	0	1	2	3	4	5	6	7	8	9
500	69 897	906	914	923	932	940	949	958	966	975
01	984	992	*001	*010	*018	*027	*036	*044	*053	*062
02	70 070	079	088	096	105	114	122	131	140	148
03	157	165	174	183	191	200	209	217	226	234
04	243	252	260	269	278	286	295	303	312	321
05	329	338	346	355	364	372	381	389	398	406
06	415	424	432	441	449	458	467	475	484	492
07	501	509	518	526	535	544	552	561	569	578
08	586	595	603	612	621	629	638	646	655	663
09	672	680	689	697	706	714	723	731	740	749
510	757	766	774	783	791	800	808	817	825	834
11	842	851	859	868	876	885	893	902	910	919
12	927	935	944	952	961	969	978	986	995	*003
13	71 012	020	029	037	046	054	063	071	079	088
14	096	105	113	122	130	139	147	155	164	172
15	181	189	198	206	214	223	231	240	248	257
16	265	273	282	290	299	307	315	324	332	341
17	349	357	366	374	383	391	399	408	416	425
18	433	441	450	458	466	475	483	492	500	508
19	517	525	533	542	550	559	567	575	584	592
520	600	609	617	625	634	642	650	659	667	675
21	684	692	700	709	717	725	734	742	750	759
22	767	775	784	792	800	809	817	825	834	842
23	850	858	867	875	883	892	900	908	917	925
24	933	941	950	958	966	975	983	991	999	*008
25	72 016	024	032	041	049	057	066	074	082	090
26	099	107	115	123	132	140	148	156	165	173
27	181	189	198	206	214	222	230	239	247	255
28	263	272	280	288	296	304	313	321	329	337
29	346	354	362	370	378	387	395	403	411	419
530	428	436	444	452	460	469	477	485	493	501
31	509	518	526	534	542	550	558	567	575	583
32	591	599	607	616	624	632	640	648	656	665
33	673	681	689	697	705	713	722	730	738	746
34	754	762	770	779	787	795	803	811	819	827
35	835	843	852	860	868	876	884	892	900	908
36	916	925	933	941	949	957	965	973	981	989
37	997	*006	*014	*022	*030	*038	*046	*054	*062	*070
38	73 078	086	094	102	111	119	127	135	143	151
39	159	167	175	183	191	199	207	215	223	231
540	239	247	255	263	272	280	288	296	304	312
41	320	328	336	344	352	360	368	376	384	392
42	400	408	416	424	432	440	448	456	464	472
43	480	488	496	504	512	520	528	536	544	552
44	560	568	576	584	592	600	608	616	624	632
45	640	648	656	664	672	679	687	695	703	711
46	719	727	735	743	751	759	767	775	783	791
47	799	807	815	823	830	838	846	854	862	870
48	878	886	894	902	910	918	926	933	941	949
49	957	965	973	981	989	997	*005	*013	*020	*028
550	74 036	044	052	060	068	076	084	092	099	107
N.	0	1	2	3	4	5	6	7	8	9

Prop. Parts

	9	8
1	0.9	0.8
2	1.8	1.6
3	2.7	2.4
4	3.6	3.2
5	4.5	4.0
6	5.4	4.8
7	6.3	5.6
8	7.2	6.4
9	8.1	7.2

	7
1	0.7
2	1.4
3	2.1
4	2.8
5	3.5
6	4.2
7	4.9
8	5.6
9	6.3

N.	0	1	2	3	4	5	6	7	8	9	Prop. Parts
550	74 036	044	052	060	068	076	084	092	099	107	
51	115	123	131	139	147	155	162	170	178	186	
52	194	202	210	218	225	233	241	249	257	265	
53	273	280	288	296	304	312	320	327	335	343	
54	351	359	367	374	382	390	398	406	414	421	
55	429	437	445	453	461	468	476	484	492	500	
56	507	515	523	531	539	547	554	562	570	578	
57	586	593	601	609	617	624	632	640	648	656	
58	663	671	679	687	695	702	710	718	726	733	
59	741	749	757	764	772	780	788	796	803	811	
560	819	827	834	842	850	858	865	873	881	889	
61	896	904	912	920	927	935	943	950	958	966	
62	974	981	989	997	*005	*012	*020	*028	*035	*043	
63	75 051	059	066	074	082	089	097	105	113	120	
64	128	136	143	151	159	166	174	182	189	197	
65	205	213	220	228	236	243	251	259	266	274	
66	282	289	297	305	312	320	328	335	343	351	
67	358	366	374	381	389	397	404	412	420	427	
68	435	442	450	458	465	473	481	488	496	504	
69	511	519	526	534	542	549	557	565	572	580	
570	587	595	603	610	618	626	633	641	648	656	

	8	7
1	0.8	0.7
2	1.6	1.4
3	2.4	2.1
4	3.2	2.8
5	4.0	3.5
6	4.8	4.2
7	5.6	4.9
8	6.4	5.6
9	7.2	6.3

N.	0	1	2	3	4	5	6	7	8	9
71	664	671	679	686	694	702	709	717	724	732
72	740	747	755	762	770	778	785	793	800	808
73	815	823	831	838	846	853	861	868	876	884
74	891	899	906	914	921	929	937	944	952	959
75	967	974	982	989	997	*005	*012	*020	*027	*035
76	76 042	050	057	065	072	080	087	095	103	110
77	118	125	133	140	148	155	163	170	178	185
78	193	200	208	215	223	230	238	245	253	260
79	268	275	283	290	298	305	313	320	328	335
580	343	350	358	365	373	380	388	395	403	410
81	418	425	433	440	448	455	462	470	477	485
82	492	500	507	515	522	530	537	545	552	559
83	567	574	582	589	597	604	612	619	626	634
84	641	649	656	664	671	678	686	693	701	708
85	716	723	730	738	745	753	760	768	775	782
86	790	797	805	812	819	827	834	842	849	856
87	864	871	879	886	893	901	908	916	923	930
88	938	945	953	960	967	975	982	989	997	*004
89	77 012	019	026	034	041	048	056	063	070	078
590	085	093	100	107	115	122	129	137	144	151
91	159	166	173	181	188	195	203	210	217	225
92	232	240	247	254	262	269	276	283	291	298
93	305	313	320	327	335	342	349	357	364	371
94	379	386	393	401	408	415	422	430	437	444
95	452	459	466	474	481	488	495	503	510	517
96	525	532	539	546	554	561	568	576	583	590
97	597	605	612	619	627	634	641	648	656	663
98	670	677	685	692	699	706	714	721	728	735
99	743	750	757	764	772	779	786	793	801	808
600	815	822	830	837	844	851	859	866	873	880
N.	0	1	2	3	4	5	6	7	8	9	Prop. Parts

N.	0	1	2	3	4	5	6	7	8	9	Prop. Parts		
600	77 815	822	830	837	844	851	859	866	873	880			
01	887	895	902	909	916	924	931	938	945	952			
02	960	967	974	981	988	996	*003	*010	*017	*025			
03	78 032	039	046	053	061	068	075	082	089	097			
04	104	111	118	125	132	140	147	154	161	168			
05	176	183	190	197	204	211	219	226	233	240			
06	247	254	262	269	276	283	290	297	305	312			
07	319	326	333	340	347	355	362	369	376	383			
08	390	398	405	412	419	426	433	440	447	455			
09	462	469	476	483	490	497	504	512	519	526			
610	533	540	547	554	561	569	576	583	590	597			
												8	**7**
11	604	611	618	625	633	640	647	654	661	668			
12	675	682	689	696	704	711	718	725	732	739	1	0.8	0.7
13	746	753	760	767	774	781	789	796	803	810	2	1.6	1.4
14	817	824	831	838	845	852	859	866	873	880	3	2.4	2.1
15	888	895	902	909	916	923	930	937	944	951	4	3.2	2.8
16	958	965	972	979	986	993	*000	*007	*014	*021	5	4.0	3.5
17	79 029	036	043	050	057	064	071	078	085	092	6	4.8	4.2
18	099	106	113	120	127	134	141	148	155	162	7	5.6	4.9
19	169	176	183	190	197	204	211	218	225	232	8	6.4	5.6
620	239	246	253	260	267	274	281	288	295	302	9	7.2	6.3
21	309	316	323	330	337	344	351	358	365	372			
22	379	386	393	400	407	414	421	428	435	442			
23	449	456	463	470	477	484	491	498	505	511			
24	518	525	532	539	546	553	560	567	574	581			
25	588	595	602	609	616	623	630	637	644	650			
26	657	664	671	678	685	692	699	706	713	720			
27	727	734	741	748	754	761	768	775	782	789			
28	796	803	810	817	824	831	837	844	851	858			
29	865	872	879	886	893	900	906	913	920	927			
630	934	941	948	955	962	969	975	982	989	996			
													6
31	80 003	010	017	024	030	037	044	051	058	065			
32	072	079	085	092	099	106	113	120	127	134	1		0.6
33	140	147	154	161	168	175	182	188	195	202	2		1.2
34	209	216	223	229	236	243	250	257	264	271	3		1.8
35	277	284	291	298	305	312	318	325	332	339	4		2.4
											5		3.0
36	346	353	359	366	373	380	387	393	400	407	6		3.6
37	414	421	428	434	441	448	455	462	468	475	7		4.2
38	482	489	496	502	509	516	523	530	536	543	8		4.8
39	550	557	564	570	577	584	591	598	604	611	9		5.4
640	618	625	632	638	645	652	659	665	672	679			
41	686	693	699	706	713	720	726	733	740	747			
42	754	760	767	774	781	787	794	801	808	814			
43	821	828	835	841	848	855	862	868	875	882			
44	889	895	902	909	916	922	929	936	943	949			
45	956	963	969	976	983	990	996	*003	*010	*017			
46	81 023	030	037	043	050	057	064	070	077	084			
47	090	097	104	111	117	124	131	137	144	151			
48	158	164	171	178	184	191	198	204	211	218			
49	224	231	238	245	251	258	265	271	278	285			
650	291	298	305	311	318	325	331	338	345	351			
N.	**0**	**1**	**2**	**3**	**4**	**5**	**6**	**7**	**8**	**9**	Prop. Parts		

N.	0	1	2	3	4	5	6	7	8	9
650	81 291	298	305	311	318	325	331	338	345	351
51	358	365	371	378	385	391	398	405	411	418
52	425	431	438	445	451	458	465	471	478	485
53	491	498	505	511	518	525	531	538	544	551
54	558	564	571	578	584	591	598	604	611	617
55	624	631	637	644	651	657	664	671	677	684
56	690	697	704	710	717	723	730	737	743	750
57	757	763	770	776	783	790	796	803	809	816
58	823	829	836	842	849	856	862	869	875	882
59	889	895	902	908	915	921	928	935	941	948
660	954	961	968	974	981	987	994	*000	*007	*014
61	82 020	027	033	040	046	053	060	066	073	079
62	086	092	099	105	112	119	125	132	138	145
63	151	158	164	171	178	184	191	197	204	210
64	217	223	230	236	243	249	256	263	269	276
65	282	289	295	302	308	315	321	328	334	341
66	347	354	360	367	373	380	387	393	400	406
67	413	419	426	432	439	445	452	458	465	471
68	478	484	491	497	504	510	517	523	530	536
69	543	549	556	562	569	575	582	588	595	601
670	607	614	620	627	633	640	646	653	659	666
71	672	679	685	692	698	705	711	718	724	730
72	737	743	750	756	763	769	776	782	789	795
73	802	808	814	821	827	834	840	847	853	860
74	866	872	879	885	892	898	905	911	918	924
75	930	937	943	950	956	963	969	975	982	988
76	995	*001	*008	*014	*020	*027	*033	*040	*046	*052
77	83 059	065	072	078	085	091	097	104	110	117
78	123	129	136	142	149	155	161	168	174	181
79	187	193	200	206	213	219	225	232	238	245
680	251	257	264	270	276	283	289	296	302	308
81	315	321	327	334	340	347	353	359	366	372
82	378	385	391	398	404	410	417	423	429	436
83	442	448	455	461	467	474	480	487	493	499
84	506	512	518	525	531	537	544	550	556	563
85	569	575	582	588	594	601	607	613	620	626
86	632	639	645	651	658	664	670	677	683	689
87	696	702	708	715	721	727	734	740	746	753
88	759	765	771	778	784	790	797	803	809	816
89	822	828	835	841	847	853	860	866	872	879
690	885	891	897	904	910	916	923	929	935	942
91	948	954	960	967	973	979	985	992	998	*004
92	84 011	017	023	029	036	042	048	055	061	067
93	073	080	086	092	098	105	111	117	123	130
94	136	142	148	155	161	167	173	180	186	192
95	198	205	211	217	223	230	236	242	248	255
96	261	267	273	280	286	292	298	305	311	317
97	323	330	336	342	348	354	361	367	373	379
98	386	392	398	404	410	417	423	429	435	442
99	448	454	460	466	473	479	485	491	497	504
700	510	516	522	528	535	541	547	553	559	566
N.	0	1	2	3	4	5	6	7	8	9

Prop. Parts

	7	6
1	0.7	0.6
2	1.4	1.2
3	2.1	1.8
4	2.8	2.4
5	3.5	3.0
6	4.2	3.6
7	4.9	4.2
8	5.6	4.8
9	6.3	5.4

N.	0	1	2	3	4	5	6	7	8	9	Prop. Parts
700	84 510	516	522	528	535	541	547	553	559	566	
01	572	578	584	590	597	603	609	615	621	628	
02	634	640	646	652	658	665	671	677	683	689	
03	696	702	708	714	720	726	733	739	745	751	
04	757	763	770	776	782	788	794	800	807	813	
05	819	825	831	837	844	850	856	862	868	874	
06	880	887	893	899	905	911	917	924	930	936	
07	942	948	954	960	967	973	979	985	991	997	
08	85 003	009	016	022	028	034	040	046	052	058	
09	065	071	077	083	089	095	101	107	114	120	
710	126	132	138	144	150	156	163	169	175	181	
11	187	193	199	205	211	217	224	230	236	242	7 / 6
12	248	254	260	266	272	278	285	291	297	303	1 / 0.7 / 0.6
13	309	315	321	327	333	339	345	352	358	364	2 / 1.4 / 1.2
14	370	376	382	388	394	400	406	412	418	425	3 / 2.1 / 1.8
15	431	437	443	449	455	461	467	473	479	485	4 / 2.8 / 2.4 ; 5 / 3.5 / 3.0
16	491	497	503	509	516	522	528	534	540	546	6 / 4.2 / 3.6
17	552	558	564	570	576	582	588	594	600	606	7 / 4.9 / 4.2
18	612	618	625	631	637	643	649	655	661	667	8 / 5.6 / 4.8
19	673	679	685	691	697	703	709	715	721	727	9 / 6.3 / 5.4
720	733	739	745	751	757	763	769	775	781	788	
21	794	800	806	812	818	824	830	836	842	848	
22	854	860	866	872	878	884	890	896	902	908	
23	914	920	926	932	938	944	950	956	962	968	
24	974	980	986	992	998	*004	*010	*016	*022	*028	
25	86 034	040	046	052	058	064	070	076	082	088	
26	094	100	106	112	118	124	130	136	141	147	
27	153	159	165	171	177	183	189	195	201	207	
28	213	219	225	231	237	243	249	255	261	267	
29	273	279	285	291	297	303	308	314	320	326	
730	332	338	344	350	356	362	368	374	380	386	
31	392	398	404	410	415	421	427	433	439	445	5
32	451	457	463	469	475	481	487	493	499	504	1 / 0.5
33	510	516	522	528	534	540	546	552	558	564	2 / 1.0 ; 3 / 1.5
34	570	576	581	587	593	599	605	611	617	623	4 / 2.0
35	629	635	641	646	652	658	664	670	676	682	5 / 2.5
36	688	694	700	705	711	717	723	729	735	741	6 / 3.0
37	747	753	759	764	770	776	782	788	794	800	7 / 3.5
38	806	812	817	823	829	835	841	847	853	859	8 / 4.0
39	864	870	876	882	888	894	900	906	911	917	9 / 4.5
740	923	929	935	941	947	953	958	964	970	976	
41	982	988	994	999	*005	*011	*017	*023	*029	*035	
42	87 040	046	052	058	064	070	075	081	087	093	
43	099	105	111	116	122	128	134	140	146	151	
44	157	163	169	175	181	186	192	198	204	210	
45	216	221	227	233	239	245	251	256	262	268	
46	274	280	286	291	297	303	309	315	320	326	
47	332	338	344	349	355	361	367	373	379	384	
48	390	396	402	408	413	419	425	431	437	442	
49	448	454	460	466	471	477	483	489	495	500	
750	506	512	518	523	529	535	541	547	552	558	
N.	0	1	2	3	4	5	6	7	8	9	Prop. Parts

N.	0	1	2	3	4	5	6	7	8	9	Prop. Parts
750	87 506	512	518	523	529	535	541	547	552	558	
51	564	570	576	581	587	593	599	604	610	616	
52	622	628	633	639	645	651	656	662	668	674	
53	679	685	691	697	703	708	714	720	726	731	
54	737	743	749	754	760	766	772	777	783	789	
55	795	800	806	812	818	823	829	835	841	846	
56	852	858	864	869	875	881	887	892	898	904	
57	910	915	921	927	933	938	944	950	955	961	
58	967	973	978	984	990	996	*001	*007	*013	*018	
59	88 024	030	036	041	047	053	058	064	070	076	
760	081	087	093	098	104	110	116	121	127	133	
61	138	144	150	156	161	167	173	178	184	190	
62	195	201	207	213	218	224	230	235	241	247	
63	252	258	264	270	275	281	287	292	298	304	
64	309	315	321	326	332	338	343	349	355	360	
65	366	372	377	383	389	395	400	406	412	417	
66	423	429	434	440	446	451	457	463	468	474	
67	480	485	491	497	502	508	513	519	525	530	
68	536	542	547	553	559	564	570	576	581	587	
69	593	598	604	610	615	621	627	632	638	643	
770	649	655	660	666	672	677	683	689	694	700	
71	705	711	717	722	728	734	739	745	750	756	
72	762	767	773	779	784	790	795	801	807	812	
73	818	824	829	835	840	846	852	857	863	868	
74	874	880	885	891	897	902	908	913	919	925	
75	930	936	941	947	953	958	964	969	975	981	
76	986	992	997	*003	*009	*014	*020	*025	*031	*037	
77	89 042	048	053	059	064	070	076	081	087	092	
78	098	104	109	115	120	126	131	137	143	148	
79	154	159	165	170	176	182	187	193	198	204	
780	209	215	221	226	232	237	243	248	254	260	
81	265	271	276	282	287	293	298	304	310	315	
82	321	326	332	337	343	348	354	360	365	371	
83	376	382	387	393	398	404	409	415	421	426	
84	432	437	443	448	454	459	465	470	476	481	
85	487	492	498	504	509	515	520	526	531	537	
86	542	548	553	559	564	570	575	581	586	592	
87	597	603	609	614	620	625	631	636	642	647	
88	653	658	664	669	675	680	686	691	697	702	
89	708	713	719	724	730	735	741	746	752	757	
790	763	768	774	779	785	790	796	801	807	812	
91	818	823	829	834	840	845	851	856	862	867	
92	873	878	883	889	894	900	905	911	916	922	
93	927	933	938	944	949	955	960	966	971	977	
94	982	988	993	998	*004	*009	*015	*020	*026	*031	
95	90 037	042	048	053	059	064	069	075	080	086	
96	091	097	102	108	113	119	124	129	135	140	
97	146	151	157	162	168	173	179	184	189	195	
98	200	206	211	217	222	227	233	238	244	249	
99	255	260	266	271	276	282	287	293	298	304	
800	309	314	320	325	331	336	342	347	352	358	
N.	0	1	2	3	4	5	6	7	8	9	Prop. Parts

	6	5
1	0.6	0.5
2	1.2	1.0
3	1.8	1.5
4	2.4	2.0
5	3.0	2.5
6	3.6	3.0
7	4.2	3.5
8	4.8	4.0
9	5.4	4.5

N.	0	1	2	3	4	5	6	7	8	9	Prop. Parts
800	90 309	314	320	325	331	336	342	347	352	358	
01	363	369	374	380	385	390	396	401	407	412	
02	417	423	428	434	439	445	450	455	461	466	
03	472	477	482	488	493	499	504	509	515	520	
04	526	531	536	542	547	553	558	563	569	574	
05	580	585	590	596	601	607	612	617	623	628	
06	634	639	644	650	655	660	666	671	677	682	
07	687	693	698	703	709	714	720	725	730	736	
08	741	747	752	757	763	768	773	779	784	789	
09	795	800	806	811	816	822	827	832	838	843	
810	849	854	859	865	870	875	881	886	891	897	
11	902	907	913	918	924	929	934	940	945	950	
12	956	961	966	972	977	982	988	993	998	*004	
13	91 009	014	020	025	030	036	041	046	052	057	
14	062	068	073	078	084	089	094	100	105	110	
15	116	121	126	132	137	142	148	153	158	164	
16	169	174	180	185	190	196	201	206	212	217	
17	222	228	233	238	243	249	254	259	265	270	
18	275	281	286	291	297	302	307	312	318	323	
19	328	334	339	344	350	355	360	365	371	376	
820	381	387	392	397	403	408	413	418	424	429	
21	434	440	445	450	455	461	466	471	477	482	
22	487	492	498	503	508	514	519	524	529	535	
23	540	545	551	556	561	566	572	577	582	587	
24	593	598	603	609	614	619	624	630	635	640	
25	645	651	656	661	666	672	677	682	687	693	
26	698	703	709	714	719	724	730	735	740	745	
27	751	756	761	766	772	777	782	787	793	798	
28	803	808	814	819	824	829	834	840	845	850	
29	855	861	866	871	876	882	887	892	897	903	
830	908	913	918	924	929	934	939	944	950	955	
31	960	965	971	976	981	986	991	997	*002	*007	
32	92 012	018	023	028	033	038	044	049	054	059	
33	065	070	075	080	085	091	096	101	106	111	
34	117	122	127	132	137	143	148	153	158	163	
35	169	174	179	184	189	195	200	205	210	215	
36	221	226	231	236	241	247	252	257	262	267	
37	273	278	283	288	293	298	304	309	314	319	
38	324	330	335	340	345	350	355	361	366	371	
39	376	381	387	392	397	402	407	412	418	423	
840	428	433	438	443	449	454	459	464	469	474	
41	480	485	490	495	500	505	511	516	521	526	
42	531	536	542	547	552	557	562	567	572	578	
43	583	588	593	598	603	609	614	619	624	629	
44	634	639	645	650	655	660	665	670	675	681	
45	686	691	696	701	706	711	716	722	727	732	
46	737	742	747	752	758	763	768	773	778	783	
47	788	793	799	804	809	814	819	824	829	834	
48	840	845	850	855	860	865	870	875	881	886	
49	891	896	901	906	911	916	921	927	932	937	
850	942	947	952	957	962	967	973	978	983	988	
N.	0	1	2	3	4	5	6	7	8	9	Prop. Parts

Prop. Parts

	6	5
1	0.6	0.5
2	1.2	1.0
3	1.8	1.5
4	2.4	2.0
5	3.0	2.5
6	3.6	3.0
7	4.2	3.5
8	4.8	4.0
9	5.4	4.5

N.	0	1	2	3	4	5	6	7	8	9	Prop. Parts
850	92 942	947	952	957	962	967	973	978	983	988	
51	993	998	*003	*008	*013	*018	*024	*029	*034	*039	
52	93 044	049	054	059	064	069	075	080	085	090	
53	095	100	105	110	115	120	125	131	136	141	
54	146	151	156	161	166	171	176	181	186	192	
55	197	202	207	212	217	222	227	232	237	242	
56	247	252	258	263	268	273	278	283	288	293	
57	298	303	308	313	318	323	328	334	339	344	
58	349	354	359	364	369	374	379	384	389	394	
59	399	404	409	414	420	425	430	435	440	445	
860	450	455	460	465	470	475	480	485	490	495	

											6	5
61	500	505	510	515	520	526	531	536	541	546		
62	551	556	561	566	571	576	581	586	591	596		
63	601	606	611	616	621	626	631	636	641	646	1 0.6	0.5
64	651	656	661	666	671	676	682	687	692	697	2 1.2	1.0
											3 1.8	1.5
65	702	707	712	717	722	727	732	737	742	747	4 2.4	2.0
											5 3.0	2.5
66	752	757	762	767	772	777	782	787	792	979	6 3.6	3.0
67	802	807	812	817	822	827	832	837	842	847	7 4.2	3.5
68	852	857	862	867	872	877	882	887	892	897	8 4.8	4.0
69	902	907	912	917	922	927	932	937	942	947	9 5.4	4.5
870	952	957	962	967	972	977	982	987	992	997		
71	94 002	007	012	017	022	027	032	037	042	047		
72	052	057	062	067	072	077	082	086	091	096		
73	101	106	111	116	121	126	131	136	141	146		
74	151	156	161	166	171	176	181	186	191	196		
75	201	206	211	216	221	226	231	236	240	245		
76	250	255	260	265	270	275	280	285	290	295		
77	300	305	310	315	320	325	330	335	340	345		
78	349	354	359	364	369	374	379	384	389	394		
79	399	404	409	414	419	424	429	433	438	443		
880	448	453	458	463	468	473	478	483	488	493		

											4
81	498	503	507	512	517	522	527	532	537	542	
82	547	552	557	562	567	571	576	581	586	591	
83	596	601	606	611	616	621	626	630	635	640	1 0.4
84	645	650	655	660	665	670	675	680	685	689	2 0.8
											3 1.2
85	694	699	704	709	714	719	724	729	734	738	4 1.6
											5 2.0
86	743	748	753	758	763	768	773	778	783	787	6 2.4
87	792	797	802	807	812	817	822	827	832	836	7 2.8
88	841	846	851	856	861	866	871	876	880	885	8 3.2
89	890	895	900	905	910	915	919	924	929	934	9 3.6
890	939	944	949	954	959	963	968	973	978	983	
91	988	993	998	*002	*007	*012	*017	*022	*027	*032	
92	95 036	041	046	051	056	061	066	071	075	080	
93	085	090	095	100	105	109	114	119	124	129	
94	134	139	143	148	153	158	163	168	173	177	
95	182	187	192	197	202	207	211	216	221	226	
96	231	236	240	245	250	255	260	265	270	274	
97	279	284	289	294	299	303	308	313	318	323	
98	328	332	337	342	347	352	357	361	366	371	
99	376	381	386	390	395	400	405	410	415	419	
900	424	429	434	439	444	448	453	458	463	468	
N.	0	1	2	3	4	5	6	7	8	9	Prop. Parts

N.	0	1	2	3	4	5	6	7	8	9	Prop. Parts
900	95 424	429	434	439	444	448	453	458	463	468	
01	472	477	482	487	492	497	501	506	511	516	
02	521	525	530	535	540	545	550	554	559	564	
03	569	574	578	583	588	593	598	602	607	612	
04	617	622	626	631	636	641	646	650	655	660	
05	665	670	674	679	684	689	694	698	703	708	
06	713	718	722	727	732	737	742	746	751	756	
07	761	766	770	775	780	785	789	794	799	804	
08	809	813	818	823	828	832	837	842	847	852	
09	856	861	866	871	875	880	885	890	895	899	
910	904	909	914	918	923	928	933	938	942	947	
11	952	957	961	966	971	976	980	985	990	995	
12	999	*004	*009	*014	*019	*023	*028	*033	*038	*042	
13	96 047	052	057	061	066	071	076	080	085	090	
14	095	099	104	109	114	118	123	128	133	137	
15	142	147	152	156	161	166	171	175	180	185	
16	190	194	199	204	209	213	218	223	227	232	
17	237	242	246	251	256	261	265	270	275	280	
18	284	289	294	298	303	308	313	317	322	327	
19	332	336	341	346	350	355	360	365	369	374	
920	379	384	388	393	398	402	407	412	417	421	
21	426	431	435	440	445	450	454	459	464	468	
22	473	478	483	487	492	497	501	506	511	515	
23	520	525	530	534	539	544	548	553	558	562	
24	567	572	577	581	586	591	595	600	605	609	
25	614	619	624	628	633	638	642	647	652	656	
26	661	666	670	675	680	685	689	694	699	703	
27	708	713	717	722	727	731	736	741	745	750	
28	755	759	764	769	774	778	783	788	792	797	
29	802	806	811	816	820	825	830	834	839	844	
930	848	853	858	862	867	872	876	881	886	890	
31	895	900	904	909	914	918	923	928	932	937	
32	942	946	951	956	960	965	970	974	979	984	
33	988	993	997	*002	*007	*011	*016	*021	*025	*030	
34	97 035	039	044	049	053	058	063	067	072	077	
35	081	086	090	095	100	104	109	114	118	123	
36	128	132	137	142	146	151	155	160	165	169	
37	174	179	183	188	192	197	202	206	211	216	
38	220	225	230	234	239	243	248	253	257	262	
39	267	271	276	280	285	290	294	299	304	308	
940	313	317	322	327	331	336	340	345	350	354	
41	359	364	368	373	377	382	387	391	396	400	
42	405	410	414	419	424	428	433	437	442	447	
43	451	456	460	465	470	474	479	483	488	493	
44	497	502	506	511	516	520	525	529	534	539	
45	543	548	552	557	562	566	571	575	580	585	
46	589	594	598	603	607	612	617	621	626	630	
47	635	640	644	649	653	658	663	667	672	676	
48	681	685	690	695	699	704	708	713	717	722	
49	727	731	736	740	745	749	754	759	763	768	
950	772	777	782	786	791	795	800	804	809	813	
N.	0	1	2	3	4	5	6	7	8	9	Prop. Parts

Prop. Parts:

	5	4
1	0.5	0.4
2	1.0	0.8
3	1.5	1.2
4	2.0	1.6
5	2.5	2.0
6	3.0	2.4
7	3.5	2.8
8	4.0	3.2
9	4.5	3.6

N.	0	1	2	3	4	5	6	7	8	9	Prop. Parts		
950	97 772	777	782	786	791	795	800	804	809	813			
51	818	823	827	832	836	841	845	850	855	859			
52	864	868	873	877	882	886	891	896	900	905			
53	909	914	918	923	928	932	937	941	946	950			
54	955	959	964	968	973	978	982	987	991	996			
55	98 000	005	009	014	019	023	028	032	037	041			
56	046	050	055	·059	064	068	073	078	082	087			
57	091	096	100	105	109	114	118	123	127	132			
58	137	141	146	150	155	159	164	168	173	177			
59	182	186	191	195	200	204	209	214	218	223			
960	227	232	236	241	245	250	254	259	263	268			
61	272	277	281	286	290	295	299	304	308	313			
62	318	322	327	331	336	340	345	349	354	358			
63	363	367	372	376	381	385	390	394	399	403			
64	408	412	417	421	426	430	435	439	444	448			
65	453	457	462	466	471	475	480	484	489	493			
66	498	502	507	511	516	520	525	529	534	538			
67	543	547	552	556	561	565	570	574	579	583			
68	588	592	597	601	605	610	614	619	623	628			
69	632	637	641	646	650	655	659	664	668	673			
970	677	682	686	691	695	700	704	709	713	717			
71	722	726	731	735	740	744	749	753	758	762		**5**	**4**
72	767	771	776	780	784	789	793	798	802	807			
73	811	816	820	825	829	834	838	843	847	851	1	0.5	0.4
74	856	860	865	869	874	878	883	887	892	896	2	1.0	0.8
75	900	905	909	914	918	923	927	932	936	941	3 4	1.5 2.0	1.2 1.6
76	945	949	954	958	963	967	972	976	981	985	5	2.5	2.0
77	989	994	998	*003	*007	*012	*016	*021	*025	*029	6	3.0	2.4
78	99 034	038	043	047	052	056	061	065	069	074	7	3.5	2.8
79	078	083	087	092	096	100	105	109	114	118	8 9	4.0 4.5	3.2 3.6
980	123	127	131	136	140	145	149	154	158	162			
81	167	171	176	180	185	189	193	198	202	207			
82	211	216	220	224	229	233	238	242	247	251			
83	255	260	264	269	273	277	282	286	291	295			
84	300	304	308	313	317	322	326	330	335	339			
85	344	348	352	357	361	366	370	374	379	383			
86	388	392	396	401	405	410	414	419	423	427			
87	432	436	441	445	449	454	458	463	467	471			
88	476	480	484	489	493	498	502	506	511	515			
89	520	524	528	533	537	542	546	550	555	559			
990	564	568	572	577	581	585	590	594	599	603			
91	607	612	616	621	625	629	634	638	642	647			
92	651	656	660	664	669	673	677	682	686	691			
93	695	699	704	708	712	717	721	726	730	734			
94	739	743	747	752	756	760	765	769	774	778			
95	782	787	791	795	800	804	808	813	817	822			
96	826	830	835	839	843	848	852	856	861	865			
97	870	874	878	883	887	891	896	900	904	909			
98	913	917	922	926	930	935	939	944	948	952			
99	957	961	965	970	974	978	983	987	991	996			
1000	00 000	004	009	013	017	022	026	030	035	039			
N.	0	1	2	3	4	5	6	7	8	9	Prop. Parts		

N.	Log_e	N.	Log_e	N.	Log_e	N.	Log_e	N.	Log_e
2	0.69 315	13	2.56 495	31	3.43 399	53	3.97 029	73	4.29 046
3	1.09 861	17	2.83 321	37	3.61 092	59	4.07 754	79	4.36 945
5	1.60 944	19	2.94 444	41	3.71 357	61	4.11 087	83	4.41 884
7	1.94 591	23	3.13 549	43	3.76 120	67	4.20 469	89	4.48 864
11	2.39 790	29	3.36 730,	47	3.85 015	71	4.26 268	97	4.57 471

For other numbers combine these, or use the formula

$$\log_e N = (\log_e 10)\,(\log_{10} N) = \frac{1}{M}\log_{10} N = 2.30258509\,\log_{10} N.$$

$$\log_{10}\left(\frac{1}{M}\right) = \log_{10}\,(2.30258509) = 0.36221569.$$

$$\log_e \pi = 1.14472989.$$

Useful Constants and Their Logarithms

N	$\text{Log}_{10}\,N$
$e = \lim_{x=\infty}\left(1 + \frac{1}{x}\right)^x = 2.718\,2813$	0.434 2945
$M = \log_{10} e = 0.434\,2945$	9.637 7843 − 10
$\frac{1}{M} = \log_e 10 = 2.302\,5851$	0.362 2157
$\pi = 3.141\,5927$	0.497 1499
$\frac{1}{\pi} = 0.318\,3099$	9.502 8501 − 10
$\frac{180}{\pi} =$ degrees in 1 radian $= 57.295\,7795$	1.758 1226
$\frac{\pi}{180} =$ radians in 1° $\quad = 0.017\,4533$	8.241 8774 − 10

Table II

LOGARITHMS

OF THE

TRIGONOMETRIC FUNCTIONS

TO

FIVE DECIMAL PLACES

'	Log Sin	d	Log Tan	c d	Log Cot	Log Cos	
0	———		———			0.00 000	60
1	6.46 373	30103	6.46 373	30103	3.53 627	0.00 000	59
2	6.76 476	17609	6.76 476	17609	3.23 524	0.00 000	58
3	6.94 085	12494	6.94 085	12494	3.05 915	0.00 000	57
4	7.06 579	9691	7.06 579	9691	2.93 421	0.00 000	56
5	7.16 270	7918	7.16 270	7918	2.83 730	0.00 000	55
6	7.24 188	6694	7.24 188	6694	2.75 812	0.00 000	54
7	7.30 882	5800	7.30 882	5800	2.69 118	0.00 000	53
8	7.36 682	5115	7.36 682	5115	2.63 318	0.00 000	52
9	7.41 797	4576	7.41 797	4576	2.58 203	0.00 000	51
10	7.46 373	4139	7.46 373	4139	2.53 627	0.00 000	50
11	7.50 512	3779	7.50 512	3779	2.49 488	0.00 000	49
12	7.54 291	3476	7.54 291	3476	2.45 709	0.00 000	48
13	7.57 767	3218	7.57 767	3219	2.42 233	0.00 000	47
14	7.60 985	2997	7.60 986	2996	2.39 014	0.00 000	46
15	7.63 982	2802	7.63 982	2803	2.36 018	0.00 000	45
16	7.66 784	2633	7.66 785	2633	2.33 215	0.00 000	44
17	7.69 417	2483	7.69 418	2482	2.30 582	9.99 999	43
18	7.71 900	2348	7.71 900	2348	2.28 100	9.99 999	42
19	7.74 248	2227	7.74 248	2228	2.25 752	9.99 999	41
20	7.76 475	2119	7.76 476	2119	2.23 524	9.99 999	40
21	7.78 594	2021	7.78 595	2020	2.21 405	9.99 999	39
22	7.80 615	1930	7.80 615	1931	2.19 385	9.99 999	38
23	7.82 545	1848	7.82 546	1848	2.17 454	9.99 999	37
24	7.84 393	1773	7.84 394	1773	2.15 606	9.99 999	36
25	7.86 166	1704	7.86 167	1704	2.13 833	9.99 999	35
26	7.87 870	1639	7.87 871	1639	2.12 129	9.99 999	34
27	7.89 509	1579	7.89 510	1579	2.10 490	9.99 999	33
28	7.91 088	1524	7.91 089	1524	2.08 911	9.99 999	32
29	7.92 612	1472	7.92 613	1473	2.07 387	9.99 998	31
30	7.94 084	1424	7.94 086	1424	2.05 914	9.99 998	30
31	7.95 508	1379	7.95 510	1379	2.04 490	9.99 998	29
32	7.96 887	1336	7.96 889	1336	2.03 111	9.99 998	28
33	7.98 223	1297	7.98 225	1297	2.01 775	9.99 998	27
34	7.99 520	1259	7.99 522	1259	2.00 478	9.99 998	26
35	8.00 779	1223	8.00 781	1223	1.99 219	9.99 998	25
36	8.02 002	1190	8.02 004	1190	1.97 996	9.99 998	24
37	8.03 192	1158	8.03 194	1159	1.96 806	9.99 997	23
38	8.04 350	1128	8.04 353	1128	1.95 647	9.99 997	22
39	8.05 478	1100	8.05 481	1100	1.94 519	9.99 997	21
40	8.06 578	1072	8.06 581	1072	1.93 419	9.99 997	20
41	8.07 650	1046	8.07 653	1047	1.92 347	9.99 997	19
42	8.08 696	1022	8.08 700	1022	1.91 300	9.99 997	18
43	8.09 718	999	8.09 722	998	1.90 278	9.99 997	17
44	8.10 717	976	8.10 720	976	1.89 280	9.99 996	16
45	8.11 693	954	8.11 696	955	1.88 304	9.99 996	15
46	8.12 647	934	8.12 651	934	1.87 349	9.99 996	14
47	8.13 581	914	8.13 585	915	1.86 415	9.99 996	13
48	8.14 495	896	8.14 500	895	1.85 500	9.99 996	12
49	8.15 391	877	8.15 395	878	1.84 605	9.99 996	11
50	8.16 268	860	8.16 273	860	1.83 727	9.99 995	10
51	8.17 128	843	8.17 133	843	1.82 867	9.99 995	9
52	8.17 971	827	8.17 976	828	1.82 024	9.99 995	8
53	8.18 798	812	8.18 804	812	1.81 196	9.99 995	7
54	8.19 610	797	8.19 616	797	1.80 384	9.99 995	6
55	8.20 407	782	8.20 413	782	1.79 587	9.99 994	5
56	8.21 189	769	8.21 195	769	1.78 805	9.99 994	4
57	8.21 958	755	8.21 964	756	1.78 036	9.99 994	3
58	8.22 713	743	8.22 720	742	1.77 280	9.99 994	2
59	8.23 456	730	8.23 462	730	1.76 538	9.99 994	1
60	8.24 186		8.24 192		1.75 808	9.99 993	0

Log Cos	d	Log Cot	c d	Log Tan	Log Sin	'

Interpolation for Log Sin and Log Tan of Small Angles and for Log Cos and Log Cot of Large Angles.

When ordinary interpolation is not sufficiently accurate,

For Small Angles,

Let N = No. of Minutes in θ.

Then

$$\log \sin \theta = \log N + S - 10,$$
$$\log \tan \theta = \log N + T - 10.$$

For Large Angles,

Let N = No. of Minutes in $(90° - \theta)$.

Then

$$\log \cos \theta = \log N + S - 10,$$
$$\log \cot \theta = \log N + T - 10.$$

Find log N from Table I, and find S and T below.

N	S	N	S
0'– 13'	6.46373	129'–134'	6.46362
14'– 42'	72	135'–140'	61
43'– 58'	. 71	141'–146'	60
59'– 71'	6.46370	147'–151'	6.46359
72'– 81'	69	152'–157'	58
82'– 91'	68	158'–162'	57
92'– 99'	6.46367	163'–167'	6.46356
100'–107'	66	168'–171'	55
108'–115'	65	172'–176'	54
116'–121'	6.46364	177'–180'	6.46353
122'–128'	63		

N	T	N	T
0'– 26'	6.46373	128'–130'	6.46393
27'– 39'	74	131'–133'	94
40'– 48'	75	134'–136'	95
49'– 56'	6.46376	137'–139'	6.46396
57'– 64'	77	140'–142'	97
64'– 69'	78	143'–145'	98
70'– 74'	6.46379	146'–148'	6.46399
75'– 80'	80	149'–150'	6.46400
81'– 85'	81	151'–153'	01
86'– 89'	6.46382	154'–156'	6.46402
90'– 94'	83	157'–158'	03
95'– 98'	84	159'–161'	04
99'–102'	6.46385	162'–163'	6.46405
103'–106'	86	164'–166'	06
107'–110'	87	167'–168'	07
111'–113'	6.46388	169'–171'	6.46408
114'–117'	89	172'–173'	09
118'–120'	90	174'–175'	10
121'–124'	6.46391	176'–178'	6.46411
125'–127'	92	179'–180'	6.46412

′	Log Sin	d	Log Tan	c d	Log Cot	Log Cos	′
0	8.24 186		8.24 192		1.75 808	9.99 993	60
1	8.24 903	717	8.24 910	718	1.75 090	9.99 993	59
2	8.25 609	706	8.25 616	706	1.74 384	9.99 993	58
3	8.26 304	695	8.26 312	696	1.73 688	9.99 993	57
4	8.26 988	684	8.26 996	684	1.73 004	9.99 992	56
5	8.27 661	673	8.27 669	673	1.72 331	9.99 992	55
6	8.28 324	663	8.28 332	663	1.71 668	9.99 992	54
7	8.28 977	653	8.28 986	654	1.71 014	9.99 992	53
8	8.29 621	644	8.29 629	643	1.70 371	9.99 992	52
9	8.30 255	634	8.30 263	634	1.69 737	9.99 991	51
10	8.30 879	624	8.30 888	625	1.69 112	9.99 991	50
11	8.31 495	616	8.31 505	617	1.68 495	9.99 991	49
12	8.32 103	608	8.32 112	607	1.67 888	9.99 990	48
13	8.32 702	599	8.32 711	599	1.67 289	9.99 990	47
14	8.33 292	590	8.33 302	591	1.66 698	9.99 990	46
15	8.33 875	583	8.33 886	584	1.66 114	9.99 990	45
16	8.34 450	575	8.34 461	575	1.65 539	9.99 989	44
17	8.35 018	568	8.35 029	568	1.64 971	9.99 989	43
18	8.35 578	560	8.35 590	561	1.64 410	9.99 989	42
19	8.36 131	553	8.36 143	553	1.63 857	9.99 989	41
20	8.36 678	547	8.36 689	546	1.63 311	9.99 988	40
21	8.37 217	539	8.37 229	540	1.62 771	9.99 988	39
22	8.37 750	533	8.37 762	533	1.62 238	9.99 988	38
23	8.38 276	526	8.38 289	527	1.61 711	9.99 987	37
24	8.38 796	520	8.38 809	520	1.61 191	9.99 987	36
25	8.39 310	514	8.39 323	514	1.60 677	9.99 986	35
26	8.39 818	508	8.39 832	509	1.60 168	9.99 986	34
27	8.40 320	502	8.40 334	502	1.59 666	9.99 986	33
28	8.40 816	496	8.40 830	496	1.59 170	9.99 986	32
29	8.41 307	491	8.41 321	491	1.58 679	9.99 985	31
30	8.41 792	485	8.41 807	486	1.58 193	9.99 985	30
31	8.42 272	480	8.42 287	480	1.57 713	9.99 985	29
32	8.42 746	474	8.42 762	475	1.57 238	9.99 984	28
33	8.43 216	470	8.43 232	470	1.56 768	9.99 984	27
34	8.43 680	464	8.43 696	464	1.56 304	9.99 984	26
35	8.44 139	459	8.44 156	460	1.55 844	9.99 983	25
36	8.44 594	455	8.44 611	455	1.55 389	9.99 983	24
37	8.45 044	450	8.45 061	450	1.54 939	9.99 983	23
38	8.45 489	445	8.45 507	446	1.54 493	9.99 982	22
39	8.45 930	441	8.45 948	441	1.54 054	9.99 982	21
40	8.46 366	436	8.46 385	437	1.53 615	9.99 982	20
41	8.46 799	433	8.46 817	432	1.53 183	9.99 981	19
42	8.47 226	427	8.47 245	428	1.52 755	9.99 981	18
43	8.47 650	424	8.47 669	424	1.52 331	9.99 981	17
44	8.48 069	419	8.48 089	420	1.51 911	9.99 980	16
45	8.48 485	416	8.48 505	416	1.51 495	9.99 980	15
46	8.48 896	411	8.48 917	412	1.51 083	9.99 979	14
47	8.49 304	408	8.49 325	408	1.50 675	9.99 979	13
48	8.49 708	404	8.49 729	404	1.50 271	9.99 979	12
49	8.50 108	400	8.50 130	401	1.49 870	9.99 978	11
50	8.50 504	396	8.50 527	397	1.49 473	9.99 978	10
51	8.50 897	393	8.50 920	393	1.49 080	9.99 977	9
52	8.51 287	390	8.51 310	390	1.48 690	9.99 977	8
53	8.51 673	386	8.51 696	386	1.48 304	9.99 977	7
54	8.52 055	382	8.52 079	383	1.47 921	9.99 976	6
55	8.52 434	379	8.52 459	380	1.47 541	9.99 976	5
56	8.52 810	376	8.52 835	376	1.47 165	9.99 975	4
57	8.53 183	373	8.53 208	373	1.46 792	9.99 975	3
58	8.53 552	369	8.53 578	370	1.46 422	9.99 974	2
59	8.53 919	367	8.53 945	367	1.46 055	9.99 974	1
60	8.54 282	363	8.54 308	363	1.45 692	9.99 974	0
	Log Cos	d	Log Cot	c d	Log Tan	Log Sin	′

Prop. Parts

	720	710	690	680	670
2	144	142	138	136	134
3	216	213	207	204	201
4	288	284	276	272	268
5	360	355	345	340	335
6	432	426	414	408	402
7	504	497	483	476	469
8	576	568	552	544	536
9	648	639	621	612	603

	660	650	640	630	620
2	132	130	128	126	124
3	198	195	192	189	186
4	264	260	256	252	248
5	330	325	320	315	310
6	396	390	384	378	372
7	462	455	448	441	434
8	528	520	512	504	496
9	594	585	576	567	558

	610	600	590	580	570
2	122	120	118	116	114
3	183	180	177	174	171
4	244	240	236	232	228
5	305	300	295	290	285
6	366	360	354	348	342
7	427	420	413	406	399
8	488	480	472	464	456
9	549	540	531	522	513

	560	550	540	530	520
2	112	110	108	106	104
3	168	165	162	159	156
4	224	220	216	212	208
5	280	275	270	265	260
6	336	330	324	318	312
7	392	385	378	371	364
8	448	440	432	424	416
9	504	495	486	477	468

	510	500	490	480	470
2	102	100	98	96	94
3	153	150	147	144	141
4	204	200	196	192	188
5	255	250	245	240	235
6	306	300	294	288	282
7	357	350	343	336	329
8	408	400	392	384	376
9	459	450	441	432	423

	460	450	440	430	420
2	92	90	88	86	84
3	138	135	132	129	126
4	184	180	176	172	168
5	230	225	220	215	210
6	276	270	264	258	252
7	322	315	308	301	294
8	368	360	352	344	336
9	414	405	396	387	378

	410	400	395	390	385
2	82	80	79.0	78	77.0
3	123	120	118.5	117	115.5
4	164	160	158.0	156	154.0
5	205	200	197.5	195	192.5
6	246	240	237.0	234	231.0
7	287	280	276.5	273	269.5
8	328	320	316.0	312	308.0
9	369	360	355.5	351	346.5

	380	375	370	365	360
2	76	75.0	74	73.0	72
3	114	112.5	111	109.5	108
4	152	150.0	148	146.0	144
5	190	187.5	185	182.5	180
6	228	225.0	222	219.0	216
7	266	262.5	259	255.5	252
8	304	300.0	296	292.0	288
9	342	337.5	333	328.5	324

Prop. Parts

'	Log Sin	d	Log Tan	c d	Log Cot	Log Cos	
0	8.54 282	360	8.54 308	361	1.45 692	9.99 974	60
1	8.54 642	357	8.54 669	358	1.45 331	9.99 973	59
2	8.54 999	355	8.55 027	355	1.44 973	9.99 973	58
3	8.55 354	351	8.55 382	352	1.44 618	9.99 972	57
4	8.55 705	349	8.55 734	349	1.44 266	9.99 972	56
5	8.56 054	346	8.56 083	346	1.43 917	9.99 971	55
6	8.56 400	343	8.56 429	344	1.43 571	9.99 971	54
7	8.56 743	341	8.56 773	341	1.43 227	9.99 970	53
8	8.57 084	337	8.57 114	338	1.42 886	9.99 970	52
9	8.57 421	336	8.57 452	336	1.42 548	9.99 969	51
10	8.57 757	332	8.57 788	333	1.42 212	9.99 969	50
11	8.58 089	330	8.58 121	330	1.41 879	9.99 968	49
12	8.58 419	328	8.58 451	328	1.41 549	9.99 968	48
13	8.58 747	325	8.58 779	326	1.41 221	9.99 967	47
14	8.59 072	323	8.59 105	323	1.40 895	9.99 967	46
15	8.59 395	320	8.59 428	321	1.40 572	9.99 967	45
16	8.59 715	318	8.59 749	319	1.40 251	9.99 966	44
17	8.60 033	316	8.60 068	316	1.39 932	9.99 966	43
18	8.60 349	313	8.60 384	314	1.39 616	9.99 965	42
19	8.60 662	311	8.60 698	311	1.39 302	9.99 964	41
20	8.60 973	309	8.61 009	310	1.38 991	9.99 964	40
21	8.61 282	307	8.61 319	307	1.38 681	9.99 963	39
22	8.61 589	305	8.61 626	305	1.38 374	9.99 963	38
23	8.61 894	302	8.61 931	303	1.38 069	9.99 962	37
24	8.62 196	301	8.62 234	301	1.37 766	9.99 962	36
25	8.62 497	298	8.62 535	299	1.37 465	9.99 961	35
26	8.62 795	296	8.62 834	297	1.37 166	9.99 961	34
27	8.63 091	294	8.63 131	295	1.36 869	9.99 960	33
28	8.63 385	293	8.63 426	292	1.36 574	9.99 960	32
29	8.63 678	290	8.63 718	291	1.36 282	9.99 959	31
30	8.63 968	288	8.64 009	289	1.35 991	9.99 959	30
31	8.64 256	287	8.64 298	287	1.35 702	9.99 958	29
32	8.64 543	284	8.64 585	285	1.35 415	9.99 958	28
33	8.64 827	283	8.64 870	284	1.35 130	9.99 957	27
34	8.65 110	281	8.65 154	281	1.34 846	9.99 956	26
35	8.65 391	279	8.65 435	280	1.34 565	9.99 956	25
36	8.65 670	277	8.65 715	278	1.34 285	9.99 955	24
37	8.65 947	276	8.65 993	276	1.34 007	9.99 955	23
38	8.66 223	274	8.66 269	274	1.33 731	9.99 954	22
39	8.66 497	272	8.66 543	273	1.33 457	9.99 954	21
40	8.66 769	270	8.66 816	271	1.33 184	9.99 953	20
41	8.67 039	269	8.67 087	269	1.32 913	9.99 952	19
42	8.67 308	267	8.67 356	268	1.32 644	9.99 952	18
43	8.67 575	266	8.67 624	266	1.32 376	9.99 951	17
44	8.67 841	263	8.67 890	264	1.32 110	9.99 951	16
45	8.68 104	263	8.68 154	263	1.31 846	9.99 950	15
46	8.68 367	260	8.68 417	261	1.31 583	9.99 949	14
47	8.68 627	259	8.68 678	260	1.31 322	9.99 949	13
48	8.68 886	258	8.68 938	258	1.31 062	9.99 948	12
49	8.69 144	256	8.69 196	257	1.30 804	9.99 948	11
50	8.69 400	254	8.69 453	255	1.30 547	9.99 947	10
51	8.69 654	253	8.69 708	254	1.30 292	9.99 946	9
52	8.69 907	252	8.69 962	252	1.30 038	9.99 946	8
53	8.70 159	250	8.70 214	251	1.29 786	9.99 945	7
54	8.70 409	249	8.70 465	249	1.29 535	9.99 944	6
55	8.70 658	247	8.70 714	248	1.29 286	9.99 944	5
56	8.70 905	246	8.70 962	246	1.29 038	9.99 943	4
57	8.71 151	244	8.71 208	245	1.28 792	9.99 942	3
58	8.71 395	243	8.71 453	244	1.28 547	9.99 942	2
59	8.71 638	242	8.71 697	243	1.28 303	9.99 941	1
60	8.71 880		8.71 940		1.28 060	9.99 940	0
	Log Cos	d	Log Cot	c d	Log Tan	Log Sin	'

Prop. Parts

	360	355	350	345
2	72	71.0	70	69.0
3	108	106.5	105	103.5
4	144	142.0	140	138.0
5	180	177.5	175	172.5
6	216	213.0	210	207.0
7	252	248.5	245	241.5
8	288	284.0	280	276.0
9	324	319.5	315	310.5

	340	335	330	325
2	68	67.0	66	65.0
3	102	100.5	99	97.5
4	136	134.0	132	130.0
5	170	167.5	165	162.5
6	204	201.0	198	195.0
7	238	234.5	231	227.5
8	272	268.0	264	260.0
9	306	301.5	297	292.5

	320	315	310	305
2	64	63.0	62	61.0
3	96	94.5	93	91.5
4	128	126.0	124	122.0
5	160	157.5	155	152.5
6	192	189.0	186	183.0
7	224	220.5	217	213.5
8	256	252.0	248	244.0
9	288	283.5	279	274.5

	300	295	290	285
2	60	59.0	58	57.0
3	90	88.5	87	85.5
4	120	118.0	116	114.0
5	150	147.5	145	142.5
6	180	177.0	174	171.0
7	210	206.5	203	199.5
8	240	236.0	232	228.0
9	270	265.5	261	256.5

	280	275	270	265
2	56	55.0	54	53.0
3	84	82.5	81	79.5
4	112	110.0	108	106.0
5	140	137.5	135	132.5
6	168	165.0	162	159.0
7	196	192.5	189	185.5
8	224	220.0	216	212.0
9	252	247.5	243	238.5

	260	255	250	245
2	52	51.0	50	49.0
3	78	76.5	75	73.5
4	104	102.0	100	98.0
5	130	127.5	125	122.5
6	156	153.0	150	147.0
7	182	178.5	175	171.5
8	208	204.0	200	196.0
9	234	229.5	225	220.5

'	Log Sin	d	Log Tan	c d	Log Cot	Log Cos	
0	8.71 880	240	8.71 940	241	1.28 060	9.99 940	60
1	8.72 120	239	8.72 181	239	1.27 819	9.99 940	59
2	8.72 359	238	8.72 420	239	1.27 580	9.99 939	58
3	8.72 597	237	8.72 659	237	1.27 341	9.99 939	57
4	8.72 834	235	8.72 896	236	1.27 104	9.99 938	56
5	8.73 069	234	8.73 132	234	1.26 868	9.99 937	55
6	8.73 303	232	8.73 366	234	1.26 634	9.99 936	54
7	8.73 535	232	8.73 600	232	1.26 400	9.99 936	53
8	8.73 767	230	8.73 832	231	1.26 168	9.99 935	52
9	8.73 997	229	8.74 063	229	1.25 937	9.99 935	51
10	8.74 226	228	8.74 292	229	1.25 708	9.99 934	50
11	8.74 454	226	8.74 521	227	1.25 479	9.99 933	49
12	8.74 680	226	8.74 748	226	1.25 252	9.99 932	48
13	8.74 906	224	8.74 974	225	1.25 026	9.99 932	47
14	8.75 130	223	8.75 199	224	1.24 801	9.99 931	46
15	8.75 353	222	8.75 423	222	1.24 577	9.99 930	45
16	8.75 575	220	8.75 645	222	1.24 355	9.99 929	44
17	8.75 795	220	8.75 867	220	1.24 133	9.99 929	43
18	8.76 015	219	8.76 087	219	1.23 913	9.99 928	42
19	8.76 234	217	8.76 306	219	1.23 694	9.99 927	41
20	8.76 451	216	8.76 525	217	1.23 475	9.99 926	40
21	8.76 667	216	8.76 742	216	1.23 258	9.99 926	39
22	8.76 883	214	8.76 958	215	1.23 042	9.99 925	38
23	8.77 097	213	8.77 173	214	1.22 827	9.99 924	37
24	8.77 310	212	8.77 387	213	1.22 613	9.99 923	36
25	8.77 522	211	8.77 600	211	1.22 400	9.99 923	35
26	8.77 733	210	8.77 811	211	1.22 189	9.99 922	34
27	8.77 943	209	8.78 022	210	1.21 978	9.99 921	33
28	8.78 152	208	8.78 232	209	1.21 768	9.99 920	32
29	8.78 360	208	8.78 441	208	1.21 559	9.99 920	31
30	8.78 568	206	8.78 649	206	1.21 351	9.99 919	30
31	8.78 774	205	8.78 855	206	1.21 145	9.99 918	29
32	8.78 979	204	8.79 061	205	1.20 939	9.99 917	28
33	8.79 183	203	8.79 266	204	1.20 734	9.99 917	27
34	8.79 386	202	8.79 470	203	1.20 530	9.99 916	26
35	8.79 588	201	8.79 673	202	1.20 327	9.99 915	25
36	8.79 789	201	8.79 875	201	1.20 125	9.99 914	24
37	8.79 990	199	8.80 076	201	1.19 924	9.99 913	23
38	8.80 189	199	8.80 277	199	1.19 723	9.99 913	22
39	8.80 388	197	8.80 476	198	1.19 524	9.99 912	21
40	8.80 585	197	8.80 674	198	1.19 326	9.99 911	20
41	8.80 782	196	8.80 872	196	1.19 128	9.99 910	19
42	8.80 978	195	8.81 068	196	1.18 932	9.99 909	18
43	8.81 173	194	8.81 264	195	1.18 736	9.99 909	17
44	8.81 367	193	8.81 459	194	1.18 541	9.99 908	16
45	8.81 560	192	8.81 653	193	1.18 347	9.99 907	15
46	8.81 752	192	8.81 846	192	1.18 154	9.99 906	14
47	8.81 944	190	8.82 038	192	1.17 962	9.99 905	13
48	8.82 134	190	8.82 230	190	1.17 770	9.99 904	12
49	8.82 324	189	8.82 420	190	1.17 580	9.99 904	11
50	8.82 513	188	8.82 610	189	1.17 390	9.99 903	10
51	8.82 701	187	8.82 799	188	1.17 201	9.99 902	9
52	8.82 888	187	8.82 987	188	1.17 013	9.99 901	8
53	8.83 075	186	8.83 175	186	1.16 825	9.99 900	7
54	8.83 261	185	8.83 361	186	1.16 639	9.99 899	6
55	8.83 446	184	8.83 547	185	1.16 453	9.99 898	5
56	8.83 630	183	8.83 732	184	1.16 268	9.99 898	4
57	8.83 813	183	8.83 916	184	1.16 084	9.99 897	3
58	8.83 996	181	8.84 100	182	1.15 900	9.99 896	2
59	8.84 177	181	8.84 282	182	1.15 718	9.99 895	1
60	8.84 358		8.84 464		1.15 536	9.99 894	0
	Log Cos	d	Log Cot	c d	Log Tan	Log Sin	'

Prop. Parts

	241	239	237	235
2	48.2	47.8	47.4	47.0
3	72.3	71.7	71.1	70.5
4	96.4	95.6	94.8	94.0
5	120.5	119.5	118.5	117.5
6	144.6	143.4	142.2	141.0
7	168.7	167.3	165.9	164.5
8	192.8	191.2	189.6	188.0
9	216.9	215.1	213.3	211.5

	234	232	229	227
2	46.8	46.4	45.8	45.4
3	70.2	69.6	68.7	68.1
4	93.6	92.8	91.6	90.8
5	117.0	116.0	114.5	113.5
6	140.4	139.2	137.4	136.2
7	163.8	162.4	160.3	158.9
8	187.2	185.6	183.2	181.6
9	210.6	208.8	206.1	204.3

	226	224	222	220
2	45.2	44.8	44.4	44.0
3	67.8	67.2	66.6	66.0
4	90.4	89.6	88.8	88.0
5	113.0	112.0	111.0	110.0
6	135.6	134.4	133.2	132.0
7	158.2	156.8	155.4	154.0
8	180.8	179.2	177.6	176.0
9	203.4	201.6	199.8	198.0

	219	217	215	213
2	43.8	43.4	43.0	42.6
3	65.7	65.1	64.5	63.9
4	87.6	86.8	86.0	85.2
5	109.5	108.5	107.5	106.5
6	131.4	130.2	129.0	127.8
7	153.3	151.9	150.5	149.1
8	175.2	173.6	172.0	170.4
9	197.1	195.3	193.5	191.7

	211	208	206	203
2	42.2	41.6	41.2	40.6
3	63.3	62.4	61.8	60.9
4	84.4	83.2	82.4	81.2
5	105.5	104.0	103.0	101.5
6	126.6	124.8	123.6	121.8
7	147.7	145.6	144.2	142.1
8	168.8	166.4	164.8	162.4
9	189.9	187.2	185.4	182.7

	201	199	197	195
2	40.2	39.8	39.4	39.0
3	60.3	59.7	59.1	58.5
4	80.4	79.6	78.8	78.0
5	100.5	99.5	98.5	97.5
6	120.6	119.4	118.2	117.0
7	140.7	139.3	137.9	136.5
8	160.8	159.2	157.6	156.0
9	180.9	179.1	177.3	175.5

	193	192	190	188
2	38.6	38.4	38.0	37.6
3	57.9	57.6	57.0	56.4
4	77.2	76.8	76.0	75.2
5	96.5	96.0	95.0	94.0
6	115.8	115.2	114.0	112.8
7	135.1	134.4	133.0	131.6
8	154.4	153.6	152.0	150.4
9	173.7	172.8	171.0	169.2

	186	184	182	181
2	37.2	36.8	36.4	36.2
3	55.8	55.2	54.6	54.3
4	74.4	73.6	72.8	72.4
5	93.0	92.0	91.0	90.5
6	111.6	110.4	109.2	108.6
7	130.2	128.8	127.4	126.7
8	148.8	147.2	145.6	144.8
9	167.4	165.6	163.8	162.9

′	Log Sin	d	Log Tan	c d	Log Cot	Log Cos	
0	8.84 358	181	8.84 464	182	1.15 536	9.99 894	60
1	8.84 539	179	8.84 646	180	1.15 354	9.99 893	59
2	8.84 718	179	8.84 826	180	1.15 174	9.99 892	58
3	8.84 897	178	8.85 006	179	1.14 994	9.99 891	57
4	8.85 075	177	8.85 185	178	1.14 815	9.99 891	56
5	8.85 252	177	8.85 363	177	1.14 637	9.99 890	55
6	8.85 429	176	8.85 540	177	1.14 460	9.99 889	54
7	8.85 605	175	8.85 717	176	1.14 283	9.99 888	53
8	8.85 780	175	8.85 893	176	1.14 107	9.99 887	52
9	8.85 955	173	8.86 069	174	1.13 931	9.99 886	51
10	8.86 128	173	8.86 243	174	1.13 757	9.99 885	50
11	8.86 301	173	8.86 417	174	1.13 583	9.99 884	49
12	8.86 474	171	8.86 591	172	1.13 409	9.99 883	48
13	8.86 645	171	8.86 763	172	1.13 237	9.99 882	47
14	8.86 816	171	8.86 935	171	1.13 065	9.99 881	46
15	8.86 987	169	8.87 106	171	1.12 894	9.99 880	45
16	8.87 156	169	8.87 277	170	1.12 723	9.99 879	44
17	8.87 325	169	8.87 447	169	1.12 553	9.99 879	43
18	8.87 494	167	8.87 616	169	1.12 384	9.99 878	42
19	8.87 661	168	8.87 785	168	1.12 215	9.99 877	41
20	8.87 829	166	8.87 953	167	1.12 047	9.99 876	40
21	8.87 995	166	8.88 120	167	1.11 880	9.99 875	39
22	8.88 161	165	8.88 287	166	1.11 713	9.99 874	38
23	8.88 326	164	8.88 453	165	1.11 547	9.99 873	37
24	8.88 490	164	8.88 618	165	1.11 382	9.99 872	36
25	8.88 654	163	8.88 783	165	1.11 217	9.99 871	35
26	8.88 817	163	8.88 948	163	1.11 052	9.99 870	34
27	8.88 980	162	8.89 111	163	1.10 889	9.99 869	33
28	8.89 142	162	8.89 274	163	1.10 726	9.99 868	32
29	8.89 304	160	8.89 437	161	1.10 563	9.99 867	31
30	8.89 464	161	8.89 598	162	1.10 402	9.99 866	30
31	8.89 625	159	8.89 760	160	1.10 240	9.99 865	29
32	8.89 784	159	8.89 920	160	1.10 080	9.99 864	28
33	8.89 943	159	8.90 080	160	1.09 920	9.99 863	27
34	8.90 102	158	8.90 240	159	1.09 760	9.99 862	26
35	8.90 260	157	8.90 399	158	1.09 601	9.99 861	25
36	8.90 417	157	8.90 557	158	1.09 443	9.99 860	24
37	8.90 574	156	8.90 715	157	1.09 285	9.99 859	23
38	8.90 730	155	8.90 872	157	1.09 128	9.99 858	22
39	8.90 885	155	8.91 029	156	1.08 971	9.99 857	21
40	8.91 040	155	8.91 185	155	1.08 815	9.99 856	20
41	8.91 195	154	8.91 340	155	1.08 660	9.99 855	19
42	8.91 349	153	8.91 495	155	1.08 505	9.99 854	18
43	8.91 502	153	8.91 650	153	1.08 350	9.99 853	17
44	8.91 655	152	8.91 803	154	1.08 197	9.99 852	16
45	8.91 807	152	8.91 957	153	1.08 043	9.99 851	15
46	8.91 959	151	8.92 110	152	1.07 890	9.99 850	14
47	8.92 110	151	8.92 262	152	1.07 738	9.99 848	13
48	8.92 261	150	8.92 414	151	1.07 586	9.99 847	12
49	8.92 411	150	8.92 565	151	1.07 435	9.99 846	11
50	8.92 561	149	8.92 716	150	1.07 284	9.99 845	10
51	8.92 710	149	8.92 866	150	1.07 134	9.99 844	9
52	8.92 859	148	8.93 016	149	1.06 984	9.99 843	8
53	8.93 007	147	8.93 165	148	1.06 835	9.99 842	7
54	8.93 154	147	8.93 313	149	1.06 687	9.99 841	6
55	8.93 301	147	8.93 462	147	1.06 538	9.99 840	5
56	8.93 448	146	8.93 609	147	1.06 391	9.99 839	4
57	8.93 594	146	8.93 756	147	1.06 244	9.99 838	3
58	8.93 740	145	8.93 903	146	1.06 097	9.99 837	2
59	8.93 885	145	8.94 049	146	1.05 951	9.99 836	1
60	8.94 030		8.94 195		1.05 805	9.99 834	0
	Log Cos	d	Log Cot	c d	Log Tan	Log Sin	′

Prop. Parts

	182	181	180	179
2	36.4	36.2	36.0	35.8
3	54.6	54.3	54.0	53.7
4	72.8	72.4	72.0	71.6
5	91.0	90.5	90.0	89.5
6	109.2	108.6	108.0	107.4
7	127.4	126.7	126.0	125.3
8	145.6	144.8	144.0	143.2
9	163.8	162.9	162.0	161.1

	178	177	176	175
2	35.6	35.4	35.2	35.0
3	53.4	53.1	52.8	52.5
4	71.2	70.8	70.4	70.0
5	89.0	88.5	88.0	87.5
6	106.8	106.2	105.6	105.0
7	124.6	123.9	123.2	122.5
8	142.4	141.6	140.8	140.0
9	160.2	159.3	158.4	157.5

	174	173	172	171
2	34.8	34.6	34.4	34.2
3	52.2	51.9	51.6	51.3
4	69.6	69.2	68.8	68.4
5	87.0	86.5	86.0	85.5
6	104.4	103.8	103.2	102.6
7	121.8	121.1	120.4	119.7
8	139.2	138.4	137.6	136.8
9	156.6	155.7	154.8	153.9

	170	169	168	167
2	34.0	33.8	33.6	33.4
3	51.0	50.7	50.4	50.1
4	68.0	67.6	67.2	66.8
5	85.0	84.5	84.0	83.5
6	102.0	101.4	100.8	100.2
7	119.0	118.3	117.6	116.9
8	136.0	135.2	134.4	133.6
9	153.0	152.1	151.2	150.3

	166	165	164	163
2	33.2	33.0	32.8	32.6
3	49.8	49.5	49.2	48.9
4	66.4	66.0	65.6	65.2
5	83.0	82.5	82.0	81.5
6	99.6	99.0	98.4	97.8
7	116.2	115.5	114.8	114.1
8	132.8	132.0	131.2	130.4
9	149.4	148.5	147.6	146.7

	162	161	160	159
2	32.4	32.2	32.0	31.8
3	48.6	48.3	48.0	47.7
4	64.8	64.4	64.0	63.6
5	81.0	80.5	80.0	79.5
6	97.2	96.6	96.0	95.4
7	113.4	112.7	112.0	111.3
8	129.6	128.8	128.0	127.2
9	145.8	144.9	144.0	143.1

	158	157	156	155
2	31.6	31.4	31.2	31.0
3	47.4	47.1	46.8	46.5
4	63.2	62.8	62.4	62.0
5	79.0	78.5	78.0	77.5
6	94.8	94.2	93.6	93.0
7	110.6	109.9	109.2	108.5
8	126.4	125.6	124.8	124.0
9	142.2	141.3	140.4	139.5

	154	153	152	151
2	30.8	30.6	30.4	30.2
3	46.2	45.9	45.6	45.3
4	61.6	61.2	60.8	60.4
5	77.0	76.5	76.0	75.5
6	92.4	91.8	91.2	90.6
7	107.8	107.1	106.4	105.7
8	123.2	122.4	121.6	120.8
9	138.6	137.7	136.8	135.9

′	Log Sin	d	Log Tan	c d	Log Cot	Log Cos	
0	8.94 030	144	8.94 195	145	1.05 805	9.99 834	60
1	8.94 174	143	8.94 340	145	1.05 660	9.99 833	59
2	8.94 317	144	8.94 485	145	1.05 515	9.99 832	58
3	8.94 461	142	8.94 630	143	1.05 370	9.99 831	57
4	8.94 603	143	8.94 773	144	1.05 227	9.99 830	56
5	8.94 746	141	8.94 917	143	1.05 083	9.99 829	55
6	8.94 887	142	8.95 060	142	1.04 940	9.99 828	54
7	8.95 029	141	8.95 202	142	1.04 798	9.99 827	53
8	8.95 170	140	8.95 344	142	1.04 656	9.99 825	52
9	8.95 310	140	8.95 486	141	1.04 514	9.99 824	51
10	8.95 450	139	8.95 627	140	1.04 373	9.99 823	50
11	8.95 589	139	8.95 767	141	1.04 233	9.99 822	49
12	8.95 728	139	8.95 908	139	1.04 092	9.99 821	48
13	8.95 867	138	8.96 047	140	1.03 953	9.99 820	47
14	8.96 005	138	8.96 187	138	1.03 813	9.99 819	46
15	8.96 143	137	8.96 325	139	1.03 675	9.99 817	45
16	8.96 280	137	8.96 464	138	1.03 536	9.99 816	44
17	8.96 417	136	8.96 602	137	1.03 398	9.99 815	43
18	8.96 553	136	8.96 739	138	1.03 261	9.99 814	42
19	8.96 689	136	8.96 877	136	1.03 123	9.99 813	41
20	8.96 825	135	8.97 013	137	1.02 987	9.99 812	40
21	8.96 960	135	8.97 150	135	1.02 850	9.99 810	39
22	8.97 095	134	8.97 285	136	1.02 715	9.99 809	38
23	8.97 229	134	8.97 421	135	1.02 579	9.99 808	37
24	8.97 363	133	8.97 556	135	1.02 444	9.99 807	36
25	8.97 496	133	8.97 691	134	1.02 309	9.99 806	35
26	8.97 629	133	8.97 825	134	1.02 175	9.99 804	34
27	8.97 762	132	8.97 959	133	1.02 041	9.99 803	33
28	8.97 894	132	8.98 092	133	1.01 908	9.99 802	32
29	8.98 026	131	8.98 225	133	1.01 775	9.99 801	31
30	8.98 157	131	8.98 358	132	1.01 642	9.99 800	30
31	8.98 288	131	8.98 490	132	1.01 510	9.99 798	29
32	8.98 419	130	8.98 622	131	1.01 378	9.99 797	28
33	8.98 549	130	8.98 753	131	1.01 247	9.99 796	27
34	8.98 679	129	8.98 884	131	1.01 116	9.99 795	26
35	8.98 808	129	8.99 015	130	1.00 985	9.99 793	25
36	8.98 937	129	8.99 145	130	1.00 855	9.99 792	24
37	8.99 066	128	8.99 275	130	1.00 725	9.99 791	23
38	8.99 194	128	8.99 405	129	1.00 595	9.99 790	22
39	8.99 322	128	8.99 534	128	1.00 466	9.99 788	21
40	8.99 450	127	8.99 662	129	1.00 338	9.99 787	20
41	8.99 577	127	8.99 791	128	1.00 209	9.99 786	19
42	8.99 704	126	8.99 919	127	1.00 081	9.99 785	18
43	8.99 830	126	9.00 046	128	0.99 954	9.99 783	17
44	8.99 956	126	9.00 174	127	0.99 826	9.99 782	16
45	9.00 082	125	9.00 301	126	0.99 699	9.99 781	15
46	9.00 207	125	9.00 427	126	0.99 573	9.99 780	14
47	9.00 332	124	9.00 553	126	0.99 447	9.99 778	13
48	9.00 456	125	9.00 679	126	0.99 321	9.99 777	12
49	9.00 581	123	9.00 805	125	0.99 195	9.99 776	11
50	9.00 704	124	9.00 930	125	0.99 070	9.99 775	10
51	9.00 828	123	9.01 055	124	0.98 945	9.99 773	9
52	9.00 951	123	9.01 179	124	0.98 821	9.99 772	8
53	9.01 074	122	9.01 303	124	0.98 697	9.99 771	7
54	9.01 196	122	9.01 427	123	0.98 573	9.99 769	6
55	9.01 318	122	9.01 550	123	0.98 450	9.99 768	5
56	9.01 440	121	9.01 673	123	0.98 327	9.99 767	4
57	9.01 561	121	9.01 796	122	0.98 204	9.99 765	3
58	9.01 682	121	9.01 918	122	0.98 082	9.99 763	2
59	9.01 803	120	9.02 040	122	0.97 960	9.99 763	1
60	9.01 923		9.02 162		0.97 838	9.99 761	0
	Log Cos	d	Log Cot	c d	Log Tan	Log Sin	′

Prop. Parts

	150	149	148	147
2	30.0	29.8	29.6	29.4
3	45.0	44.7	44.4	44.1
4	60.0	59.6	59.2	58.8
5	75.0	74.5	74.0	73.5
6	90.0	89.4	88.8	88.2
7	105.0	104.3	103.6	102.9
8	120.0	119.2	118.4	117.6
9	135.0	134.1	133.2	132.3

	146	145	144	143
2	29.2	29.0	28.8	28.6
3	43.8	43.5	43.2	42.9
4	58.4	58.0	57.6	57.2
5	73.0	72.5	72.0	71.5
6	87.6	87.0	86.4	85.8
7	102.2	101.5	100.8	100.1
8	116.8	116.0	115.2	114.4
9	131.4	130.5	129.6	128.7

	142	141	140	139
2	28.4	28.2	28.0	27.8
3	42.6	42.3	42.0	41.7
4	56.8	56.4	56.0	55.6
5	71.0	70.5	70.0	69.5
6	85.2	84.6	84.0	83.4
7	99.4	98.7	98.0	97.3
8	113.6	112.8	112.0	111.2
9	127.8	126.9	126.0	125.1

	138	137	136	135
2	27.6	27.4	27.2	27.0
3	41.4	41.1	40.8	40.5
4	55.2	54.8	54.4	54.0
5	69.0	68.5	68.0	67.5
6	82.8	82.2	81.6	81.0
7	96.6	95.9	95.2	94.5
8	110.4	109.6	108.8	108.0
9	124.2	123.3	122.4	121.5

	134	133	132	131
2	26.8	26.6	26.4	26.2
3	40.2	39.9	39.6	39.3
4	53.6	53.2	52.8	52.4
5	67.0	66.5	66.0	65.5
6	80.4	79.8	79.2	78.6
7	93.8	93.1	92.4	91.7
8	107.2	106.4	105.6	104.8
9	120.6	119.7	118.8	117.9

	130	129	128	127
2	26.0	25.8	25.6	25.4
3	39.0	38.7	38.4	38.1
4	52.0	51.6	51.2	50.8
5	65.0	64.5	64.0	63.5
6	78.0	77.4	76.8	76.2
7	91.0	90.3	89.6	88.9
8	104.0	103.2	102.4	101.6
9	117.0	116.1	115.2	114.3

	126	125	124	123
2	25.2	25.0	24.8	24.6
3	37.8	37.5	37.2	36.9
4	50.4	50.0	49.6	49.2
5	63.0	62.5	62.0	61.5
6	75.6	75.0	74.4	73.8
7	88.2	87.5	86.8	86.1
8	100.8	100.0	99.2	98.4
9	113.4	112.5	111.6	110.7

	122	121	120
2	24.4	24.2	24.0
3	36.6	36.3	36.0
4	48.8	48.4	48.0
5	61.0	60.5	60.0
6	73.2	72.6	72.0
7	85.4	84.7	84.0
8	97.6	96.8	96.0
9	109.8	108.9	108.0

′	Log Sin	d	Log Tan	c d	Log Cot	Log Cos	
0	9.01 923	120	9.02 162	121	0.97 838	9.99 761	60
1	9.02 043	120	9.02 283	121	0.97 717	9.99 760	59
2	9.02 163	120	9.02 404	121	0.97 596	9.99 759	58
3	9.02 283	119	9.02 525	120	0.97 475	9.99 757	57
4	9.02 402	118	9.02 645	121	0.97 355	9.99 756	56
5	9.02 520	119	9.02 766	119	0.97 234	9.99 755	55
6	9.02 639	118	9.02 885	120	0.97 115	9.99 753	54
7	9.02 757	117	9.03 005	119	0.96 995	9.99 752	53
8	9.02 874	118	9.03 124	118	0.96 876	9.99 751	52
9	9.02 992	117	9.03 242	119	0.96 758	9.99 749	51
10	9.03 109	117	9.03 361	118	0.96 639	9.99 748	50
11	9.03 226	116	9.03 479	118	0.96 521	9.99 747	49
12	9.03 342	116	9.03 597	117	0.96 403	9.99 745	48
13	9.03 458	116	9.03 714	118	0.96 286	9.99 744	47
14	9.03 574	116	9.03 832	116	0.96 168	9.99 742	46
15	9.03 690	115	9.03 948	117	0.96 052	9.99 741	45
16	9.03 805	115	9.04 065	116	0.95 935	9.99 740	44
17	9.03 920	114	9.04 181	116	0.95 819	9.99 738	43
18	9.04 034	115	9.04 297	116	0.95 703	9.99 737	42
19	9.04 149	113	9.04 413	115	0.95 587	9.99 736	41
20	9.04 262	114	9.04 528	115	0.95 472	9.99 734	40
21	9.04 376	114	9.04 643	115	0.95 357	9.99 733	39
22	9.04 490	113	9.04 758	115	0.95 242	9.99 731	38
23	9.04 603	112	9.04 873	114	0.95 127	9.99 730	37
24	9.04 715	113	9.04 987	114	0.95 013	9.99 728	36
25	9.04 828	112	9.05 101	113	0.94 899	9.99 727	35
26	9.04 940	112	9.05 214	114	0.94 786	9.99 726	34
27	9.05 052	112	9.05 328	113	0.94 672	9.99 724	33
28	9.05 164	111	9.05 441	112	0.94 559	9.99 723	32
29	9.05 275	111	9.05 553	113	0.94 447	9.99 721	31
30	9.05 386	111	9.05 666	112	0.94 334	9.99 720	30
31	9.05 497	110	9.05 778	112	0.94 222	9.99 718	29
32	9.05 607	110	9.05 890	112	0.94 110	9.99 717	28
33	9.05 717	110	9.06 002	111	0.93 998	9.99 716	27
34	9.05 827	110	9.06 113	111	0.93 887	9.99 714	26
35	9.05 937	109	9.06 224	111	0.93 776	9.99 713	25
36	9.06 046	109	9.06 335	110	0.93 665	9.99 711	24
37	9.06 155	109	9.06 445	111	0.93 555	9.99 710	23
38	9.06 264	108	9.06 556	110	0.93 444	9.99 708	22
39	9.06 372	109	9.06 666	109	0.93 334	9.99 707	21
40	9.06 481	108	9.06 775	110	0.93 225	9.99 705	20
41	9.06 589	107	9.06 885	109	0.93 115	9.99 704	19
42	9.06 696	108	9.06 994	109	0.93 006	9.99 702	18
43	9.06 804	107	9.07 103	108	0.92 897	9.99 701	17
44	9.06 911	107	9.07 211	109	0.92 789	9.99 699	16
45	9.07 018	106	9.07 320	108	0.92 680	9.99 698	15
46	9.07 124	107	9.07 428	108	0.92 572	9.99 696	14
47	9.07 231	106	9.07 536	107	0.92 464	9.99 695	13
48	9.07 337	105	9.07 643	108	0.92 357	9.99 693	12
49	9.07 442	106	9.07 751	107	0.92 249	9.99 692	11
50	9.07 548	105	9.07 858	106	0.92 142	9.99 690	10
51	9.07 653	105	9.07 964	107	0.92 036	9.99 689	9
52	9.07 758	105	9.08 071	106	0.91 929	9.99 687	8
53	9.07 863	105	9.08 177	106	0.91 823	9.99 686	7
54	9.07 968	104	9.08 283	106	0.91 717	9.99 684	6
55	9.08 072	104	9.08 389	106	0.91 611	9.99 683	5
56	9.08 176	104	9.08 495	105	0.91 505	9.99 681	4
57	9.08 280	103	9.08 600	105	0.91 400	9.99 680	3
58	9.08 383	103	9.08 705	105	0.91 295	9.99 678	2
59	9.08 486	103	9.08 810	104	0.91 190	9.99 677	1
60	9.08 589		9.08 914		0.91 086	9.99 675	0
	Log Cos	d	Log Cot	c d	Log Tan	Log Sin	′

Prop. Parts

	121	120	119
1	12.1	12.0	11.9
2	24.2	24.0	23.8
3	36.3	36.0	35.7
4	48.4	48.0	47.6
5	60.5	60.0	59.5
6	72.6	72.0	71.4
7	84.7	84.0	83.3
8	96.8	96.0	95.2
9	108.9	108.0	107.1

	118	117	116
1	11.8	11.7	11.6
2	23.6	23.4	23.2
3	35.4	35.1	34.8
4	47.2	46.8	46.4
5	59.0	58.5	58.0
6	70.8	70.2	69.6
7	82.6	81.9	81.2
8	94.4	93.6	92.8
9	106.2	105.3	104.4

	115	114	113
1	11.5	11.4	11.3
2	23.0	22.8	22.6
3	34.5	34.2	33.9
4	46.0	45.6	45.2
5	57.5	57.0	56.5
6	69.0	68.4	67.8
7	80.5	79.8	79.1
8	92.0	91.2	90.4
9	103.5	102.6	101.7

	112	111	110
1	11.2	11.1	11.0
2	22.4	22.2	22.0
3	33.6	33.3	33.0
4	44.8	44.4	44.0
5	56.0	55.5	55.0
6	67.2	66.6	66.0
7	78.4	77.7	77.0
8	89.6	88.8	88.0
9	100.8	99.9	99.0

	109	108	107	106
1	10.9	10.8	10.7	10.6
2	21.8	21.6	21.4	21.2
3	32.7	32.4	32.1	31.8
4	43.6	43.2	42.8	42.4
5	54.5	54.0	53.5	53.0
6	65.4	64.8	64.2	63.6
7	76.3	75.6	74.9	74.2
8	87.2	86.4	85.6	84.8
9	98.1	97.2	96.3	95.4

′	Log Sin	d	Log Tan	c d	Log Cot	Log Cos			Prop. Parts		
0	9.08 589	103	9.08 914	105	0.91 086	9.99 675	60				
1	9.08 692	103	9.09 019	104	0.90 981	9.99 674	59				
2	9.08 795	102	9.09 123	104	0.90 877	9.99 672	58				
3	9.08 897	102	9.09 227	103	0.90 773	9.99 670	57				
4	9.08 999	102	9.09 330	104	0.90 670	9.99 669	56				
5	9.09 101	101	9.09 434	103	0.90 566	9.99 667	55		**105**	**104**	**103**	**102**
6	9.09 202	102	9.09 537	103	0.90 463	9.99 666	54	1	10.5	10.4	10.3	10.2
7	9.09 304	101	9.09 640	102	0.90 360	9.99 664	53	2	21.0	20.8	20.6	20.4
8	9.09 405	101	9.09 742	103	0.90 258	9.99 663	52	3	31.5	31.2	30.9	30.6
9	9.09 506	100	9.09 845	102	0.90 155	9.99 661	51	4	42.0	41.6	41.2	40.8
10	9.09 606	101	9.09 947	102	0.90 053	9.99 659	50	5	52.5	52.0	51.5	51.0
11	9.09 707	100	9.10 049	101	0.89 951	9.99 658	49	6	63.0	62.4	61.8	61.2
12	9.09 807	100	9.10 150	102	0.89 850	9.99 656	48	7	73.5	72.8	72.1	71.4
13	9.09 907	99	9.10 252	101	0.89 748	9.99 655	47	8	84.0	83.2	82.4	81.6
14	9.10 006	100	9.10 353	101	0.89 647	9.99 653	46	9	94.5	93.6	92.7	91.8
15	9.10 106	99	9.10 454	101	0.89 546	9.99 651	45					
16	9.10 205	99	9.10 555	101	0.89 445	9.99 650	44					
17	9.10 304	98	9.10 656	100	0.89 344	9.99 648	43					
18	9.10 402	99	9.10 756	100	0.89 244	9.99 647	42					
19	9.10 501	98	9.10 856	100	0.89 144	9.99 645	41			**101**	**99**	**98**	**97**
20	9.10 599	98	9.10 956	100	0.89 044	9.99 643	40	1	10.1	9.9	9.8	9.7
21	9.10 697	98	9.11 056	99	0.88 944	9.99 642	39	2	20.2	19.8	19.6	19.4
22	9.10 795	98	9.11 155	99	0.88 845	9.99 640	38	3	30.3	29.7	29.4	29.1
23	9.10 893	97	9.11 254	99	0.88 746	9.99 638	37	4	40.4	39.6	39.2	38.8
24	9.10 990	97	9.11 353	99	0.88 647	9.99 637	36	5	50.5	49.5	49.0	48.5
25	9.11 087	97	9.11 452	99	0.88 548	9.99 635	35	6	60.6	59.4	58.8	58.2
26	9.11 184	97	9.11 551	98	0.88 449	9.99 633	34	7	70.7	69.3	68.6	67.9
27	9.11 281	96	9.11 649	98	0.88 351	9.99 632	33	8	80.8	79.2	78.4	77.6
28	9.11 377	97	9.11 747	98	0.88 253	9.99 630	32	9	90.9	89.1	88.2	87.3
29	9.11 474	96	9.11 845	98	0.88 155	9.99 629	31					
30	9.11 570	96	9.11 943	97	0.88 057	9.99 627	30					
31	9.11 666	95	9.12 040	98	0.87 960	9.99 625	29					
32	9.11 761	96	9.12 138	97	0.87 862	9.99 624	28					
33	9.11 857	95	9.12 235	97	0.87 765	9.99 622	27			**96**	**95**	**94**	**93**
34	9.11 952	95	9.12 332	96	0.87 668	9.99 620	26	1	9.6	9.5	9.4	9.3
35	9.12 047	95	9.12 428	97	0.87 572	9.99 618	25	2	19.2	19.0	18.8	18.6
36	9.12 142	94	9.12 525	96	0.87 475	9.99 617	24	3	28.8	28.5	28.2	27.9
37	9.12 236	95	9.12 621	96	0.87 379	9.99 615	23	4	38.4	38.0	37.6	37.2
38	9.12 331	94	9.12 717	96	0.87 283	9.99 613	22	5	48.0	47.5	47.0	46.5
39	9.12 425	94	9.12 813	96	0.87 187	9.99 612	21	6	57.6	57.0	56.4	55.8
40	9.12 519	93	9.12 909	95	0.87 091	9.99 610	20	7	67.2	66.5	65.8	65.1
41	9.12 612	94	9.13 004	95	0.86 996	9.99 608	19	8	76.8	76.0	75.2	74.4
42	9.12 706	93	9.13 099	95	0.86 901	9.99 607	18	9	86.4	85.5	84.6	83.7
43	9.12 799	93	9.13 194	95	0.86 806	9.99 605	17					
44	9.12 892	93	9.13 289	95	0.86 711	9.99 603	16					
45	9.12 985	93	9.13 384	94	0.86 616	9.99 601	15					
46	9.13 078	93	9.13 478	95	0.86 522	9.99 600	14					
47	9.13 171	92	9.13 573	94	0.86 427	9.99 598	13			**92**	**91**	**90**
48	9.13 263	92	9.13 667	94	0.86 333	9.99 596	12	1	9.2	9.1	9.0
49	9.13 355	92	9.13 761	93	0.86 239	9.99 595	11	2	18.4	18.2	18.0
50	9.13 447	92	9.13 854	94	0.86 146	9.99 593	10	3	27.6	27.3	27.0
51	9.13 539	91	9.13 948	93	0.86 052	9.99 591	9	4	36.8	36.4	36.0
52	9.13 630	92	9.14 041	93	0.85 959	9.99 589	8	5	46.0	45.5	45.0
53	9.13 722	91	9.14 134	93	0.85 866	9.99 588	7	6	55.2	54.6	54.0
54	9.13 813	91	9.14 227	93	0.85 773	9.99 586	6	7	64.4	63.7	63.0
55	9.13 904	90	9.14 320	92	0.85 680	9.99 584	5	8	73.6	72.8	72.0
56	9.13 994	91	9.14 412	92	0.85 588	9.99 582	4	9	82.8	81.9	81.0
57	9.14 085	90	9.14 504	93	0.85 496	9.99 581	3				
58	9.14 175	91	9.14 597	91	0.85 403	9.99 579	2				
59	9.14 266	90	9.14 688	92	0.85 312	9.99 577	1				
60	9.14 356		9.14 780		0.85 220	9.99 575	0				
	Log Cos	d	Log Cot	c d	Log Tan	Log Sin	′		Prop. Parts		

′	Log Sin	d	Log Tan	c d	Log Cot	Log Cos	
0	9.14 356	89	9.14 780	92	0.85 220	9.99 575	60
1	9.14 445	90	9.14 872	91	0.85 128	9.99 574	59
2	9.14 535	89	9.14 963	91	0.85 037	9.99 572	58
3	9.14 624	90	9.15 054	91	0.84 946	9.99 570	57
4	9.14 714	89	9.15 145	91	0.84 855	9.99 568	56
5	9.14 803	88	9.15 236	91	0.84 764	9.99 566	55
6	9.14 891	89	9.15 327	90	0.84 673	9.99 565	54
7	9.14 980	89	9.15 417	91	0.84 583	9.99 563	53
8	9.15 069	88	9.15 508	90	0.84 492	9.99 561	52
9	9.15 157	88	9.15 598	90	0.84 402	9.99 559	51
10	9.15 245	88	9.15 688	89	0.84 312	9.99 557	50
11	9.15 333	88	9.15 777	90	0.84 223	9.99 556	49
12	9.15 421	87	9.15 867	89	0.84 133	9.99 554	48
13	9.15 508	88	9.15 956	90	0.84 044	9.99 552	47
14	9.15 596	87	9.16 046	89	0.83 954	9.99 550	46
15	9.15 683	87	9.16 135	89	0.83 865	9.99 548	45
16	9.15 770	87	9.16 224	88	0.83 776	9.99 546	44
17	9.15 857	87	9.16 312	89	0.83 688	9.99 545	43
18	9.15 944	86	9.16 401	88	0.83 599	9.99 543	42
19	9.16 030	86	9.16 489	88	0.83 511	9.99 541	41
20	9.16 116	87	9.16 577	88	0.83 423	9.99 539	40
21	9.16 203	86	9.16 665	88	0.83 335	9.99 537	39
22	9.16 289	85	9.16 753	88	0.83 247	9.99 535	38
23	9.16 374	86	9.16 841	87	0.83 159	9.99 533	37
24	9.16 460	85	9.16 928	88	0.83 072	9.99 532	36
25	9.16 545	86	9.17 016	87	0.82 984	9.99 530	35
26	9.16 631	85	9.17 103	87	0.82 897	9.99 528	34
27	9.16 716	85	9.17 190	87	0.82 810	9.99 526	33
28	9.16 801	85	9.17 277	86	0.82 723	9.99 524	32
29	9.16 886	84	9.17 363	87	0.82 637	9.99 522	31
30	9.16 970	85	9.17 450	86	0.82 550	9.99 520	30
31	9.17 055	84	9.17 536	86	0.82 464	9.99 518	29
32	9.17 139	84	9.17 622	86	0.82 378	9.99 517	28
33	9.17 223	84	9.17 708	86	0.82 292	9.99 515	27
34	9.17 307	84	9.17 794	86	0.82 206	9.99 513	26
35	9.17 391	83	9.17 880	85	0.82 120	9.99 511	25
36	9.17 474	84	9.17 965	86	0.82 035	9.99 509	24
37	9.17 558	83	9.18 051	85	0.81 949	9.99 507	23
38	9.17 641	83	9.18 136	85	0.81 864	9.99 505	22
39	9.17 724	83	9.18 221	85	0.81 779	9.99 503	21
40	9.17 807	83	9.18 306	85	0.81 694	9.99 501	20
41	9.17 890	83	9.18 391	84	0.81 609	9.99 499	19
42	9.17 973	82	9.18 475	85	0.81 525	9.99 497	18
43	9.18 055	82	9.18 560	84	0.81 440	9.99 495	17
44	9.18 137	83	9.18 644	84	0.81 356	9.99 494	16
45	9.18 220	82	9.18 728	84	0.81 272	9.99 492	15
46	9.18 302	81	9.18 812	84	0.81 188	9.99 490	14
47	9.18 383	82	9.18 896	83	0.81 104	9.99 488	13
48	9.18 465	82	9.18 979	84	0.81 021	9.99 486	12
49	9.18 547	81	9.19 063	83	0.80 937	9.99 484	11
50	9.18 628	81	9.19 146	83	0.80 854	9.99 482	10
51	9.18 709	81	9.19 229	83	0.80 771	9.99 480	9
52	9.18 790	81	9.19 312	83	0.80 688	9.99 478	8
53	9.18 871	81	9.19 395	83	0.80 605	9.99 476	7
54	9.18 952	81	9.19 478	83	0.80 522	9.99 474	6
55	9.19 033	80	9.19 561	82	0.80 439	9.99 472	5
56	9.19 113	80	9.19 643	82	0.80 357	9.99 470	4
57	9.19 193	80	9.19 725	82	0.80 275	9.99 468	3
58	9.19 273	80	9.19 807	82	0.80 193	9.99 466	2
59	9.19 353	80	9.19 889	82	0.80 111	9.99 464	1
60	9.19 433		9.19 971		0.80 029	9.99 462	0
	Log Cos	d	Log Cot	c d	Log Tan	Log Sin	′

Prop. Parts

	92	91	90	89
1	9.2	9.1	9.0	8.9
2	18.4	18.2	18.0	17.8
3	27.6	27.3	27.0	26.7
4	36.8	36.4	36.0	35.6
5	46.0	45.5	45.0	44.5
6	55.2	54.6	54.0	53.4
7	64.4	63.7	63.0	62.3
8	73.6	72.8	72.0	71.2
9	82.8	81.9	81.0	80.1

	88	87	86
1	8.8	8.7	8.6
2	17.6	17.4	17.2
3	26.4	26.1	25.8
4	35.2	34.8	34.4
5	44.0	43.5	43.0
6	52.8	52.2	51.6
7	61.6	60.9	60.2
8	70.4	69.6	68.8
9	79.2	78.3	77.4

	85	84	83
1	8.5	8.4	8.3
2	17.0	16.8	16.6
3	25.5	25.2	24.9
4	34.0	33.6	33.2
5	42.5	42.0	41.5
6	51.0	50.4	49.8
7	59.5	58.8	58.1
8	68.0	67.2	66.4
9	76.5	75.6	74.7

	82	81	80
1	8.2	8.1	8.0
2	16.4	16.2	16.0
3	24.6	24.3	24.0
4	32.8	32.4	32.0
5	41.0	40.5	40.0
6	49.2	48.6	48.0
7	57.4	56.7	56.0
8	65.6	64.8	64.0
9	73.8	72.9	72.0

Prop. Parts

′	Log Sin	d	Log Tan	c d	Log Cot	Log Cos		Prop. Parts
0	9.19 433	80	9.19 971	82	0.80 029	9.99 462	60	
1	9.19 513	79	9.20 053	81	0.79 947	9.99 460	59	
2	9.19 592	80	9.20 134	82	0.79 866	9.99 458	58	
3	9.19 672	79	9.20 216	81	0.79 784	9.99 456	57	
4	9.19 751	79	9.20 297	81	0.79 703	9.99 454	56	

									82	81	80
5	9.19 830	79	9.20 378	81	0.79 622	9.99 452	55	1	8.2	8.1	8.0
6	9.19 909	79	9.20 459	81	0.79 541	9.99 450	54	2	16.4	16.2	16.0
7	9.19 988	79	9.20 540	81	0.79 460	9.99 448	53	3	24.6	24.3	24.0
8	9.20 067	78	9.20 621	80	0.79 379	9.99 446	52	4	32.8	32.4	32.0
9	9.20 145	78	9.20 701	81	0.79 299	9.99 444	51	5	41.0	40.5	40.0
10	9.20 223	79	9.20 782	80	0.79 218	9.99 442	50	6	49.2	48.6	48.0
11	9.20 302	78	9.20 862	80	0.79 138	9.99 440	49	7	57.4	56.7	56.0
12	9.20 380	78	9.20 942	80	0.79 058	9.99 438	48	8	65.6	64.8	64.0
13	9.20 458	77	9.21 022	80	0.78 978	9.99 436	47	9	73.8	72.9	72.0
14	9.20 535	78	9.21 102	80	0.78 898	9.99 434	46				

									79	78	77
15	9.20 613	78	9.21 182	79	0.78 818	9.99 432	45	1	7.9	7.8	7.7
16	9.20 691	77	9.21 261	80	0.78 739	9.99 429	44	2	15.8	15.6	15.4
17	9.20 768	77	9.21 341	79	0.78 659	9.99 427	43	3	23.7	23.4	23.1
18	9.20 845	77	9.21 420	79	0.78 580	9.99 425	42	4	31.6	31.2	30.8
19	9.20 922	77	9.21 499	79	0.78 501	9.99 423	41	5	39.5	39.0	38.5
20	9.20 999	77	9.21 578	79	0.78 422	9.99 421	40	6	47.4	46.8	46.2
21	9.21 076	77	9.21 657	79	0.78 343	9.99 419	39	7	55.3	54.6	53.9
22	9.21 153	76	9.21 736	78	0.78 264	9.99 417	38	8	63.2	62.4	61.6
23	9.21 229	77	9.21 814	79	0.78 186	9.99 415	37	9	71.1	70.2	69.3
24	9.21 306	76	9.21 893	78	0.78 107	9.99 413	36				

									76	75	74
25	9.21 382	76	9.21 971	78	0.78 029	9.99 411	35	1	7.6	7.5	7.4
26	9.21 458	76	9.22 049	78	0.77 951	9.99 409	34	2	15.2	15.0	14.8
27	9.21 534	76	9.22 127	78	0.77 873	9.99 407	33	3	22.8	22.5	22.2
28	9.21 610	75	9.22 205	78	0.77 795	9.99 404	32	4	30.4	30.0	29.6
29	9.21 685	76	9.22 283	78	0.77 717	9.99 402	31	5	38.0	37.5	37.0
30	9.21 761	75	9.22 361	77	0.77 639	9.99 400	30	6	45.6	45.0	44.4
31	9.21 836	76	9.22 438	78	0.77 562	9.99 398	29	7	53.2	52.5	51.8
32	9.21 912	75	9.22 516	77	0.77 484	9.99 396	28	8	60.8	60.0	59.2
33	9.21 987	75	9.22 593	77	0.77 407	9.99 394	27	9	68.4	67.5	66.6
34	9.22 062	75	9.22 670	77	0.77 330	9.99 392	26				

									73	72	71
35	9.22 137	74	9.22 747	77	0.77 253	9.99 390	25	1	7.3	7.2	7.1
36	9.22 211	75	9.22 824	77	0.77 176	9.99 388	24	2	14.6	14.4	14.2
37	9.22 286	75	9.22 901	76	0.77 099	9.99 385	23	3	21.9	21.6	21.3
38	9.22 361	74	9.22 977	77	0.77 023	9.99 383	22	4	29.2	28.8	28.4
39	9.22 435	74	9.23 054	76	0.76 946	9.99 381	21	5	36.5	36.0	35.5
40	9.22 509	74	9.23 130	76	0.76 870	9.99 379	20	6	43.8	43.2	42.6
41	9.22 583	74	9.23 206	77	0.76 794	9.99 377	19	7	51.1	50.4	49.7
42	9.22 657	74	9.23 283	76	0.76 717	9.99 375	18	8	58.4	57.6	56.8
43	9.22 731	74	9.23 359	76	0.76 641	9.99 372	17	9	65.7	64.8	63.9
44	9.22 805	73	9.23 435	75	0.76 565	9.99 370	16				
45	9.22 878	74	9.23 510	76	0.76 490	9.99 368	15				
46	9.22 952	73	9.23 586	75	0.76 414	9.99 366	14				
47	9.23 025	73	9.23 661	76	0.76 339	9.99 364	13				
48	9.23 098	73	9.23 737	75	0.76 263	9.99 362	12				
49	9.23 171	73	9.23 812	75	0.76 188	9.99 359	11				
50	9.23 244	73	9.23 887	75	0.76 113	9.99 357	10				
51	9.23 317	73	9.23 962	75	0.76 038	9.99 355	9				
52	9.23 390	72	9.24 037	75	0.75 963	9.99 353	8				
53	9.23 462	73	9.24 112	74	0.75 888	9.99 351	7				
54	9.23 535	72	9.24 186	75	0.75 814	9.99 348	6				
55	9.23 607	72	9.24 261	74	0.75 739	9.99 346	5				
56	9.23 679	73	9.24 335	75	0.75 665	9.99 344	4				
57	9.23 752	71	9.24 410	74	0.75 590	9.99 342	3				
58	9.23 823	72	9.24 484	74	0.75 516	9.99 340	2				
59	9.23 895	72	9.24 558	74	0.75 442	9.99 337	1				
60	9.23 967		9.24 632		0.75 368	9.99 335	0				

| | Log Cos | d | Log Cot | c d | Log Tan | Log Sin | ′ | | Prop. Parts |

′	Log Sin	d	Log Tan	c d	Log Cot	Log Cos	d			Prop. Parts		
0	9.23 967	72	9.24 632	74	0.75 368	9.99 335	2	60				
1	9.24 039	71	9.24 706	73	0.75 294	9.99 333	2	59				
2	9.24 110	71	9.24 779	74	0.75 221	9.99 331	3	58				
3	9.24 181	72	9.24 853	73	0.75 147	9.99 328	2	57				
4	9.24 253	71	9.24 926	74	0.75 074	9.99 326	2	56		**74**	**73**	**72**
5	9.24 324	71	9.25 000	73	0.75 000	9.99 324	2	55		74	73	72
6	9.24 395	71	9.25 073	73	0.74 927	9.99 322	2	54	1	7.4	7.3	7.2
7	9.24 466	70	9.25 146	73	0.74 854	9.99 319	3	53	2	14.8	14.6	14.4
8	9.24 536	71	9.25 219	73	0.74 781	9.99 317	2	52	3	22.2	21.9	21.6
9	9.24 607	70	9.25 292	73	0.74 708	9.99 315	2	51	4	29.6	29.2	28.8
									5	37.0	36.5	36.0
10	9.24 677	71	9.25 365	72	0.74 635	9.99 313	3	50	6	44.4	43.8	43.2
11	9.24 748	70	9.25 437	73	0.74 563	9.99 310	2	49	7	51.8	51.1	50.4
12	9.24 818	70	9.25 510	72	0.74 490	9.99 308	2	48	8	59.2	58.4	57.6
13	9.24 888	70	9.25 582	73	0.74 418	9.99 306	2	47	9	66.6	65.7	64.8
14	9.24 958	70	9.25 655	72	0.74 345	9.99 304	3	46				
15	9.25 028	70	9.25 727	72	0.74 273	9.99 301	2	45				
16	9.25 098	70	9.25 799	72	0.74 201	9.99 299	2	44				
17	9.25 168	69	9.25 871	72	0.74 129	9.99 297	2	43				
18	9.25 237	70	9.25 943	72	0.74 057	9.99 294	2	42		**71**	**70**	**69**
19	9.25 307	69	9.26 015	71	0.73 985	9.99 292	2	41	1	7.1	7.0	6.9
20	9.25 376	69	9.26 086	72	0.73 914	9.99 290	2	40	2	14.2	14.0	13.8
21	9.25 445	69	9.26 158	71	0.73 842	9.99 288	3	39	3	21.3	21.0	20.7
22	9.25 514	69	9.26 229	72	0.73 771	9.99 285	2	38	4	28.4	28.0	27.6
23	9.25 583	69	9.26 301	71	0.73 699	9.99 283	2	37	5	35.5	35.0	34.5
24	9.25 652	69	9.26 372	71	0.73 628	9.99 281	3	36	6	42.6	42.0	41.4
25	9.25 721	69	9.26 443	71	0.73 557	9.99 278	2	35	7	49.7	49.0	48.3
26	9.25 790	68	9.26 514	71	0.73 486	9.99 276	2	34	8	56.8	56.0	55.2
27	9.25 858	69	9.26 585	70	0.73 415	9.99 274	3	33	9	63.9	63.0	62.1
28	9.25 927	68	9.26 655	71	0.73 345	9.99 271	2	32				
29	9.25 995	68	9.26 726	71	0.73 274	9.99 269	2	31				
30	9.26 063	68	9.26 797	70	0.73 203	9.99 267	3	30				
31	9.26 131	68	9.26 867	70	0.73 133	9.99 264	2	29				
32	9.26 199	68	9.26 937	71	0.73 063	9.99 262	2	28				
33	9.26 267	68	9.27 008	70	0.72 992	9.99 260	3	27		**68**	**67**	**66**
34	9.26 335	68	9.27 078	70	0.72 922	9.99 257	2	26	1	6.8	6.7	6.6
35	9.26 403	67	9.27 148	70	0.72 852	9.99 255	3	25	2	13.6	13.4	13.2
36	9.26 470	68	9.27 218	70	0.72 782	9.99 252	2	24	3	20.4	20.1	19.8
37	9.26 538	67	9.27 288	69	0.72 712	9.99 250	2	23	4	27.2	26.8	26.4
38	9.26 605	67	9.27 357	70	0.72 643	9.99 248	3	22	5	34.0	33.5	33.0
39	9.26 672	67	9.27 427	69	0.72 573	9.99 245	2	21	6	40.8	40.2	39.6
40	9.26 739	67	9.27 496	70	0.72 504	9.99 243	2	20	7	47.6	46.9	46.2
41	9.26 806	67	9.27 566	69	0.72 434	9.99 241	3	19	8	54.4	53.6	52.8
42	9.26 873	67	9.27 635	69	0.72 365	9.99 238	2	18	9	61.2	60.3	59.4
43	9.26 940	67	9.27 704	69	0.72 296	9.99 236	3	17				
44	9.27 007	66	9.27 773	69	0.72 227	9.99 233	2	16				
45	9.27 073	67	9.27 842	69	0.72 158	9.99 231	2	15				
46	9.27 140	66	9.27 911	69	0.72 089	9.99 229	3	14				
47	9.27 206	67	9.27 980	69	0.72 020	9.99 226	2	13				
48	9.27 273	66	9.28 049	68	0.71 951	9.99 224	3	12		**65**	**3**	
49	9.27 339	66	9.28 117	69	0.71 883	9.99 221	2	11	1	6.5	0.3	
50	9.27 405	66	9.28 186	68	0.71 814	9.99 219	2	10	2	13.0	0.6	
51	9.27 471	66	9.28 254	69	0.71 746	9.99 217	3	9	3	19.5	0.9	
52	9.27 537	65	9.28 323	68	0.71 677	9.99 214	2	8	4	26.0	1.2	
53	9.27 602	66	9.28 391	68	0.71 609	9.99 212	3	7	5	32.5	1.5	
54	9.27 668	66	9.28 459	68	0.71 541	9.99 209	2	6	6	39.0	1.8	
55	9.27 734	65	9.28 527	68	0.71 473	9.99 207	3	5	7	45.5	2.1	
56	9.27 799	65	9.28 595	67	0.71 405	9.99 204	2	4	8	52.0	2.4	
57	9.27 864	65	9.28 662	68	0.71 338	9.99 202	2	3	9	58.5	2.7	
58	9.27 930	66	9.28 730	68	0.71 270	9.99 200	3	2				
59	9.27 995	65	9.28 798	67	0.71 202	9.99 197	2	1				
60	9.28 060		9.28 865		0.71 135	9.99 195		0				
	Log Cos	d	Log Cot	c d	Log Tan	Log Sin	d	′		Prop. Parts		

′	Log Sin	d	Log Tan	c d	Log Cot	Log Cos	d		Prop. Parts		
0	9.28 060	65	9.28 865	68	0.71 135	9.99 195	3	**60**			
1	9.28 125	65	9.28 933	67	0.71 067	9.99 192	2	59			
2	9.28 190	64	9.29 000	67	0.71 000	9.99 190	2	58			
3	9.28 254	65	9.29 067	67	0.70 933	9.99 187	2	57			
4	9.28 319	65	9.29 134	67	0.70 866	9.99 185	3	56			
5	9.28 384	64	9.29 201	67	0.70 799	9.99 182	2	**55**		**68**	**67**	**66**
6	9.28 448	64	9.29 268	67	0.70 732	9.99 180	3	54	1	6.8	6.7	6.6
7	9.28 512	65	9.29 335	67	0.70 665	9.99 177	2	53	2	13.6	13.4	13.2
8	9.28 577	64	9.29 402	66	0.70 598	9.99 175	3	52	3	20.4	20.1	19.8
9	9.28 641	64	9.29 468	67	0.70 532	9.99 172	2	51	4	27.2	26.8	26.4
10	9.28 705	64	9.29 535	66	0.70 465	9.99 170	3	**50**	5	34.0	33.5	33.0
11	9.28 769	64	9.29 601	67	0.70 399	9.99 167	2	49	6	40.8	40.2	39.6
12	9.28 833	63	9.29 668	66	0.70 332	9.99 165	3	48	7	47.6	46.9	46.2
13	9.28 896	64	9.29 734	66	0.70 266	9.99 162	2	47	8	54.4	53.6	52.8
14	9.28 960	64	9.29 800	66	0.70 200	9.99 160	3	46	9	61.2	60.3	59.4
15	9.29 024	63	9.29 866	66	0.70 134	9.99 157	2	**45**			
16	9.29 087	63	9.29 932	66	0.70 068	9.99 155	3	44			
17	9.29 150	64	9.29 998	66	0.70 002	9.99 152	2	43			
18	9.29 214	63	9.30 064	66	0.69 936	9.99 150	3	42			
19	9.29 277	63	9.30 130	65	0.69 870	9.99 147	2	41		**65**	**64**	**63**
20	9.29 340	63	9.30 195	66	0.69 805	9.99 145	3	**40**	1	6.5	6.4	6.3
21	9.29 403	63	9.30 261	65	0.69 739	9.99 142	2	39	2	13.0	12.8	12.6
22	9.29 466	63	9.30 326	65	0.69 674	9.99 140	3	38	3	19.5	19.2	18.9
23	9.29 529	62	9.30 391	66	0.69 609	9.99 137	2	37	4	26.0	25.6	25.2
24	9.29 591	63	9.30 457	65	0.69 543	9.99 135	3	36	5	32.5	32.0	31.5
25	9.29 654	62	9.30 522	65	0.69 478	9.99 132	2	**35**	6	39.0	38.4	37.8
26	9.29 716	63	9.30 587	65	0.69 413	9.99 130	3	34	7	45.5	44.8	44.1
27	9.29 779	62	9.30 652	65	0.69 348	9.99 127	3	33	8	52.0	51.2	50.4
28	9.29 841	62	9.30 717	65	0.69 283	9.99 124	2	32	9	58.5	57.6	56.7
29	9.29 903	63	9.30 782	64	0.69 218	9.99 122	3	31			
30	9.29 966	62	9.30 846	65	0.69 154	9.99 119	2	**30**			
31	9.30 028	62	9.30 911	64	0.69 089	9.99 117	3	29			
32	9.30 090	61	9.30 975	65	0.69 025	9.99 114	2	28		**62**	**61**	**60**
33	9.30 151	62	9.31 040	64	0.68 960	9.99 112	3	27	1	6.2	6.1	6.0
34	9.30 213	62	9.31 104	64	0.68 896	9.99 109	3	26	2	12.4	12.2	12.0
35	9.30 275	61	9.31 168	65	0.68 832	9.99 106	2	**25**	3	18.6	18.3	18.0
36	9.30 336	62	9.31 233	64	0.68 767	9.99 104	3	24	4	24.8	24.4	24.0
37	9.30 398	61	9.31 297	64	0.68 703	9.99 101	2	23	5	31.0	30.5	30.0
38	9.30 459	62	9.31 361	64	0.68 639	9.99 099	3	22	6	37.2	36.6	36.0
39	9.30 521	61	9.31 425	64	0.68 575	9.99 096	3	21	7	43.4	42.7	42.0
40	9.30 582	61	9.31 489	63	0.68 511	9.99 093	2	**20**	8	49.6	48.8	48.0
41	9.30 643	61	9.31 552	64	0.68 448	9.99 091	3	19	9	55.8	54.9	54.0
42	9.30 704	61	9.31 616	63	0.68 384	9.99 088	2	18			
43	9.30 765	61	9.31 679	64	0.68 321	9.99 086	3	17			
44	9.30 826	61	9.31 743	63	0.68 257	9.99 083	3	16			
45	9.30 887	60	9.31 806	64	0.68 194	9.99 080	2	**15**			
46	9.30 947	61	9.31 870	63	0.68 130	9.99 078	3	14		**59**	**3**	**2**
47	9.31 008	60	9.31 933	63	0.68 067	9.99 075	3	13	1	5.9	0.3	0.2
48	9.31 068	61	9.31 996	63	0.68 004	9.99 072	3	12	2	11.8	0.6	0.4
49	9.31 129	60	9.32 059	63	0.67 941	9.99 070	3	11	3	17.7	0.9	0.6
50	9.31 189	61	9.32 122	63	0.67 878	9.99 067	3	**10**	4	23.6	1.2	0.8
51	9.31 250	60	9.32 185	63	0.67 815	9.99 064	2	9	5	29.5	1.5	1.0
52	9.31 310	60	9.32 248	63	0.67 752	9.99 062	3	8	6	35.4	1.8	1.2
53	9.31 370	60	9.32 311	62	0.67 689	9.99 059	3	7	7	41.3	2.1	1.4
54	9.31 430	60	9.32 373	63	0.67 627	9.99 056	2	6	8	47.2	2.4	1.6
55	9.31 490	59	9.32 436	62	0.67 564	9.99 054	3	**5**	9	53.1	2.7	1.8
56	9.31 549	60	9.32 498	63	0.67 502	9.99 051	3	4			
57	9.31 609	60	9.32 561	62	0.67 439	9.99 048	2	3			
58	9.31 669	59	9.32 623	62	0.67 377	9.99 046	3	2			
59	9.31 728	60	9.32 685	62	0.67 315	9.99 043	3	1			
60	9.31 788		9.32 747		0.67 253	9.99 040		**0**			
	Log Cos	d	Log Cot	c d	Log Tan	Log Sin	d	′		Prop. Parts		

′	Log Sin	d	Log Tan	c d	Log Cot	Log Cos	d	
0	9.31 788	59	9.32 747	63	0.67 253	9.99 040	2	60
1	9.31 847	60	9.32 810	62	0.67 190	9.99 038	3	59
2	9.31 907	59	9.32 872	61	0.67 128	9.99 035	3	58
3	9.31 966	59	9.32 933	62	0.67 067	9.99 032	2	57
4	9.32 025	59	9.32 995	62	0.67 005	9.99 030	3	56
5	9.32 084	59	9.33 057	62	0.66 943	9.99 027	3	55
6	9.32 143	59	9.33 119	61	0.66 881	9.99 024	2	54
7	9.32 202	59	9.33 180	62	0.66 820	9.99 022	3	53
8	9.32 261	58	9.33 242	61	0.66 758	9.99 019	3	52
9	9.32 319	59	9.33 303	62	0.66 697	9.99 016	3	51
10	9.32 378	59	9.33 365	61	0.66 635	9.99 013	2	50
11	9.32 437	58	9.33 426	61	0.66 574	9.99 011	3	49
12	9.32 495	58	9.33 487	61	0.66 513	9.99 008	3	48
13	9.32 553	59	9.33 548	61	0.66 452	9.99 005	3	47
14	9.32 612	58	9.33 609	61	0.66 391	9.99 002	2	46
15	9.32 670	58	9.33 670	61	0.66 330	9.99 000	3	45
16	9.32 728	58	9.33 731	61	0.66 269	9.98 997	3	44
17	9.32 786	58	9.33 792	61	0.66 208	9.98 994	3	43
18	9.32 844	58	9.33 853	60	0.66 147	9.98 991	2	42
19	9.32 902	58	9.33 913	61	0.66 087	9.98 989	3	41
20	9.32 960	58	9.33 974	60	0.66 026	9.98 986	3	40
21	9.33 018	57	9.34 034	61	0.65 966	9.98 983	3	39
22	9.33 075	58	9.34 095	60	0.65 905	9.98 980	2	38
23	9.33 133	57	9.34 155	60	0.65 845	9.98 978	3	37
24	9.33 190	58	9.34 215	61	0.65 785	9.98 975	3	36
25	9.33 248	57	9.34 276	60	0.65 724	9.98 972	3	35
26	9.33 305	57	9.34 336	60	0.65 664	9.98 969	2	34
27	9.33 362	58	9.34 396	60	0.65 604	9.98 967	3	33
28	9.33 420	57	9.34 456	60	0.65 544	9.98 964	3	32
29	9.33 477	57	9.34 516	60	0.65 484	9.98 961	3	31
30	9.33 534	57	9.34 576	59	0.65 424	9.98 958	3	30
31	9.33 591	56	9.34 635	60	0.65 365	9.98 955	2	29
32	9.33 647	57	9.34 695	60	0.65 305	9.98 953	3	28
33	9.33 704	57	9.34 755	59	0.65 245	9.98 950	3	27
34	9.33 761	57	9.34 814	60	0.65 186	9.98 947	3	26
35	9.33 818	56	9.34 874	59	0.65 126	9.98 944	3	25
36	9.33 874	57	9.34 933	59	0.65 067	9.98 941	3	24
37	9.33 931	56	9.34 992	59	0.65 008	9.98 938	2	23
38	9.33 987	56	9.35 051	60	0.64 949	9.98 936	3	22
39	9.34 043	57	9.35 111	59	0.64 889	9.98 933	3	21
40	9.34 100	56	9.35 170	59	0.64 830	9.98 930	3	20
41	9.34 156	56	9.35 229	59	0.64 771	9.98 927	3	19
42	9.34 212	56	9.35 288	59	0.64 712	9.98 924	3	18
43	9.34 268	56	9.35 347	58	0.64 653	9.98 921	2	17
44	9.34 324	56	9.35 405	59	0.64 595	9.98 919	3	16
45	9.34 380	56	9.35 464	59	0.64 536	9.98 916	3	15
46	9.34 436	55	9.35 523	58	0.64 477	9.98 913	3	14
47	9.34 491	56	9.35 581	59	0.64 419	9.98 910	3	13
48	9.34 547	55	9.35 640	58	0.64 360	9.98 907	3	12
49	9.34 602	56	9.35 698	59	0.64 302	9.98 904	3	11
50	9.34 658	55	9.35 757	58	0.64 243	9.98 901	3	10
51	9.34 713	56	9.35 815	58	0.64 185	9.98 898	2	9
52	9.34 769	55	9.35 873	58	0.64 127	9.98 896	3	8
53	9.34 824	55	9.35 931	58	0.64 069	9.98 893	3	7
54	9.34 879	55	9.35 989	58	0.64 011	9.98 890	3	6
55	9.34 934	55	9.36 047	58	0.63 953	9.98 887	3	5
56	9.34 989	55	9.36 105	58	0.63 895	9.98 884	3	4
57	9.35 044	55	9.36 163	58	0.63 837	9.98 881	3	3
58	9.35 099	55	9.36 221	58	0.63 779	9.98 878	3	2
59	9.35 154	55	9.36 279	57	0.63 721	9.98 875	3	1
60	9.35 209		9.36 336		0.63 664	9.98 872		0
	Log Cos	d	Log Cot	c d	Log Tan	Log Sin	d	′

Prop. Parts

	63	62	61
1	6.3	6.2	6.1
2	12.6	12.4	12.2
3	18.9	18.6	18.3
4	25.2	24.8	24.4
5	31.5	31.0	30.5
6	37.8	37.2	36.6
7	44.1	43.4	42.7
8	50.4	49.6	48.8
9	56.7	55.8	54.9

	60	59	58
1	6.0	5.9	5.8
2	12.0	11.8	11.6
3	18.0	17.7	17.4
4	24.0	23.6	23.2
5	30.0	29.5	29.0
6	36.0	35.4	34.8
7	42.0	41.3	40.6
8	48.0	47.2	46.4
9	54.0	53.1	52.2

	57	56	55
1	5.7	5.6	5.5
2	11.4	11.2	11.0
3	17.1	16.8	16.5
4	22.8	22.4	22.0
5	28.5	28.0	27.5
6	34.2	33.6	33.0
7	39.9	39.2	38.5
8	45.6	44.8	44.0
9	51.3	50.4	49.5

	3	2
1	0.3	0.2
2	0.6	0.4
3	0.9	0.6
4	1.2	0.8
5	1.5	1.0
6	1.8	1.2
7	2.1	1.4
8	2.4	1.6
9	2.7	1.8

Prop. Parts

′	Log Sin	d	Log Tan	c d	Log Cot	Log Cos	d		Prop. Parts
0	9.35 209	54	9.36 336	58	0.63 664	9.98 872	3	60	
1	9.35 263	55	9.36 394	58	0.63 606	9.98 869	2	59	
2	9.35 318	55	9.36 452	57	0.63 548	9.98 867	3	58	
3	9.35 373	54	9.36 509	57	0.63 491	9.98 864	3	57	
4	9.35 427	54	9.36 566	58	0.63 434	9.98 861	3	56	
5	9.35 481	55	9.36 624	57	0.63 376	9.98 858	3	55	
6	9.35 536	54	9.36 681	57	0.63 319	9.98 855	3	54	
7	9.35 590	54	9.36 738	57	0.63 262	9.98 852	3	53	
8	9.35 644	54	9.36 795	57	0.63 205	9.98 849	3	52	
9	9.35 698	54	9.36 852	57	0.63 148	9.98 846	3	51	
10	9.35 752	54	9.36 909	57	0.63 091	9.98 843	3	50	
11	9.35 806	54	9.36 966	57	0.63 034	9.98 840	3	49	
12	9.35 860	54	9.37 023	57	0.62 977	9.98 837	3	48	
13	9.35 914	54	9.37 080	57	0.62 920	9.98 834	3	47	
14	9.35 968	54	9.37 137	56	0.62 863	9.98 831	3	46	
15	9.36 022	53	9.37 193	57	0.62 807	9.98 828	3	45	
16	9.36 075	54	9.37 250	56	0.62 750	9.98 825	3	44	
17	9.36 129	53	9.37 306	57	0.62 694	9.98 822	3	43	
18	9.36 182	54	9.37 363	56	0.62 637	9.98 819	3	42	
19	9.36 236	53	9.37 419	57	0.62 581	9.98 816	3	41	
20	9.36 289	53	9.37 476	56	0.62 524	9.98 813	3	40	
21	9.36 342	53	9.37 532	56	0.62 468	9.98 810	3	39	
22	9.36 395	54	9.37 588	56	0.62 412	9.98 807	3	38	
23	9.36 449	53	9.37 644	56	0.62 356	9.98 804	3	37	
24	9.36 502	53	9.37 700	56	0.62 300	9.98 801	3	36	
25	9.36 555	53	9.37 756	56	0.62 244	9.98 798	3	35	
26	9.36 608	52	9.37 812	56	0.62 188	9.98 795	3	34	
27	9.36 660	53	9.37 868	56	0.62 132	9.98 792	3	33	
28	9.36 713	53	9.37 924	56	0.62 076	9.98 789	3	32	
29	9.36 766	53	9.37 980	55	0.62 020	9.98 786	3	31	
30	9.36 819	52	9.38 035	56	0.61 965	9.98 783	3	30	
31	9.36 871	53	9.38 091	56	0.61 909	9.98 780	3	29	
32	9.36 924	52	9.38 147	55	0.61 853	9.98 777	3	28	
33	9.36 976	52	9.38 202	55	0.61 798	9.98 774	3	27	
34	9.37 028	53	9.38 257	56	0.61 743	9.98 771	3	26	
35	9.37 081	52	9.38 313	55	0.61 687	9.98 768	3	25	
36	9.37 133	52	9.38 368	55	0.61 632	9.98 765	3	24	
37	9.37 185	52	9.38 423	56	0.61 577	9.98 762	3	23	
38	9.37 237	52	9.38 479	55	0.61 521	9.98 759	3	22	
39	9.37 289	52	9.38 534	55	0.61 466	9.98 756	3	21	
40	9.37 341	52	9.38 589	55	0.61 411	9.98 753	3	20	
41	9.37 393	52	9.38 644	55	0.61 356	9.98 750	4	19	
42	9.37 445	52	9.38 699	55	0.61 301	9.98 746	3	18	
43	9.37 497	52	9.38 754	54	0.61 246	9.98 743	3	17	
44	9.37 549	51	9.38 808	55	0.61 192	9.98 740	3	16	
45	9.37 600	52	9.38 863	55	0.61 137	9.98 737	3	15	
46	9.37 652	51	9.38 918	54	0.61 082	9.98 734	3	14	
47	9.37 703	52	9.38 972	55	0.61 028	9.98 731	3	13	
48	9.37 755	51	9.39 027	55	0.60 973	9.98 728	3	12	
49	9.37 806	52	9.39 082	54	0.60 918	9.98 725	3	11	
50	9.37 858	51	9.39 136	54	0.60 864	9.98 722	3	10	
51	9.37 909	51	9.39 190	55	0.60 810	9.98 719	4	9	
52	9.37 960	51	9.39 245	54	0.60 755	9.98 715	3	8	
53	9.38 011	51	9.39 299	54	0.60 701	9.98 712	3	7	
54	9.38 062	51	9.39 353	54	0.60 647	9.98 709	3	6	
55	9.38 113	51	9.39 407	54	0.60 593	9.98 706	3	5	
56	9.38 164	51	9.39 461	54	0.60 539	9.98 703	3	4	
57	9.38 215	51	9.39 515	54	0.60 485	9.98 700	3	3	
58	9.38 266	51	9.39 569	54	0.60 431	9.98 697	3	2	
59	9.38 317	51	9.39 623	54	0.60 377	9.98 694	4	1	
60	9.38 368		9.39 677		0.60 323	9.98 690		0	
	Log Cos	d	Log Cot	c d	Log Tan	Log Sin	d	′	Prop. Parts

Prop. Parts

	58	57	56
1	5.8	5.7	5.6
2	11.6	11.4	11.2
3	17.4	17.1	16.8
4	23.2	22.8	22.4
5	29.0	28.5	28.0
6	34.8	34.2	33.6
7	40.6	39.9	39.2
8	46.4	45.6	44.8
9	52.2	51.3	50.4

	55	54	53
1	5.5	5.4	5.3
2	11.0	10.8	10.6
3	16.5	16.2	15.9
4	22.0	21.6	21.2
5	27.5	27.0	26.5
6	33.0	32.4	31.8
7	38.5	37.8	37.1
8	44.0	43.2	42.4
9	49.5	48.6	47.7

	52	51
1	5.2	5.1
2	10.4	10.2
3	15.6	15.3
4	20.8	20.4
5	26.0	25.5
6	31.2	30.6
7	36.4	35.7
8	41.6	40.8
9	46.8	45.9

	4	3	2
1	0.4	0.3	0.2
2	0.8	0.6	0.4
3	1.2	0.9	0.6
4	1.6	1.2	0.8
5	2.0	1.5	1.0
6	2.4	1.8	1.2
7	2.8	2.1	1.4
8	3.2	2.4	1.6
9	3.6	2.7	1.8

'	Log Sin	d	Log Tan	cd	Log Cot	Log Cos	d	
0	9.38 368	50	9.39 677	54	0.60 323	9.98 690	3	60
1	9.38 418	51	9.39 731	54	0.60 269	9.98 687	3	59
2	9.38 469	50	9.39 785	53	0.60 215	9.98 684	3	58
3	9.38 519	51	9.39 838	54	0.60 162	9.98 681	3	57
4	9.38 570	50	9.39 892	53	0.60 108	9.98 678	3	56
5	9.38 620	50	9.39 945	54	0.60 055	9.98 675	4	55
6	9.38 670	51	9.39 999	53	0.60 001	9.98 671	3	54
7	9.38 721	50	9.40 052	54	0.59 948	9.98 668	3	53
8	9.38 771	50	9.40 106	53	0.59 894	9.98 665	3	52
9	9.38 821	50	9.40 159	53	0.59 841	9.98 662	3	51
10	9.38 871	50	9.40 212	54	0.59 788	9.98 659	3	50
11	9.38 921	50	9.40 266	53	0.59 734	9.98 656	4	49
12	9.38 971	50	9.40 319	53	0.59 681	9.98 652	3	48
13	9.39 021	50	9.40 372	53	0.59 628	9.98 649	3	47
14	9.39 071	50	9.40 425	53	0.59 575	9.98 646	3	46
15	9.39 121	49	9.40 478	53	0.59 522	9.98 643	3	45
16	9.39 170	50	9.40 531	53	0.59 469	9.98 640	4	44
17	9.39 220	50	9.40 584	52	0.59 416	9.98 636	3	43
18	9.39 270	49	9.40 636	53	0.59 364	9.98 633	3	42
19	9.39 319	50	9.40 689	53	0.59 311	9.98 630	3	41
20	9.39 369	49	9.40 742	53	0.59 258	9.98 627	4	40
21	9.39 418	49	9.40 795	52	0.59 205	9.98 623	3	39
22	9.39 467	50	9.40 847	53	0.59 153	9.98 620	3	38
23	9.39 517	49	9.40 900	52	0.59 100	9.98 617	3	37
24	9.39 566	49	9.40 952	53	0.59 048	9.98 614	4	36
25	9.39 615	49	9.41 005	52	0.58 995	9.98 610	3	35
26	9.39 664	49	9.41 057	52	0.58 943	9.98 607	3	34
27	9.39 713	49	9.41 109	52	0.58 891	9.98 604	3	33
28	9.39 762	49	9.41 161	53	0.58 839	9.98 601	4	32
29	9.39 811	49	9.41 214	52	0.58 786	9.98 597	3	31
30	9.39 860	49	9.41 266	52	0.58 734	9.98 594	3	30
31	9.39 909	49	9.41 318	52	0.58 682	9.98 591	2	29
32	9.39 958	48	9.41 370	52	0.58 630	9.98 588	4	28
33	9.40 006	49	9.41 422	52	0.58 578	9.98 584	3	27
34	9.40 055	48	9.41 474	52	0.58 526	9.98 581	3	26
35	9.40 103	49	9.41 526	52	0.58 474	9.98 578	4	25
36	9.40 152	48	9.41 578	51	0.58 422	9.98 574	3	24
37	9.40 200	49	9.41 629	52	0.58 371	9.98 571	3	23
38	9.40 249	48	9.41 681	52	0.58 319	9.98 568	3	22
39	9.40 297	49	9.41 733	51	0.58 267	9.98 565	4	21
40	9.40 346	48	9.41 784	52	0.58 216	9.98 561	3	20
41	9.40 394	48	9.41 836	51	0.58 164	9.98 558	3	19
42	9.40 442	48	9.41 887	52	0.58 113	9.98 555	4	18
43	9.40 490	48	9.41 939	51	0.58 061	9.98 551	3	17
44	9.40 538	48	9.41 990	51	0.58 010	9.98 548	3	16
45	9.40 586	48	9.42 041	52	0.57 959	9.98 545	4	15
46	9.40 634	48	9.42 093	51	0.57 907	9.98 541	3	14
47	9.40 682	48	9.42 144	51	0.57 856	9.98 538	3	13
48	9.40 730	48	9.42 195	51	0.57 805	9.98 535	4	12
49	9.40 778	47	9.42 246	51	0.57 754	9.98 531	3	11
50	9.40 825	48	9.42 297	51	0.57 703	9.98 528	3	10
51	9.40 873	48	9.42 348	51	0.57 652	9.98 525	4	9
52	9.40 921	47	9.42 399	51	0.57 601	9.98 521	3	8
53	9.40 968	48	9.42 450	51	0.57 550	9.98 518	3	7
54	9.41 016	47	9.42 501	51	0.57 499	9.98 515	4	6
55	9.41 063	48	9.42 552	51	0.57 448	9.98 511	3	5
56	9.41 111	47	9.42 603	50	0.57 397	9.98 508	3	4
57	9.41 158	47	9.42 653	51	0.57 347	9.98 505	3	3
58	9.41 205	47	9.42 704	51	0.57 296	9.98 501	3	2
59	9.41 252	48	9.42 755	50	0.57 245	9.98 498	4	1
60	9.41 300		9.42 805		0.57 195	9.98 494		0
	Log Cos	d	Log Cot	cd	Log Tan	Log Sin	d	'

Prop. Parts

	54	53	52
1	5.4	5.3	5.2
2	10.8	10.6	10.4
3	16.2	15.9	15.6
4	21.6	21.2	20.8
5	27.0	26.5	26.0
6	32.4	31.8	31.2
7	37.8	37.1	36.4
8	43.2	42.4	41.6
9	48.6	47.7	46.8

	51	50	49
1	5.1	5.0	4.9
2	10.2	10.0	9.8
3	15.3	15.0	14.7
4	20.4	20.0	19.6
5	25.5	25.0	24.5
6	30.6	30.0	29.4
7	35.7	35.0	34.3
8	40.8	40.0	39.2
9	45.9	45.0	44.1

	48	47
1	4.8	4.7
2	9.6	9.4
3	14.4	14.1
4	19.2	18.8
5	24.0	23.5
6	28.8	28.2
7	33.6	32.9
8	38.4	37.6
9	43.2	42.3

	4	3
1	0.4	0.3
2	0.8	0.6
3	1.2	0.9
4	1.6	1.2
5	2.0	1.5
6	2.4	1.8
7	2.8	2.1
8	3.2	2.4
9	3.6	2.7

Prop. Parts

′	Log Sin	d	Log Tan	c d	Log Cot	Log Cos	d		Prop. Parts		
0	9.41 300	47	9.42 805	51	0.57 195	9.98 494	3	60			
1	9.41 347	47	9.42 856	50	0.57 144	9.98 491	3	59			
2	9.41 394	47	9.42 906	51	0.57 094	9.98 488	4	58			
3	9.41 441	47	9.42 957	50	0.57 043	9.98 484	3	57			
4	9.41 488	47	9.43 007	50	0.56 993	9.98 481	4	56			
5	9.41 535	47	9.43 057	51	0.56 943	9.98 477	3	55	**51**	**50**	**49**
6	9.41 582	46	9.43 108	50	0.56 892	9.98 474	3	54	1	5.1	5.0	4.9
7	9.41 628	47	9.43 158	50	0.56 842	9.98 471	4	53	2	10.2	10.0	9.8
8	9.41 675	47	9.43 208	50	0.56 792	9.98 467	3	52	3	15.3	15.0	14.7
9	9.41 722	46	9.43 258	50	0.56 742	9.98 464	4	51	4	20.4	20.0	19.6
10	9.41 768	47	9.43 308	50	0.56 692	9.98 460	3	50	5	25.5	25.0	24.5
11	9.41 815	46	9.43 358	50	0.56 642	9.98 457	4	49	6	30.6	30.0	29.4
12	9.41 861	47	9.43 408	50	0.56 592	9.98 453	3	48	7	35.7	35.0	34.3
13	9.41 908	46	9.43 458	50	0.56 542	9.98 450	3	47	8	40.8	40.0	39.2
14	9.41 954	47	9.43 508	50	0.56 492	9.98 447	4	46	9	45.9	45.0	44.1
15	9.42 001	46	9.43 558	49	0.56 442	9.98 443	3	45			
16	9.42 047	46	9.43 607	50	0.56 393	9.98 440	4	44			
17	9.42 093	47	9.43 657	50	0.56 343	9.98 436	3	43			
18	9.42 140	46	9.43 707	49	0.56 293	9.98 433	4	42			
19	9.42 186	46	9.43 756	50	0.56 244	9.98 429	3	41		**48**	**47**	**46**
20	9.42 232	46	9.43 806	49	0.56 194	9.98 426	4	40	1	4.8	4.7	4.6
21	9.42 278	46	9.43 855	50	0.56 145	9.98 422	3	39	2	9.6	9.4	9.2
22	9.42 324	46	9.43 905	49	0.56 095	9.98 419	4	38	3	14.4	14.1	13.8
23	9.42 370	46	9.43 954	50	0.56 046	9.98 415	3	37	4	19.2	18.8	18.4
24	9.42 416	45	9.44 004	49	0.55 996	9.98 412	3	36	5	24.0	23.5	23.0
25	9.42 461	46	9.44 053	49	0.55 947	9.98 409	4	35	6	28.8	28.2	27.6
26	9.42 507	46	9.44 102	49	0.55 898	9.98 405	3	34	7	33.6	32.9	32.2
27	9.42 553	46	9.44 151	50	0.55 849	9.98 402	4	33	8	38.4	37.6	36.8
28	9.42 599	45	9.44 201	49	0.55 799	9.98 398	3	32	9	43.2	42.3	41.4
29	9.42 644	46	9.44 250	49	0.55 750	9.98 395	4	31			
30	9.42 690	45	9.44 299	49	0.55 701	9.98 391	3	30			
31	9.42 735	46	9.44 348	49	0.55 652	9.98 388	4	29			
32	9.42 781	45	9.44 397	49	0.55 603	9.98 384	3	28		**45**	**44**
33	9.42 826	46	9.44 446	49	0.55 554	9.98 381	4	27			
34	9.42 872	45	9.44 495	49	0.55 505	9.98 377	4	26	1	4.5	4.4
35	9.42 917	45	9.44 544	48	0.55 456	9.98 373	3	25	2	9.0	8.8
36	9.42 962	46	9.44 592	49	0.55 408	9.98 370	4	24	3	13.5	13.2
37	9.43 008	45	9.44 641	49	0.55 359	9.98 366	3	23	4	18.0	17.6
38	9.43 053	45	9.44 690	48	0.55 310	9.98 363	4	22	5	22.5	22.0
39	9.43 098	45	9.44 738	49	0.55 262	9.98 359	4	21	6	27.0	26.4
40	9.43 143	45	9.44 787	49	0.55 213	9.98 356	3	20	7	31.5	30.8
41	9.43 188	45	9.44 836	48	0.55 164	9.98 352	4	19	8	36.0	35.2
42	9.43 233	45	9.44 884	49	0.55 116	9.98 349	4	18	9	40.5	39.6
43	9.43 278	45	9.44 933	48	0.55 067	9.98 345	4	17			
44	9.43 323	44	9.44 981	48	0.55 019	9.98 342	4	16			
45	9.43 367	45	9.45 029	49	0.54 971	9.98 338	4	15			
46	9.43 412	45	9.45 078	48	0.54 922	9.98 334	3	14			
47	9.43 457	45	9.45 126	48	0.54 874	9.98 331	4	13		**4**	**3**
48	9.43 502	44	9.45 174	48	0.54 826	9.98 327	3	12	1	0.4	0.3
49	9.43 546	45	9.45 222	49	0.54 778	9.98 324	4	11	2	0.8	0.6
50	9.43 591	44	9.45 271	48	0.54 729	9.98 320	3	10	3	1.2	0.9
51	9.43 635	45	9.45 319	48	0.54 681	9.98 317	4	9	4	1.6	1.2
52	9.43 680	44	9.45 367	48	0.54 633	9.98 313	4	8	5	2.0	1.5
53	9.43 724	45	9.45 415	48	0.54 585	9.98 309	3	7	6	2.4	1.8
54	9.43 769	44	9.45 463	48	0.54 537	9.98 306	4	6	7	2.8	2.1
55	9.43 813	44	9.45 511	48	0.54 489	9.98 302	3	5	8	3.2	2.4
56	9.43 857	44	9.45 559	47	0.54 441	9.98 299	4	4	9	3.6	2.7
57	9.43 901	45	9.45 606	48	0.54 394	9.98 295	4	3			
58	9.43 946	44	9.45 654	48	0.54 346	9.98 291	3	2			
59	9.43 990	44	9.45 702	48	0.54 298	9.98 288	4	1			
60	9.44 034		9.45 750		0.54 250	9.98 284		0			
	Log Cos	d	Log Cot	c|d	Log Tan	Log Sin	d	′	Prop. Parts		

′	Log Sin	d	Log Tan	c d	Log Cot	Log Cos	d		Prop. Parts
0	9.44 034	44	9.45 750	47	0.54 250	9.98 284	3	60	
1	9.44 078	44	9.45 797	48	0.54 203	9.98 281	4	59	
2	9.44 122	44	9.45 845	47	0.54 155	9.98 277	4	58	
3	9.44 166	44	9.45 892	48	0.54 108	9.98 273	3	57	
4	9.44 210	43	9.45 940	47	0.54 060	9.98 270	4	56	

										48	47	46

5	9.44 253	44	9.45 987	48	0.54 013	9.98 266	4	55
6	9.44 297	44	9.46 035	47	0.53 965	9.98 262	3	54
7	9.44 341	44	9.46 082	48	0.53 918	9.98 259	4	53
8	9.44 385	43	9.46 130	47	0.53 870	9.98 255	4	52
9	9.44 428	44	9.46 177	47	0.53 823	9.98 251	3	51

10	9.44 472	44	9.46 224	47	0.53 776	9.98 248	4	50
11	9.44 516	43	9.46 271	48	0.53 729	9.98 244	4	49
12	9.44 559	43	9.46 319	47	0.53 681	9.98 240	3	48
13	9.44 602	44	9.46 366	47	0.53 634	9.98 237	4	47
14	9.44 646	43	9.46 413	47	0.53 587	9.98 233	4	46

15	9.44 689	44	9.46 460	47	0.53 540	9.98 229	3	45
16	9.44 733	43	9.46 507	47	0.53 493	9.98 226	4	44
17	9.44 776	43	9.46 554	47	0.53 446	9.98 222	4	43
18	9.44 819	43	9.46 601	47	0.53 399	9.98 218	3	42
19	9.44 862	43	9.46 648	46	0.53 352	9.98 215	4	41

20	9.44 905	43	9.46 694	47	0.53 306	9.98 211	4	40
21	9.44 948	44	9.46 741	47	0.53 259	9.98 207	3	39
22	9.44 992	43	9.46 788	47	0.53 212	9.98 204	4	38
23	9.45 035	42	9.46 835	46	0.53 165	9.98 200	4	37
24	9.45 077	43	9.46 881	47	0.53 119	9.98 196	4	36

25	9.45 120	43	9.46 928	47	0.53 072	9.98 192	3	35
26	9.45 163	43	9.46 975	46	0.53 025	9.98 189	4	34
27	9.45 206	43	9.47 021	47	0.52 979	9.98 185	4	33
28	9.45 249	43	9.47 068	46	0.52 932	9.98 181	4	32
29	9.45 292	42	9.47 114	46	0.52 886	9.98 177	3	31

30	9.45 334	43	9.47 160	47	0.52 840	9.98 174	4	30
31	9.45 377	42	9.47 207	46	0.52 793	9.98 170	4	29
32	9.45 419	43	9.47 253	46	0.52 747	9.98 166	4	28
33	9.45 462	42	9.47 299	47	0.52 701	9.98 162	3	27
34	9.45 504	43	9.47 346	46	0.52 654	9.98 159	4	26

35	9.45 547	42	9.47 392	46	0.52 608	9.98 155	4	25
36	9.45 589	43	9.47 438	46	0.52 562	9.98 151	4	24
37	9.45 632	42	9.47 484	46	0.52 516	9.98 147	3	23
38	9.45 674	42	9.47 530	46	0.52 470	9.98 144	4	22
39	9.45 716	42	9.47 576	46	0.52 424	9.98 140	4	21

40	9.45 758	43	9.47 622	46	0.52 378	9.98 136	4	20
41	9.45 801	42	9.47 668	46	0.52 332	9.98 132	3	19
42	9.45 843	42	9.47 714	46	0.52 286	9.98 129	4	18
43	9.45 885	42	9.47 760	46	0.52 240	9.98 125	4	17
44	9.45 927	42	9.47 806	46	0.52 194	9.98 121	4	16

45	9.45 969	42	9.47 852	45	0.52 148	9.98 117	4	15
46	9.46 011	42	9.47 897	46	0.52 103	9.98 113	3	14
47	9.46 053	42	9.47 943	46	0.52 057	9.98 110	4	13
48	9.46 095	41	9.47 989	46	0.52 011	9.98 106	4	12
49	9.46 136	42	9.48 035	45	0.51 965	9.98 102	4	11

50	9.46 178	42	9.48 080	46	0.51 920	9.98 098	4	10
51	9.46 220	42	9.48 126	45	0.51 874	9.98 094	4	9
52	9.46 262	41	9.48 171	46	0.51 829	9.98 090	3	8
53	9.46 303	42	9.48 217	45	0.51 783	9.98 087	4	7
54	9.46 345	41	9.48 262	45	0.51 738	9.98 083	4	6

55	9.46 386	42	9.48 307	46	0.51 693	9.98 079	4	5
56	9.46 428	41	9.48 353	45	0.51 647	9.98 075	4	4
57	9.46 469	42	9.48 398	45	0.51 602	9.98 071	4	3
58	9.46 511	41	9.48 443	46	0.51 557	9.98 067	4	2
59	9.46 552	42	9.48 489	45	0.51 511	9.98 063	3	1
60	9.46 594		9.48 534		0.51 466	9.98 060		0

| | Log Cos | d | Log Cot | c d | Log Tan | Log Sin | d | ′ | Prop. Parts |

Prop. Parts

	48	47	46
1	4.8	4.7	4.6
2	9.6	9.4	9.2
3	14.4	14.1	13.8
4	19.2	18.8	18.4
5	24.0	23.5	23.0
6	28.8	28.2	27.6
7	33.6	32.9	32.2
8	38.4	37.6	36.8
9	43.2	42.3	41.4

	45	44	43
1	4.5	4.4	4.3
2	9.0	8.8	8.6
3	13.5	13.2	12.9
4	18.0	17.6	17.2
5	22.5	22.0	21.5
6	27.0	26.4	25.8
7	31.5	30.8	30.1
8	36.0	35.2	34.4
9	40.5	39.6	38.7

	42	41
1	4.2	4.1
2	8.4	8.2
3	12.6	12.3
4	16.8	16.4
5	21.0	20.5
6	25.2	24.6
7	29.4	28.7
8	33.6	32.8
9	37.8	36.9

	4	3
1	0.4	0.3
2	0.8	0.6
3	1.2	0.9
4	1.6	1.2
5	2.0	1.5
6	2.4	1.8
7	2.8	2.1
8	3.2	2.4
9	3.6	2.7

′	Log Sin	d	Log Tan	c d	Log Cot	Log Cos	d	
0	9.46 594		9.48 534		0.51 466	9.98 060		60
1	9.46 635	41	9.48 579	45	0.51 421	9.98 056	4	59
2	9.46 676	41	9.48 624	45	0.51 376	9.98 052	4	58
3	9.46 717	41	9.48 669	45	0.51 331	9.98 048	4	57
4	9.46 758	41	9.48 714	45	0.51 286	9.98 044	4	56
5	9.46 800	42	9.48 759	45	0.51 241	9.98 040	4	55
6	9.46 841	41	9.48 804	45	0.51 196	9.98 036	4	54
7	9.46 882	41	9.48 849	45	0.51 151	9.98 032	3	53
8	9.46 923	41	9.48 894	45	0.51 106	9.98 029	4	52
9	9.46 964	41	9.48 939	45	0.51 061	9.98 025	4	51
10	9.47 005	41	9.48 984	45	0.51 016	9.98 021	4	50
11	9.47 045	40	9.49 029	45	0.50 971	9.98 017	4	49
12	9.47 086	41	9.49 073	44	0.50 927	9.98 013	4	48
13	9.47 127	41	9.49 118	45	0.50 882	9.98 009	4	47
14	9.47 168	41	9.49 163	45	0.50 837	9.98 005	4	46
15	9.47 209	41	9.49 207	44	0.50 793	9.98 001	4	45
16	9.47 249	40	9.49 252	45	0.50 748	9.97 997	4	44
17	9.47 290	41	9.49 296	44	0.50 704	9.97 993	4	43
18	9.47 330	40	9.49 341	45	0.50 659	9.97 989	4	42
19	9.47 371	41	9.49 385	44	0.50 615	9.97 986	3	41
20	9.47 411	40	9.49 430	45	0.50 570	9.97 982	4	40
21	9.47 452	41	9.49 474	44	0.50 526	9.97 978	4	39
22	9.47 492	40	9.49 519	45	0.50 481	9.97 974	4	38
23	9.47 533	41	9.49 563	44	0.50 437	9.97 970	4	37
24	9.47 573	40	9.49 607	44	0.50 393	9.97 966	4	36
25	9.47 613	40	9.49 652	45	0.50 348	9.97 962	4	35
26	9.47 654	41	9.49 696	44	0.50 304	9.97 958	4	34
27	9.47 694	40	9.49 740	44	0.50 260	9.97 954	4	33
28	9.47 734	40	9.49 784	44	0.50 216	9.97 950	4	32
29	9.47 774	40	9.49 828	44	0.50 172	9.97 946	4	31
30	9.47 814	40	9.49 872	44	0.50 128	9.97 942	4	30
31	9.47 854	40	9.49 916	44	0.50 084	9.97 938	4	29
32	9.47 894	40	9.49 960	44	0.50 040	9.97 934	4	28
33	9.47 934	40	9.50 004	44	0.49 996	9.97 930	4	27
34	9.47 974	40	9.50 048	44	0.49 952	9.97 926	4	26
35	9.48 014	40	9.50 092	44	0.49 908	9.97 922	4	25
36	9.48 054	40	9.50 136	44	0.49 864	9.97 918	4	24
37	9.48 094	40	9.50 180	43	0.49 820	9.97 914	4	23
38	9.48 133	39	9.50 223	44	0.49 777	9.97 910	4	22
39	9.48 173	40	9.50 267	44	0.49 733	9.97 906	4	21
40	9.48 213	40	9.50 311	44	0.49 689	9.97 902	4	20
41	9.48 252	39	9.50 355	43	0.49 645	9.97 898	4	19
42	9.48 292	40	9.50 398	44	0.49 602	9.97 894	4	18
43	9.48 332	40	9.50 442	43	0.49 558	9.97 890	4	17
44	9.48 371	39	9.50 485	44	0.49 515	9.97 886	4	16
45	9.48 411	40	9.50 529	43	0.49 471	9.97 882	4	15
46	9.48 450	39	9.50 572	44	0.49 428	9.97 878	4	14
47	9.48 490	40	9.50 616	43	0.49 384	9.97 874	4	13
48	9.48 529	39	9.50 659	44	0.49 341	9.97 870	4	12
49	9.48 568	39	9.50 703	43	0.49 297	9.97 866	4	11
50	9.48 607	39	9.50 746	43	0.49 254	9.97 861	5	10
51	9.48 647	40	9.50 789	43	0.49 211	9.97 857	4	9
52	9.48 686	39	9.50 833	44	0.49 167	9.97 853	4	8
53	9.48 725	39	9.50 876	43	0.49 124	9.97 849	4	7
54	9.48 764	39	9.50 919	43	0.49 081	9.97 845	4	6
55	9.48 803	39	9.50 962	43	0.49 038	9.97 841	4	5
56	9.48 842	39	9.51 005	43	0.48 995	9.97 837	4	4
57	9.48 881	39	9.51 048	43	0.48 952	9.97 833	4	3
58	9.48 920	39	9.51 092	44	0.48 908	9.97 829	4	2
59	9.48 959	39	9.51 135	43	0.48 865	9.97 825	4	1
60	9.48 998	39	9.51 178	43	0.48 822	9.97 821	4	0
	Log Cos	d	Log Cot	c d	Log Tan	Log Sin	d	′

Prop. Parts

	45	44	43
1	4.5	4.4	4.3
2	9.0	8.8	8.6
3	13.5	13.2	12.9
4	18.0	17.6	17.2
5	22.5	22.0	21.5
6	27.0	26.4	25.8
7	31.5	30.8	30.1
8	36.0	35.2	34.4
9	40.5	39.6	38.7

	42	41	40
1	4.2	4.1	4.0
2	8.4	8.2	8.0
3	12.6	12.3	12.0
4	16.8	16.4	16.0
5	21.0	20.5	20.0
6	25.2	24.6	24.0
7	29.4	28.7	28.0
8	33.6	32.8	32.0
9	37.8	36.9	36.0

	39	5
1	3.9	0.5
2	7.8	1.0
3	11.7	1.5
4	15.6	2.0
5	19.5	2.5
6	23.4	3.0
7	27.3	3.5
8	31.2	4.0
9	35.1	4.5

	4	3
1	0.4	0.3
2	0.8	0.6
3	1.2	0.9
4	1.6	1.2
5	2.0	1.5
6	2.4	1.8
7	2.8	2.1
8	3.2	2.4
9	3.6	2.7

′	Log Sin	d	Log Tan	c d	Log Cot	Log Cos	d		Prop. Parts		
0	9.48 998	39	9.51 178	43	0.48 822	9.97 821	4	60			
1	9.49 037	39	9.51 221	43	0.48 779	9.97 817	5	59			
2	9.49 076	39	9.51 264	42	0.48 736	9.97 812	4	58			
3	9.49 115	38	9.51 306	43	0.48 694	9.97 808	4	57			
4	9.49 153	39	9.51 349	43	0.48 651	9.97 804	4	56			
5	9.49 192	39	9.51 392	43	0.48 608	9.97 800	4	55			
6	9.49 231	38	9.51 435	43	0.48 565	9.97 796	4	54			
7	9.49 269	39	9.51 478	42	0.48 522	9.97 792	4	53			
8	9.49 308	39	9.51 520	43	0.48 480	9.97 788	4	52	**43**	**42**	**41**
9	9.49 347	38	9.51 563	43	0.48 437	9.97 784	5	51	1 4.3	4.2	4.1
10	9.49 385	39	9.51 606	42	0.48 394	9.97 779	4	50	2 8.6	8.4	8.2
11	9.49 424	38	9.51 648	43	0.48 352	9.97 775	4	49	3 12.9	12.6	12.3
12	9.49 462	38	9.51 691	43	0.48 309	9.97 771	4	48	4 17.2	16.8	16.4
13	9.49 500	39	9.51 734	42	0.48 266	9.97 767	4	47	5 21.5	21.0	20.5
14	9.49 539	38	9.51 776	43	0.48 224	9.97 763	4	46	6 25.8	25.2	24.6
15	9.49 577	38	9.51 819	42	0.48 181	9.97 759	5	45	7 30.1	29.4	28.7
16	9.49 615	39	9.51 861	42	0.48 139	9.97 754	4	44	8 34.4	33.6	32.8
17	9.49 654	38	9.51 903	43	0.48 097	9.97 750	4	43	9 38.7	37.8	36.9
18	9.49 692	38	9.51 946	42	0.48 054	9.97 746	4	42			
19	9.49 730	38	9.51 988	43	0.48 012	9.97 742	4	41			
20	9.49 768	38	9.52 031	42	0.47 969	9.97 738	4	40			
21	9.49 806	38	9.52 073	42	0.47 927	9.97 734	5	39			
22	9.49 844	38	9.52 115	42	0.47 885	9.97 729	4	38			
23	9.49 882	38	9.52 157	43	0.47 843	9.97 725	4	37			
24	9.49 920	38	9.52 200	42	0.47 800	9.97 721	4	36			
25	9.49 958	38	9.52 242	42	0.47 758	9.97 717	4	35	**39**	**38**	**37**
26	9.49 996	38	9.52 284	42	0.47 716	9.97 713	5	34	1 3.9	3.8	3.7
27	9.50 034	38	9.52 326	42	0.47 674	9.97 708	4	33	2 7.8	7.6	7.4
28	9.50 072	38	9.52 368	42	0.47 632	9.97 704	4	32	3 11.7	11.4	11.1
29	9.50 110	38	9.52 410	42	0.47 590	9.97 700	4	31	4 15.6	15.2	14.8
30	9.50 148	37	9.52 452	42	0.47 548	9.97 696	5	30	5 19.5	19.0	18.5
31	9.50 185	38	9.52 494	42	0.47 506	9.97 691	4	29	6 23.4	22.8	22.2
32	9.50 223	38	9.52 536	42	0.47 464	9.97 687	4	28	7 27.3	26.6	25.9
33	9.50 261	37	9.52 578	42	0.47 422	9.97 683	4	27	8 31.2	30.4	29.6
34	9.50 298	38	9.52 620	41	0.47 380	9.97 679	5	26	9 35.1	34.2	33.3
35	9.50 336	38	9.52 661	42	0.47 339	9.97 674	4	25			
36	9.50 374	37	9.52 703	42	0.47 297	9.97 670	4	24			
37	9.50 411	38	9.52 745	42	0.47 255	9.97 666	4	23			
38	9.50 449	37	9.52 787	42	0.47 213	9.97 662	5	22			
39	9.50 486	37	9.52 829	41	0.47 171	9.97 657	4	21			
40	9.50 523	38	9.52 870	42	0.47 130	9.97 653	4	20			
41	9.50 561	37	9.52 912	41	0.47 088	9.97 649	4	19			
42	9.50 598	37	9.52 953	42	0.47 047	9.97 645	5	18	**36**	**5**	**4**
43	9.50 635	38	9.52 995	42	0.47 005	9.97 640	4	17	1 3.6	0.5	0.4
44	9.50 673	37	9.53 037	41	0.46 963	9.97 636	4	16	2 7.2	1.0	0.8
45	9.50 710	37	9.53 078	42	0.46 922	9.97 632	4	15	3 10.8	1.5	1.2
46	9.50 747	37	9.53 120	41	0.46 880	9.97 628	5	14	4 14.4	2.0	1.6
47	9.50 784	37	9.53 161	41	0.46 839	9.97 623	4	13	5 18.0	2.5	2.0
48	9.50 821	37	9.53 202	42	0.46 798	9.97 619	4	12	6 21.6	3.0	2.4
49	9.50 858	38	9.53 244	41	0.46 756	9.97 615	5	11	7 25.2	3.5	2.8
50	9.50 896	37	9.53 285	42	0.46 715	9.97 610	4	10	8 28.8	4.0	3.2
51	9.50 933	37	9.53 327	41	0.46 673	9.97 606	4	9	9 32.4	4.5	3.6
52	9.50 970	37	9.53 368	41	0.46 632	9.97 602	5	8			
53	9.51 007	36	9.53 409	41	0.46 591	9.97 597	4	7			
54	9.51 043	37	9.53 450	42	0.46 550	9.97 593	4	6			
55	9.51 080	37	9.53 492	41	0.46 508	9.97 589	5	5			
56	9.51 117	37	9.53 533	41	0.46 467	9.97 584	4	4			
57	9.51 154	37	9.53 574	41	0.46 426	9.97 580	4	3			
58	9.51 191	36	9.53 615	41	0.46 385	9.97 576	5	2			
59	9.51 227	37	9.53 656	41	0.46 344	9.97 571	4	1			
60	9.51 264		9.53 697		0.46 303	9.97 567		0			
	Log Cos	d	Log Cot	c d	Log Tan	Log Sin	d	′	Prop. Parts		

'	Log Sin	d	Log Tan	c d	Log Cot	Log Cos	d	Prop. Parts				
0	9.51 264	37	9.53 697	41	0.46 303	9.97 567		60				
1	9.51 301	37	9.53 738	41	0.46 262	9.97 563	4	59				
2	9.51 338	36	9.53 779	41	0.46 221	9.97 558	5	58				
3	9.51 374	37	9.53 820	41	0.46 180	9.97 554	4	57				
4	9.51 411	36	9.53 861	41	0.46 139	9.97 550	4	56				
5	9.51 447	37	9.53 902	41	0.46 098	9.97 545	5	55				
6	9.51 484	36	9.53 943	41	0.46 057	9.97 541	4	54				
7	9.51 520	37	9.53 984	41	0.46 016	9.97 536	5	53				
8	9.51 557	36	9.54 025	40	0.45 975	9.97 532	4	52				
9	9.51 593	36	9.54 065	41	0.45 935	9.97 528	4	51		**41**	**40**	**39**
10	9.51 629	37	9.54 106	41	0.45 894	9.97 523	5	50	1	4.1	4.0	3.9
11	9.51 666	36	9.54 147	40	0.45 853	9.97 519	4	49	2	8.2	8.0	7.8
12	9.51 702	36	9.54 187	41	0.45 813	9.97 515	4	48	3	12.3	12.0	11.7
13	9.51 738	36	9.54 228	41	0.45 772	9.97 510	5	47	4	16.4	16.0	15.6
14	9.51 774	37	9.54 269	40	0.45 731	9.97 506	4	46	5	20.5	20.0	19.5
15	9.51 811	36	9.54 309	41	0.45 691	9.97 501	5	45	6	24.6	24.0	23.4
16	9.51 847	36	9.54 350	40	0.45 650	9.97 497	4	44	7	28.7	28.0	27.3
17	9.51 883	36	9.54 390	41	0.45 610	9.97 492	5	43	8	32.8	32.0	31.2
18	9.51 919	36	9.54 431	40	0.45 569	9.97 488	4	42	9	36.9	36.0	35.1
19	9.51 955	36	9.54 471	41	0.45 529	9.97 484	4	41				
20	9.51 991	36	9.54 512	40	0.45 488	9.97 479	5	40				
21	9.52 027	36	9.54 552	41	0.45 448	9.97 475	4	39				
22	9.52 063	36	9.54 593	40	0.45 407	9.97 470	5	38				
23	9.52 099	36	9.54 633	40	0.45 367	9.97 466	5	37				
24	9.52 135	36	9.54 673	41	0.45 327	9.97 461	4	36				
25	9.52 171	36	9.54 714	40	0.45 286	9.97 457	4	35		**37**	**36**	**35**
26	9.52 207	35	9.54 754	40	0.45 246	9.97 453	5	34	1	3.7	3.6	3.5
27	9.52 242	36	9.54 794	41	0.45 206	9.97 448	4	33	2	7.4	7.2	7.0
28	9.52 278	36	9.54 835	40	0.45 165	9.97 444	5	32	3	11.1	10.8	10.5
29	9.52 314	36	9.54 875	40	0.45 125	9.97 439	4	31	4	14.8	14.4	14.0
30	9.52 350	35	9.54 915	40	0.45 085	9.97 435	5	30	5	18.5	18.0	17.5
31	9.52 385	36	9.54 955	40	0.45 045	9.97 430	4	29	6	22.2	21.6	21.0
32	9.52 421	35	9.54 995	40	0.45 005	9.97 426	5	28	7	25.9	25.2	24.5
33	9.52 456	36	9.55 035	40	0.44 965	9.97 421	4	27	8	29.6	28.8	28.0
34	9.52 492	35	9.55 075	40	0.44 925	9.97 417	5	26	9	33.3	32.4	31.5
35	9.52 527	36	9.55 115	40	0.44 885	9.97 412	4	25				
36	9.52 563	35	9.55 155	40	0.44 845	9.97 408	5	24				
37	9.52 598	36	9.55 195	40	0.44 805	9.97 403	4	23				
38	9.52 634	35	9.55 235	40	0.44 765	9.97 399	5	22				
39	9.52 669	36	9.55 275	40	0.44 725	9.97 394	4	21				
40	9.52 705	35	9.55 315	40	0.44 685	9.97 390	5	20				
41	9.52 740	35	9.55 355	40	0.44 645	9.97 385	4	19				
42	9.52 775	36	9.55 395	39	0.44 605	9.97 381	5	18		**34**	**5**	**4**
43	9.52 811	35	9.55 434	40	0.44 566	9.97 376	4	17	1	3.4	0.5	0.4
44	9.52 846	35	9.55 474	40	0.44 526	9.97 372	5	16	2	6.8	1.0	0.8
45	9.52 881	35	9.55 514	40	0.44 486	9.97 367	4	15	3	10.2	1.5	1.2
46	9.52 916	35	9.55 554	39	0.44 446	9.97 363	5	14	4	13.6	2.0	1.6
47	9.52 951	35	9.55 593	40	0.44 407	9.97 358	5	13	5	17.0	2.5	2.0
48	9.52 986	35	9.55 633	40	0.44 367	9.97 353	4	12	6	20.4	3.0	2.4
49	9.53 021	35	9.55 673	39	0.44 327	9.97 349	5	11	7	23.8	3.5	2.8
50	9.53 056	36	9.55 712	40	0.44 288	9.97 344	4	10	8	27.2	4.0	3.2
51	9.53 092	34	9.55 752	39	0.44 248	9.97 340	5	9	9	30.6	4.5	3.6
52	9.53 126	35	9.55 791	40	0.44 209	9.97 335	4	8				
53	9.53 161	35	9.55 831	39	0.44 169	9.97 331	5	7				
54	9.53 196	35	9.55 870	40	0.44 130	9.97 326	5	6				
55	9.53 231	35	9.55 910	39	0.44 090	9.97 322	4	5				
56	9.53 266	35	9.55 949	40	0.44 051	9.97 317	5	4				
57	9.53 301	35	9.55 989	39	0.44 011	9.97 312	4	3				
58	9.53 336	34	9.56 028	39	0.43 972	9.97 308	5	2				
59	9.53 370	35	9.56 067	40	0.43 933	9.97 303	4	1				
60	9.53 405		9.56 107		0.43 893	9.97 299		0				
	Log Cos	d	Log Cot	c d	Log Tan	Log Sin	d	'	Prop. Parts			

′	Log Sin	d	Log Tan	c d	Log Cot	Log Cos	d	′	Prop. Parts		
0	9.53 405	35	9.56 107	39	0.43 893	9.97 299	5	60			
1	9.53 440	35	9.56 146	39	0.43 854	9.97 294	5	59			
2	9.53 475	34	9.56 185	39	0.43 815	9.97 289	4	58			
3	9.53 509	35	9.56 224	40	0.43 776	9.97 285	5	57			
4	9.53 544	34	9.56 264	39	0.43 736	9.97 280	4	56			
5	9.53 578	35	9.56 303	39	0.43 697	9.97 276	5	55			
6	9.53 613	34	9.56 342	39	0.43 658	9.97 271	5	54			
7	9.53 647	35	9.56 381	39	0.43 619	9.97 266	4	53			
8	9.53 682	34	9.56 420	39	0.43 580	9.97 262	5	52		40	39	38
9	9.53 716	35	9.56 459	39	0.43 541	9.97 257	5	51	1	4.0	3.9	3.8
10	9.53 751	34	9.56 498	39	0.43 502	9.97 252	4	50	2	8.0	7.8	7.6
11	9.53 785	34	9.56 537	39	0.43 463	9.97 248	5	49	3	12.0	11.7	11.4
12	9.53 819	35	9.56 576	39	0.43 424	9.97 243	5	43	4	16.0	15.6	15.2
13	9.53 854	34	9.56 615	39	0.43 385	9.97 238	4	47	5	20.0	19.5	19.0
14	9.53 888	34	9.56 654	39	0.43 346	9.97 234	5	46	6	24.0	23.4	22.8
15	9.53 922	35	9.56 693	39	0.43 307	9.97 229	5	45	7	28.0	27.3	26.6
16	9.53 957	34	9.56 732	39	0.43 268	9.97 224	4	44	8	32.0	31.2	30.4
17	9.53 991	34	9.56 771	39	0.43 229	9.97 220	5	43	9	36.0	35.1	34.2
18	9.54 025	34	9.56 810	39	0.43 190	9.97 215	5	42			
19	9.54 059	34	9.56 849	38	0.43 151	9.97 210	4	41			
20	9.54 093	34	9.56 887	39	0.43 113	9.97 206	5	40			
21	9.54 127	34	9.56 926	39	0.43 074	9.97 201	5	39			
22	9.54 161	34	9.56 965	39	0.43 035	9.97 196	4	38			
23	9.54 195	34	9.57 004	38	0.42 996	9.97 192	5	37			
24	9.54 229	34	9.57 042	39	0.42 958	9.97 187	5	36			
25	9.54 263	34	9.57 081	39	0.42 919	9.97 182	4	35		37	35	34
26	9.54 297	34	9.57 120	38	0.42 880	9.97 178	5	34	1	3.7	3.5	3.4
27	9.54 331	34	9.57 158	39	0.42 842	9.97 173	5	33	2	7.4	7.0	6.8
28	9.54 365	34	9.57 197	38	0.42 803	9.97 168	5	32	3	11.1	10.5	10.2
29	9.54 399	34	9.57 235	39	0.42 765	9.97 163	4	31	4	14.8	14.0	13.6
30	9.54 433	33	9.57 274	38	0.42 726	9.97 159	5	30	5	18.5	17.5	17.0
31	9.54 466	34	9.57 312	39	0.42 688	9.97 154	5	29	6	22.2	21.0	20.4
32	9.54 500	34	9.57 351	38	0.42 649	9.97 149	4	28	7	25.9	24.5	23.8
33	9.54 534	33	9.57 389	39	0.42 611	9.97 145	5	27	8	29.6	28.0	27.2
34	9.54 567	34	9.57 428	38	0.42 572	9.97 140	5	26	9	33.3	31.5	30.6
35	9.54 601	34	9.57 466	38	0.42 534	9.97 135	5	25			
36	9.54 635	33	9.57 504	39	0.42 496	9.97 130	4	24			
37	9.54 668	34	9.57 543	38	0.42 457	9.97 126	5	23			
38	9.54 702	33	9.57 581	38	0.42 419	9.97 121	5	22			
39	9.54 735	34	9.57 619	39	0.42 381	9.97 116	5	21			
40	9.54 769	33	9.57 658	38	0.42 342	9.97 111	4	20			
41	9.54 802	34	9.57 696	38	0.42 304	9.97 107	5	19			
42	9.54 836	33	9.57 734	38	0.42 266	9.97 102	5	18		33	5	4
43	9.54 869	34	9.57 772	38	0.42 228	9.97 097	5	17	1	3.3	0.5	0.4
44	9.54 903	33	9.57 810	39	0.42 190	9.97 092	5	16	2	6.6	1.0	0.8
45	9.54 936	33	9.57 849	38	0.42 151	9.97 087	4	15	3	9.9	1.5	1.2
46	9.54 969	34	9.57 887	38	0.42 113	9.97 083	5	14	4	13.2	2.0	1.6
47	9.55 003	33	9.57 925	38	0.42 075	9.97 078	5	13	5	16.5	2.5	2.0
48	9.55 036	33	9.57 963	38	0.42 037	9.97 073	5	12	6	19.8	3.0	2.4
49	9.55 069	33	9.58 001	38	0.41 999	9.97 068	5	11	7	23.1	3.5	2.8
50	9.55 102	34	9.58 039	38	0.41 961	9.97 063	4	10	8	26.4	4.0	3.2
51	9.55 136	33	9.58 077	38	0.41 923	9.97 059	5	9	9	29.7	4.5	3.6
52	9.55 169	33	9.58 115	38	0.41 885	9.97 054	5	8			
53	9.55 202	33	9.58 153	38	0.41 847	9.97 049	5	7			
54	9.55 235	33	9.58 191	38	0.41 809	9.97 044	5	6			
55	9.55 268	33	9.58 229	38	0.41 771	9.97 039	4	5			
56	9.55 301	33	9.58 267	37	0.41 733	9.97 035	5	4			
57	9.55 334	33	9.58 304	38	0.41 696	9.97 030	5	3			
58	9.55 367	33	9.58 342	38	0.41 658	9.97 025	5	2			
59	9.55 400	33	9.58 380	38	0.41 620	9.97 020	5	1			
60	9.55 433		9.58 418		0.41 582	9.97 015		0			
	Log Cos	d	Log Cot	c d	Log Tan	Log Sin	d	′	Prop. Parts		

′	Log Sin	d	Log Tan	c d	Log Cot	Log Cos	d		Prop. Parts		
0	9.55 433	33	9.58 418	37	0.41 582	9.97 015	5	60			
1	9.55 466	33	9.58 455	38	0.41 545	9.97 010	5	59			
2	9.55 499	33	9.58 493	38	0.41 507	9.97 005	4	58			
3	9.55 532	32	9.58 531	38	0.41 469	9.97 001	5	57			
4	9.55 564	33	9.58 569	37	0.41 431	9.96 996	5	56			
5	9.55 597	33	9.58 606	38	0.41 394	9.96 991	5	55			
6	9.55 630	33	9.58 644	37	0.41 356	9.96 986	5	54			
7	9.55 663	32	9.58 681	38	0.41 319	9.96 981	5	53			
8	9.55 695	33	9.58 719	38	0.41 281	9.96 976	5	52			
9	9.55 728	33	9.58 757	37	0.41 243	9.96 971	5	51		**38**	**37**	**36**
10	9.55 761	32	9.58 794	38	0.41 206	9.96 966	4	50	1	3.8	3.7	3.6
11	9.55 793	33	9.58 832	37	0.41 168	9.96 962	5	49	2	7.6	7.4	7.2
12	9.55 826	32	9.58 869	38	0.41 131	9.96 957	5	48	3	11.4	11.1	10.8
13	9.55 858	33	9.58 907	37	0.41 093	9.96 952	5	47	4	15.2	14.8	14.4
14	9.55 891	32	9.58 944	37	0.41 056	9.96 947	5	46	5	19.0	18.5	18.0
15	9.55 923	33	9.58 981	38	0.41 019	9.96 942	5	45	6	22.8	22.2	21.6
16	9.55 956	32	9.59 019	37	0.40 981	9.96 937	5	44	7	26.6	25.9	25.2
17	9.55 988	33	9.59 056	38	0.40 944	9.96 932	5	43	8	30.4	29.6	28.8
18	9.56 021	32	9.59 094	37	0.40 906	9.96 927	5	42	9	34.2	33.3	32.4
19	9.56 053	32	9.59 131	37	0.40 869	9.96 922	5	41			
20	9.56 085	33	9.59 168	37	0.40 832	9.96 917	5	40			
21	9.56 118	32	9.59 205	38	0.40 795	9.96 912	5	39			
22	9.56 150	32	9.59 243	37	0.40 757	9.96 907	4	38			
23	9.56 182	33	9.59 280	37	0.40 720	9.96 903	5	37			
24	9.56 215	32	9.59 317	37	0.40 683	9.96 898	5	36			
25	9.56 247	32	9.59 354	37	0.40 646	9.96 893	5	35		**33**	**32**	**31**
26	9.56 279	32	9.59 391	38	0.40 609	9.96 888	5	34			
27	9.56 311	32	9.59 429	37	0.40 571	9.96 883	5	33	1	3.3	3.2	3.1
28	9.56 343	32	9.59 466	37	0.40 534	9.96 878	5	32	2	6.6	6.4	6.2
29	9.56 375	33	9.59 503	37	0.40 497	9.96 873	5	31	3	9.9	9.6	9.3
30	9.56 408	32	9.59 540	37	0.40 460	9.96 868	5	30	4	13.2	12.8	12.4
31	9.56 440	32	9.59 577	37	0.40 423	9.96 863	5	29	5	16.5	16.0	15.5
32	9.56 472	32	9.59 614	37	0.40 386	9.96 858	5	28	6	19.8	19.2	18.6
33	9.56 504	32	9.59 651	37	0.40 349	9.96 853	5	27	7	23.1	22.4	21.7
34	9.56 536	32	9.59 688	37	0.40 312	9.96 848	5	26	8	26.4	25.6	24.8
35	9.56 568	31	9.59 725	37	0.40 275	9.96 843	5	25	9	29.7	28.8	27.9
36	9.56 599	32	9.59 762	37	0.40 238	9.96 838	5	24			
37	9.56 631	32	9.59 799	36	0.40 201	9.96 833	5	23			
38	9.56 663	32	9.59 835	37	0.40 165	9.96 828	5	22			
39	9.56 695	32	9.59 872	37	0.40 128	9.96 823	5	21			
40	9.56 727	32	9.59 909	37	0.40 091	9.96 818	5	20			
41	9.56 759	31	9.59 946	37	0.40 054	9.96 813	5	19			
42	9.56 790	32	9.59 983	36	0.40 017	9.96 808	5	18		**6**	**5**	**4**
43	9.56 822	32	9.60 019	37	0.39 981	9.96 803	5	17	1	0.6	0.5	0.4
44	9.56 854	32	9.60 056	37	0.39 944	9.96 798	5	16	2	1.2	1.0	0.8
45	9.56 886	31	9.60 093	37	0.39 907	9.96 793	5	15	3	1.8	1.5	1.2
46	9.56 917	32	9.60 130	36	0.39 870	9.96 788	5	14	4	2.4	2.0	1.6
47	9.56 949	31	9.60 166	37	0.39 834	9.96 783	5	13	5	3.0	2.5	2.0
48	9.56 980	32	9.60 203	37	0.39 797	9.96 778	6	12	6	3.6	3.0	2.4
49	9.57 012	32	9.60 240	36	0.39 760	9.96 772	5	11	7	4.2	3.5	2.8
50	9.57 044	31	9.60 276	37	0.39 724	9.96 767	5	10	8	4.8	4.0	3.2
51	9.57 075	32	9.60 313	36	0.39 687	9.96 762	5	9	9	5.4	4.5	3.6
52	9.57 107	31	9.60 349	37	0.39 651	9.96 757	5	8			
53	9.57 138	31	9.60 386	36	0.39 614	9.96 752	5	7			
54	9.57 169	32	9.60 422	37	0.39 578	9.96 747	5	6			
55	9.57 201	31	9.60 459	36	0.39 541	9.96 742	5	5			
56	9.57 232	32	9.60 495	37	0.39 505	9.96 737	5	4			
57	9.57 264	31	9.60 532	36	0.39 468	9.96 732	5	3			
58	9.57 295	31	9.60 568	37	0.39 432	9.96 727	5	2			
59	9.57 326	32	9.60 605	36	0.39 395	9.96 722	5	1			
60	9.57 358		9.60 641		0.39 359	9.96 717		0			
	Log Cos	d	Log Cot	c d	Log Tan	Log Sin	d	′	Prop. Parts		

′	Log Sin	d	Log Tan	c d	Log Cot	Log Cos	d		Prop. Parts		
0	9.57 358	31	9.60 641	36	0.39 359	9.96 717	6	60			
1	9.57 389	31	9.60 677	37	0.39 323	9.96 711	5	59			
2	9.57 420	31	9.60 714	36	0.39 286	9.96 706	5	58			
3	9.57 451	31	9.60 750	36	0.39 250	9.96 701	5	57			
4	9.57 482	32	9.60 786	37	0.39 214	9.96 696	5	56			
5	9.57 514	31	9.60 823	36	0.39 177	9.96 691	5	55			
6	9.57 545	31	9.60 859	36	0.39 141	9.96 686	5	54			
7	9.57 576	31	9.60 895	36	0.39 105	9.96 681	5	53			
8	9.57 607	31	9.60 931	36	0.39 069	9.96 676	6	52			
9	9.57 638	31	9.60 967	37	0.39 033	9.96 670	5	51	**37**	**36**	**35**
10	9.57 669	31	9.61 004	36	0.38 996	9.96 665	5	50	1 3.7	3.6	3.5
11	9.57 700	31	9.61 040	36	0.38 960	9.96 660	5	49	2 7.4	7.2	7.0
12	9.57 731	31	9.61 076	36	0.38 924	9.96 655	5	48	3 11.1	10.8	10.5
13	9.57 762	31	9.61 112	36	0.38 888	9.96 650	5	47	4 14.8	14.4	14.0
14	9.57 793	31	9.61 148	36	0.38 852	9.96 645	5	46	5 18.5	18.0	17.5
15	9.57 824	31	9.61 184	36	0.38 816	9.96 640	6	45	6 22.2	21.6	21.0
16	9.57 855	30	9.61 220	36	0.38 780	9.96 634	5	44	7 25.9	25.2	24.5
17	9.57 885	31	9.61 256	36	0.38 744	9.96 629	5	43	8 29.6	28.8	28.0
18	9.57 916	31	9.61 292	36	0.38 708	9.96 624	5	42	9 33.3	32.4	31.5
19	9.57 947	31	9.61 328	36	0.38 672	9.96 619	5	41			
20	9.57 978	30	9.61 364	36	0.38 636	9.96 614	6	40			
21	9.58 008	31	9.61 400	36	0.38 600	9.96 608	5	39			
22	9.58 039	31	9.61 436	36	0.38 564	9.96 603	5	38			
23	9.58 070	31	9.61 472	36	0.38 528	9.96 598	5	37			
24	9.58 101	30	9.61 508	36	0.38 492	9.96 593	5	36			
25	9.58 131	31	9.61 544	35	0.38 456	9.96 588	6	35	**32**	**31**	**30**
26	9.58 162	30	9.61 579	36	0.38 421	9.96 582	5	34	1 3.2	3.1	3.0
27	9.58 192	31	9.61 615	36	0.38 385	9.96 577	5	33	2 6.4	6.2	6.0
28	9.58 223	30	9.61 651	36	0.38 349	9.96 572	5	32	3 9.6	9.3	9.0
29	9.58 253	31	9.61 687	35	0.38 313	9.96 567	5	31	4 12.8	12.4	12.0
30	9.58 284	30	9.61 722	36	0.38 278	9.96 562	6	30	5 16.0	15.5	15.0
31	9.58 314	31	9.61 758	36	0.38 242	9.96 556	5	29	6 19.2	18.6	18.0
32	9.58 345	30	9.61 794	36	0.38 206	9.96 551	5	28	7 22.4	21.7	21.0
33	9.58 375	31	9.61 830	35	0.38 170	9.96 546	5	27	8 25.6	24.8	24.0
34	9.58 406	30	9.61 865	36	0.38 135	9.96 541	6	26	9 28.8	27.9	27.0
35	9.58 436	31	9.61 901	35	0.38 099	9.96 535	5	25			
36	9.58 467	30	9.61 936	36	0.38 064	9.96 530	5	24			
37	9.58 497	30	9.61 972	36	0.38 028	9.96 525	5	23			
38	9.58 527	30	9.62 008	35	0.37 992	9.96 520	6	22			
39	9.58 557	31	9.62 043	36	0.37 957	9.96 514	5	21			
40	9.58 588	30	9.62 079	35	0.37 921	9.96 509	5	20			
41	9.58 618	30	9.62 114	36	0.37 886	9.96 504	6	19			
42	9.58 648	30	9.62 150	35	0.37 850	9.96 498	5	18	**29**	**6**	**5**
43	9.58 678	31	9.62 185	36	0.37 815	9.96 493	5	17	1 2.9	0.6	0.5
44	9.58 709	30	9.62 221	35	0.37 779	9.96 488	5	16	2 5.8	1.2	1.0
45	9.58 739	30	9.62 256	36	0.37 744	9.96 483	6	15	3 8.7	1.8	1.5
46	9.58 769	30	9.62 292	35	0.37 708	9.96 477	5	14	4 11.6	2.4	2.0
47	9.58 799	30	9.62 327	35	0.37 673	9.96 472	5	13	5 14.5	3.0	2.5
48	9.58 829	30	9.62 362	36	0.37 638	9.96 467	6	12	6 17.4	3.6	3.0
49	9.58 859	30	9.62 398	35	0.37 602	9.96 461	5	11	7 20.3	4.2	3.5
50	9.58 889	30	9.62 433	35	0.37 567	9.96 456	5	10	8 23.2	4.8	4.0
51	9.58 919	30	9.62 468	36	0.37 532	9.96 451	6	9	9 26.1	5.4	4.5
52	9.58 949	30	9.62 504	35	0.37 496	9.96 445	5	8			
53	9.58 979	30	9.62 539	35	0.37 461	9.96 440	5	7			
54	9.59 009	30	9.62 574	35	0.37 426	9.96 435	6	6			
55	9.59 039	30	9.62 609	36	0.37 391	9.96 429	5	5			
56	9.59 069	29	9.62 645	35	0.37 355	9.96 424	5	4			
57	9.59 098	30	9.62 680	35	0.37 320	9.96 419	6	3			
58	9.59 128	30	9.62 715	35	0.37 285	9.96 413	5	2			
59	9.59 158	30	9.62 750	35	0.37 250	9.96 408	5	1			
60	9.59 188		9.62 785		0.37 215	9.96 403		0			
	Log Cos	d	Log Cot	c d	Log Tan	Log Sin	d	′	Prop. Parts		

′	Log Sin	d	Log Tan	c d	Log Cot	Log Cos	d	
0	9.59 188	30	9.62 785	35	0.37 215	9.96 403	6	60
1	9.59 218	29	9.62 820	35	0.37 180	9.96 3?7	5	59
2	9.59 247	30	9.62 855	35	0.37 145	9.96 392	5	58
3	9.59 277	30	9.62 890	36	0.37 110	9.96 387	6	57
4	9.59 307	29	9.62 926	35	0.37 074	9.96 381	5	56
5	9.59 336	30	9.62 961	35	0.37 039	9.96 376	6	55
6	9.59 366	30	9.62 996	35	0.37 004	9.96 370	5	54
7	9.59 396	29	9.63 031	35	0.36 969	9.96 365	5	53
8	9.59 425	30	9.63 066	35	0.36 934	9.96 360	5	52
9	9.59 455	29	9.63 101	34	0.36 899	9.96 354	5	51
10	9.59 484	30	9.63 135	35	0.36 865	9.96 349	6	50
11	9.59 514	29	9.63 170	35	0.36 830	9.96 343	5	49
12	9.59 543	30	9.63 205	35	0.36 795	9.96 338	5	48
13	9.59 573	29	9.63 240	35	0.36 760	9.96 333	6	47
14	9.59 602	30	9.63 275	35	0.36 725	9.96 327	5	46
15	9.59 632	29	9.63 310	35	0.36 690	9.96 322	6	45
16	9.59 661	29	9.63 345	34	0.36 655	9.96 316	5	44
17	9.59 690	30	9.63 379	35	0.36 621	9.96 311	6	43
18	9.59 720	29	9.63 414	35	0.36 586	9.96 305	5	42
19	9.59 749	29	9.63 449	35	0.36 551	9.96 300	6	41
20	9.59 778	30	9.63 484	35	0.36 516	9.96 294	5	40
21	9.59 808	29	9.63 519	34	0.36 481	9.96 289	5	39
22	9.59 837	29	9.63 553	35	0.36 447	9.96 284	6	38
23	9.59 866	29	9.63 588	35	0.36 412	9.96 278	5	37
24	9.59 895	29	9.63 623	34	0.36 377	9.96 273	6	36
25	9.59 924	30	9.63 657	35	0.36 343	9.96 267	5	35
26	9.59 954	29	9.63 692	34	0.36 308	9.96 262	6	34
27	9.59 983	29	9.63 726	35	0.36 274	9.96 256	5	33
28	9.60 012	29	9.63 761	35	0.36 239	9.96 251	6	32
29	9.60 041	29	9.63 796	34	0.36 204	9.96 245	5	31
30	9.60 070	29	9.63 830	35	0.36 170	9.96 240	6	30
31	9.60 099	29	9.63 865	34	0.36 135	9.96 234	5	29
32	9.60 128	29	9.63 899	35	0.36 101	9.96 229	6	28
33	9.60 157	29	9.63 934	34	0.36 066	9.96 223	5	27
34	9.60 186	29	9.63 968	35	0.36 032	9.96 218	6	26
35	9.60 215	29	9.64 003	34	0.35 997	9.96 212	5	25
36	9.60 244	29	9.64 037	35	0.35 963	9.96 207	6	24
37	9.60 273	29	9.64 072	34	0.35 928	9.96 201	5	23
38	9.60 302	29	9.64 106	34	0.35 894	9.96 196	6	22
39	9.60 331	28	9.64 140	35	0.35 860	9.96 190	5	21
40	9.60 359	29	9.64 175	34	0.35 825	9.96 185	6	20
41	9.60 388	29	9.64 209	34	0.35 791	9.96 179	5	19
42	9.60 417	29	9.64 243	35	0.35 757	9.96 174	6	18
43	9.60 446	28	9.64 278	34	0.35 722	9.96 168	6	17
44	9.60 474	29	9.64 312	34	0.35 688	9.96 162	5	16
45	9.60 503	29	9.64 346	35	0.35 654	9.96 157	6	15
46	9.60 532	29	9.64 381	34	0.35 619	9.96 151	5	14
47	9.60 561	28	9.64 415	34	0.35 585	9.96 146	6	13
48	9.60 589	29	9.64 449	34	0.35 551	9.96 140	5	12
49	9.60 618	28	9.64 483	34	0.35 517	9.96 135	6	11
50	9.60 646	29	9.64 517	35	0.35 483	9.96 129	6	10
51	9.60 675	29	9.64 552	34	0.35 448	9.96 123	5	9
52	9.60 704	28	9.64 586	34	0.35 414	9.96 118	6	8
53	9.60 732	29	9.64 620	34	0.35 380	9.96 112	5	7
54	9.60 761	28	9.64 654	34	0.35 346	9.96 107	6	6
55	9.60 789	29	9.64 688	34	0.35 312	9.96 101	6	5
56	9.60 818	28	9.64 722	34	0.35 278	9.96 095	5	4
57	9.60 846	29	9.64 756	34	0.35 244	9.96 090	6	3
58	9.60 875	28	9.64 790	34	0.35 210	9.96 084	6	2
59	9.60 903	28	9.64 824	34	0.35 176	9.96 079	5	1
60	9.60 931		9.64 858		0.35 142	9.96 073		0
	Log Cos	d	Log Cot	c d	Log Tan	Log Sin	d	′

Prop. Parts

	36	35	34
1	3.6	3.5	3.4
2	7.2	7.0	6.8
3	10.8	10.5	10.2
4	14.4	14.0	13.6
5	18.0	17.5	17.0
6	21.6	21.0	20.4
7	25.2	24.5	23.8
8	28.8	28.0	27.2
9	32.4	31.5	30.6

	30	29	28
1	3.0	2.9	2.8
2	6.0	5.8	5.6
3	9.0	8.7	8.4
4	12.0	11.6	11.2
5	15.0	14.5	14.0
6	18.0	17.4	16.8
7	21.0	20.3	19.6
8	24.0	23.2	22.4
9	27.0	26.1	25.2

	6	5
1	0.6	0.5
2	1.2	1.0
3	1.8	1.5
4	2.4	2.0
5	3.0	2.5
6	3.6	3.0
7	4.2	3.5
8	4.8	4.0
9	5.4	4.5

'	Log Sin	d	Log Tan	c d	Log Cot	Log Cos	d		Prop. Parts		
0	9.60 931	29	9.64 858	34	0.35 142	9.96 073	6	60			
1	9.60 960	28	9.64 892	34	0.35 108	9.96 067	5	59			
2	9.60 988	28	9.64 926	34	0.35 074	9.96 062	6	58			
3	9.61 016	29	9.64 960	34	0.35 040	9.96 056	6	57			
4	9.61 045	28	9.64 994	34	0.35 006	9.96 050	5	56			
5	9.61 073	28	9.65 028	34	0.34 972	9.96 045	6	55			
6	9.61 101	28	9.65 062	34	0.34 938	9.96 039	5	54			
7	9.61 129	29	9.65 096	34	0.34 904	9.96 034	6	53			
8	9.61 158	28	9.65 130	34	0.34 870	9.96 028	6	52			
9	9.61 186	28	9.65 164	33	0.34 836	9.96 022	5	51	**34**	**33**	**29**
10	9.61 214	28	9.65 197	34	0.34 803	9.96 017	6	50	1	3.4	3.3	2.9
11	9.61 242	28	9.65 231	34	0.34 769	9.96 011	6	49	2	6.8	6.6	5.8
12	9.61 270	28	9.65 265	34	0.34 735	9.96 005	5	48	3	10.2	9.9	8.7
13	9.61 298	28	9.65 299	34	0.34 701	9.96 000	6	47	4	13.6	13.2	11.6
14	9.61 326	28	9.65 333	33	0.34 667	9.95 994	6	46	5	17.0	16.5	14.5
15	9.61 354	28	9.65 366	34	0.34 634	9.95 988	6	45	6	20.4	19.8	17.4
16	9.61 382	29	9.65 400	34	0.34 600	9.95 982	5	44	7	23.8	23.1	20.3
17	9.61 411	27	9.65 434	33	0.34 566	9.95 977	6	43	8	27.2	26.4	23.2
18	9.61 438	28	9.65 467	34	0.34 533	9.95 971	6	42	9	30.6	29.7	26.1
19	9.61 466	28	9.65 501	34	0.34 499	9.95 965	5	41			
20	9.61 494	28	9.65 535	33	0.34 465	9.95 960	6	40			
21	9.61 522	28	9.65 568	34	0.34 432	9.95 954	6	39			
22	9.61 550	28	9.65 602	34	0.34 398	9.95 948	6	38			
23	9.61 578	28	9.65 636	33	0.34 364	9.95 942	5	37			
24	9.61 606	28	9.65 669	34	0.34 331	9.95 937	6	36			
25	9.61 634	28	9.65 703	33	0.34 297	9.95 931	6	35		**28**	**27**
26	9.61 662	27	9.65 736	34	0.34 264	9.95 925	5	34		**28**	**27**
27	9.61 689	28	9.65 770	33	0.34 230	9.95 920	6	33	1	2.8	2.7
28	9.61 717	28	9.65 803	34	0.34 197	9.95 914	6	32	2	5.6	5.4
29	9.61 745	28	9.65 837	33	0.34 163	9.95 908	6	31	3	8.4	8.1
30	9.61 773	27	9.65 870	34	0.34 130	9.95 902	5	30	4	11.2	10.8
31	9.61 800	28	9.65 904	33	0.34 096	9.95 897	6	29	5	14.0	13.5
32	9.61 828	28	9.65 937	34	0.34 063	9.95 891	6	28	6	16.8	16.2
33	9.61 856	27	9.65 971	33	0.34 029	9.95 885	6	27	7	19.6	18.9
34	9.61 883	28	9.66 004	34	0.33 996	9.95 879	6	26	8	22.4	21.6
35	9.61 911	28	9.66 038	33	0.33 962	9.95 873	5	25	9	25.2	24.3
36	9.61 939	27	9.66 071	33	0.33 929	9.95 868	6	24			
37	9.61 966	28	9.66 104	34	0.33 896	9.95 862	6	23			
38	9.61 994	27	9.66 138	33	0.33 862	9.95 856	6	22			
39	9.62 021	28	9.66 171	33	0.33 829	9.95 850	6	21			
40	9.62 049	27	9.66 204	34	0.33 796	9.95 844	5	20			
41	9.62 076	28	9.66 238	33	0.33 762	9.95 839	6	19			
42	9.62 104	27	9.66 271	33	0.33 729	9.95 833	6	18			
43	9.62 131	28	9.66 304	33	0.33 696	9.95 827	6	17		**6**	**5**
44	9.62 159	27	9.66 337	34	0.33 663	9.95 821	6	16	1	0.6	0.5
45	9.62 186	28	9.66 371	33	0.33 629	9.95 815	5	15	2	1.2	1.0
46	9.62 214	27	9.66 404	33	0.33 596	9.95 810	6	14	3	1.8	1.5
47	9.62 241	27	9.66 437	33	0.33 563	9.95 804	6	13	4	2.4	2.0
48	9.62 268	28	9.66 470	33	0.33 530	9.95 798	6	12	5	3.0	2.5
49	9.62 296	27	9.66 503	34	0.33 497	9.95 792	6	11	6	3.6	3.0
50	9.62 323	27	9.66 537	33	0.33 463	9.95 786	6	10	7	4.2	3.5
51	9.62 350	27	9.66 570	33	0.33 430	9.95 780	5	9	8	4.8	4.0
52	9.62 377	28	9.66 603	33	0.33 397	9.95 775	6	8	9	5.4	4.5
53	9.62 405	27	9.66 636	33	0.33 364	9.95 769	6	7			
54	9.62 432	27	9.66 669	33	0.33 331	9.95 763	6	6			
55	9.62 459	27	9.66 702	33	0.33 298	9.95 757	6	5			
56	9.62 486	27	9.66 735	33	0.33 265	9.95 751	6	4			
57	9.62 513	28	9.66 768	33	0.33 232	9.95 745	6	3			
58	9.62 541	27	9.66 801	33	0.33 199	9.95 739	6	2			
59	9.62 568	27	9.66 834	33	0.33 166	9.95 733	5	1			
60	9.62 595		9.66 867		0.33 133	9.95 728		0			
	Log Cos	d	Log Cot	c d	Log Tan	Log Sin	d	'	Prop. Parts		

′	Log Sin	d	Log Tan	c d	Log Cot	Log Cos	d	
0	9.62 595	27	9.66 867	33	0.33 133	9.95 728	6	60
1	9.62 622	27	9.66 900	33	0.33 100	9.95 722	6	59
2	9.62 649	27	9.66 933	33	0.33 067	9.95 716	6	58
3	9.62 676	27	9.66 966	33	0.33 034	9.95 710	6	57
4	9.62 703	27	9.66 999	33	0.33 001	9.95 704	6	56
5	9.62 730	27	9.67 032	33	0.32 968	9.95 698	6	55
6	9.62 757	27	9.67 065	33	0.32 935	9.95 692	6	54
7	9.62 784	27	9.67 098	33	0.32 902	9.95 686	6	53
8	9.62 811	27	9.67 131	32	0.32 869	9.95 680	6	52
9	9.62 838	27	9.67 163	33	0.32 837	9.95 674	6	51
10	9.62 865	27	9.67 196	33	0.32 804	9.95 668	5	50
11	9.62 892	26	9.67 229	33	0.32 771	9.95 663	6	49
12	9.62 918	27	9.67 262	33	0.32 738	9.95 657	6	48
13	9.62 945	27	9.67 295	32	0.32 705	9.95 651	6	47
14	9.62 972	27	9.67 327	33	0.32 673	9.95 645	6	46
15	9.62 999	27	9.67 360	33	0.32 640	9.95 639	6	45
16	9.63 026	26	9.67 393	33	0.32 607	9.95 633	6	44
17	9.63 052	27	9.67 426	32	0.32 574	9.95 627	6	43
18	9.63 079	27	9.67 458	33	0.32 542	9.95 621	6	42
19	9.63 106	27	9.67 491	33	0.32 509	9.95 615	6	41
20	9.63 133	26	9.67 524	32	0.32 476	9.95 609	6	40
21	9.63 159	27	9.67 556	33	0.32 444	9.95 603	6	39
22	9.63 186	27	9.67 589	33	0.32 411	9.95 597	6	38
23	9.63 213	26	9.67 622	32	0.32 378	9.95 591	6	37
24	9.63 239	27	9.67 654	33	0.32 346	9.95 585	6	36
25	9.63 266	26	9.67 687	32	0.32 313	9.95 579	6	35
26	9.63 292	27	9.67 719	33	0.32 281	9.95 573	6	34
27	9.63 319	26	9.67 752	33	0.32 248	9.95 567	6	33
28	9.63 345	27	9.67 785	32	0.32 215	9.95 561	6	32
29	9.63 372	26	9.67 817	33	0.32 183	9.95 555	6	31
30	9.63 398	27	9.67 850	32	0.32 150	9.95 549	6	30
31	9.63 425	26	9.67 882	33	0.32 118	9.95 543	6	29
32	9.63 451	27	9.67 915	32	0.32 085	9.95 537	6	28
33	9.63 478	26	9.67 947	33	0.32 053	9.95 531	6	27
34	9.63 504	27	9.67 980	32	0.32 020	9.95 525	6	26
35	9.63 531	26	9.68 012	32	0.31 988	9.95 519	6	25
36	9.63 557	26	9.68 044	33	0.31 956	9.95 513	6	24
37	9.63 583	27	9.68 077	32	0.31 923	9.95 507	7	23
38	9.63 610	26	9.68 109	33	0.31 891	9.95 500	6	22
39	9.63 636	26	9.68 142	32	0.31 858	9.95 494	6	21
40	9.63 662	27	9.68 174	32	0.31 826	9.95 488	6	20
41	9.63 689	26	9.68 206	33	0.31 794	9.95 482	6	19
42	9.63 715	26	9.68 239	32	0.31 761	9.95 476	6	18
43	9.63 741	26	9.68 271	32	0.31 729	9.95 470	6	17
44	9.63 767	27	9.68 303	33	0.31 697	9.95 464	6	16
45	9.63 794	26	9.68 336	32	0.31 664	9.95 458	6	15
46	9.63 820	26	9.68 368	32	0.31 632	9.95 452	6	14
47	9.63 846	26	9.68 400	32	0.31 600	9.95 446	6	13
48	9.63 872	26	9.68 432	33	0.31 568	9.95 440	6	12
49	9.63 898	26	9.68 465	32	0.31 535	9.95 434	7	11
50	9.63 924	26	9.68 497	32	0.31 503	9.95 427	6	10
51	9.63 950	26	9.68 529	32	0.31 471	9.95 421	6	9
52	9.63 976	26	9.68 561	32	0.31 439	9.95 415	6	8
53	9.64 002	26	9.68 593	33	0.31 407	9.95 409	6	7
54	9.64 028	26	9.68 626	32	0.31 374	9.95 403	6	6
55	9.64 054	26	9.68 658	32	0.31 342	9.95 397	6	5
56	9.64 080	26	9.68 690	32	0.31 310	9.95 391	7	4
57	9.64 106	26	9.68 722	32	0.31 278	9.95 384	6	3
58	9.64 132	26	9.68 754	32	0.31 246	9.95 378	6	2
59	9.64 158	26	9.68 786	32	0.31 214	9.95 372	6	1
60	9.64 184		9.68 818		0.31 182	9.95 366		0
	Log Cos	d	Log Cot	c d	Log Tan	Log Sin	d	′

Prop. Parts

	33	32	27
1	3.3	3.2	2.7
2	6.6	6.4	5.4
3	9.9	9.6	8.1
4	13.2	12.8	10.8
5	16.5	16.0	13.5
6	19.8	19.2	16.2
7	23.1	22.4	18.9
8	26.4	25.6	21.6
9	29.7	28.8	24.3

	26	7
1	2.6	0.7
2	5.2	1.4
3	7.8	2.1
4	10.4	2.8
5	13.0	3.5
6	15.6	4.2
7	18.2	4.9
8	20.8	5.6
9	23.4	6.3

	6	5
1	0.6	0.5
2	1.2	1.0
3	1.8	1.5
4	2.4	2.0
5	3.0	2.5
6	3.6	3.0
7	4.2	3.5
8	4.8	4.0
9	5.4	4.5

′	Log Sin	d	Log Tan	c d	Log Cot	Log Cos	d		Prop. Parts
0	9.64 184	26	9.68 818	32	0.31 182	9.95 366	6	60	
1	9.64 210	26	9.68 850	32	0.31 150	9.95 360	6	59	
2	9.64 236	26	9.68 882	32	0.31 118	9.95 354	6	58	
3	9.64 262	26	9.68 914	32	0.31 086	9.95 348	7	57	
4	9.64 288	25	9.68 946	32	0.31 054	9.95 341	6	56	
5	9.64 313	26	9.68 978	32	0.31 022	9.95 335	6	55	
6	9.64 339	26	9.69 010	32	0.30 990	9.95 329	6	54	
7	9.64 365	26	9.69 042	32	0.30 958	9.95 323	6	53	
8	9.64 391	26	9.69 074	32	0.30 926	9.95 317	7	52	
9	9.64 417	25	9.69 106	32	0.30 894	9.95 310	6	51	

	32	31	26
1	3.2	3.1	2.6
2	6.4	6.2	5.2
3	9.6	9.3	7.8
4	12.8	12.4	10.4
5	16.0	15.5	13.0
6	19.2	18.6	15.6
7	22.4	21.7	18.2
8	25.6	24.8	20.8
9	28.8	27.9	23.4

′	Log Sin	d	Log Tan	c d	Log Cot	Log Cos	d	
10	9.64 442	26	9.69 138	32	0.30 862	9.95 304	6	50
11	9.64 468	26	9.69 170	32	0.30 830	9.95 298	6	49
12	9.64 494	25	9.69 202	32	0.30 798	9.95 292	6	48
13	9.64 519	26	9.69 234	32	0.30 766	9.95 286;	7	47
14	9.64 545	26	9.69 266	32	0.30 734	9.95 279	6	46
15	9.64 571	25	9.69 298	31	0.30 702	9.95 273	6	45
16	9.64 596	26	9.69 329	32	0.30 671	9.95 267	6	44
17	9.64 622	25	9.69 361	32	0.30 639	9.95 261	7	43
18	9.64 647	26	9.69 393	32	0.30 607	9.95 254	6	42
19	9.64 673	25	9.69 425	32	0.30 575	9.95 248	6	41
20	9.64 698	26	9.69 457	31	0.30 543	9.95 242	6	40
21	9.64 724	25	9.69 488	32	0.30 512	9.95 236	7	39
22	9.64 749	26	9.69 520	32	0.30 480	9.95 229	6	38
23	9.64 775	25	9.69 552	32	0.30 448	9.95 223	6	37
24	9.64 800	26	9.69 584	31	0.30 416	9.95 217	6	36
25	9.64 826	25	9.69 615	32	0.30 385	9.95 211	7	35
26	9.64 851	26	9.69 647	32	0.30 353	9.95 204	6	34
27	9.64 877	25	9.69 679	31	0.30 321	9.95 198	6	33
28	9.64 902	25	9.69 710	32	0.30 290	9.95 192	7	32
29	9.64 927	26	9.69 742	32	0.30 258	9.95 185	6	31

	25	24
1	2.5	2.4
2	5.0	4.8
3	7.5	7.2
4	10.0	9.6
5	12.5	12.0
6	15.0	14.4
7	17.5	16.8
8	20.0	19.2
9	22.5	21.6

′	Log Sin	d	Log Tan	c d	Log Cot	Log Cos	d	
30	9.64 953	25	9.69 774	31	0.30 226	9.95 179	6	30
31	9.64 978	25	9.69 805	32	0.30 195	9.95 173	6	29
32	9.65 003	26	9.69 837	31	0.30 163	9.95 167	7	28
33	9.65 029	25	9.69 868	32	0.30 132	9.95 160	6	27
34	9.65 054	25	9.69 900	32	0.30 100	9.95 154	6	26
35	9.65 079	25	9.69 932	31	0.30 068	9.95 148	7	25
36	9.65 104	26	9.69 963	32	0.30 037	9.95 141	6	24
37	9.65 130	25	9.69 995	31	0.30 005	9.95 135	6	23
38	9.65 155	25	9.70 026	32	0.29 974	9.95 129	7	22
39	9.65 180	25	9.70 058	31	0.29 942	9.95 122	6	21
40	9.65 205	25	9.70 089	32	0.29 911	9.95 116	6	20
41	9.65 230	25	9.70 121	31	0.29 879	9.95 110	7	19
42	9.65 255	26	9.70 152	32	0.29 848	9.95 103	6	18
43	9.65 281	25	9.70 184	31	0.29 816	9.95 097	7	17
44	9.65 306	25	9.70 215	32	0.29 785	9.95 090	6	16
45	9.65 331	25	9.70 247	31	0.29 753	9.95 084	6	15
46	9.65 356	25	9.70 278	31	0.29 722	9.95 078	7	14
47	9.65 381	25	9.70 309	32	0.29 691	9.95 071	6	13
48	9.65 406	25	9.70 341	31	0.29 659	9.95 065	6	12
49	9.65 431	25	9.70 372	32	0.29 628	9.95 059	7	11

	7	6
1	0.7	0.6
2	1.4	1.2
3	2.1	1.8
4	2.8	2.4
5	3.5	3.0
6	4.2	3.6
7	4.9	4.2
8	5.6	4.8
9	6.3	5.4

′	Log Sin	d	Log Tan	c d	Log Cot	Log Cos	d	
50	9.65 456	25	9.70 404	31	0.29 596	9.95 052	6	10
51	9.65 481	25	9.70 435	31	0.29 565	9.95 046	7	9
52	9.65 506	25	9.70 466	32	0.29 534	9.95 039	6	8
53	9.65 531	25	9.70 498	31	0.29 502	9.95 033	6	7
54	9.65 556	24	9.70 529	31	0.29 471	9.95 027	7	6
55	9.65 580	25	9.70 560	32	0.29 440	9.95 020	6	5
56	9.65 605	25	9.70 592	31	0.29 408	9.95 014	7	4
57	9.65 630	25	9.70 623	31	0.29 377	9.95 007	6	3
58	9.65 655	25	9.70 654	31	0.29 346	9.95 001	6	2
59	9.65 680	25	9.70 685	32	0.29 315	9.94 995	7	1
60	9.65 705		9.70 717		0.29 283	9.94 988		0

	Log Cos	d	Log Cot	c d	Log Tan	Log Sin	d	′	Prop. Parts

′	Log Sin	d	Log Tan	c d	Log Cot	Log Cos	d		Prop. Parts		
0	9.65 705	24	9.70 717	31	0.29 283	9.94 988	6	60			
1	9.65 729	25	9.70 748	31	0.29 252	9.94 982	7	59			
2	9.65 754	25	9.70 779	31	0.29 221	9.94 975	6	58			
3	9.65 779	25	9.70 810	31	0.29 190	9.94 969	7	57			
4	9.65 804	24	9.70 841	32	0.29 159	9.94 962	6	56			
5	9.65 828	25	9.70 873	31	0.29 127	9.94 956	7	55			
6	9.65 853	25	9.70 904	31	0.29 096	9.94 949	6	54			
7	9.65 878	24	9.70 935	31	0.29 065	9.94 943	7	53			
8	9.65 902	25	9.70 966	31	0.29 034	9.94 936	6	52			
9	9.65 927	25	9.70 997	31	0.29 003	9.94 930	7	51		**32**	**31**	**30**
10	9.65 952	24	9.71 028	31	0.28 972	9.94 923	6	50	1	3.2	3.1	3.0
11	9.65 976	25	9.71 059	31	0.28 941	9.94 917	6	49	2	6.4	6.2	6.0
12	9.66 001	24	9.71 090	31	0.28 910	9.94 911	7	48	3	9.6	9.3	9.0
13	9.66 025	25	9.71 121	32	0.28 879	9.94 904	6	47	4	12.8	12.4	12.0
14	9.66 050	25	9.71 153	31	0.28 847	9.94 898	7	46	5	16.0	15.5	15.0
15	9.66 075	24	9.71 184	31	0.28 816	9.94 891	6	45	6	19.2	18.6	18.0
16	9.66 099	25	9.71 215	31	0.28 785	9.94 885	7	44	7	22.4	21.7	21.0
17	9.66 124	24	9.71 246	31	0.28 754	9.94 878	7	43	8	25.6	24.8	24.0
18	9.66 148	25	9.71 277	31	0.28 723	9.94 871	6	42	9	28.8	27.9	27.0
19	9.66 173	24	9.71 308	31	0.28 692	9.94 865	7	41			
20	9.66 197	24	9.71 339	31	0.28 661	9.94 858	6	40			
21	9.66 221	25	9.71 370	31	0.28 630	9.94 852	7	39			
22	9.66 246	24	9.71 401	30	0.28 599	9.94 845	6	38			
23	9.66 270	25	9.71 431	31	0.28 569	9.94 839	7	37			
24	9.66 295	24	9.71 462	31	0.28 538	9.94 832	6	36			
25	9.66 319	24	9.71 493	31	0.28 507	9.94 826	7	35		**25**	**24**	**23**
26	9.66 343	25	9.71 524	31	0.28 476	9.94 819	6	34	1	2.5	2.4	2.3
27	9.66 368	24	9.71 555	31	0.28 445	9.94 813	7	33	2	5.0	4.8	4.6
28	9.66 392	24	9.71 586	31	0.28 414	9.94 806	7	32	3	7.5	7.2	6.9
29	9.66 416	25	9.71 617	31	0.28 383	9.94 799	6	31	4	10.0	9.6	9.2
30	9.66 441	24	9.71 648	31	0.28 352	9.94 793	7	30	5	12.5	12.0	11.5
31	9.66 465	24	9.71 679	30	0.28 321	9.94 786	6	29	6	15.0	14.4	13.8
32	9.66 489	24	9.71 709	31	0.28 291	9.94 780	7	28	7	17.5	16.8	16.1
33	9.66 513	24	9.71 740	31	0.28 260	9.94 773	6	27	8	20.0	19.2	18.4
34	9.66 537	25	9.71 771	31	0.28 229	9.94 767	7	26	9	22.5	21.6	20.7
35	9.66 562	24	9.71 802	31	0.28 198	9.94 760	7	25			
36	9.66 586	24	9.71 833	30	0.28 167	9.94 753	6	24			
37	9.66 610	24	9.71 863	31	0.28 137	9.94 747	7	23			
38	9.66 634	24	9.71 894	31	0.28 106	9.94 740	6	22			
39	9.66 658	24	9.71 925	30	0.28 075	9.94 734	7	21			
40	9.66 682	24	9.71 955	31	0.28 045	9.94 727	7	20			
41	9.66 706	25	9.71 986	31	0.28 014	9.94 720	6	19			
42	9.66 731	24	9.72 017	31	0.27 983	9.94 714	7	18		**7**	**6**	
43	9.66 755	24	9.72 048	30	0.27 952	9.94 707	7	17	1	0.7	0.6	
44	9.66 779	24	9.72 078	31	0.27 922	9.94 700	6	16	2	1.4	1.2	
45	9.66 803	24	9.72 109	31	0.27 891	9.94 694	7	15	3	2.1	1.8	
46	9.66 827	24	9.72 140	30	0.27 860	9.94 687	7	14	4	2.8	2.4	
47	9.66 851	24	9.72 170	31	0.27 830	9.94 680	6	13	5	3.5	3.0	
48	9.66 875	24	9.72 201	30	0.27 799	9.94 674	7	12	6	4.2	3.6	
49	9.66 899	23	9.72 231	31	0.27 769	9.94 667	7	11	7	4.9	4.2	
50	9.66 922	24	9.72 262	31	0.27 738	9.94 660	6	10	8	5.6	4.8	
51	9.66 946	24	9.72 293	30	0.27 707	9.94 654	7	9	9	6.3	5.4	
52	9.66 970	24	9.72 323	31	0.27 677	9.94 647	7	8			
53	9.66 994	24	9.72 354	30	0.27 646	9.94 640	6	7			
54	9.67 018	24	9.72 384	31	0.27 616	9.94 634	7	6			
55	9.67 042	24	9.72 415	30	0.27 585	9.94 627	7	5			
56	9.67 066	24	9.72 445	31	0.27 555	9.94 620	6	4			
57	9.67 090	23	9.72 476	30	0.27 524	9.94 614	7	3			
58	9.67 113	24	9.72 506	31	0.27 494	9.94 607	7	2			
59	9.67 137	24	9.72 537	30	0.27 463	9.94 600	7	1			
60	9.67 161		9.72 567		0.27 433	9.94 593		0			
	Log Cos	d	Log Cot	c d	Log Tan	Log Sin	d	′	Prop. Parts		

′	Log Sin	d	Log Tan	c d	Log Cot	Log Cos	d		Prop. Parts		
0	9.67 161	24	9.72 567	31	0.27 433	9.94 593	6	60			
1	9.67 185	23	9.72 598	30	0.27 402	9.94 587	7	59			
2	9.67 208	24	9.72 628	31	0.27 372	9.94 580	7	58			
3	9.67 232	24	9.72 659	30	0.27 341	9.94 573	6	57			
4	9.67 256	24	9.72 689	31	0.27 311	9.94 567	7	56			
5	9.67 280	23	9.72 720	30	0.27 280	9.94 560	7	55			
6	9.67 303	24	9.72 750	30	0.27 250	9.94 553	7	54			
7	9.67 327	23	9.72 780	31	0.27 220	9.94 546	6	53			
8	9.67 350	24	9.72 811	30	0.27 189	9.94 540	7	52		31	30	29
9	9.67 374	24	9.72 841	31	0.27 159	9.94 533	7	51			
10	9.67 398	23	9.72 872	30	0.27 128	9.94 526	7	50	1	3.1	3.0	2.9
11	9.67 421	24	9.72 902	30	0.27 098	9.94 519	6	49	2	6.2	6.0	5.8
12	9.67 445	23	9.72 932	31	0.27 068	9.94 513	7	48	3	9.3	9.0	8.7
13	9.67 468	24	9.72 963	30	0.27 037	9.94 506	7	47	4	12.4	12.0	11.6
14	9.67 492	23	9.72 993	30	0.27 007	9.94 499	7	46	5	15.5	15.0	14.5
15	9.67 515	24	9.73 023	31	0.26 977	9.94 492	7	45	6	18.6	18.0	17.4
16	9.67 539	23	9.73 054	30	0.26 946	9.94 485	6	44	7	21.7	21.0	20.3
17	9.67 562	24	9.73 084	30	0.26 916	9.94 479	7	43	8	24.8	24.0	23.2
18	9.67 586	23	9.73 114	30	0.26 886	9.94 472	7	42	9	27.9	27.0	26.1
19	9.67 609	24	9.73 144	31	0.26 856	9.94 465	7	41			
20	9.67 633	23	9.73 175	30	0.26 825	9.94 458	7	40			
21	9.67 656	24	9.73 205	30	0.26 795	9.94 451	6	39			
22	9.67 680	23	9.73 235	30	0.26 765	9.94 445	7	38			
23	9.67 703	23	9.73 265	30	0.26 735	9.94 438	7	37			
24	9.67 726	24	9.73 295	31	0.26 705	9.94 431	7	36			
25	9.67 750	23	9.73 326	30	0.26 674	9.94 424	7	35		24	23	22
26	9.67 773	23	9.73 356	30	0.26 644	9.94 417	7	34			
27	9.67 796	24	9.73 386	30	0.26 614	9.94 410	6	33	1	2.4	2.3	2.2
28	9.67 820	23	9.73 416	30	0.26 584	9.94 404	7	32	2	4.8	4.6	4.4
29	9.67 843	23	9.73 446	30	0.26 554	9.94 397	7	31	3	7.2	6.9	6.6
30	9.67 866	24	9.73 476	31	0.26 524	9.94 390	7	30	4	9.6	9.2	8.8
31	9.67 890	23	9.73 507	30	0.26 493	9.94 383	7	29	5	12.0	11.5	11.0
32	9.67 913	23	9.73 537	30	0.26 463	9.94 376	7	28	6	14.4	13.8	13.2
33	9.67 936	23	9.73 567	30	0.26 433	9.94 369	7	27	7	16.8	16.1	15.4
34	9.67 959	23	9.73 597	30	0.26 403	9.94 362	7	26	8	19.2	18.4	17.6
35	9.67 982	24	9.73 627	30	0.26 373	9.94 355	6	25	9	21.6	20.7	19.8
36	9.68 006	23	9.73 657	30	0.26 343	9.94 349	7	24			
37	9.68 029	23	9.73 687	30	0.26 313	9.94 342	7	23			
38	9.68 052	23	9.73 717	30	0.26 283	9.94 335	7	22			
39	9.68 075	23	9.73 747	30	0.26 253	9.94 328	7	21			
40	9.68 098	23	9.73 777	30	0.26 223	9.94 321	7	20			
41	9.68 121	23	9.73 807	30	0.26 193	9.94 314	7	19			
42	9.68 144	23	9.73 837	30	0.26 163	9.94 307	7	18		7	6	
43	9.68 167	23	9.73 867	30	0.26 133	9.94 300	7	17	1	0.7	0.6	
44	9.68 190	23	9.73 897	30	0.26 103	9.94 293	7	16	2	1.4	1.2	
45	9.68 213	24	9.73 927	30	0.26 073	9.94 286	7	15	3	2.1	1.8	
46	9.68 237	23	9.73 957	30	0.26 043	9.94 279	6	14	4	2.8	2.4	
47	9.68 260	23	9.73 987	30	0.26 013	9.94 273	7	13	5	3.5	3.0	
48	9.68 283	22	9.74 017	30	0.25 983	9.94 266	7	12	6	4.2	3.6	
49	9.68 305	23	9.74 047	30	0.25 953	9.94 259	7	11	7	4.9	4.2	
50	9.68 328	23	9.74 077	30	0.25 923	9.94 252	7	10	8	5.6	4.8	
51	9.68 351	23	9.74 107	30	0.25 893	9.94 245	7	9	9	6.3	5.4	
52	9.68 374	23	9.74 137	29	0.25 863	9.94 238	7	8			
53	9.68 397	23	9.74 166	30	0.25 834	9.94 231	7	7			
54	9.68 420	23	9.74 196	30	0.25 804	9.94 224	7	6			
55	9.68 443	23	9.74 226	30	0.25 774	9.94 217	7	5			
56	9.68 466	23	9.74 256	30	0.25 744	9.94 210	7	4			
57	9.68 489	23	9.74 286	30	0.25 714	9.94 203	7	3			
58	9.68 512	22	9.74 316	29	0.25 684	9.94 196	7	2			
59	9.68 534	23	9.74 345	30	0.25 655	9.94 189	7	1			
60	9.68 557		9.74 375		0.25 625	9.94 182		0			
	Log Cos	d	Log Cot	c d	Log Tan	Log Sin	d	′		Prop. Parts		

′	Log Sin	d	Log Tan	c d	Log Cot	Log Cos	d		Prop. Parts
0	9.68 557	23	9.74 375	30	0.25 625	9.94 182	7	60	
1	9.68 580	23	9.74 405	30	0.25 595	9.94 175	7	59	
2	9.68 603	22	9.74 435	30	0.25 565	9.94 168	7	58	
3	9.68 625	23	9.74 465	29	0.25 535	9.94 161	7	57	
4	9.68 648	23	9.74 494	30	0.25 506	9.94 154	7	56	
5	9.68 671	23	9.74 524	30	0.25 476	9.94 147	7	55	
6	9.68 694	22	9.74 554	29	0.25 446	9.94 140	7	54	
7	9.68 716	23	9.74 583	30	0.25 417	9.94 133	7	53	
8	9.68 739	23	9.74 613	30	0.25 387	9.94 126	7	52	
9	9.68 762	22	9.74 643	30	0.25 357	9.94 119	7	51	
10	9.68 784	23	9.74 673	29	0.25 327	9.94 112	7	50	
11	9.68 807	22	9.74 702	30	0.25 298	9.94 105	7	49	
12	9.68 829	23	9.74 732	30	0.25 268	9.94 098	8	48	
13	9.68 852	23	9.74 762	29	0.25 238	9.94 090	7	47	
14	9.68 875	22	9.74 791	30	0.25 209	9.94 083	7	46	
15	9.68 897	23	9.74 821	30	0.25 179	9.94 076	7	45	
16	9.68 920	22	9.74 851	29	0.25 149	9.94 069	7	44	
17	9.68 942	23	9.74 880	30	0.25 120	9.94 062	7	43	
18	9.68 965	22	9.74 910	29	0.25 090	9.94 055	7	42	
19	9.68 987	23	9.74 939	30	0.25 061	9.94 048	7	41	
20	9.69 010	22	9.74 969	29	0.25 031	9.94 041	7	40	
21	9.69 032	23	9.74 998	30	0.25 002	9.94 034	7	39	
22	9.69 055	22	9.75 028	30	0.24 972	9.94 027	7	38	
23	9.69 077	23	9.75 058	29	0.24 942	9.94 020	8	37	
24	9.69 100	22	9.75 087	30	0.24 913	9.94 012	7	36	
25	9.69 122	22	9.75 117	29	0.24 883	9.94 005	7	35	
26	9.69 144	23	9.75 146	30	0.24 854	9.93 998	7	34	
27	9.69 167	22	9.75 176	29	0.24 824	9.93 991	7	33	
28	9.69 189	23	9.75 205	30	0.24 795	9.93 984	7	32	
29	9.69 212	22	9.75 235	29	0.24 765	9.93 977	7	31	
30	9.69 234	22	9.75 264	29	0.24 736	9.93 970	7	30	
31	9.69 256	23	9.75 294	29	0.24 706	9.93 963	8	29	
32	9.69 279	22	9.75 323	30	0.24 677	9.93 955	7	28	
33	9.69 301	22	9.75 353	29	0.24 647	9.93 948	7	27	
34	9.69 323	22	9.75 382	29	0.24 618	9.93 941	7	26	
35	9.69 345	23	9.75 411	30	0.24 589	9.93 934	7	25	
36	9.69 368	22	9.75 441	29	0.24 559	9.93 927	7	24	
37	9.69 390	22	9.75 470	30	0.24 530	9.93 920	8	23	
38	9.69 412	22	9.75 500	29	0.24 500	9.93 912	7	22	
39	9.69 434	22	9.75 529	29	0.24 471	9.93 905	7	21	
40	9.69 456	23	9.75 558	30	0.24 442	9.93 898	7	20	
41	9.69 479	22	9.75 588	29	0.24 412	9.93 891	7	19	
42	9.69 501	22	9.75 617	30	0.24 383	9.93 884	8	18	
43	9.69 523	22	9.75 647	29	0.24 353	9.93 876	7	17	
44	9.69 545	22	9.75 676	29	0.24 324	9.93 869	7	16	
45	9.69 567	22	9.75 705	30	0.24 295	9.93 862	7	15	
46	9.69 589	22	9.75 735	29	0.24 265	9.93 855	8	14	
47	9.69 611	22	9.75 764	29	0.24 236	9.93 847	7	13	
48	9.69 633	22	9.75 793	29	0.24 207	9.93 840	7	12	
49	9.69 655	22	9.75 822	30	0.24 178	9.93 833	7	11	
50	9.69 677	22	9.75 852	29	0.24 148	9.93 826	7	10	
51	9.69 699	22	9.75 881	29	0.24 119	9.93 819	8	9	
52	9.69 721	22	9.75 910	29	0.24 090	9.93 811	7	8	
53	9.69 743	22	9.75 939	30	0.24 061	9.93 804	7	7	
54	9.69 765	22	9.75 969	29	0.24 031	9.93 797	8	6	
55	9.69 787	22	9.75 998	29	0.24 002	9.93 789	7	5	
56	9.69 809	22	9.76 027	29	0.23 973	9.93 782	7	4	
57	9.69 831	22	9.76 056	30	0.23 944	9.93 775	7	3	
58	9.69 853	22	9.76 086	29	0.23 914	9.93 768	8	2	
59	9.69 875	22	9.76 115	29	0.23 885	9.93 760	7	1	
60	9.69 897		9.76 144		0.23 856	9.93 753		0	
	Log Cos	d	Log Cot	c d	Log Tan	Log Sin	d	′	Prop. Parts

Prop. Parts:

	30	29	23
1	3.0	2.9	2.3
2	6.0	5.8	4.6
3	9.0	8.7	6.9
4	12.0	11.6	9.2
5	15.0	14.5	11.5
6	18.0	17.4	13.8
7	21.0	20.3	16.1
8	24.0	23.2	18.4
9	27.0	26.1	20.7

	22	8	7
1	2.2	0.8	0.7
2	4.4	1.6	1.4
3	6.6	2.4	2.1
4	8.8	3.2	2.8
5	11.0	4.0	3.5
6	13.2	4.8	4.2
7	15.4	5.6	4.9
8	17.6	6.4	5.6
9	19.8	7.2	6.3

′	Log Sin	d	Log Tan	c d	Log Cot	Log Cos	d		Prop. Parts
0	9.69 897	22	9.76 144	29	0.23 856	9.93 753	7	60	
1	9.69 919	22	9.76 173	29	0.23 827	9.93 746	8	59	
2	9.69 941	22	9.76 202	29	0.23 798	9.93 738	7	58	
3	9.69 963	21	9.76 231	30	0.23 769	9.93 731	7	57	
4	9.69 984	22	9.76 261	29	0.23 739	9.93 724	7	56	
5	9.70 006	22	9.76 290	29	0.23 710	9.93 717	8	55	
6	9.70 028	22	9.76 319	29	0.23 681	9.93 709	7	54	
7	9.70 050	22	9.76 348	29	0.23 652	9.93 702	7	53	
8	9.70 072	21	9.76 377	29	0.23 623	9.93 695	8	52	
9	9.70 093	22	9.76 406	29	0.23 594	9.93 687	7	51	
									30 29 28
10	9.70 115	22	9.76 435	29	0.23 565	9.93 680	7	50	1 3.0 2.9 2.8
11	9.70 137	22	9.76 464	29	0.23 536	9.93 673	8	49	2 6.0 5.8 5.6
12	9.70 159	21	9.76 493	29	0.23 507	9.93 665	7	48	3 9.0 8.7 8.4
13	9.70 180	22	9.76 522	29	0.23 478	9.93 658	8	47	4 12.0 11.6 11.2
14	9.70 202	22	9.76 551	29	0.23 449	9.93 650	7	46	5 15.0 14.5 14.0
									6 18.0 17.4 16.8
15	9.70 224	21	9.76 580	29	0.23 420	9.93 643	7	45	7 21.0 20.3 19.6
16	9.70 245	22	9.76 609	30	0.23 391	9.93 636	8	44	8 24.0 23.2 22.4
17	9.70 267	21	9.76 639	29	0.23 361	9.93 628	7	43	9 27.0 26.1 25.2
18	9.70 288	22	9.76 668	29	0.23 332	9.93 621	7	42	
19	9.70 310	22	9.76 697	28	0.23 303	9.93 614	8	41	
20	9.70 332	21	9.76 725	29	0.23 275	9.93 606	7	40	
21	9.70 353	22	9.76 754	29	0.23 246	9.93 599	8	39	
22	9.70 375	21	9.76 783	29	0.23 217	9.93 591	7	38	
23	9.70 396	22	9.76 812	29	0.23 188	9.93 584	7	37	
24	9.70 418	21	9.76 841	29	0.23 159	9.93 577	8	36	
25	9.70 439	22	9.76 870	29	0.23 130	9.93 569	7	35	22 21
26	9.70 461	21	9.76 899	29	0.23 101	9.93 562	8	34	1 2.2 2.1
27	9.70 482	22	9.76 928	29	0.23 072	9.93 554	7	33	2 4.4 4.2
28	9.70 504	21	9.76 957	29	0.23 043	9.93 547	8	32	3 6.6 6.3
29	9.70 525	22	9.76 986	29	0.23 014	9.93 539	7	31	4 8.8 8.4
30	9.70 547	21	9.77 015	29	0.22 985	9.93 532	7	30	5 11.0 10.5
31	9.70 568	22	9.77 044	29	0.22 956	9.93 525	8	29	6 13.2 12.6
32	9.70 590	21	9.77 073	28	0.22 927	9.93 517	7	28	7 15.4 14.7
33	9.70 611	22	9.77 101	29	0.22 899	9.93 510	8	27	8 17.6 16.8
34	9.70 633	21	9.77 130	29	0.22 870	9.93 502	7	26	9 19.8 18.9
35	9.70 654	21	9.77 159	29	0.22 841	9.93 495	8	25	
36	9.70 675	22	9.77 188	29	0.22 812	9.93 487	7	24	
37	9.70 697	21	9.77 217	29	0.22 783	9.93 480	8	23	
38	9.70 718	21	9.77 246	28	0.22 754	9.93 472	7	22	
39	9.70 739	22	9.77 274	29	0.22 726	9.93 465	8	21	
40	9.70 761	21	9.77 303	29	0.22 697	9.93 457	7	20	
41	9.70 782	21	9.77 332	29	0.22 668	9.93 450	8	19	
42	9.70 803	21	9.77 361	29	0.22 639	9.93 442	7	18	8 7
43	9.70 824	22	9.77 390	28	0.22 610	9.93 435	8	17	1 0.8 0.7
44	9.70 846	21	9.77 418	29	0.22 582	9.93 427	7	16	2 1.6 1.4
45	9.70 867	21	9.77 447	29	0.22 553	9.93 420	8	15	3 2.4 2.1
46	9.70 888	21	9.77 476	29	0.22 524	9.93 412	7	14	4 3.2 2.8
47	9.70 909	22	9.77 505	28	0.22 495	9.93 405	8	13	5 4.0 3.5
48	9.70 931	21	9.77 533	29	0.22 467	9.93 397	7	12	6 4.8 4.2
49	9.70 952	21	9.77 562	29	0.22 438	9.93 390	8	11	7 5.6 4.9
50	9.70 973	21	9.77 591	28	0.22 409	9.93 382	7	10	8 6.4 5.6
51	9.70 994	21	9.77 619	29	0.22 381	9.93 375	8	9	9 7.2 6.3
52	9.71 015	21	9.77 648	29	0.22 352	9.93 367	7	8	
53	9.71 036	22	9.77 677	29	0.22 323	9.93 360	8	7	
54	9.71 058	21	9.77 706	28	0.22 294	9.93 352	8	6	
55	9.71 079	21	9.77 734	29	0.22 266	9.93 344	7	5	
56	9.71 100	21	9.77 763	28	0.22 237	9.93 337	8	4	
57	9.71 121	21	9.77 791	29	0.22 209	9.93 329	7	3	
58	9.71 142	21	9.77 820	29	0.22 180	9.93 322	8	2	
59	9.71 163	21	9.77 849	28	0.22 151	9.93 314	7	1	
60	9.71 184		9.77 877		0.22 123	9.93 307		0	
	Log Cos	d	Log Cot	c d	Log Tan	Log Sin	d	′	Prop. Parts

′	Log Sin	d	Log Tan	c d	Log Cot	Log Cos	d		Prop. Parts
0	9.71 184	21	9.77 877	29	0.22 123	9.93 307	8	60	
1	9.71 205	21	9.77 906	29	0.22 094	9.93 299	8	59	
2	9.71 226	21	9.77 935	28	0.22 065	9.93 291	8	58	
3	9.71 247	21	9.77 963	29	0.22 037	9.93 284	7	57	
4	9.71 268	21	9.77 992	28	0.22 008	9.93 276	8	56	
5	9.71 289	21	9.78 020	29	0.21 980	9.93 269	7	55	
6	9.71 310	21	9.78 049	28	0.21 951	9.93 261	8	54	
7	9.71 331	21	9.78 077	29	0.21 923	9.93 253	8	53	
8	9.71 352	21	9.78 106	29	0.21 894	9.93 246	7	52	
9	9.71 373	20	9.78 135	28	0.21 865	9.93 238	8	51	
10	9.71 393	21	9.78 163	29	0.21 837	9.93 230	8	50	
11	9.71 414	21	9.78 192	28	0.21 808	9.93 223	7	49	
12	9.71 435	21	9.78 220	29	0.21 780	9.93 215	8	48	
13	9.71 456	21	9.78 249	28	0.21 751	9.93 207	8	47	
14	9.71 477	21	9.78 277	29	0.21 723	9.93 200	7	46	
									29 **28** **21**
15	9.71 498	21	9.78 306	28	0.21 694	9.93 192	8	45	1 2.9 2.8 2.1
16	9.71 519	20	9.78 334	29	0.21 666	9.93 184	8	44	2 5.8 5.6 4.2
17	9.71 539	21	9.78 363	28	0.21 637	9.93 177	7	43	3 8.7 8.4 6.3
18	9.71 560	21	9.78 391	28	0.21 609	9.93 169	8	42	4 11.6 11.2 8.4
19	9.71 581	21	9.78 419	29	0.21 581	9.93 161	7	41	5 14.5 14.0 10.5
20	9.71 602	20	9.78 448	28	0.21 552	9.93 154	8	40	6 17.4 16.8 12.6
21	9.71 622	21	9.78 476	29	0.21 524	9.93 146	8	39	7 20.3 19.6 14.7
22	9.71 643	21	9.78 505	28	0.21 495	9.93 138	7	38	8 23.2 22.4 16.8
23	9.71 664	21	9.78 533	29	0.21 467	9.93 131	8	37	9 26.1 25.2 18.9
24	9.71 685	20	9.78 562	28	0.21 438	9.93 123	8	36	
25	9.71 705	21	9.78 590	28	0.21 410	9.93 115	7	35	
26	9.71 726	21	9.78 618	29	0.21 382	9.93 108	8	34	
27	9.71 747	21	9.78 647	28	0.21 353	9.93 100	8	33	
28	9.71 767	21	9.78 675	29	0.21 325	9.93 092	8	32	
29	9.71 788	21	9.78 704	28	0.21 296	9.93 084	7	31	
30	9.71 809	20	9.78 732	28	0.21 268	9.93 077	8	30	
31	9.71 829	21	9.78 760	29	0.21 240	9.93 069	8	29	
32	9.71 850	20	9.78 789	28	0.21 211	9.93 061	8	28	
33	9.71 870	21	9.78 817	28	0.21 183	9.93 053	7	27	
34	9.71 891	20	9.78 845	29	0.21 155	9.93 046	8	26	
35	9.71 911	21	9.78 874	28	0.21 126	9.93 038	8	25	
36	9.71 932	20	9.78 902	28	0.21 098	9.93 030	8	24	
37	9.71 952	21	9.78 930	29	0.21 070	9.93 022	8	23	**20** **8** **7**
38	9.71 973	21	9.78 959	28	0.21 041	9.93 014	7	22	1 2.0 0.8 0.7
39	9.71 994	20	9.78 987	28	0.21 013	9.93 007	8	21	2 4.0 1.6 1.4
40	9.72 014	20	9.79 015	28	0.20 985	9.92 999	8	20	3 6.0 2.4 2.1
41	9.72 034	21	9.79 043	29	0.20 957	9.92 991	8	19	4 8.0 3.2 2.8
42	9.72 055	20	9.79 072	28	0.20 928	9.92 983	7	18	5 10.0 4.0 3.5
43	9.72 075	21	9.79 100	28	0.20 900	9.92 976	8	17	6 12.0 4.8 4.2
44	9.72 096	20	9.79 128	28	0.20 872	9.92 968	8	16	7 14.0 5.6 4.9
45	9.72 116	21	9.79 156	29	0.20 844	9.92 960	8	15	8 16.0 6.4 5.6
46	9.72 137	20	9.79 185	28	0.20 815	9.92 952	8	14	9 18.0 7.2 6.3
47	9.72 157	20	9.79 213	28	0.20 787	9.92 944	8	13	
48	9.72 177	21	9.79 241	28	0.20 759	9.92 936	7	12	
49	9.72 198	20	9.79 269	28	0.20 731	9.92 929	8	11	
50	9.72 218	20	9.79 297	29	0.20 703	9.92 921	8	10	
51	9.72 238	21	9.79 326	28	0.20 674	9.92 913	8	9	
52	9.72 259	20	9.79 354	28	0.20 646	9.92 905	8	8	
53	9.72 279	20	9.79 382	28	0.20 618	9.92 897	8	7	
54	9.72 299	21	9.79 410	28	0.20 590	9.92 889	8	6	
55	9.72 320	20	9.79 438	28	0.20 562	9.92 881	8	5	
56	9.72 340	20	9.79 466	29	0.20 534	9.92 874	8	4	
57	9.72 360	21	9.79 495	28	0.20 505	9.92 866	8	3	
58	9.72 381	20	9.79 523	28	0.20 477	9.92 858	8	2	
59	9.72 401	20	9.79 551	28	0.20 449	9.92 850	8	1	
60	9.72 421		9.79 579		0.20 421	9.92 842		0	
	Log Cos	d	Log Cot	c d	Log Tan	Log Sin	d	′	Prop. Parts

′	Log Sin	d	Log Tan	c d	Log Cot	Log Cos	d		Prop. Parts		
0	9.72 421	20	9.79 579	28	0.20 421	9.92 842	8	60				
1	9.72 441	20	9.79 607	28	0.20 393	9.92 834	8	59				
2	9.72 461	21	9.79 635	28	0.20 365	9.92 826	8	58				
3	9.72 482	20	9.79 663	28	0.20 337	9.92 818	8	57				
4	9.72 502	20	9.79 691	28	0.20 309	9.92 810	7	56				
5	9.72 522	20	9.79 719	28	0.20 281	9.92 803	8	55				
6	9.72 542	20	9.79 747	29	0.20 253	9.92 795	8	54				
7	9.72 562	20	9.79 776	28	0.20 224	9.92 787	8	53				
8	9.72 582	20	9.79 804	28	0.20 196	9.92 779	8	52		29	28	27
9	9.72 602	20	9.79 832	28	0.20 168	9.92 771	8	51	1	2.9	2.8	2.7
10	9.72 622	21	9.79 860	28	0.20 140	9.92 763	8	50	2	5.8	5.6	5.4
11	9.72 643	20	9.79 888	28	0.20 112	9.92 755	8	49	3	8.7	8.4	8.1
12	9.72 663	20	9.79 916	28	0.20 084	9.92 747	8	48	4	11.6	11.2	10.8
13	9.72 683	20	9.79 944	28	0.20 056	9.92 739	8	47	5	14.5	14.0	13.5
14	9.72 703	20	9.79 972	28	0.20 028	9.92 731	8	46	6	17.4	16.8	16.2
15	9.72 723	20	9.80 000	28	0.20 000	9.92 723	8	45	7	20.3	19.6	18.9
16	9.72 743	20	9.80 028	28	0.19 972	9.92 715	8	44	8	23.2	22.4	21.6
17	9.72 763	20	9.80 056	28	0.19 944	9.92 707	8	43	9	26.1	25.2	24.3
18	9.72 783	20	9.80 084	28	0.19 916	9.92 699	8	42				
19	9.72 803	20	9.80 112	28	0.19 888	9.92 691	8	41				
20	9.72 823	20	9.80 140	28	0.19 860	9.92 683	8	40				
21	9.72 843	20	9.80 168	27	0.19 832	9.92 675	8	39				
22	9.72 863	20	9.80 195	28	0.19 805	9.92 667	8	38				
23	9.72 883	19	9.80 223	28	0.19 777	9.92 659	8	37				
24	9.72 902	20	9.80 251	28	0.19 749	9.92 651	8	36				
25	9.72 922	20	9.80 279	28	0.19 721	9.92 643	8	35		21	20	19
26	9.72 942	20	9.80 307	28	0.19 693	9.92 635	8	34	1	2.1	2.0	1.9
27	9.72 962	20	9.80 335	28	0.19 665	9.92 627	8	33	2	4.2	4.0	3.8
28	9.72 982	20	9.80 363	28	0.19 637	9.92 619	8	32	3	6.3	6.0	5.7
29	9.73 002	20	9.80 391	28	0.19 609	9.92 611	8	31	4	8.4	8.0	7.6
30	9.73 022	19	9.80 419	28	0.19 581	9.92 603	8	30	5	10.5	10.0	9.5
31	9.73 041	20	9.80 447	27	0.19 553	9.92 595	8	29	6	12.6	12.0	11.4
32	9.73 061	20	9.80 474	28	0.19 526	9.92 587	8	28	7	14.7	14.0	13.3
33	9.73 081	20	9.80 502	28	0.19 498	9.92 579	8	27	8	16.8	16.0	15.2
34	9.73 101	20	9.80 530	28	0.19 470	9.92 571	8	26	9	18.9	18.0	17.1
35	9.73 121	19	9.80 558	28	0.19 442	9.92 563	8	25				
36	9.73 140	20	9.80 586	28	0.19 414	9.92 555	9	24				
37	9.73 160	20	9.80 614	28	0.19 386	9.92 546	8	23				
38	9.73 180	20	9.80 642	27	0.19 358	9.92 538	8	22				
39	9.73 200	19	9.80 669	28	0.19 331	9.92 530	8	21				
40	9.73 219	20	9.80 697	28	0.19 303	9.92 522	8	20				
41	9.73 239	20	9.80 725	28	0.19 275	9.92 514	8	19				
42	9.73 259	19	9.80 753	28	0.19 247	9.92 506	8	18		9	8	7
43	9.73 278	20	9.80 781	27	0.19 219	9.92 498	8	17	1	0.9	0.8	0.7
44	9.73 298	20	9.80 808	28	0.19 192	9.92 490	8	16	2	1.8	1.6	1.4
45	9.73 318	19	9.80 836	28	0.19 164	9.92 482	9	15	3	2.7	2.4	2.1
46	9.73 337	20	9.80 864	28	0.19 136	9.92 473	8	14	4	3.6	3.2	2.8
47	9.73 357	20	9.80 892	27	0.19 108	9.92 465	8	13	5	4.5	4.0	3.5
48	9.73 377	19	9.80 919	28	0.19 081	9.92 457	8	12	6	5.4	4.8	4.2
49	9.73 396	20	9.80 947	28	0.19 053	9.92 449	8	11	7	6.3	5.6	4.9
50	9.73 416	19	9.80 975	28	0.19 025	9.92 441	8	10	8	7.2	6.4	5.6
51	9.73 435	20	9.81 003	27	0.18 997	9.92 433	8	9	9	8.1	7.2	6.3
52	9.73 455	19	9.81 030	28	0.18 970	9.92 425	9	8				
53	9.73 474	20	9.81 058	28	0.18 942	9.92 416	8	7				
54	9.73 494	19	9.81 086	27	0.18 914	9.92 408	8	6				
55	9.73 513	20	9.81 113	28	0.18 887	9.92 400	8	5				
56	9.73 533	19	9.81 141	28	0.18 859	9.92 392	8	4				
57	9.73 552	20	9.81 169	27	0.18 831	9.92 384	8	3				
58	9.73 572	19	9.81 196	28	0.18 804	9.92 376	9	2				
59	9.73 591	20	9.81 224	28	0.18 776	9.92 367	8	1				
60	9.73 611		9.81 252		0.18 748	9.92 359		0				
	Log Cos	d	Log Cot	c d	Log Tan	Log Sin	d	′		Prop. Parts		

′	Log Sin	d	Log Tan	c d	Log Cot	Log Cos	d	
0	9.73 611	19	9.81 252	27	0.18 748	9.92 359	8	60
1	9.73 630	20	9.81 279	28	0.18 721	9.92 351	8	59
2	9.73 650	19	9.81 307	28	0.18 693	9.92 343	8	58
3	9.73 669	20	9.81 335	27	0.18 665	9.92 335	8	57
4	9.73 689	19	9.81 362	28	0.18 638	9.92 326	9 / 8	56
5	9.73 708	19	9.81 390	28	0.18 610	9.92 318	8	55
6	9.73 727	20	9.81 418	27	0.18 582	9.92 310	8	54
7	9.73 747	19	9.81 445	28	0.18 555	9.92 302	8	53
8	9.73 766	19	9.81 473	27	0.18 527	9.92 293	9	52
9	9.73 785	20	9.81 500	28	0.18 500	9.92 285	8	51
10	9.73 805	19	9.81 528	28	0.18 472	9.92 277	8	50
11	9.73 824	19	9.81 556	27	0.18 444	9.92 269	8	49
12	9.73 843	20	9.81 583	28	0.18 417	9.92 260	9	48
13	9.73 863	19	9.81 611	27	0.18 389	9.92 252	8	47
14	9.73 882	19	9.81 638	28	0.18 362	9.92 244	8	46
15	9.73 901	20	9.81 666	27	0.18 334	9.92 235	9	45
16	9.73 921	19	9.81 693	28	0.18 307	9.92 227	8	44
17	9.73 940	19	9.81 721	27	0.18 279	9.92 219	8	43
18	9.73 959	19	9.81 748	28	0.18 252	9.92 211	8	42
19	9.73 978	19	9.81 776	27	0.18 224	9.92 202	9	41
20	9.73 997	20	9.81 803	28	0.18 197	9.92 194	8	40
21	9.74 017	19	9.81 831	27	0.18 169	9.92 186	8	39
22	9.74 036	19	9.81 858	28	0.18 142	9.92 177	9	38
23	9.74 055	19	9.81 886	27	0.18 114	9.92 169	8	37
24	9.74 074	19	9.81 913	28	0.18 087	9.92 161	8	36
25	9.74 093	20	9.81 941	27	0.18 059	9.92 152	9	35
26	9.74 113	19	9.81 968	28	0.18 032	9.92 144	8	34
27	9.74 132	19	9.81 996	27	0.18 004	9.92 136	8	33
28	9.74 151	19	9.82 023	28	0.17 977	9.92 127	9	32
29	9.74 170	19	9.82 051	27	0.17 949	9.92 119	8	31
30	9.74 189	19	9.82 078	28	0.17 922	9.92 111	8	30
31	9.74 208	19	9.82 106	27	0.17 894	9.92 102	9	29
32	9.74 227	19	9.82 133	28	0.17 867	9.92 094	8	28
33	9.74 246	19	9.82 161	27	0.17 839	9.92 086	8	27
34	9.74 265	19	9.82 188	27	0.17 812	9.92 077	9	26
35	9.74 284	19	9.82 215	28	0.17 785	9.92 069	8	25
36	9.74 303	19	9.82 243	27	0.17 757	9.92 060	9	24
37	9.74 322	19	9.82 270	28	0.17 730	9.92 052	8	23
38	9.74 341	19	9.82 298	27	0.17 702	9.92 044	8	22
39	9.74 360	19	9.82 325	27	0.17 675	9.92 035	9	21
40	9.74 379	19	9.82 352	28	0.17 648	9.92 027	8	20
41	9.74 398	19	9.82 380	27	0.17 620	9.92 018	9	19
42	9.74 417	19	9.82 407	28	0.17 593	9.92 010	8	18
43	9.74 436	19	9.82 435	27	0.17 565	9.92 002	8	17
44	9.74 455	19	9.82 462	27	0.17 538	9.91 993	9	16
45	9.74 474	19	9.82 489	28	0.17 511	9.91 985	8	15
46	9.74 493	19	9.82 517	27	0.17 483	9.91 976	9	14
47	9.74 512	19	9.82 544	27	0.17 456	9.91 968	8	13
48	9.74 531	18	9.82 571	28	0.17 429	9.91 959	9	12
49	9.74 549	19	9.82 599	27	0.17 401	9.91 951	8	11
50	9.74 568	19	9.82 626	27	0.17 374	9.91 942	9	10
51	9.74 587	19	9.82 653	28	0.17 347	9.91 934	8	9
52	9.74 606	19	9.82 681	27	0.17 319	9.91 925	9	8
53	9.74 625	19	9.82 708	27	0.17 292	9.91 917	8	7
54	9.74 644	18	9.82 735	27	0.17 265	9.91 908	9	6
55	9.74 662	19	9.82 762	28	0.17 238	9.91 900	8	5
56	9.74 681	19	9.82 790	27	0.17 210	9.91 891	9	4
57	9.74 700	19	9.82 817	27	0.17 183	9.91 883	8	3
58	9.74 719	18	9.82 844	28	0.17 156	9.91 874	9	2
59	9.74 737	19	9.82 871	28	0.17 129	9.91 866	8 / 9	1
60	9.74 756		9.82 899		0.17 101	9.91 857		0
	Log Cos	d	Log Cot	c d	Log Tan	Log Sin	d	′

Prop. Parts

	28	27	20
1	2.8	2.7	2.0
2	5.6	5.4	4.0
3	8.4	8.1	6.0
4	11.2	10.8	8.0
5	14.0	13.5	10.0
6	16.8	16.2	12.0
7	19.6	18.9	14.0
8	22.4	21.6	16.0
9	25.2	24.3	18.0

	19	18
1	1.9	1.8
2	3.8	3.6
3	5.7	5.4
4	7.6	7.2
5	9.5	9.0
6	11.4	10.8
7	13.3	12.6
8	15.2	14.4
9	17.1	16.2

	9	8
1	0.9	0.8
2	1.8	1.6
3	2.7	2.4
4	3.6	3.2
5	4.5	4.0
6	5.4	4.8
7	6.3	5.6
8	7.2	6.4
9	8.1	7.2

'	Log Sin	d	Log Tan	c d	Log Cot	Log Cos	d	
0	9.74 756	19	9.82 899	27	0.17 101	9.91 857	8	60
1	9.74 775	19	9.82 926	27	0.17 074	9.91 849	8	59
2	9.74 794	18	9.82 953	27	0.17 047	9.91 840	8	58
3	9.74 812	19	9.82 980	28	0.17 020	9.91 832	9	57
4	9.74 831	19	9.83 008		0.16 992	9.91 823	8	56
5	9.74 850	18	9.83 035	27	0.16 965	9.91 815	8	55
6	9.74 868	18	9.83 062	27	0.16 938	9.91 806	8	54
7	9.74 887	19	9.83 089	28	0.16 911	9.91 798	8	53
8	9.74 906	18	9.83 117	27	0.16 883	9.91 789	8	52
9	9.74 924	19	9.83 144	27	0.16 856	9.91 781	9	51
10	9.74 943	18	9.83 171	27	0.16 829	9.91 772	9	50
11	9.74 961	19	9.83 198	27	0.16 802	9.91 763	8	49
12	9.74 980	19	9.83 225	27	0.16 775	9.91 755	9	48
13	9.74 999	18	9.83 252	28	0.16 748	9.91 746	8	47
14	9.75 017	19	9.83 280	27	0.16 720	9.91 738	9	46
15	9.75 036	18	9.83 307	27	0.16 693	9.91 729	9	45
16	9.75 054	19	9.83 334	27	0.16 666	9.91 720	8	44
17	9.75 073	18	9.83 361	27	0.16 639	9.91 712	9	43
18	9.75 091	19	9.83 388	27	0.16 612	9.91 703	8	42
19	9.75 110	18	9.83 415	27	0.16 585	9.91 695	9	41
20	9.75 128	19	9.83 442	28	0.16 558	9.91 686	9	40
21	9.75 147	18	9.83 470	27	0.16 530	9.91 677	8	39
22	9.75 165	19	9.83 497	27	0.16 503	9.91 669	9	38
23	9.75 184	18	9.83 524	27	0.16 476	9.91 660	9	37
24	9.75 202	19	9.83 551	27	0.16 449	9.91 651	8	36
25	9.75 221	18	9.83 578	27	0.16 422	9.91 643	9	35
26	9.75 239	19	9.83 605	27	0.16 395	9.91 634	9	34
27	9.75 258	18	9.83 632	27	0.16 368	9.91 625	8	33
28	9.75 276	18	9.83 659	27	0.16 341	9.91 617	9	32
29	9.75 294	19	9.83 686	27	0.16 314	9.91 608	9	31
30	9.75 313	18	9.83 713	27	0.16 287	9.91 599	8	30
31	9.75 331	19	9.83 740	28	0.16 260	9.91 591	9	29
32	9.75 350	18	9.83 768	27	0.16 232	9.91 582	9	28
33	9.75 368	18	9.83 795	27	0.16 205	9.91 573	8	27
34	9.75 386	19	9.83 822	27	0.16 178	9.91 565	9	26
35	9.75 405	18	9.83 849	27	0.16 151	9.91 556	9	25
36	9.75 423	18	9.83 876	27	0.16 124	9.91 547	9	24
37	9.75 441	18	9.83 903	27	0.16 097	9.91 538	8	23
38	9.75 459	19	9.83 930	27	0.16 070	9.91 530	9	22
39	9.75 478	18	9.83 957	27	0.16 043	9.91 521	9	21
40	9.75 496	18	9.83 984	27	0.16 016	9.91 512	8	20
41	9.75 514	19	9.84 011	27	0.15 989	9.91 504	9	19
42	9.75 533	18	9.84 038	27	0.15 962	9.91 495	9	18
43	9.75 551	18	9.84 065	27	0.15 935	9.91 486	9	17
44	9.75 569	18	9.84 092	27	0.15 908	9.91 477	8	16
45	9.75 587	18	9.84 119	27	0.15 881	9.91 469	9	15
46	9.75 605	19	9.84 146	27	0.15 854	9.91 460	9	14
47	9.75 624	18	9.84 173	27	0.15 827	9.91 451	9	13
48	9.75 642	18	9.84 200	27	0.15 800	9.91 442	9	12
49	9.75 660	18	9.84 227	27	0.15 773	9.91 433	8	11
50	9.75 678	18	9.84 254	26	0.15 746	9.91 425	9	10
51	9.75 696	18	9.84 280	27	0.15 720	9.91 416	9	9
52	9.75 714	19	9.84 307	27	0.15 693	9.91 407	9	8
53	9.75 733	18	9.84 334	27	0.15 666	9.91 398	9	7
54	9.75 751	18	9.84 361	27	0.15 639	9.91 389	8	6
55	9.75 769	18	9.84 388	27	0.15 612	9.91 381	9	5
56	9.75 787	18	9.84 415	27	0.15 585	9.91 372	9	4
57	9.75 805	18	9.84 442	27	0.15 558	9.91 363	9	3
58	9.75 823	18	9.84 469	27	0.15 531	9.91 354	9	2
59	9.75 841	18	9.84 496	27	0.15 504	9.91 345	9	1
60	9.75 859		9.84 523		0.15 477	9.91 336		0
	Log Cos	d	Log Cot	c d	Log Tan	Log Sin	d	'

Prop. Parts

	28	27	26
1	2.8	2.7	2.6
2	5.6	5.4	5.2
3	8.4	8.1	7.8
4	11.2	10.8	10.4
5	14.0	13.5	13.0
6	16.8	16.2	15.6
7	19.6	18.9	18.2
8	22.4	21.6	20.8
9	25.2	24.3	23.4

	19	18
1	1.9	1.8
2	3.8	3.6
3	5.7	5.4
4	7.6	7.2
5	9.5	9.0
6	11.4	10.8
7	13.3	12.6
8	15.2	14.4
9	17.1	16.2

	9	8
1	0.9	0.8
2	1.8	1.6
3	2.7	2.4
4	3.6	3.2
5	4.5	4.0
6	5.4	4.8
7	6.3	5.6
8	7.2	6.4
9	8.1	7.2

'	Log Sin	d	Log Tan	c d	Log Cot	Log Cos	d		Prop. Parts
0	9.75 859	18	9.84 523	27	0.15 477	9.91 336	8	60	
1	9.75 877	18	9.84 550	26	0.15 450	9.91 328	9	59	
2	9.75 895	18	9.84 576	27	0.15 424	9.91 319	9	58	
3	9.75 913	18	9.84 603	27	0.15 397	9.91 310	9	57	
4	9.75 931	18	9.84 630	27	0.15 370	9.91 301	9	56	
5	9.75 949	18	9.84 657	27	0.15 343	9.91 292	9	55	
6	9.75 967	18	9.84 684	27	0.15 316	9.91 283	9	54	
7	9.75 985	18	9.84 711	27	0.15 289	9.91 274	8	53	
8	9.76 003	18	9.84 738	26	0.15 262	9.91 266	9	52	
9	9.76 021	18	9.84 764	27	0.15 236	9.91 257	9	51	**27** **26** **18**
10	9.76 039	18	9.84 791	27	0.15 209	9.91 248	9	50	1 2.7 2.6 1.8
11	9.76 057	18	9.84 818	27	0.15 182	9.91 239	9	49	2 5.4 5.2 3.6
12	9.76 075	18	9.84 845	27	0.15 155	9.91 230	9	48	3 8.1 7.8 5.4
13	9.76 093	18	9.84 872	27	0.15 128	9.91 221	9	47	4 10.8 10.4 7.2
14	9.76 111	18	9.84 899	26	0.15 101	9.91 212	9	46	5 13.5 13.0 9.0
15	9.76 129	17	9.84 925	27	0.15 075	9.91 203	9	45	6 16.2 15.6 10.8
16	9.76 146	18	9.84 952	27	0.15 048	9.91 194	9	44	7 18.9 18.2 12.6
17	9.76 164	18	9.84 979	27	0.15 021	9.91 185	9	43	8 21.6 20.8 14.4
18	9.76 182	18	9.85 006	27	0.14 994	9.91 176	9	42	9 24.3 23.4 16.2
19	9.76 200	18	9.85 033	26	0.14 967	9.91 167	9	41	
20	9.76 218	18	9.85 059	27	0.14 941	9.91 158	9	40	
21	9.76 236	17	9.85 086	27	0.14 914	9.91 149	8	39	
22	9.76 253	18	9.85 113	27	0.14 887	9.91 141	9	38	
23	9.76 271	18	9.85 140	26	0.14 860	9.91 132	9	37	
24	9.76 289	18	9.85 166	27	0.14 834	9.91 123	9	36	
25	9.76 307	17	9.85 193	27	0.14 807	9.91 114	9	35	**17** **10**
26	9.76 324	18	9.85 220	27	0.14 780	9.91 105	9	34	
27	9.76 342	18	9.85 247	26	0.14 753	9.91 096	9	33	1 1.7 1.0
28	9.76 360	18	9.85 273	27	0.14 727	9.91 087	9	32	2 3.4 2.0
29	9.76 378	17	9.85 300	27	0.14 700	9.91 078	9	31	3 5.1 3.0
30	9.76 395	18	9.85 327	27	0.14 673	9.91 069	9	30	4 6.8 4.0
31	9.76 413	18	9.85 354	26	0.14 646	9.91 060	9	29	5 8.5 5.0
32	9.76 431	17	9.85 380	27	0.14 620	9.91 051	9	28	6 10.2 6.0
33	9.76 448	18	9.85 407	27	0.14 593	9.91 042	9	27	7 11.9 7.0
34	9.76 466	18	9.85 434	26	0.14 566	9.91 033	10	26	8 13.6 8.0
35	9.76 484	17	9.85 460	27	0.14 540	9.91 023	9	25	9 15.3 9.0
36	9.76 501	18	9.85 487	27	0.14 513	9.91 014	9	24	
37	9.76 519	18	9.85 514	26	0.14 486	9.91 005	9	23	
38	9.76 537	17	9.85 540	27	0.14 460	9.90 996	9	22	
39	9.76 554	18	9.85 567	27	0.14 433	9.90 987	9	21	
40	9.76 572	18	9.85 594	26	0.14 406	9.90 978	9	20	
41	9.76 590	17	9.85 620	27	0.14 380	9.90 969	9	19	
42	9.76 607	18	9.85 647	27	0.14 353	9.90 960	9	18	
43	9.76 625	17	9.85 674	26	0.14 326	9.90 951	9	17	**9** **8**
44	9.76 642	18	9.85 700	27	0.14 300	9.90 942	9	16	1 0.9 0.8
45	9.76 660	17	9.85 727	27	0.14 273	9.90 933	9	15	2 1.8 1.6
46	9.76 677	18	9.85 754	26	0.14 246	9.90 924	9	14	3 2.7 2.4
47	9.76 695	17	9.85 780	27	0.14 220	9.90 915	9	13	4 3.6 3.2
48	9.76 712	18	9.85 807	27	0.14 193	9.90 906	10	12	5 4.5 4.0
49	9.76 730	17	9.85 834	26	0.14 166	9.90 896	9	11	6 5.4 4.8
50	9.76 747	18	9.85 860	27	0.14 140	9.90 887	9	10	7 6.3 5.6
51	9.76 765	17	9.85 887	26	0.14 113	9.90 878	9	9	8 7.2 6.4
52	9.76 782	18	9.85 913	27	0.14 087	9.90 869	9	8	9 8.1 7.2
53	9.76 800	17	9.85 940	27	0.14 060	9.90 860	9	7	
54	9.76 817	18	9.85 967	26	0.14 033	9.90 851	9	6	
55	9.76 835	17	9.85 993	27	0.14 007	9.90 842	10	5	
56	9.76 852	18	9.86 020	26	0.13 980	9.90 832	9	4	
57	9.76 870	17	9.86 046	27	0.13 954	9.90 823	9	3	
58	9.76 887	17	9.86 073	27	0.13 927	9.90 814	9	2	
59	9.76 904	18	9.86 100	26	0.13 900	9.90 805	9	1	
60	9.76 922		9.86 126		0.13 874	9.90 796		0	
	Log Cos	d	Log Cot	c d	Log Tan	Log Sin	d	'	Prop. Parts

′	Log Sin	d	Log Tan	c d	Log Cot	Log Cos	d		Prop. Parts
0	9.76 922	17	9.86 126	27	0.13 874	9.90 796	9	60	
1	9.76 939	18	9.86 153	26	0.13 847	9.90 787	10	59	
2	9.76 957	17	9.86 179	27	0.13 821	9.90 777	9	58	
3	9.76 974	17	9.86 206	26	0.13 794	9.90 768	9	57	
4	9.76 991	18	9.86 232	27	0.13 768	9.90 759	9	56	
5	9.77 009	17	9.86 259	26	0.13 741	9.90 750	9	55	
6	9.77 026	17	9.86 285	27	0.13 715	9.90 741	10	54	
7	9.77 043	18	9.86 312	26	0.13 688	9.90 731	9	53	
8	9.77 061	17	9.86 338	27	0.13 662	9.90 722	9	52	
9	9.77 078	17	9.86 365	27	0.13 635	9.90 713	9	51	
									27 **26** **18**
									1 2.7 2.6 1.8
10	9.77 095	17	9.86 392	26	0.13 608	9.90 704	10	50	2 5.4 5.2 3.6
11	9.77 112	18	9.86 418	27	0.13 582	9.90 694	9	49	3 8.1 7.8 5.4
12	9.77 130	17	9.86 445	26	0.13 555	9.90 685	9	48	4 10.8 10.4 7.2
13	9.77 147	17	9.86 471	27	0.13 529	9.90 676	9	47	5 13.5 13.0 9.0
14	9.77 164	17	9.86 498	26	0.13 502	9.90 667	10	46	6 16.2 15.6 10.8
									7 18.9 18.2 12.6
15	9.77 181	18	9.86 524	27	0.13 476	9.90 657	9	45	8 21.6 20.8 14.4
16	9.77 199	17	9.86 551	26	0.13 449	9.90 648	9	44	9 24.3 23.4 16.2
17	9.77 216	17	9.86 577	26	0.13 423	9.90 639	9	43	
18	9.77 233	17	9.86 603	27	0.13 397	9.90 630	10	42	
19	9.77 250	18	9.86 630	26	0.13 370	9.90 620	9	41	
20	9.77 268	17	9.86 656	27	0.13 344	9.90 611	9	40	
21	9.77 285	17	9.86 683	26	0.13 317	9.90 602	10	39	
22	9.77 302	17	9.86 709	27	0.13 291	9.90 592	9	38	
23	9.77 319	17	9.86 736	26	0.13 264	9.90 583	9	37	
24	9.77 336	17	9.86 762	27	0.13 238	9.90 574	9	36	
25	9.77 353	17	9.86 789	26	0.13 211	9.90 565	10	35	**17** **16**
26	9.77 370	17	9.86 815	27	0.13 185	9.90 555	9	34	1 1.7 1.6
27	9.77 387	18	9.86 842	26	0.13 158	9.90 546	9	33	2 3.4 3.2
28	9.77 405	17	9.86 868	26	0.13 132	9.90 537	10	32	3 5.1 4.8
29	9.77 422	17	9.86 894	27	0.13 106	9.90 527	9	31	4 6.8 6.4
									5 8.5 8.0
30	9.77 439	17	9.86 921	26	0.13 079	9.90 518	9	30	6 10.2 9.6
31	9.77 456	17	9.86 947	27	0.13 053	9.90 509	10	29	7 11.9 11.2
32	9.77 473	17	9.86 974	26	0.13 026	9.90 499	9	28	8 13.6 12.8
33	9.77 490	17	9.87 000	27	0.13 000	9.90 490	10	27	9 15.3 14.4
34	9.77 507	17	9.87 027	26	0.12 973	9.90 480	9	26	
35	9.77 524	17	9.87 053	26	0.12 947	9.90 471	9	25	
36	9.77 541	17	9.87 079	27	0.12 921	9.90 462	10	24	
37	9.77 558	17	9.87 106	26	0.12 894	9.90 452	9	23	
38	9.77 575	17	9.87 132	26	0.12 868	9.90 443	9	22	
39	9.77 592	17	9.87 158	27	0.12 842	9.90 434	10	21	
40	9.77 609	17	9.87 185	26	0.12 815	9.90 424	9	20	
41	9.77 626	17	9.87 211	27	0.12 789	9.90 415	10	19	
42	9.77 643	17	9.87 238	26	0.12 762	9.90 405	9	18	
43	9.77 660	17	9.87 264	26	0.12 736	9.90 396	10	17	**10** **9**
44	9.77 677	17	9.87 290	27	0.12 710	9.90 386	9	16	1 1.0 0.9
									2 2.0 1.8
45	9.77 694	17	9.87 317	26	0.12 683	9.90 377	9	15	3 3.0 2.7
46	9.77 711	17	9.87 343	26	0.12 657	9.90 368	10	14	4 4.0 3.6
47	9.77 728	16	9.87 369	27	0.12 631	9.90 358	9	13	5 5.0 4.5
48	9.77 744	17	9.87 396	26	0.12 604	9.90 349	9	12	6 6.0 5.4
49	9.77 761	17	9.87 422	26	0.12 578	9.90 339	9	11	7 7.0 6.3
									8 8.0 7.2
50	9.77 778	17	9.87 448	27	0.12 552	9.90 330	10	10	9 9.0 8.1
51	9.77 795	17	9.87 475	26	0.12 525	9.90 320	9	9	
52	9.77 812	17	9.87 501	26	0.12 499	9.90 311	10	8	
53	9.77 829	17	9.87 527	27	0.12 473	9.90 301	9	7	
54	9.77 846	16	9.87 554	26	0.12 446	9.90 292	10	6	
55	9.77 862	17	9.87 580	26	0.12 420	9.90 282	9	5	
56	9.77 879	17	9.87 606	27	0.12 394	9.90 273	9	4	
57	9.77 896	17	9.87 633	26	0.12 367	9.90 263	9	3	
58	9.77 913	17	9.87 659	26	0.12 341	9.90 254	10	2	
59	9.77 930	16	9.87 685	26	0.12 315	9.90 244	9	1	
60	9.77 946		9.87 711		0.12 289	9.90 235		0	
	Log Cos	d	Log Cot	c d	Log Tan	Log Sin	d	′	Prop. Parts

′	Log Sin	d	Log Tan	c d	Log Cot	Log Cos	d		Prop. Parts		
0	9.77 946	17	9.87 711	27	0.12 289	9.90 235	10	60			
1	9.77 963	17	9.87 738	26	0.12 262	9.90 225	9	59			
2	9.77 980	17	9.87 764	26	0.12 236	9.90 216	10	58			
3	9.77 997	16	9.87 790	27	0.12 210	9.90 206	9	57			
4	9.78 013	17	9.87 817	26	0.12 183	9.90 197	10	56			
5	9.78 030	17	9.87 843	26	0.12 157	9.90 187	9	55			
6	9.78 047	16	9.87 869	26	0.12 131	9.90 178	10	54			
7	9.78 063	17	9.87 895	27	0.12 105	9.90 168	9	53			
8	9.78 080	17	9.87 922	26	0.12 078	9.90 159	10	52			
9	9.78 097	16	9.87 948	26	0.12 052	9.90 149	10	51			
10	9.78 113	17	9.87 974	26	0.12 026	9.90 139	9	50			
11	9.78 130	17	9.88 000	27	0.12 000	9.90 130	10	49			
12	9.78 147	16	9.88 027	26	0.11 973	9.90 120	9	48			
13	9.78 163	17	9.88 053	26	0.11 947	9.90 111	10	47			
14	9.78 180	17	9.88 079	26	0.11 921	9.90 101	10	46			
15	9.78 197	16	9.88 105	26	0.11 895	9.90 091	9	45	**27**	**26**	**17**
16	9.78 213	17	9.88 131	27	0.11 869	9.90 082	10	44	1 2.7	2.6	1.7
17	9.78 230	16	9.88 158	26	0.11 842	9.90 072	9	43	2 5.4	5.2	3.4
18	9.78 246	17	9.88 184	26	0.11 816	9.90 063	10	42	3 8.1	7.8	5.1
19	9.78 263	17	9.88 210	26	0.11 790	9.90 053	10	41	4 10.8	10.4	6.8
20	9.78 280	16	9.88 236	26	0.11 764	9.90 043	9	40	5 13.5	13.0	8.5
21	9.78 296	17	9.88 262	27	0.11 738	9.90 034	10	39	6 16.2	15.6	10.2
22	9.78 313	16	9.88 289	26	0.11 711	9.90 024	10	38	7 18.9	18.2	11.9
23	9.78 329	17	9.88 315	26	0.11 685	9.90 014	9	37	8 21.6	20.8	13.6
24	9.78 346	16	9.88 341	26	0.11 659	9.90 005	10	36	9 24.3	23.4	15.3
25	9.78 362	17	9.88 367	26	0.11 633	9.89 995	10	35			
26	9.78 379	16	9.88 393	27	0.11 607	9.89 985	10	34			
27	9.78 395	17	9.88 420	26	0.11 580	9.89 976	10	33			
28	9.78 412	16	9.88 446	26	0.11 554	9.89 966	10	32			
29	9.78 428	17	9.88 472	26	0.11 528	9.89 956	9	31			
30	9.78 445	16	9.88 498	26	0.11 502	9.89 947	10	30			
31	9.78 461	17	9.88 524	26	0.11 476	9.89 937	10	29			
32	9.78 478	16	9.88 550	27	0.11 450	9.89 927	9	28			
33	9.78 494	16	9.88 577	26	0.11 423	9.89 918	10	27			
34	9.78 510	17	9.88 603	26	0.11 397	9.89 908	10	26			
35	9.78 527	16	9.88 629	26	0.11 371	9.89 898	10	25			
36	9.78 543	17	9.88 655	26	0.11 345	9.89 888	9	24			
37	9.78 560	16	9.88 681	26	0.11 319	9.89 879	10	23	**16**	**10**	**9**
38	9.78 576	16	9.88 707	26	0.11 293	9.89 869	10	22	1 1.6	1.0	0.9
39	9.78 592	17	9.88 733	26	0.11 267	9.89 859	10	21	2 3.2	2.0	1.8
40	9.78 609	16	9.88 759	27	0.11 241	9.89 849	9	20	3 4.8	3.0	2.7
41	9.78 625	17	9.88 786	26	0.11 214	9.89 840	10	19	4 6.4	4.0	3.6
42	9.78 642	16	9.88 812	26	0.11 188	9.89 830	10	18	5 8.0	5.0	4.5
43	9.78 658	16	9.88 838	26	0.11 162	9.89 820	10	17	6 9.6	6.0	5.4
44	9.78 674	17	9.88 864	26	0.11 136	9.89 810	9	16	7 11.2	7.0	6.3
45	9.78 691	16	9.88 890	26	0.11 110	9.89 801	10	15	8 12.8	8.0	7.2
46	9.78 707	16	9.88 916	26	0.11 084	9.89 791	10	14	9 14.4	9.0	8.1
47	9.78 723	16	9.88 942	26	0.11 058	9.89 781	10	13			
48	9.78 739	17	9.88 968	26	0.11 032	9.89 771	10	12			
49	9.78 756	16	9.88 994	26	0.11 006	9.89 761	9	11			
50	9.78 772	16	9.89 020	26	0.10 980	9.89 752	10	10			
51	9.78 788	17	9.89 046	27	0.10 954	9.89 742	10	9			
52	9.78 805	16	9.89 073	26	0.10 927	9.89 732	10	8			
53	9.78 821	16	9.89 099	26	0.10 901	9.89 722	10	7			
54	9.78 837	16	9.89 125	26	0.10 875	9.89 712	10	6			
55	9.78 853	16	9.89 151	26	0.10 849	9.89 702	9	5			
56	9.78 869	17	9.89 177	26	0.10 823	9.89 693	10	4			
57	9.78 886	16	9.89 203	26	0.10 797	9.89 683	10	3			
58	9.78 902	16	9.89 229	26	0.10 771	9.89 673	10	2			
59	9.78 918	16	9.89 255	26	0.10 745	9.89 663	10	1			
60	9.78 934		9.89 281		0.10 719	9.89 653		0			
	Log Cos	d	Log Cot	c d	Log Tan	Log Sin	d	′	Prop. Parts		

′	Log Sin	d	Log Tan	c d	Log Cot	Log Cos	d		Prop. Parts
0	9.78 934	16	9.89 281	26	0.10 719	9.89 653	10	60	
1	9.78 950	17	9.89 307	26	0.10 693	9.89 643	10	59	
2	9.78 967	16	9.89 333	26	0.10 667	9.89 633	9	58	
3	9.78 983	16	9.89 359	26	0.10 641	9.89 624	10	57	
4	9.78 999	16	9.89 385	26	0.10 615	9.89 614	10	56	
5	9.79 015	16	9.89 411	26	0.10 589	9.89 604	10	55	
6	9.79 031	16	9.89 437	26	0.10 563	9.89 594	10	54	
7	9.79 047	16	9.89 463	26	0.10 537	9.89 584	10	53	
8	9.79 063	16	9.89 489	26	0.10 511	9.89 574	10	52	
9	9.79 079	16	9.89 515	26	0.10 485	9.89 564	10	51	
										26	25	17
10	9.79 095	16	9.89 541	26	0.10 459	9.89 554	10	50	1	2.6	2.5	1.7
11	9.79 111	17	9.89 567	26	0.10 433	9.89 544	10	49	2	5.2	5.0	3.4
12	9.79 128	16	9.89 593	26	0.10 407	9.89 534	10	48	3	7.8	7.5	5.1
13	9.79 144	16	9.89 619	26	0.10 381	9.89 524	10	47	4	10.4	10.0	6.8
14	9.79 160	16	9.89 645	26	0.10 355	9.89 514	10	46	5	13.0	12.5	8.5
									6	15.6	15.0	10.2
15	9.79 176	16	9.89 671	26	0.10 329	9.89 504	9	45	7	18.2	17.5	11.9
16	9.79 192	16	9.89 697	26	0.10 303	9.89 495	10	44	8	20.8	20.0	13.6
17	9.79 208	16	9.89 723	26	0.10 277	9.89 485	10	43	9	23.4	22.5	15.3
18	9.79 224	16	9.89 749	26	0.10 251	9.89 475	10	42	
19	9.79 240	16	9.89 775	26	0.10 225	9.89 465	10	41	
20	9.79 256	16	9.89 801	26	0.10 199	9.89 455	10	40	
21	9.79 272	16	9.89 827	26	0.10 173	9.89 445	10	39	
22	9.79 288	16	9.89 853	26	0.10 147	9.89 435	10	38	
23	9.79 304	15	9.89 879	26	0.10 121	9.89 425	10	37	
24	9.79 319	16	9.89 905	26	0.10 095	9.89 415	10	36	
										16	15	11
25	9.79 335	16	9.89 931	26	0.10 069	9.89 405	10	35	1	1.6	1.5	1.1
26	9.79 351	16	9.89 957	26	0.10 043	9.89 395	10	34	2	3.2	3.0	2.2
27	9.79 367	16	9.89 983	26	0.10 017	9.89 385	10	33	3	4.8	4.5	3.3
28	9.79 383	16	9.90 009	26	0.09 991	9.89 375	11	32	4	6.4	6.0	4.4
29	9.79 399	16	9.90 035	26	0.09 965	9.89 364	10	31	5	8.0	7.5	5.5
30	9.79 415	16	9.90 061	25	0.09 939	9.89 354	10	30	6	9.6	9.0	6.6
31	9.79 431	16	9.90 086	26	0.09 914	9.89 344	10	29	7	11.2	10.5	7.7
32	9.79 447	16	9.90 112	26	0.09 888	9.89 334	10	28	8	12.8	12.0	8.8
33	9.79 463	15	9.90 138	26	0.09 862	9.89 324	10	27	9	14.4	13.5	9.9
34	9.79 478	16	9.90 164	26	0.09 836	9.89 314	10	26	
35	9.79 494	16	9.90 190	26	0.09 810	9.89 304	10	25	
36	9.79 510	16	9.90 216	26	0.09 784	9.89 294	10	24	
37	9.79 526	16	9.90 242	26	0.09 758	9.89 284	10	23	
38	9.79 542	16	9.90 268	26	0.09 732	9.89 274	10	22	
39	9.79 558	15	9.90 294	26	0.09 706	9.89 264	10	21	
40	9.79 573	16	9.90 320	26	0.09 680	9.89 254	10	20	
41	9.79 589	16	9.90 346	25	0.09 654	9.89 244	11	19	
42	9.79 605	16	9.90 371	26	0.09 629	9.89 233	10	18		10	9
43	9.79 621	15	9.90 397	26	0.09 603	9.89 223	10	17	1	1.0	0.9
44	9.79 636	16	9.90 423	26	0.09 577	9.89 213	10	16	2	2.0	1.8
45	9.79 652	16	9.90 449	26	0.09 551	9.89 203	10	15	3	3.0	2.7
46	9.79 668	16	9.90 475	26	0.09 525	9.89 193	10	14	4	4.0	3.6
47	9.79 684	15	9.90 501	26	0.09 499	9.89 183	10	13	5	5.0	4.5
48	9.79 699	16	9.90 527	26	0.09 473	9.89 173	11	12	6	6.0	5.4
49	9.79 715	16	9.90 553	25	0.09 447	9.89 162	10	11	7	7.0	6.3
50	9.79 731	15	9.90 578	26	0.09 422	9.89 152	10	10	8	8.0	7.2
51	9.79 746	16	9.90 604	26	0.09 396	9.89 142	10	9	9	9.0	8.1
52	9.79 762	16	9.90 630	26	0.09 370	9.89 132	10	8	
53	9.79 778	15	9.90 656	26	0.09 344	9.89 122	10	7	
54	9.79 793	16	9.90 682	26	0.09 318	9.89 112	11	6	
55	9.79 809	16	9.90 708	26	0.09 292	9.89 101	10	5	
56	9.79 825	15	9.90 734	25	0.09 266	9.89 091	10	4	
57	9.79 840	16	9.90 759	26	0.09 241	9.89 081	10	3	
58	9.79 856	16	9.90 785	26	0.09 215	9.89 071	11	2	
59	9.79 872	15	9.90 811	26	0.09 189	9.89 060	10	1	
60	9.79 887		9.90 837		0.09 163	9.89 050		0	
	Log Cos	d	Log Cot	c d	Log Tan	Log Sin	d	′	Prop. Parts

'	Log Sin	d	Log Tan	c d	Log Cot	Log Cos	d		Prop. Parts
0	9.79 887	16	9.90 837	26	0.09 163	9.89 050		60	
1	9.79 903	15	9.90 863	26	0.09 137	9.89 040	10	59	
2	9.79 918	16	9.90 889	25	0.09 111	9.89 030	10	58	
3	9.79 934	16	9.90 914	26	0.09 086	9.89 020	10	57	
4	9.79 950	15	9.90 940	26	0.09 060	9.89 009	11	56	
5	9.79 965	16	9.90 966	26	0.09 034	9.88 999	10	55	
6	9.79 981	16	9.90 992	26	0.09 008	9.88 989	10	54	
7	9.79 996	16	9.91 018	25	0.08 982	9.88 978	11	53	
8	9.80 012	15	9.91 043	26	0.08 957	9.88 968	10	52	
9	9.80 027	16	9.91 069	26	0.08 931	9.88 958	10	51	
10	9.80 043	15	9.91 095	26	0.08 905	9.88 948	10	50	
11	9.80 058	16	9.91 121	26	0.08 879	9.88 937	11	49	
12	9.80 074	15	9.91 147	25	0.08 853	9.88 927	10	48	
13	9.80 089	16	9.91 172	26	0.08 828	9.88 917	10	47	
14	9.80 105	15	9.91 198	26	0.08 802	9.88 906	11	46	
15	9.80 120	16	9.91 224	26	0.08 776	9.88 896	10	45	**26** **25** **16**
16	9.80 136	15	9.91 250	26	0.08 750	9.88 886	10	44	1 2.6 2.5 1.6
17	9.80 151	15	9.91 276	25	0.08 724	9.88 875	11	43	2 5.2 5.0 3.2
18	9.80 166	16	9.91 301	26	0.08 699	9.88 865	10	42	3 7.8 7.5 4.8
19	9.80 182	15	9.91 327	26	0.08 673	9.88 855	11	41	4 10.4 10.0 6.4
20	9.80 197	16	9.91 353	26	0.08 647	9.88 844		40	5 13.0 12.5 8.0
21	9.80 213	15	9.91 379	25	0.08 621	9.88 834	10	39	6 15.6 15.0 9.6
22	9.80 228	16	9.91 404	26	0.08 596	9.88 824	10	38	7 18.2 17.5 11.2
23	9.80 244	15	9.91 430	26	0.08 570	9.88 813	10	37	8 20.8 20.0 12.8
24	9.80 259	15	9.91 456	26	0.08 544	9.88 803	10	36	9 23.4 22.5 14.4
25	9.80 274	16	9.91 482	25	0.08 518	9.88 793	11	35	
26	9.80 290	15	9.91 507	26	0.08 493	9.88 782	10	34	
27	9.80 305	15	9.91 533	26	0.08 467	9.88 772	11	33	
28	9.80 320	16	9.91 559	26	0.08 441	9.88 761	10	32	
29	9.80 336	15	9.91 585	25	0.08 415	9.88 751	10	31	
30	9.80 351	15	9.91 610	26	0.08 390	9.88 741	11	30	
31	9.80 366	16	9.91 636	26	0.08 364	9.88 730	10	29	
32	9.80 382	15	9.91 662	26	0.08 338	9.88 720	11	28	
33	9.80 397	15	9.91 688	25	0.08 312	9.88 709	10	27	
34	9.80 412	16	9.91 713	26	0.08 287	9.88 699	11	26	
35	9.80 428	15	9.91 739	26	0.08 261	9.88 688	10	25	
36	9.80 443	15	9.91 765	26	0.08 235	9.88 678	10	24	
37	9.80 458	15	9.91 791	25	0.08 209	9.88 668	11	23	**15** **11** **10**
38	9.80 473	16	9.91 816	26	0.08 184	9.88 657	10	22	1 1.5 1.1 1.0
39	9.80 489	15	9.91 842	26	0.08 158	9.88 647	11	21	2 3.0 2.2 2.0
40	9.80 504	15	9.91 868	25	0.08 132	9.88 636		20	3 4.5 3.3 3.0
41	9.80 519	15	9.91 893	26	0.08 107	9.88 626	11	19	4 6.0 4.4 4.0
42	9.80 534	16	9.91 919	26	0.08 081	9.88 615	10	18	5 7.5 5.5 5.0
43	9.80 550	15	9.91 945	26	0.08 055	9.88 605	10	17	6 9.0 6.6 6.0
44	9.80 565	15	9.91 971	25	0.08 029	9.88 594	10	16	7 10.5 7.7 7.0
45	9.80 580	15	9.91 996	26	0.08 004	9.88 584	11	15	8 12.0 8.8 8.0
46	9.80 595	15	9.92 022	26	0.07 978	9.88 573	10	14	9 13.5 9.9 9.0
47	9.80 610	15	9.92 048	25	0.07 952	9.88 563	11	13	
48	9.80 625	16	9.92 073	26	0.07 927	9.88 552	10	12	
49	9.80 641	15	9.92 099	26	0.07 901	9.88 542	11	11	
50	9.80 656	15	9.92 125	25	0.07 875	9.88 531	10	10	
51	9.80 671	15	9.92 150	26	0.07 850	9.88 521	10	9	
52	9.80 686	15	9.92 176	26	0.07 824	9.88 510	11	8	
53	9.80 701	15	9.92 202	25	0.07 798	9.88 499	10	7	
54	9.80 716	15	9.92 227	26	0.07 773	9.88 489	11	6	
55	9.80 731	15	9.92 253	26	0.07 747	9.88 478	10	5	
56	9.80 746	16	9.92 279	25	0.07 721	9.88 468	11	4	
57	9.80 762	15	9.92 304	26	0.07 696	9.88 457	10	3	
58	9.80 777	15	9.92 330	26	0.07 670	9.88 447	11	2	
59	9.80 792	15	9.92 356	25	0.07 644	9.88 436	11	1	
60	9.80 807		9.92 381		0.07 619	9.88 425		0	
	Log Cos	d	Log Cot	c d	Log Tan	Log Sin	d	'	Prop. Parts

′	Log Sin	d	Log Tan	c d	Log Cot	Log Cos	d	
0	9.80 807	15	9.92 381	26	0.07 619	9.88 425	10	60
1	9.80 822	15	9.92 407	26	0.07 593	9.88 415	11	59
2	9.80 837	15	9.92 433	25	0.07 567	9.88 404	10	58
3	9.80 852	15	9.92 458	26	0.07 542	9.88 394	11	57
4	9.80 867	15	9.92 484	26	0.07 516	9.88 383	11	56
5	9.80 882	15	9.92 510	25	0.07 490	9.88 372	10	55
6	9.80 897	15	9.92 535	26	0.07 465	9.88 362	11	54
7	9.80 912	15	9.92 561	26	0.07 439	9.88 351	11	53
8	9.80 927	15	9.92 587	25	0.07 413	9.88 340	10	52
9	9.80 942	15	9.92 612	26	0.07 388	9.88 330	11	51
10	9.80 957	15	9.92 638	25	0.07 362	9.88 319	11	50
11	9.80 972	15	9.92 663	26	0.07 337	9.88 308	10	49
12	9.80 987	15	9.92 689	26	0.07 311	9.88 298	11	48
13	9.81 002	15	9.92 715	25	0.07 285	9.88 287	11	47
14	9.81 017	15	9.92 740	26	0.07 260	9.88 276	10	46
15	9.81 032	15	9.92 766	26	0.07 234	9.88 266	11	45
16	9.81 047	14	9.92 792	25	0.07 208	9.88 255	11	44
17	9.81 061	15	9.92 817	26	0.07 183	9.88 244	10	43
18	9.81 076	15	9.92 843	25	0.07 157	9.88 234	11	42
19	9.81 091	15	9.92 868	26	0.07 132	9.88 223	11	41
20	9.81 106	15	9.92 894	26	0.07 106	9.88 212	11	40
21	9.81 121	15	9.92 920	25	0.07 080	9.88 201	10	39
22	9.81 136	15	9.92 945	26	0.07 055	9.88 191	11	38
23	9.81 151	15	9.92 971	25	0.07 029	9.88 180	11	37
24	9.81 166	14	9.92 996	26	0.07 004	9.88 169	11	36
25	9.81 180	15	9.93 022	26	0.06 978	9.88 158	10	35
26	9.81 195	15	9.93 048	25	0.06 952	9.88 148	11	34
27	9.81 210	15	9.93 073	26	0.06 927	9.88 137	11	33
28	9.81 225	15	9.93 099	25	0.06 901	9.88 126	11	32
29	9.81 240	14	9.93 124	26	0.06 876	9.88 115	10	31
30	9.81 254	15	9.93 150	25	0.06 850	9.88 105	11	30
31	9.81 269	15	9.93 175	26	0.06 825	9.88 094	11	29
32	9.81 284	15	9.93 201	26	0.06 799	9.88 083	11	28
33	9.81 299	15	9.93 227	25	0.06 773	9.88 072	11	27
34	9.81 314	14	9.93 252	26	0.06 748	9.88 061	10	26
35	9.81 328	15	9.93 278	25	0.06 722	9.88 051	11	25
36	9.81 343	15	9.93 303	26	0.06 697	9.88 040	11	24
37	9.81 358	14	9.93 329	25	0.06 671	9.88 029	11	23
38	9.81 372	15	9.93 354	26	0.06 646	9.88 018	11	22
39	9.81 387	15	9.93 380	26	0.06 620	9.88 007	11	21
40	9.81 402	15	9.93 406	25	0.06 594	9.87 996	11	20
41	9.81 417	14	9.93 431	26	0.06 569	9.87 985	10	19
42	9.81 431	15	9.93 457	25	0.06 543	9.87 975	11	18
43	9.81 446	15	9.93 482	26	0.06 518	9.87 964	11	17
44	9.81 461	14	9.93 508	25	0.06 492	9.87 953	11	16
45	9.81 475	15	9.93 533	26	0.06 467	9.87 942	11	15
46	9.81 490	15	9.93 559	25	0.06 441	9.87 931	11	14
47	9.81 505	14	9.93 584	26	0.06 416	9.87 920	11	13
48	9.81 519	15	9.93 610	26	0.06 390	9.87 909	11	12
49	9.81 534	15	9.93 636	25	0.06 364	9.87 898	11	11
50	9.81 549	14	9.93 661	26	0.06 339	9.87 887	10	10
51	9.81 563	15	9.93 687	25	0.06 313	9.87 877	11	9
52	9.81 578	14	9.93 712	26	0.06 288	9.87 866	11	8
53	9.81 592	15	9.93 738	25	0.06 262	9.87 855	11	7
54	9.81 607	15	9.93 763	26	0.06 237	9.87 844	11	6
55	9.81 622	14	9.93 789	25	0.06 211	9.87 833	11	5
56	9.81 636	15	9.93 814	26	0.06 186	9.87 822	11	4
57	9.81 651	14	9.93 840	25	0.06 160	9.87 811	11	3
58	9.81 665	15	9.93 865	26	0.06 135	9.87 800	11	2
59	9.81 680	14	9.93 891	25	0.06 109	9.87 789	11	1
60	9.81 694		9.93 916		0.06 084	9.87 778		0
	Log Cos	d	Log Cot	c d	Log Tan	Log Sin	d	′

Prop. Parts

	26	25	15
1	2.6	2.5	1.5
2	5.2	5.0	3.0
3	7.8	7.5	4.5
4	10.4	10.0	6.0
5	13.0	12.5	7.5
6	15.6	15.0	9.0
7	18.2	17.5	10.5
8	20.8	20.0	12.0
9	23.4	22.5	13.5

	14	11	10
1	1.4	1.1	1.0
2	2.8	2.2	2.0
3	4.2	3.3	3.0
4	5.6	4.4	4.0
5	7.0	5.5	5.0
6	8.4	6.6	6.0
7	9.8	7.7	7.0
8	11.2	8.8	8.0
9	12.6	9.9	9.0

Prop. Parts

′	Log Sin	d	Log Tan	c d	Log Cot	Log Cos	d		Prop. Parts
0	9.81 694	15	9.93 916	26	0.06 084	9.87 778	11	60	
1	9.81 709	14	9.93 942	25	0.06 058	9.87 767	11	59	
2	9.81 723	15	9.93 967	26	0.06 033	9.87 756	11	58	
3	9.81 738	14	9.93 993	25	0.06 007	9.87 745	11	57	
4	9.81 752	15	9.94 018	26	0.05 982	9.87 734	11	56	
5	9.81 767	14	9.94 044	25	0.05 956	9.87 723	11	55	
6	9.81 781	15	9.94 069	26	0.05 931	9.87 712	11	54	
7	9.81 796	14	9.94 095	25	0.05 905	9.87 701	11	53	
8	9.81 810	15	9.94 120	26	0.05 880	9.87 690	11	52	
9	9.81 825	14	9.94 146	25	0.05 854	9.87 679	11	51	
10	9.81 839	15	9.94 171	26	0.05 829	9.87 668	11	50	
11	9.81 854	14	9.94 197	25	0.05 803	9.87 657	11	49	
12	9.81 868	14	9.94 222	26	0.05 778	9.87 646	11	48	
13	9.81 882	15	9.94 248	25	0.05 752	9.87 635	11	47	
14	9.81 897	14	9.94 273	26	0.05 727	9.87 624	11	46	

		26	**25**	**15**
15	9.81 911	15	9.94 299	25	0.05 701	9.87 613	12	45
16	9.81 926	14	9.94 324	26	0.05 676	9.87 601	11	44
17	9.81 940	15	9.94 350	25	0.05 650	9.87 590	11	43
18	9.81 955	14	9.94 375	26	0.05 625	9.87 579	11	42
19	9.81 969	14	9.94 401	25	0.05 599	9.87 568	11	41

Prop. Parts tables:

	26	25	15
1	2.6	2.5	1.5
2	5.2	5.0	3.0
3	7.8	7.5	4.5
4	10.4	10.0	6.0
5	13.0	12.5	7.5
6	15.6	15.0	9.0
7	18.2	17.5	10.5
8	20.8	20.0	12.0
9	23.4	22.5	13.5

′	Log Sin	d	Log Tan	c d	Log Cot	Log Cos	d	
20	9.81 983	15	9.94 426	26	0.05 574	9.87 557	11	40
21	9.81 998	14	9.94 452	25	0.05 548	9.87 546	11	39
22	9.82 012	14	9.94 477	26	0.05 523	9.87 535	11	38
23	9.82 026	15	9.94 503	25	0.05 497	9.87 524	11	37
24	9.82 041	14	9.94 528	26	0.05 472	9.87 513	12	36
25	9.82 055	14	9.94 554	25	0.05 446	9.87 501	11	35
26	9.82 069	15	9.94 579	25	0.05 421	9.87 490	11	34
27	9.82 084	14	9.94 604	26	0.05 396	9.87 479	11	33
28	9.82 098	14	9.94 630	25	0.05 370	9.87 468	11	32
29	9.82 112	14	9.94 655	26	0.05 345	9.87 457	11	31
30	9.82 126	15	9.94 681	25	0.05 319	9.87 446	12	30
31	9.82 141	14	9.94 706	26	0.05 294	9.87 434	11	29
32	9.82 155	14	9.94 732	25	0.05 268	9.87 423	11	28
33	9.82 169	15	9.94 757	26	0.05 243	9.87 412	11	27
34	9.82 184	14	9.94 783	25	0.05 217	9.87 401	11	26
35	9.82 198	14	9.94 808	26	0.05 192	9.87 390	12	25
36	9.82 212	14	9.94 834	25	0.05 166	9.87 378	11	24
37	9.82 226	14	9.94 859	25	0.05 141	9.87 367	11	23
38	9.82 240	15	9.94 884	26	0.05 116	9.87 356	11	22
39	9.82 255	14	9.94 910	25	0.05 090	9.87 345	11	21

	14	12	11
1	1.4	1.2	1.1
2	2.8	2.4	2.2
3	4.2	3.6	3.3
4	5.6	4.8	4.4
5	7.0	6.0	5.5
6	8.4	7.2	6.6
7	9.8	8.4	7.7
8	11.2	9.6	8.8
9	12.6	10.8	9.9

′	Log Sin	d	Log Tan	c d	Log Cot	Log Cos	d	
40	9.82 269	14	9.94 935	26	0.05 065	9.87 334	12	20
41	9.82 283	14	9.94 961	25	0.05 039	9.87 322	11	19
42	9.82 297	14	9.94 986	26	0.05 014	9.87 311	11	18
43	9.82 311	15	9.95 012	25	0.04 988	9.87 300	12	17
44	9.82 326	14	9.95 037	25	0.04 963	9.87 288	11	16
45	9.82 340	14	9.95 062	26	0.04 938	9.87 277	11	15
46	9.82 354	14	9.95 088	25	0.04 912	9.87 266	11	14
47	9.82 368	14	9.95 113	26	0.04 887	9.87 255	12	13
48	9.82 382	14	9.95 139	25	0.04 861	9.87 243	11	12
49	9.82 396	14	9.95 164	26	0.04 836	9.87 232	11	11
50	9.82 410	14	9.95 190	25	0.04 810	9.87 221	12	10
51	9.82 424	15	9.95 215	25	0.04 785	9.87 209	11	9
52	9.82 439	14	9.95 240	26	0.04 760	9.87 198	11	8
53	9.82 453	14	9.95 266	25	0.04 734	9.87 187	12	7
54	9.82 467	14	9.95 291	26	0.04 709	9.87 175	11	6
55	9.82 481	14	9.95 317	25	0.04 683	9.87 164	11	5
56	9.82 495	14	9.95 342	26	0.04 658	9.87 153	12	4
57	9.82 509	14	9.95 368	25	0.04 632	9.87 141	11	3
58	9.82 523	14	9.95 393	25	0.04 607	9.87 130	11	2
59	9.82 537	14	9.95 418	26	0.04 582	9.87 119	12	1
60	9.82 551		9.95 444		0.04 556	9.87 107		0

	Log Cos	d	Log Cot	c d	Log Tan	Log Sin	d	′	Prop. Parts

48°

′	Log Sin	d	Log Tan	c d	Log Cot	Log Cos	d		Prop. Parts
0	9.82 551	14	9.95 444	25	0.04 556	9.87 107	11	**60**	
1	9.82 565	14	9.95 469	26	0.04 531	9.87 096	11	59	
2	9.82 579	14	9.95 495	25	0.04 505	9.87 085	12	58	
3	9.82 593	14	9.95 520	25	0.04 480	9.87 073	11	57	
4	9.82 607	14	9.95 545	26	0.04 455	9.87 062	12	56	
5	9.82 621	14	9.95 571	25	0.04 429	9.87 050	11	**55**	
6	9.82 635	14	9.95 596	26	0.04 404	9.87 039	11	54	
7	9.82 649	14	9.95 622	25	0.04 378	9.87 028	12	53	
8	9.82 663	14	9.95 647	25	0.04 353	9.87 016	11	52	
9	9.82 677	14	9.95 672	26	0.04 328	9.87 005	12	51	
10	9.82 691	14	9.95 698	25	0.04 302	9.86 993	11	**50**	
11	9.82 705	14	9.95 723	25	0.04 277	9.86 982	12	49	
12	9.82 719	14	9.95 748	26	0.04 252	9.86 970	11	48	
13	9.82 733	14	9.95 774	25	0.04 226	9.86 959	12	47	
14	9.82 747	14	9.95 799	26	0.04 201	9.86 947	11	46	

		26	**25**	**14**
1		2.6	2.5	1.4
2		5.2	5.0	2.8
3		7.8	7.5	4.2
4		10.4	10.0	5.6
5		13.0	12.5	7.0
6		15.6	15.0	8.4
7		18.2	17.5	9.8
8		20.8	20.0	11.2
9		23.4	22.5	12.6

′	Log Sin	d	Log Tan	c d	Log Cot	Log Cos	d	
15	9.82 761	14	9.95 825	25	0.04 175	9.86 936	12	**45**
16	9.82 775	13	9.95 850	25	0.04 150	9.86 924	11	44
17	9.82 788	14	9.95 875	26	0.04 125	9.86 913	11	43
18	9.82 802	14	9.95 901	25	0.04 099	9.86 902	12	42
19	9.82 816	14	9.95 926	26	0.04 074	9.86 890	11	41
20	9.82 830	14	9.95 952	25	0.04 048	9.86 879	12	**40**
21	9.82 844	14	9.95 977	25	0.04 023	9.86 867	12	39
22	9.82 858	14	9.96 002	26	0.03 998	9.86 855	11	38
23	9.82 872	13	9.96 028	25	0.03 972	9.86 844	12	37
24	9.82 885	14	9.96 053	25	0.03 947	9.86 832	11	36
25	9.82 899	14	9.96 078	26	0.03 922	9.86 821	12	**35**
26	9.82 913	14	9.96 104	25	0.03 896	9.86 809	11	34
27	9.82 927	14	9.96 129	26	0.03 871	9.86 798	12	33
28	9.82 941	14	9.96 155	25	0.03 845	9.86 786	11	32
29	9.82 955	13	9.96 180	25	0.03 820	9.86 775	12	31
30	9.82 968	14	9.96 205	26	0.03 795	9.86 763	11	**30**
31	9.82 982	14	9.96 231	25	0.03 769	9.86 752	12	29
32	9.82 996	14	9.96 256	25	0.03 744	9.86 740	12	28
33	9.83 010	13	9.96 281	26	0.03 719	9.86 728	11	27
34	9.83 023	14	9.96 307	25	0.03 693	9.86 717	12	26
35	9.83 037	14	9.96 332	25	0.03 668	9.86 705	11	**25**
36	9.83 051	14	9.96 357	26	0.03 643	9.86 694	12	24
37	9.83 065	13	9.96 383	25	0.03 617	9.86 682	12	23

		13	**12**	**11**
1		1.3	1.2	1.1
2		2.6	2.4	2.2
3		3.9	3.6	3.3
4		5.2	4.8	4.4
5		6.5	6.0	5.5
6		7.8	7.2	6.6
7		9.1	8.4	7.7
8		10.4	9.6	8.8
9		11.7	10.8	9.9

′	Log Sin	d	Log Tan	c d	Log Cot	Log Cos	d	
38	9.83 078	14	9.96 408	25	0.03 592	9.86 670	11	22
39	9.83 092	14	9.96 433	26	0.03 567	9.86 659	12	21
40	9.83 106	14	9.96 459	25	0.03 541	9.86 647	12	**20**
41	9.83 120	13	9.96 484	26	0.03 516	9.86 635	11	19
42	9.83 133	14	9.96 510	25	0.03 490	9.86 624	12	18
43	9.83 147	14	9.96 535	25	0.03 465	9.86 612	12	17
44	9.83 161	13	9.96 560	26	0.03 440	9.86 600	11	16
45	9.83 174	14	9.96 586	25	0.03 414	9.86 589	12	**15**
46	9.83 188	14	9.96 611	25	0.03 389	9.86 577	12	14
47	9.83 202	13	9.96 636	26	0.03 364	9.86 565	11	13
48	9.83 215	14	9.96 662	25	0.03 338	9.86 554	12	12
49	9.83 229	13	9.96 687	25	0.03 313	9.86 542	12	11
50	9.83 242	14	9.96 712	26	0.03 288	9.86 530	12	**10**
51	9.83 256	14	9.96 738	25	0.03 262	9.86 518	11	9
52	9.83 270	13	9.96 763	25	0.03 237	9.86 507	12	8
53	9.83 283	14	9.96 788	26	0.03 212	9.86 495	12	7
54	9.83 297	13	9.96 814	25	0.03 186	9.86 483	11	6
55	9.83 310	14	9.96 839	25	0.03 161	9.86 472	12	**5**
56	9.83 324	14	9.96 864	26	0.03 136	9.86 460	12	4
57	9.83 338	13	9.96 890	25	0.03 110	9.86 448	12	3
58	9.83 351	14	9.96 915	25	0.03 085	9.86 436	11	2
59	9.83 365	13	9.96 940	26	0.03 060	9.86 425	12	1
60	9.83 378		9.96 966		0.03 034	9.86 413		**0**
	Log Cos	d	Log Cot	c d	Log Tan	Log Sin	d	′	Prop. Parts

'	Log Sin	d	Log Tan	c d	Log Cot	Log Cos	d		Prop. Parts		
0	9.83 378	14	9.96 966	25	0.03 034	9.86 413	12	60			
1	9.83 392	13	9.96 991	25	0.03 009	9.86 401	12	59			
2	9.83 405	14	9.97 016	26	0.02 984	9.86 389	12	58			
3	9.83 419	13	9.97 042	25	0.02 958	9.86 377	11	57			
4	9.83 432	14	9.97 067	25	0.02 933	9.86 366	12	56			
5	9.83 446	13	9.97 092	26	0.02 908	9.86 354	12	55			
6	9.83 459	14	9.97 118	25	0.02 882	9.86 342	12	54			
7	9.83 473	13	9.97 143	25	0.02 857	9.86 330	12	53			
8	9.83 486	14	9.97 168	25	0.02 832	9.86 318	12	52			
9	9.83 500	13	9.97 193	26	0.02 807	9.86 306	11	51			
10	9.83 513	14	9.97 219	25	0.02 781	9.86 295	12	50			
11	9.83 527	13	9.97 244	25	0.02 756	9.86 283	12	49			
12	9.83 540	14	9.97 269	26	0.02 731	9.86 271	12	48			
13	9.83 554	13	9.97 295	25	0.02 705	9.86 259	12	47			
14	9.83 567	14	9.97 320	25	0.02 680	9.86 247	12	46	**26**	**25**	**14**
15	9.83 581	13	9.97 345	26	0.02 655	9.86 235	12	45	1 2.6	2.5	1.4
16	9.83 594	14	9.97 371	25	0.02 629	9.86 223	12	44	2 5.2	5.0	2.8
17	9.83 608	13	9.97 396	25	0.02 604	9.86 211	11	43	3 7.8	7.5	4.2
18	9.83 621	13	9.97 421	26	0.02 579	9.86 200	12	42	4 10.4	10.0	5.6
19	9.83 634	14	9.97 447	25	0.02 553	9.86 188	12	41	5 13.0	12.5	7.0
20	9.83 648	13	9.97 472	25	0.02 528	9.86 176	12	40	6 15.6	15.0	8.4
21	9.83 661	13	9.97 497	26	0.02 503	9.86 164	12	39	7 18.2	17.5	9.8
22	9.83 674	14	9.97 523	25	0.02 477	9.86 152	12	38	8 20.8	20.0	11.2
23	9.83 688	13	9.97 548	25	0.02 452	9.86 140	12	37	9 23.4	22.5	12.6
24	9.83 701	14	9.97 573	25	0.02 427	9.86 128	12	36			
25	9.83 715	13	9.97 598	26	0.02 402	9.86 116	12	35			
26	9.83 728	13	9.97 624	25	0.02 376	9.86 104	12	34			
27	9.83 741	14	9.97 649	25	0.02 351	9.86 092	12	33			
28	9.83 755	13	9.97 674	26	0.02 326	9.86 080	12	32			
29	9.83 768	13	9.97 700	25	0.02 300	9.86 068	12	31			
30	9.83 781	14	9.97 725	25	0.02 275	9.86 056	12	30			
31	9.83 795	13	9.97 750	26	0.02 250	9.86 044	12	29			
32	9.83 808	13	9.97 776	25	0.02 224	9.86 032	12	28			
33	9.83 821	13	9.97 801	25	0.02 199	9.86 020	12	27			
34	9.83 834	14	9.97 826	25	0.02 174	9.86 008	12	26			
35	9.83 848	13	9.97 851	26	0.02 149	9.85 996	12	25			
36	9.83 861	13	9.97 877	25	0.02 123	9.85 984	12	24			
37	9.83 874	13	9.97 902	25	0.02 098	9.85 972	12	23	**13**	**12**	**11**
38	9.83 887	14	9.97 927	26	0.02 073	9.85 960	12	22	1 1.3	1.2	1.1
39	9.83 901	13	9.97 953	25	0.02 047	9.85 948	12	21	2 2.6	2.4	2.2
40	9.83 914	13	9.97 978	25	0.02 022	9.85 936	12	20	3 3.9	3.6	3.3
41	9.83 927	13	9.98 003	26	0.01 997	9.85 924	12	19	4 5.2	4.8	4.4
42	9.83 940	14	9.98 029	25	0.01 971	9.85 912	12	18	5 6.5	6.0	5.5
43	9.83 954	13	9.98 054	25	0.01 946	9.85 900	12	17	6 7.8	7.2	6.6
44	9.83 967	13	9.98 079	25	0.01 921	9.85 888	12	16	7 9.1	8.4	7.7
45	9.83 980	13	9.98 104	26	0.01 896	9.85 876	12	15	8 10.4	9.6	8.8
46	9.83 993	13	9.98 130	25	0.01 870	9.85 864	13	14	9 11.7	10.8	9.9
47	9.84 006	14	9.98 155	25	0.01 845	9.85 851	12	13			
48	9.84 020	13	9.98 180	26	0.01 820	9.85 839	12	12			
49	9.84 033	13	9.98 206	25	0.01 794	9.85 827	12	11			
50	9.84 046	13	9.98 231	25	0.01 769	9.85 815	12	10			
51	9.84 059	13	9.98 256	25	0.01 744	9.85 803	12	9			
52	9.84 072	13	9.98 281	26	0.01 719	9.85 791	12	8			
53	9.84 085	13	9.98 307	25	0.01 693	9.85 779	13	7			
54	9.84 098	14	9.98 332	25	0.01 668	9.85 766	12	6			
55	9.84 112	13	9.98 357	26	0.01 643	9.85 754	12	5			
56	9.84 125	13	9.98 383	25	0.01 617	9.85 742	12	4			
57	9.84 138	13	9.98 408	25	0.01 592	9.85 730	12	3			
58	9.84 151	13	9.98 433	25	0.01 567	9.85 718	12	2			
59	9.84 164	13	9.98 458	26	0.01 542	9.85 706	13	1			
60	9.84 177		9.98 484		0.01 516	9.85 693		0			
	Log Cos	d	Log Cot	c d	Log Tan	Log Sin	d	'	Prop. Parts		

′	Log Sin	d	Log Tan	c d	Log Cot	Log Cos	d		Prop. Parts		
0	9.84 177	13	9.98 484	25	0.01 516	9.85 693	12	60			
1	9.84 190	13	9.98 509	25	0.01 491	9.85 681	12	59			
2	9.84 203	13	9.98 534	26	0.01 466	9.85 669	12	58			
3	9.84 216	13	9.98 560	25	0.01 440	9.85 657	12	57			
4	9.84 229	13	9.98 585	25	0.01 415	9.85 645	13	56			
5	9.84 242	13	9.98 610	25	0.01 390	9.85 632	12	55			
6	9.84 255	14	9.98 635	26	0.01 365	9.85 620	12	54			
7	9.84 269	13	9.98 661	25	0.01 339	9.85 608	12	53			
8	9.84 282	13	9.98 686	25	0.01 314	9.85 596	13	52			
9	9.84 295	13	9.98 711	26	0.01 289	9.85 583	12	51			
10	9.84 308	13	9.98 737	25	0.01 263	9.85 571	12	50			
11	9.84 321	13	9.98 762	25	0.01 238	9.85 559	12	49			
12	9.84 334	13	9.98 787	25	0.01 213	9.85 547	13	48			
13	9.84 347	13	9.98 812	26	0.01 188	9.85 534	12	47			
14	9.84 360	13	9.98 838	25	0.01 162	9.85 522	12	46	**26**	**25**	**14**
15	9.84 373	12	9.98 863	25	0.01 137	9.85 510	12	45	1 2.6	2.5	1.4
16	9.84 385	13	9.98 888	25	0.01 112	9.85 497	12	44	2 5.2	5.0	2.8
17	9.84 398	13	9.98 913	26	0.01 087	9.85 485	12	43	3 7.8	7.5	4.2
18	9.84 411	13	9.98 939	25	0.01 061	9.85 473	13	42	4 10.4	10.0	5.6
19	9.84 424	13	9.98 964	25	0.01 036	9.85 460	12	41	5 13.0	12.5	7.0
20	9.84 437	13	9.98 989	26	0.01 011	9.85 448	12	40	6 15.6	15.0	8.4
21	9.84 450	13	9.99 015	25	0.00 985	9.85 436	13	39	7 18.2	17.5	9.8
22	9.84 463	13	9.99 040	25	0.00 960	9.85 423	12	38	8 20.8	20.0	11.2
23	9.84 476	13	9.99 065	25	0.00 935	9.85 411	12	37	9 23.4	22.5	12.6
24	9.84 489	13	9.99 090	26	0.00 910	9.85 399	13	36			
25	9.84 502	13	9.99 116	25	0.00 884	9.85 386	12	35			
26	9.84 515	13	9.99 141	25	0.00 859	9.85 374	13	34			
27	9.84 528	12	9.99 166	25	0.00 834	9.85 361	12	33			
28	9.84 540	13	9.99 191	26	0.00 809	9.85 349	12	32			
29	9.84 553	13	9.99 217	25	0.00 783	9.85 337	13	31			
30	9.84 566	13	9.99 242	25	0.00 758	9.85 324	12	30			
31	9.84 579	13	9.99 267	26	0.00 733	9.85 312	13	29			
32	9.84 592	13	9.99 293	25	0.00 707	9.85 299	12	28			
33	9.84 605	13	9.99 318	25	0.00 682	9.85 287	13	27			
34	9.84 618	12	9.99 343	25	0.00 657	9.85 274	12	26			
35	9.84 630	13	9.99 368	26	0.00 632	9.85 262	12	25			
36	9.84 643	13	9.99 394	25	0.00 606	9.85 250	13	24			
37	9.84 656	13	9.99 419	25	0.00 581	9.85 237	12	23		**13**	**12**
38	9.84 669	13	9.99 444	25	0.00 556	9.85 225	13	22	1	1.3	1.2
39	9.84 682	12	9.99 469	26	0.00 531	9.85 212	12	21	2	2.6	2.4
40	9.84 694	13	9.99 495	25	0.00 505	9.85 200	13	20	3	3.9	3.6
41	9.84 707	13	9.99 520	25	0.00 480	9.85 187	12	19	4	5.2	4.8
42	9.84 720	13	9.99 545	25	0.00 455	9.85 175	13	18	5	6.5	6.0
43	9.84 733	12	9.99 570	26	0.00 430	9.85 162	12	17	6	7.8	7.2
44	9.84 745	13	9.99 596	25	0.00 404	9.85 150	13	16	7	9.1	8.4
45	9.84 758	13	9.99 621	25	0.00 379	9.85 137	12	15	8	10.4	9.6
46	9.84 771	13	9.99 646	26	0.00 354	9.85 125	13	14	9	11.7	10.8
47	9.84 784	12	9.99 672	25	0.00 328	9.85 112	12	13			
48	9.84 796	13	9.99 697	25	0.00 303	9.85 100	13	12			
49	9.84 809	13	9.99 722	25	0.00 278	9.85 087	13	11			
50	9.84 822	13	9.99 747	26	0.00 253	9.85 074	12	10			
51	9.84 835	12	9.99 773	25	0.00 227	9.85 062	13	9			
52	9.84 847	13	9.99 798	25	0.00 202	9.85 049	12	8			
53	9.84 860	13	9.99 823	25	0.00 177	9.85 037	13	7			
54	9.84 873	12	9.99 848	26	0.00 152	9.85 024	12	6			
55	9.84 885	13	9.99 874	25	0.00 126	9.85 012	13	5			
56	9.84 898	13	9.99 899	25	0.00 101	9.84 999	13	4			
57	9.84 911	12	9.99 924	25	0.00 076	9.84 986	12	3			
58	9.84 923	13	9.99 949	26	0.00 051	9.84 974	13	2			
59	9.84 936	13	9.99 975	25	0.00 025	9.84 961	12	1			
60	9.84 949		0.00 000		0.00 000	9.84 949		0			
	Log Cos	d	Log Cot	c d	Log Tan	Log Sin	d	′	Prop. Parts		

TABLE III

VALUES

OF THE

TRIGONOMETRIC FUNCTIONS

TO

FIVE DECIMAL PLACES

′	Sin	Tan	Cot	Cos	
0	.00000	.00000	———	1.0000	60
1	029	029	3437.7	000	59
2	058	058	1718.9	000	58
3	087	087	1145.9	000	57
4	116	116	859.44	000	56
5	.00145	.00145	687.55	1.0000	55
6	175	175	572.96	000	54
7	204	204	491.11	000	53
8	233	233	429.72	000	52
9	262	262	381.97	000	51
10	.00291	.00291	343.77	1.0000	50
11	320	320	312.52	.99999	49
12	349	349	286.48	999	48
13	378	378	264.44	999	47
14	407	407	245.55	999	46
15	.00436	.00436	229.18	.99999	45
16	465	465	214.86	999	44
17	495	495	202.22	999	43
18	524	524	190.98	999	42
19	553	553	180.93	998	41
20	.00582	.00582	171.89	.99998	40
21	611	611	163.70	998	39
22	640	640	156.26	998	38
23	669	669	149.47	998	37
24	698	698	143.24	998	36
25	.00727	.00727	137.51	.99997	35
26	756	756	132.22	997	34
27	785	785	127.32	997	33
28	814	815	122.77	997	32
29	844	844	118.54	996	31
30	.00873	.00873	114.59	.99996	30
31	902	902	110.89	996	29
32	931	931	107.43	996	28
33	960	960	104.17	995	27
34	.00989	.00989	101.11	995	26
35	.01018	.01018	98.218	.99995	25
36	047	047	95.489	995	24
37	076	076	92.908	994	23
38	105	105	90.463	994	22
39	134	135	88.144	994	21
40	.01164	.01164	85.940	.99993	20
41	193	193	83.844	993	19
42	222	222	81.847	993	18
43	251	251	79.943	992	17
44	280	280	78.126	992	16
45	.01309	.01309	76.390	.99991	15
46	338	338	74.729	991	14
47	367	367	73.139	991	13
48	396	396	71.615	990	12
49	425	425	70.153	990	11
50	.01454	.01455	68.750	.99989	10
51	483	484	67.402	989	9
52	513	513	66.105	989	8
53	542	542	64.858	988	7
54	571	571	63.657	988	6
55	.01600	.01600	62.499	.99987	5
56	629	629	61.383	987	4
57	658	658	60.306	986	3
58	687	687	59.266	986	2
59	716	716	58.261	985	1
60	.01745	.01746	57.290	.99985	0
	Cos	Cot	Tan	Sin	′

89°

′	Sin	Tan	Cot	Cos	
0	.01745	.01746	57.290	.99985	60
1	774	775	56.351	984	59
2	803	804	55.442	984	58
3	832	833	54.561	983	57
4	862	862	53.709	983	56
5	.01891	.01891	52.882	.99982	55
6	920	920	52.081	982	54
7	949	949	51.303	981	53
8	.01978	.01978	50.549	980	52
9	.02007	.02007	49.816	980	51
10	.02036	.02036	49.104	.99979	50
11	065	066	48.412	979	49
12	094	095	47.740	978	48
13	123	124	47.085	977	47
14	152	153	46.449	977	46
15	.02181	.02182	45.829	.99976	45
16	211	211	45.226	976	44
17	240	240	44.639	975	43
18	269	269	44.066	974	42
19	298	298	43.508	974	41
20	.02327	.02328	42.964	.99973	40
21	356	357	42.433	972	39
22	385	386	41.916	972	38
23	414	415	41.411	971	37
24	443	444	40.917	970	36
25	.02472	.02473	40.436	.99969	35
26	501	502	39.965	969	34
27	530	531	39.506	968	33
28	560	560	39.057	967	32
29	589	589	38.618	966	31
30	.02618	.02619	38.188	.99966	30
31	647	648	37.769	965	29
32	676	677	37.358	964	28
33	705	706	36.956	963	27
34	734	735	36.563	963	26
35	.02763	.02764	36.178	.99962	25
36	792	793	35.801	961	24
37	821	822	35.431	960	23
38	850	851	35.070	959	22
39	879	881	34.715	959	21
40	.02908	.02910	34.368	.99958	20
41	938	939	34.027	957	19
42	967	968	33.694	956	18
43	.02996	.02997	33.366	955	17
44	.03025	.03026	33.045	954	16
45	.03054	.03055	32.730	.99953	15
46	083	084	32.421	952	14
47	112	114	32.118	952	13
48	141	143	31.821	951	12
49	170	172	31.528	950	11
50	.03199	.03201	31.242	.99949	10
51	228	230	30.960	948	9
52	257	259	30.683	947	8
53	286	288	30.412	946	7
54	316	317	30.145	945	6
55	.03345	.03346	29.882	.99944	5
56	374	376	29.624	943	4
57	403	405	29.371	942	3
58	432	434	29.122	941	2
59	461	463	28.877	940	1
60	.03490	.03492	28.636	.99939	0
	Cos	Cot	Tan	Sin	′

88°

′	Sin	Tan	Cot	Cos	
0	.03490	.03492	28.636	.99939	60
1	519	521	.399	938	59
2	548	550	28.166	937	58
3	577	579	27.937	936	57
4	606	609	.712	935	56
5	.03635	.03638	27.490	.99934	55
6	664	667	.271	933	54
7	693	696	27.057	932	53
8	723	725	26.845	931	52
9	752	754	.637	930	51
10	.03781	.03783	26.432	.99929	50
11	810	812	.230	927	49
12	839	842	26.031	926	48
13	868	871	25.835	925	47
14	897	900	.642	924	46
15	.03926	.03929	25.452	.99923	45
16	955	958	.264	922	44
17	.03984	.03987	25.080	921	43
18	04013	04016	24.898	919	42
19	042	046	.719	918	41
20	.04071	.04075	24.542	.99917	40
21	100	104	.368	916	39
22	129	133	.196	915	38
23	159	162	24.026	913	37
24	188	191	23.859	912	36
25	.04217	.04220	23.695	.99911	35
26	246	250	.532	910	34
27	275	279	.372	909	33
28	304	308	.214	907	32
29	333	337	23.058	906	31
30	.04362	.04366	22.904	.99905	30
31	391	395	.752	904	29
32	420	424	.602	902	28
33	449	454	.454	901	27
34	478	483	.308	900	26
35	.04507	.04512	22.164	.99898	25
36	536	541	22.022	897	24
37	565	570	21.881	896	23
38	594	599	.743	894	22
39	623	628	.606	893	21
40	.04653	.04658	21.470	.99892	20
41	682	687	.337	890	19
42	711	716	.205	889	18
43	740	745	21.075	888	17
44	769	774	20.946	886	16
45	.04798	.04803	20.819	.99885	15
46	827	833	.693	883	14
47	856	862	.569	882	13
48	885	891	.446	881	12
49	914	920	.325	879	11
50	.04943	.04949	20.206	.99878	10
51	.04972	.04978	20.087	876	9
52	.05001	.05007	19.970	875	8
53	030	037	.855	873	7
54	059	066	.740	872	6
55	.05088	.05095	19.627	.99870	5
56	117	124	.516	869	4
57	146	153	.405	867	3
58	175	182	.296	866	2
59	205	212	.188	864	1
60	.05234	.05241	19.081	.99863	0
	Cos	Cot	Tan	Sin	′

87°

′	Sin	Tan	Cot	Cos	
0	.05234	.05241	19.081	.99863	60
1	263	270	18.976	861	59
2	292	299	.871	860	58
3	321	328	.768	858	57
4	350	357	.666	857	56
5	.05379	.05387	18.564	.99855	55
6	408	416	.464	854	54
7	437	445	.366	852	53
8	466	474	.268	851	52
9	495	503	.171	849	51
10	.05524	.05533	18.075	.99847	50
11	553	562	17.980	846	49
12	582	591	.886	844	48
13	611	620	.793	842	47
14	640	649	.702	841	46
15	.05669	.05678	17.611	.99839	45
16	698	708	.521	838	44
17	727	737	.431	836	43
18	756	766	.343	834	42
19	785	795	.256	833	41
20	.05814	.05824	17.169	.99831	40
21	844	854	17.084	829	39
22	873	883	16.999	827	38
23	902	912	.915	826	37
24	931	941	.832	824	36
25	.05960	.05970	16.750	.99822	35
26	.05989	.05999	.668	821	34
27	.06018	.06029	.587	819	33
28	047	058	.507	817	32
29	076	087	.428	815	31
30	.06105	.06116	16.350	.99813	30
31	134	145	.272	812	29
32	163	175	.195	810	28
33	192	204	.119	808	27
34	221	233	16.043	806	26
35	.06250	.06262	15.969	.99804	25
36	279	291	.895	803	24
37	308	321	.821	801	23
38	337	350	.748	799	22
39	366	379	.676	797	21
40	.06395	.06408	15.605	.99795	20
41	424	438	.534	793	19
42	453	467	.464	792	18
43	482	496	.394	790	17
44	511	525	.325	788	16
45	.06540	.06554	15.257	.99786	15
46	569	584	.189	784	14
47	598	613	.122	782	13
48	627	642	15.056	780	12
49	656	671	14.990	778	11
50	.06685	.06700	14.924	.99776	10
51	714	730	.860	774	9
52	743	759	.795	772	8
53	773	788	.732	770	7
54	802	817	.669	768	6
55	.06831	.06847	14.606	.99766	5
56	860	876	.544	764	4
57	889	905	.482	762	3
58	918	934	.421	760	2
59	947	963	.361	758	1
60	.06976	.06993	14.301	.99756	0
	Cos	Cot	Tan	Sin	′

86°

′	Sin	Tan	Cot	Cos	
0	.06976	.06993	14.301	.99756	60
1	.07005	.07022	.241	754	59
2	034	051	.182	752	58
3	063	080	.124	750	57
4	092	110	.065	748	56
5	.07121	.07139	14.008	.99746	55
6	150	168	13.951	744	54
7	179	197	.894	742	53
8	208	227	.838	740	52
9	237	256	.782	738	51
10	.07266	.07285	13.727	.99736	50
11	295	314	.672	734	49
12	324	344	.617	731	48
13	353	373	.563	729	47
14	382	402	.510	727	46
15	.07411	.07431	13.457	.99725	45
16	440	461	.404	723	44
17	469	490	.352	721	43
18	498	519	.300	719	42
19	527	548	.248	716	41
20	.07556	.07578	13.197	.99714	40
21	585	607	.146	712	39
22	614	636	.096	710	38
23	643	665	13.046	708	37
24	672	695	12.996	705	36
25	.07701	.07724	12.947	.99703	35
26	730	753	.898	701	34
27	759	782	.850	699	33
28	788	812	.801	696	32
29	817	841	.754	694	31
30	.07846	.07870	12.706	.99692	30
31	875	899	.659	689	29
32	904	929	.612	687	28
33	933	958	.566	685	27
34	962	.07987	.520	683	26
35	.07991	.08017	12.474	.99680	25
36	.08020	046	.429	678	24
37	049	075	.384	676	23
38	078	104	.339	673	22
39	107	134	.295	671	21
40	.08136	.08163	12.251	.99668	20
41	165	192	.207	666	19
42	194	221	.163	664	18
43	223	251	.120	661	17
44	252	280	.077	659	16
45	.08281	.08309	12.035	.99657	15
46	310	339	11.992	654	14
47	339	368	.950	652	13
48	368	397	.909	649	12
49	397	427	.867	647	11
50	.08426	.08456	11.826	.99644	10
51	455	485	.785	642	9
52	484	514	.745	639	8
53	513	544	.705	637	7
54	542	573	.664	635	6
55	.08571	.08602	11.625	.99632	5
56	600	632	.585	630	4
57	629	661	.546	627	3
58	658	690	.507	625	2
59	687	720	.468	622	1
60	.08716	.08749	11.430	.99619	0
	Cos	Cot	Tan	Sin	′

85°

′	Sin	Tan	Cot	Cos	
0	.08716	.08749	11.430	.99619	60
1	745	778	.392	617	59
2	774	807	.354	614	58
3	803	837	.316	612	57
4	831	866	.279	609	56
5	.08860	.08895	11.242	.99607	55
6	889	925	.205	604	54
7	918	954	.168	602	53
8	947	.08983	.132	599	52
9	.08976	.09013	.095	596	51
10	.09005	.09042	11.059	.99594	50
11	034	071	11.024	591	49
12	063	101	10.988	588	48
13	092	130	.953	586	47
14	121	159	.918	583	46
15	.09150	.09189	10.883	.99580	45
16	179	218	.848	578	44
17	208	247	.814	575	43
18	237	277	.780	572	42
19	266	306	.746	570	41
20	.09295	.09335	10.712	.99567	40
21	324	365	.678	564	39
22	353	394	.645	562	38
23	382	423	.612	559	37
24	411	453	.579	556	36
25	.09440	.09482	10.546	.99553	35
26	469	511	.514	551	34
27	498	541	.481	548	33
28	527	570	.449	545	32
29	556	600	.417	542	31
30	.09585	.09629	10.385	.99540	30
31	614	658	.354	537	29
32	642	688	.322	534	28
33	671	717	.291	531	27
34	700	746	.260	528	26
35	.09729	.09776	10.229	.99526	25
36	758	805	.199	523	24
37	787	834	.168	520	23
38	816	864	.138	517	22
39	845	893	.108	514	21
40	.09874	.09923	10.078	.99511	20
41	903	952	.048	508	19
42	932	.09981	10.019	506	18
43	961	.10011	9.9893	503	17
44	.09990	040	.9601	500	16
45	.10019	.10069	9.9310	.99497	15
46	048	099	.9021	494	14
47	077	128	.8734	491	13
48	106	158	.8448	488	12
49	135	187	.8164	485	11
50	.10164	.10216	9.7882	.99482	10
51	192	246	.7601	479	9
52	221	275	.7322	476	8
53	250	305	.7044	473	7
54	279	334	.6768	470	6
55	.10308	.10363	9.6493	.99467	5
56	337	393	.6220	464	4
57	366	422	.5949	461	3
58	395	452	.5679	458	2
59	424	481	.5411	455	1
60	.10453	.10510	9.5144	.99452	0
	Cos	Cot	Tan	Sin	′

84°

′	Sin	Tan	Cot	Cos	
0	.10453	.10510	9.5144	.99452	**60**
1	482	540	.4878	449	59
2	511	569	.4614	446	58
3	540	599	.4352	443	57
4	569	628	.4090	440	56
5	.10597	.10657	9.3831	.99437	**55**
6	626	687	.3572	434	54
7	655	716	.3315	431	53
8	684	746	.3060	428	52
9	713	775	.2806	424	51
10	.10742	.10805	9.2553	.99421	**50**
11	771	834	.2302	418	49
12	800	863	.2052	415	48
13	829	893	.1803	412	47
14	858	922	.1555	409	46
15	.10887	.10952	9.1309	.99406	**45**
16	916	.10981	.1065	402	44
17	945	.11011	.0821	399	43
18	.10973	040	.0579	396	42
19	.11002	070	.0338	393	41
20	.11031	.11099	9.0098	.99390	**40**
21	060	128	8.9860	386	39
22	089	158	.9623	383	38
23	118	187	.9387	380	37
24	147	217	.9152	377	36
25	.11176	.11246	8.8919	.99374	**35**
26	205	276	.8686	370	34
27	234	305	.8455	367	33
28	263	335	.8225	364	32
29	291	364	.7996	360	31
30	.11320	.11394	8.7769	.99357	**30**
31	349	423	.7542	354	29
32	378	452	.7317	351	28
33	407	482	.7093	347	27
34	436	511	.6870	344	26
35	.11465	.11541	8.6648	.99341	**25**
36	494	570	.6427	337	24
37	523	600	.6208	334	23
38	552	629	.5989	331	22
39	580	659	.5772	327	21
40	.11609	.11688	8.5555	.99324	**20**
41	638	718	.5340	320	19
42	667	747	.5126	317	18
43	696	777	.4913	314	17
44	725	806	.4701	310	16
45	.11754	.11836	8.4490	.99307	**15**
46	783	865	.4280	303	14
47	812	895	.4071	300	13
48	840	924	.3863	297	12
49	869	954	.3656	293	11
50	.11898	.11983	8.3450	.99290	**10**
51	927	.12013	.3245	286	9
52	956	042	.3041	283	8
53	.11985	072	.2838	279	7
54	.12014	101	.2636	276	6
55	.12043	.12131	8.2434	.99272	**5**
56	071	160	.2234	269	4
57	100	190	.2035	265	3
58	129	219	.1837	262	2
59	158	249	.1640	258	1
60	.12187	.12278	8.1443	.99255	**0**
	Cos	Cot	Tan	Sin	′

83°

′	Sin	Tan	Cot	Cos	
0	.12187	.12278	8.1443	.99255	**60**
1	216	308	.1248	251	59
2	245	338	.1054	248	58
3	274	367	.0860	244	57
4	302	397	.0667	240	56
5	.12331	.12426	8.0476	.99237	**55**
6	360	456	.0285	233	54
7	389	485	8.0095	230	53
8	418	515	7.9906	226	52
9	447	544	.9718	222	51
10	.12476	.12574	7.9530	.99219	**50**
11	504	603	.9344	215	49
12	533	633	.9158	211	48
13	562	662	.8973	208	47
14	591	692	.8789	204	46
15	.12620	.12722	7.8606	.99200	**45**
16	649	751	.8424	197	44
17	678	781	.8243	193	43
18	706	810	.8062	189	42
19	735	840	.7882	186	41
20	.12764	.12869	7.7704	.99182	**40**
21	793	899	.7525	178	39
22	822	929	.7348	175	38
23	851	958	.7171	171	37
24	880	.12988	.6996	167	36
25	.12908	.13017	7.6821	.99163	**35**
26	937	047	.6647	160	34
27	966	076	.6473	156	33
28	.12995	106	.6301	152	32
29	.13024	136	.6129	148	31
30	.13053	.13165	7.5958	.99144	**30**
31	081	195	.5787	141	29
32	110	224	.5618	137	28
33	139	254	.5449	133	27
34	168	284	.5281	129	26
35	.13197	.13313	7.5113	.99125	**25**
36	226	343	.4947	122	24
37	254	372	.4781	118	23
38	283	402	.4615	114	22
39	312	432	.4451	110	21
40	.13341	.13461	7.4287	.99106	**20**
41	370	491	.4124	102	19
42	399	521	.3962	098	18
43	427	550	.3800	094	17
44	456	580	.3639	091	16
45	.13485	.13609	7.3479	.99087	**15**
46	514	639	.3319	083	14
47	543	669	.3160	079	13
48	572	698	.3002	075	12
49	600	728	.2844	071	11
50	.13629	.13758	7.2687	.99067	**10**
51	658	787	.2531	063	9
52	687	817	.2375	059	8
53	716	846	.2220	055	7
54	744	876	.2066	051	6
55	.13773	.13906	7.1912	.99047	**5**
56	802	935	.1759	043	4
57	831	965	.1607	039	3
58	860	.13995	.1455	035	2
59	889	.14024	.1304	031	1
60	.13917	.14054	7.1154	.99027	**0**
	Cos	Cot	Tan	Sin	′

82°

′	Sin	Tan	Cot	Cos	
0	.13917	.14054	7.1154	.99027	**60**
1	946	084	.1004	023	59
2	.13975	113	.0855	019	58
3	.14004	143	.0706	015	57
4	033	173	.0558	011	56
5	.14061	.14202	7.0410	.99006	**55**
6	090	232	.0264	.99002	54
7	119	262	7.0117	.98998	53
8	148	291	6.9972	994	52
9	177	321	.9827	990	51
10	.14205	.14351	6.9682	.98986	**50**
11	234	381	.9538	982	49
12	263	410	.9395	978	48
13	292	440	.9252	973	47
14	320	470	.9110	969	46
15	.14349	.14499	6.8969	.98965	**45**
16	378	529	.8828	961	44
17	407	559	.8687	957	43
18	436	588	.8548	953	42
19	464	618	.8408	948	41
20	.14493	.14648	6.8269	.98944	**40**
21	522	678	.8131	940	39
22	551	707	.7994	936	38
23	580	737	.7856	931	37
24	608	767	.7720	927	36
25	.14637	.14796	6.7584	.98923	**35**
26	666	826	.7448	919	34
27	695	856	.7313	914	33
28	723	886	.7179	910	32
29	752	915	.7045	906	31
30	.14781	.14945	6.6912	.98902	**30**
31	810	.14975	.6779	897	29
32	838	.15005	.6646	893	28
33	867	034	.6514	889	27
34	896	064	.6383	884	26
35	.14925	.15094	6.6252	.98880	**25**
36	954	124	.6122	876	24
37	.14982	153	.5992	871	23
38	.15011	183	.5863	867	22
39	040	213	.5734	863	21
40	.15069	.15243	6.5606	.98858	**20**
41	097	272	.5478	854	19
42	126	302	.5350	849	18
43	155	332	.5223	845	17
44	184	362	.5097	841	16
45	.15212	.15391	6.4971	.98836	**15**
46	241	421	.4846	832	14
47	270	451	.4721	827	13
48	299	481	.4596	823	12
49	327	511	.4472	818	11
50	.15356	.15540	6.4348	.98814	**10**
51	385	570	.4225	809	9
52	414	600	.4103	805	8
53	442	630	.3980	800	7
54	471	660	.3859	796	6
55	.15500	.15689	6.3737	.98791	**5**
56	529	719	.3617	787	4
57	557	749	.3496	782	3
58	586	779	.3376	778	2
59	615	809	.3257	773	1
60	.15643	.15838	6.3138	.98769	**0**
	Cos	Cot	Tan	Sin	′

′	Sin	Tan	Cot	Cos	
0	.15643	.15838	6.3138	.98769	**60**
1	672	868	.3019	764	59
2	701	898	.2901	760	58
3	730	928	.2783	755	57
4	758	958	.2666	751	56
5	.15787	.15988	6.2549	.98746	**55**
6	816	.16017	.2432	741	54
7	845	047	.2316	737	53
8	873	077	.2200	732	52
9	902	107	.2085	728	51
10	.15931	.16137	6.1970	.98723	**50**
11	959	167	.1856	718	49
12	.15988	196	.1742	714	48
13	.16017	226	.1628	709	47
14	046	256	.1515	704	46
15	.16074	.16286	6.1402	.98700	**45**
16	103	316	.1290	695	44
17	132	346	.1178	690	43
18	160	376	.1066	686	42
19	189	405	.0955	681	41
20	.16218	.16435	6.0844	.98676	**40**
21	246	465	.0734	671	39
22	275	495	.0624	667	38
23	304	525	.0514	662	37
24	333	555	.0405	657	36
25	.16361	.16585	6.0296	.98652	**35**
26	390	615	.0188	648	34
27	419	645	6.0080	643	33
28	447	674	5.9972	638	32
29	476	704	.9865	633	31
30	.16505	.16734	5.9758	.98629	**30**
31	533	764	.9651	624	29
32	562	794	.9545	619	28
33	591	824	.9439	614	27
34	620	854	.9333	609	26
35	.16648	.16884	5.9228	.98604	**25**
36	677	914	.9124	600	24
37	706	944	.9019	595	23
38	734	.16974	.8915	590	22
39	763	.17004	.8811	585	21
40	.16792	.17033	5.8708	.98580	**20**
41	820	063	.8605	575	19
42	849	093	.8502	570	18
43	878	123	.8400	565	17
44	906	153	.8298	561	16
45	.16935	.17183	5.8197	.98556	**15**
46	964	213	.8095	551	14
47	.16992	243	.7994	546	13
48	.17021	273	.7894	541	12
49	050	303	.7794	536	11
50	.17078	.17333	5.7694	.98531	**10**
51	107	363	.7594	526	9
52	136	393	.7495	521	8
53	164	423	.7396	516	7
54	193	453	.7297	511	6
55	.17222	.17483	5.7199	.98506	**5**
56	250	513	.7101	501	4
57	279	543	.7004	496	3
58	308	573	.6906	491	2
59	336	603	.6809	486	1
60	.17365	.17633	5.6713	.98481	**0**
	Cos	Cot	Tan	Sin	′

'	Sin	Tan	Cot	Cos	
0	.17365	.17633	5.6713	.98481	60
1	393	663	.6617	476	59
2	422	693	.6521	471	58
3	451	723	.6425	466	57
4	479	753	.6329	461	56
5	.17508	.17783	5.6234	.98455	55
6	537	813	.6140	450	54
7	565	843	.6045	445	53
8	594	873	.5951	440	52
9	623	903	.5857	435	51
10	.17651	.17933	5.5764	.98430	50
11	680	963	.5671	425	49
12	708	.17993	.5578	420	48
13	737	.18023	.5485	414	47
14	766	053	.5393	409	46
15	.17794	.18083	5.5301	.98404	45
16	823	113	.5209	399	44
17	852	143	.5118	394	43
18	880	173	.5026	389	42
19	909	203	.4936	383	41
20	.17937	.18233	5.4845	.98378	40
21	966	263	.4755	373	39
22	.17995	293	.4665	368	38
23	.18023	323	.4575	362	37
24	052	353	.4486	357	36
25	.18081	.18384	5.4397	.98352	35
26	109	414	.4308	347	34
27	138	444	.4219	341	33
28	166	474	.4131	336	32
29	195	504	.4043	331	31
30	.18224	.18534	5.3955	.98325	30
31	252	564	.3868	320	29
32	281	594	.3781	315	28
33	309	624	.3694	310	27
34	338	654	.3607	304	26
35	.18367	.18684	5.3521	.98299	25
36	395	714	.3435	294	24
37	424	745	.3349	288	23
38	452	775	.3263	283	22
39	481	805	.3178	277	21
40	.18509	.18835	5.3093	.98272	20
41	538	865	.3008	267	19
42	567	895	.2924	261	18
43	595	925	.2839	256	17
44	624	955	.2755	250	16
45	.18652	.18986	5.2672	.98245	15
46	681	.19016	.2588	240	14
47	710	046	.2505	234	13
48	738	076	.2422	229	12
49	767	106	.2339	223	11
50	.18795	.19136	5.2257	.98218	10
51	824	166	.2174	212	9
52	852	197	.2092	207	8
53	881	227	.2011	201	7
54	910	257	.1929	196	6
55	.18938	.19287	5.1848	.98190	5
56	967	317	.1767	185	4
57	.18995	347	.1686	179	3
58	.19024	378	.1606	174	2
59	052	408	.1526	168	1
60	.19081	.19438	5.1446	.98163	0
	Cos	Cot	Tan	Sin	'

79°

'	Sin	Tan	Cot	Cos	
0	.19081	.19438	5.1446	.98163	60
1	109	468	.1366	157	59
2	138	498	.1286	152	58
3	167	529	.1207	146	57
4	195	559	.1128	140	56
5	.19224	.19589	5.1049	.98135	55
6	252	619	.0970	129	54
7	281	649	.0892	124	53
8	309	680	.0814	118	52
9	338	710	.0736	112	51
10	.19366	.19740	5.0658	.98107	50
11	395	770	.0581	101	49
12	423	801	.0504	096	48
13	452	831	.0427	090	47
14	481	861	.0350	084	46
15	.19509	.19801	5.0273	.98079	45
16	538	921	.0197	073	44
17	566	952	.0121	067	43
18	595	.19982	5.0045	061	42
19	623	.20012	4.9969	056	41
20	.19652	.20042	4.9894	.98050	40
21	680	073	.9819	044	39
22	709	103	.9744	039	38
23	737	133	.9669	033	37
24	766	164	.9594	027	36
25	.19794	.20194	4.9520	.98021	35
26	823	224	.9446	016	34
27	851	254	.9372	010	33
28	880	285	.9298	.98004	32
29	908	315	.9225	.97998	31
30	.19937	.20345	4.9152	.97992	30
31	965	376	.9078	987	29
32	.19994	406	.9006	981	28
33	.20022	436	.8933	975	27
34	051	466	.8860	969	26
35	.20079	.20497	4.8788	.97963	25
36	108	527	.8716	958	24
37	136	557	.8644	952	23
38	165	588	.8573	946	22
39	193	618	.8501	940	21
40	.20222	.20648	4.8430	.97934	20
41	250	679	.8359	928	19
42	279	709	.8288	922	18
43	307	739	.8218	916	17
44	336	770	.8147	910	16
45	.20364	.20800	4.8077	.97905	15
46	393	830	.8007	899	14
47	421	861	.7937	893	13
48	450	891	.7867	887	12
49	478	921	.7798	881	11
50	.20507	.20952	4.7729	.97875	10
51	535	.20982	.7659	869	9
52	563	.21013	.7591	863	8
53	592	043	.7522	857	7
54	620	073	.7453	851	6
55	.20649	.21104	4.7385	.97845	5
56	677	134	.7317	839	4
57	706	164	.7249	833	3
58	734	195	.7181	827	2
59	763	225	.7114	821	1
60	.20791	.21256	4.7046	.97815	0
	Cos	Cot	Tan	Sin	'

78°

'	Sin	Tan	Cot	Cos	
0	.20791	.21256	4.7046	.97815	60
1	820	286	.6979	809	59
2	848	316	.6912	803	58
3	877	347	.6845	797	57
4	905	377	.6779	791	56
5	.20933	.21408	4.6712	.97784	55
6	962	438	.6646	778	54
7	.20990	469	.6580	772	53
8	.21019	499	.6514	766	52
9	047	529	.6448	760	51
10	.21076	.21560	4.6382	.97754	50
11	104	590	.6317	748	49
12	132	621	.6252	742	48
13	161	651	.6187	735	47
14	189	682	.6122	729	46
15	.21218	.21712	4.6057	.97723	45
16	246	743	.5993	717	44
17	275	773	.5928	711	43
18	303	804	.5864	705	42
19	331	834	.5800	698	41
20	.21360	.21864	4.5736	.97692	40
21	388	895	.5673	686	39
22	417	925	.5609	680	38
23	445	956	.5546	673	37
24	474	.21986	.5483	667	36
25	.21502	.22017	4.5420	.97661	35
26	530	047	.5357	655	34
27	559	078	.5294	648	33
28	587	108	.5232	642	32
29	616	139	.5169	636	31
30	.21644	.22169	4.5107	.97630	30
31	672	200	.5045	623	29
32	701	231	.4983	617	28
33	729	261	.4922	611	27
34	758	292	.4860	604	26
35	.21786	.22322	4.4799	.97598	25
36	814	353	.4737	592	24
37	843	383	.4676	585	23
38	871	414	.4615	579	22
39	899	444	.4555	573	21
40	.21928	.22475	4.4494	.97566	20
41	956	505	.4434	560	19
42	.21985	536	.4373	553	18
43	.22013	567	.4313	547	17
44	041	597	.4253	541	16
45	.22070	.22628	4.4194	.97534	15
46	098	658	.4134	528	14
47	126	689	.4075	521	13
48	155	719	.4015	515	12
49	183	750	.3956	508	11
50	.22212	.22781	4.3897	.97502	10
51	240	811	.3838	496	9
52	268	842	.3779	489	8
53	297	872	.3721	483	7
54	325	903	.3662	476	6
55	.22353	.22934	4.3604	.97470	5
56	382	964	.3546	463	4
57	410	.22995	.3488	457	3
58	438	.23026	.3430	450	2
59	467	056	.3372	444	1
60	.22495	.23087	4.3315	.97437	0
	Cos	Cot	Tan	Sin	'

77°

'	Sin	Tan	Cot	Cos	
0	.22495	.23087	4.3315	.97437	60
1	523	117	.3257	430	59
2	552	148	.3200	424	58
3	580	179	.3143	417	57
4	608	209	.3086	411	56
5	.22637	.23240	4.3029	.97404	55
6	665	271	.2972	398	54
7	693	301	.2916	391	53
8	722	332	.2859	384	52
9	750	363	.2803	378	51
10	.22778	.23393	4.2747	.97371	50
11	807	424	.2691	365	49
12	835	455	.2635	358	48
13	863	485	.2580	351	47
14	892	516	.2524	345	46
15	.22920	.23547	4.2468	.97338	45
16	948	578	.2413	331	44
17	.22977	608	.2358	325	43
18	.23005	639	.2303	318	42
19	033	670	.2248	311	41
20	.23062	.23700	4.2193	.97304	40
21	090	731	.2139	298	39
22	118	762	.2084	291	38
23	146	793	.2030	284	37
24	175	823	.1976	278	36
25	.23203	.23854	4.1922	.97271	35
26	231	885	.1868	264	34
27	260	916	.1814	257	33
28	288	946	.1760	251	32
29	316	.23977	.1706	244	31
30	.23345	.24008	4.1653	.97237	30
31	373	039	.1600	230	29
32	401	069	.1547	223	28
33	429	100	.1493	217	27
34	458	131	.1441	210	26
35	.23486	.24162	4.1388	.97203	25
36	514	193	.1335	196	24
37	542	223	.1282	189	23
38	571	254	.1230	182	22
39	599	285	.1178	176	21
40	.23627	.24316	4.1126	.97169	20
41	656	347	.1074	162	19
42	684	377	.1022	155	18
43	712	408	.0970	148	17
44	740	439	.0918	141	16
45	.23769	.24470	4.0867	.97134	15
46	797	501	.0815	127	14
47	825	532	.0764	120	13
48	853	562	.0713	113	12
49	882	593	.0662	106	11
50	.23910	.24624	4.0611	.97100	10
51	938	655	.0560	093	9
52	966	686	.0509	086	8
53	.23995	717	.0459	079	7
54	.24023	747	.0408	072	6
55	.24051	.24778	4.0358	.97065	5
56	079	809	.0308	058	4
57	108	840	.0257	051	3
58	136	871	.0207	044	2
59	164	902	.0158	037	1
60	.24192	.24933	4.0108	.97030	0
	Cos	Cot	Tan	Sin	'

76°

′	Sin	Tan	Cot	Cos	
0	.24192	.24933	4.0108	.97030	**60**
1	220	964	.0058	023	59
2	249	.24995	4.0009	015	58
3	277	.25026	3.9959	008	57
4	305	056	.9910	.97001	56
5	.24333	.25087	3.9861	.96994	**55**
6	362	118	.9812	987	54
7	390	149	.9763	980	53
8	418	180	.9714	973	52
9	446	211	.9665	966	51
10	.24474	.25242	3.9617	.96959	**50**
11	503	273	.9568	952	49
12	531	304	.9520	945	48
13	559	335	.9471	937	47
14	587	366	.9423	930	46
15	.24615	.25397	3.9375	.96923	**45**
16	644	428	.9327	916	44
17	672	459	.9279	909	43
18	700	490	.9232	902	42
19	728	521	.9184	894	41
20	.24756	.25552	3.9136	.96887	**40**
21	784	583	.9089	880	39
22	813	614	.9042	873	38
23	841	645	.8995	866	37
24	869	676	.8947	858	36
25	.24897	.25707	3.8900	.96851	**35**
26	925	738	.8854	844	34
27	954	769	.8807	837	33
28	.24982	800	.8760	829	32
29	.25010	831	.8714	822	31
30	.25038	.25862	3.8667	.96815	**30**
31	066	893	.8621	807	29
32	094	924	.8575	800	28
33	122	955	.8528	793	27
34	151	.25986	.8482	786	26
35	.25179	.26017	3.8436	.96778	**25**
36	207	048	.8391	771	24
37	235	079	.8345	764	23
38	263	110	.8299	756	22
39	291	141	.8254	749	21
40	.25320	.26172	3.8208	.96742	**20**
41	348	203	.8163	734	19
42	376	235	.8118	727	18
43	404	266	.8073	719	17
44	432	297	.8028	712	16
45	.25460	.26328	3.7983	.96705	**15**
46	488	359	.7938	697	14
47	516	390	.7893	690	13
48	545	421	.7848	682	12
49	573	452	.7804	675	11
50	.25601	.26483	3.7760	.96667	**10**
51	629	515	.7715	660	9
52	657	546	.7671	653	8
53	685	577	.7627	645	7
54	713	608	.7583	638	6
55	.25741	.26639	3.7539	.96630	**5**
56	769	670	.7495	623	4
57	798	701	.7451	615	3
58	826	733	.7408	608	2
59	854	764	.7364	600	1
60	.25882	.26795	3.7321	.96593	**0**
	Cos	Cot	Tan	Sin	′

′	Sin	Tan	Cot	Cos	
0	.25882	.26795	3.7321	.96593	**60**
1	910	826	.7277	585	59
2	938	857	.7234	578	58
3	966	888	.7191	570	57
4	.25994	920	.7148	562	56
5	.26022	.26951	3.7105	.96555	**55**
6	050	.26982	.7062	547	54
7	079	.27013	.7019	540	53
8	107	044	.6976	532	52
9	135	076	.6933	524	51
10	.26163	.27107	3.6891	.96517	**50**
11	191	138	.6848	509	49
12	219	169	.6806	502	48
13	247	201	.6764	494	47
14	275	232	.6722	486	46
15	.26303	.27263	3.6680	.96479	**45**
16	331	294	.6638	471	44
17	359	326	.6596	463	43
18	387	357	.6554	456	42
19	415	388	.6512	448	41
20	.26443	.27419	3.6470	.96440	**40**
21	471	451	.6429	433	39
22	500	482	.6387	425	38
23	528	513	.6346	417	37
24	556	545	.6305	410	36
25	.26584	.27576	3.6264	.96402	**35**
26	612	607	.6222	394	34
27	640	638	.6181	386	33
28	668	670	.6140	379	32
29	696	701	.6100	371	31
30	.26724	.27732	3.6059	.96363	**30**
31	752	764	.6018	355	29
32	780	795	.5978	347	28
33	808	826	.5937	340	27
34	836	858	.5897	332	26
35	.26864	.27889	3.5856	.96324	**25**
36	892	921	.5816	316	24
37	920	952	.5776	308	23
38	948	.27983	.5736	301	22
39	.26976	.28015	.5696	293	21
40	.27004	.28046	3.5656	.96285	**20**
41	032	077	.5616	277	19
42	060	109	.5576	269	18
43	088	140	.5536	261	17
44	116	172	.5497	253	16
45	.27144	.28203	3.5457	.96246	**15**
46	172	234	.5418	238	14
47	200	266	.5379	230	13
48	228	297	.5339	222	12
49	256	329	.5300	214	11
50	.27284	.28360	3.5261	.96206	**10**
51	312	391	.5222	198	9
52	340	423	.5183	190	8
53	368	454	.5144	182	7
54	396	486	.5105	174	6
55	.27424	.28517	3.5067	.96166	**5**
56	452	549	.5028	158	4
57	480	580	.4989	150	3
58	508	612	.4951	142	2
59	536	643	.4912	134	1
60	.27564	.28675	3.4874	.96126	**0**
	Cos	Cot	Tan	Sin	′

′	Sin	Tan	Cot	Cos		′	Sin	Tan	Cot	Cos	
0	.27564	.28675	3.4874	.96126	60	0	.29237	.30573	3.2709	.95630	60
1	592	706	.4836	118	59	1	265	605	.2675	622	59
2	620	738	.4798	110	58	2	293	637	.2641	613	58
3	648	769	.4760	102	57	3	321	669	.2607	605	57
4	676	801	.4722	094	56	4	348	700	.2573	596	56
5	.27704	.28832	3.4684	.96086	55	5	.29376	.30732	3.2539	.95588	55
6	731	864	.4646	078	54	6	404	764	.2506	579	54
7	759	895	.4608	070	53	7	432	796	.2472	571	53
8	787	927	.4570	062	52	8	460	828	.2438	562	52
9	815	958	.4533	054	51	9	487	860	.2405	554	51
10	.27843	.28990	3.4495	.96046	50	10	.29515	.30891	3.2371	.95545	50
11	871	.29021	.4458	037	49	11	543	923	.2338	536	49
12	899	053	.4420	029	48	12	571	955	.2305	528	48
13	927	084	.4383	021	47	13	599	.30987	.2272	519	47
14	955	116	.4346	013	46	14	626	.31019	.2238	511	46
15	.27983	.29147	3.4308	.96005	45	15	.29654	.31051	3.2205	.95502	45
16	.28011	179	.4271	.95997	44	16	682	083	.2172	493	44
17	039	210	.4234	989	43	17	710	115	.2139	485	43
18	067	242	.4197	981	42	18	737	147	.2106	476	42
19	095	274	.4160	972	41	19	765	178	.2073	467	41
20	.28123	.29305	3.4124	.95964	40	20	.29793	.31210	3.2041	.95459	40
21	150	337	.4087	956	39	21	821	242	.2008	450	39
22	178	368	.4050	948	38	22	849	274	.1975	441	38
23	206	400	.4014	940	37	23	876	306	.1943	433	37
24	234	432	.3977	931	36	24	904	338	.1910	424	36
25	.28262	.29463	3.3941	.95923	35	25	.29932	.31370	3.1878	.95415	35
26	290	495	.3904	915	34	26	960	402	.1845	407	34
27	318	526	.3868	907	33	27	.29987	434	.1813	398	33
28	346	558	.3832	898	32	28	.30015	466	.1780	389	32
29	374	590	.3796	890	31	29	043	498	.1748	380	31
30	.28402	.29621	3.3759	.95882	30	30	.30071	.31530	3.1716	.95372	30
31	429	653	.3723	874	29	31	098	562	.1684	363	29
32	457	685	.3687	865	28	32	126	594	.1652	354	28
33	485	716	.3652	857	27	33	154	626	.1620	345	27
34	513	748	.3616	849	26	34	182	658	.1588	337	26
35	.28541	.29780	3.3580	.95841	25	35	.30209	.31690	3.1556	.95328	25
36	569	811	.3544	832	24	36	237	722	.1524	319	24
37	597	843	.3509	824	23	37	265	754	.1492	310	23
38	625	875	.3473	816	22	38	292	786	.1460	301	22
39	652	906	.3438	807	21	39	320	818	.1429	293	21
40	.28680	.29938	3.3402	.95799	20	40	.30348	.31850	3.1397	.95284	20
41	708	.29970	.3367	791	19	41	376	882	.1366	275	19
42	736	.30001	.3332	782	18	42	403	914	.1334	266	18
43	764	033	.3297	774	17	43	431	946	.1303	257	17
44	792	065	.3261	766	16	44	459	.31978	.1271	248	16
45	.28820	.30097	3.3226	.95757	15	45	.30486	.32010	3.1240	.95240	15
46	847	128	.3191	749	14	46	514	042	.1209	231	14
47	875	160	.3156	740	13	47	542	074	.1178	222	13
48	903	192	.3122	732	12	48	570	106	.1146	213	12
49	931	224	.3087	724	11	49	597	139	.1115	204	11
50	.28959	.30255	3.3052	.95715	10	50	.30625	.32171	3.1084	.95195	10
51	.28987	287	.3017	707	9	51	653	203	.1053	186	9
52	.29015	319	.2983	698	8	52	680	235	.1022	177	8
53	042	351	.2948	690	7	53	708	267	.0991	168	7
54	070	382	.2914	681	6	54	736	299	.0961	159	6
55	.29098	.30414	3.2879	.95673	5	55	.30763	.32331	3.0930	.95150	5
56	126	446	.2845	664	4	56	791	363	.0899	142	4
57	154	478	.2811	656	3	57	819	396	.0868	133	3
58	182	509	.2777	647	2	58	846	428	.0838	124	2
59	209	541	.2743	639	1	59	874	460	.0807	115	1
60	.29237	.30573	3.2709	.95630	0	60	.30902	.32492	3.0777	.95106	0
	Cos	Cot	Tan	Sin	′		Cos	Cot	Tan	Sin	′

′	Sin	Tan	Cot	Cos	
0	.30902	.32492	3.0777	.95106	60
1	929	524	.0746	097	59
2	957	556	.0716	088	58
3	.30985	588	.0686	079	57
4	.31012	621	.0655	070	56
5	.31040	.32653	3.0625	.95061	55
6	068	685	.0595	052	54
7	095	717	.0565	043	53
8	123	749	.0535	033	52
9	151	782	.0505	024	51
10	.31178	.32814	3.0475	.95015	50
11	206	846	.0445	.95006	49
12	233	878	.0415	.94997	48
13	261	911	.0385	988	47
14	289	943	.0356	979	46
15	.31316	.32975	3.0326	.94970	45
16	344	.33007	.0296	961	44
17	372	040	.0267	952	43
18	399	072	.0237	943	42
19	427	104	.0208	933	41
20	.31454	.33136	3.0178	.94924	40
21	482	169	.0149	915	39
22	510	201	.0120	906	38
23	537	233	.0090	897	37
24	565	266	.0061	888	36
25	.31593	.33298	3.0032	.94878	35
26	620	330	3.0003	869	34
27	648	363	2.9974	860	33
28	675	395	.9945	851	32
29	703	427	.9916	842	31
30	.31730	.33460	2.9887	.94832	30
31	758	492	.9858	823	29
32	786	524	.9829	814	28
33	813	557	.9800	805	27
34	841	589	.9772	795	26
35	.31868	.33621	2.9743	.94786	25
36	896	654	.9714	777	24
37	923	686	.9686	768	23
38	951	718	.9657	758	22
39	.31979	751	.9629	749	21
40	.32006	.33783	2.9600	.94740	20
41	034	816	.9572	730	19
42	061	848	.9544	721	18
43	089	881	.9515	712	17
44	116	913	.9487	702	16
45	.32144	.33945	2.9459	.94693	15
46	171	.33978	.9431	684	14
47	199	.34010	.9403	674	13
48	227	043	.9375	665	12
49	254	075	.9347	656	11
50	.32282	.34108	2.9319	.94646	10
51	309	140	.9291	637	9
52	337	173	.9263	627	8
53	364	205	.9235	618	7
54	392	238	.9208	609	6
55	.32419	.34270	2.9180	.94599	5
56	447	303	.9152	590	4
57	474	335	.9125	580	3
58	502	368	.9097	571	2
59	529	400	.9070	561	1
60	.32557	.34433	2.9042	.94552	0
	Cos	Cot	Tan	Sin	′

71°

′	Sin	Tan	Cot	Cos	
0	.32557	.34433	2.9042	.94552	60
1	584	465	.9015	542	59
2	612	498	.8987	533	58
3	639	530	.8960	523	57
4	667	563	.8933	514	56
5	.32694	.34596	2.8905	.94504	55
6	722	628	.8878	495	54
7	749	661	.8851	485	53
8	777	693	.8824	476	52
9	804	726	.8797	466	51
10	.32832	.34758	2.8770	.94457	50
11	859	791	.8743	447	49
12	887	824	.8716	438	48
13	914	856	.8689	428	47
14	942	889	.8662	418	46
15	.32969	.34922	2.8636	.94409	45
16	.32997	954	.8609	399	44
17	.33024	.34987	.8582	390	43
18	051	.35020	.8556	380	42
19	079	052	.8529	370	41
20	.33106	.35085	2.8502	.94361	40
21	134	118	.8476	351	39
22	161	150	.8449	342	38
23	189	183	.8423	332	37
24	216	216	.8397	322	36
25	.33244	.35248	2.8370	.94313	35
26	271	281	.8344	303	34
27	298	314	.8318	293	33
28	326	346	.8291	284	32
29	353	379	.8265	274	31
30	.33381	.35412	2.8239	.94264	30
31	408	445	.8213	254	29
32	436	477	.8187	245	28
33	463	510	.8161	235	27
34	490	543	.8135	225	26
35	.33518	.35576	2.8109	.94215	25
36	545	608	.8083	206	24
37	573	641	.8057	196	23
38	600	674	.8032	186	22
39	627	707	.8006	176	21
40	.33655	.35740	2.7980	.94167	20
41	682	772	.7955	157	19
42	710	805	.7929	147	18
43	737	838	.7903	137	17
44	764	871	.7878	127	16
45	.33792	.35904	2.7852	.94118	15
46	819	937	.7827	108	14
47	846	.35969	.7801	098	13
48	874	.36002	.7776	088	12
49	901	035	.7751	078	11
50	.33929	.36068	2.7725	.94068	10
51	956	101	.7700	058	9
52	.33983	134	.7675	049	8
53	.34011	167	.7650	039	7
54	038	199	.7625	029	6
55	.34065	.36232	2.7600	.94019	5
56	093	265	.7575	.94009	4
57	120	298	.7550	.93999	3
58	147	331	.7525	989	2
59	175	364	.7500	979	1
60	.34202	.36397	2.7475	.93969	0
	Cos	Cot	Tan	Sin	′

70°

′	Sin	Tan	Cot	Cos	
0	.34202	.36397	2.7475	.93969	60
1	229	430	.7450	959	59
2	257	463	.7425	949	58
3	284	496	.7400	939	57
4	311	529	.7376	929	56
5	.34339	.36562	2.7351	.93919	55
6	366	595	.7326	909	54
7	393	628	.7302	899	53
8	421	661	.7277	889	52
9	448	694	.7253	879	51
10	.34475	.36727	2.7228	.93869	50
11	503	760	.7204	859	49
12	530	793	.7179	849	48
13	557	826	.7155	839	47
14	584	859	.7130	829	46
15	.34612	.36892	2.7106	.93819	45
16	639	925	.7082	809	44
17	666	958	.7058	799	43
18	694	.36991	.7034	789	42
19	721	.37024	.7009	779	41
20	.34748	.37057	2.6985	.93769	40
21	775	090	.6961	759	39
22	803	123	.6937	748	38
23	830	157	.6913	738	37
24	857	190	.6889	728	36
25	.34884	.37223	2.6865	.93718	35
26	912	256	.6841	708	34
27	939	289	.6818	698	33
28	966	322	.6794	688	32
29	.34993	355	.6770	677	31
30	.35021	.37388	2.6746	.93667	30
31	048	422	.6723	657	29
32	075	455	.6699	647	28
33	102	488	.6675	637	27
34	130	521	.6652	626	26
35	.35157	.37554	2.6628	.93616	25
36	184	588	.6605	606	24
37	211	621	.6581	596	23
38	239	654	.6558	585	22
39	266	687	.6534	575	21
40	.35293	.37720	2.6511	.93565	20
41	320	754	.6488	555	19
42	347	787	.6464	544	18
43	375	820	.6441	534	17
44	402	853	.6418	524	16
45	.35429	.37887	2.6395	.93514	15
46	456	920	.6371	503	14
47	484	953	.6348	493	13
48	511	.37986	.6325	483	12
49	538	.38020	.6302	472	11
50	.35565	.38053	2.6279	.93462	10
51	592	086	.6256	452	9
52	619	120	.6233	441	8
53	647	153	.6210	431	7
54	674	186	.6187	420	6
55	.35701	.38220	2.6165	.93410	5
56	728	253	.6142	400	4
57	755	286	.6119	389	3
58	782	320	.6096	379	2
59	810	353	.6074	368	1
60	.35837	.38386	2.6051	.93358	0
	Cos	Cot	Tan	Sin	′

69°

′	Sin	Tan	Cot	Cos	
0	.35837	.38386	2.6051	.93358	60
1	864	420	.6028	348	59
2	891	453	.6006	337	58
3	918	487	.5983	327	57
4	945	520	.5961	316	56
5	.35973	.38553	2.5938	.93306	55
6	.36000	587	.5916	295	54
7	027	620	.5893	285	53
8	054	654	.5871	274	52
9	081	687	.5848	264	51
10	.36108	.38721	2.5826	.93253	50
11	135	754	.5804	243	49
12	162	787	.5782	232	48
13	190	821	.5759	222	47
14	217	854	.5737	211	46
15	.36244	.38888	2.5715	.93201	45
16	271	921	.5693	190	44
17	298	955	.5671	180	43
18	325	.38988	.5649	169	42
19	352	.39022	.5627	159	41
20	.36379	.39055	2.5605	.93148	40
21	406	089	.5583	137	39
22	434	122	.5561	127	38
23	461	156	.5539	116	37
24	488	190	.5517	106	36
25	.36515	.39223	2.5495	.93095	35
26	542	257	.5473	084	34
27	569	290	.5452	074	33
28	596	324	.5430	063	32
29	623	357	.5408	052	31
30	.36650	.39391	2.5386	.93042	30
31	677	425	.5365	031	29
32	704	458	.5343	020	28
33	731	492	.5322	.93010	27
34	758	526	.5300	.92999	26
35	.36785	.39559	2.5279	.92988	25
36	812	593	.5257	978	24
37	839	626	.5236	967	23
38	867	660	.5214	956	22
39	894	694	.5193	945	21
40	.36921	.39727	2.5172	.92935	20
41	948	761	.5150	924	19
42	.36975	795	.5129	913	18
43	.37002	829	.5108	902	17
44	029	862	.5086	892	16
45	.37056	.39896	2.5065	.92881	15
46	083	930	.5044	870	14
47	110	963	.5023	859	13
48	137	.39997	.5002	849	12
49	164	.40031	.4981	838	11
50	.37191	.40065	2.4960	.92827	10
51	218	098	.4939	816	9
52	245	132	.4918	805	8
53	272	166	.4897	794	7
54	299	200	.4876	784	6
55	.37326	.40234	2.4855	.92773	5
56	353	267	.4834	762	4
57	380	301	.4813	751	3
58	407	335	.4792	740	2
59	434	369	.4772	729	1
60	.37461	.40403	2.4751	.92718	0
	Cos	Cot	Tan	Sin	′

68°

′	Sin	Tan	Cot	Cos	
0	.37461	.40403	2.4751	.92718	60
1	488	436	.4730	707	59
2	515	470	.4709	697	58
3	542	504	.4689	686	57
4	569	538	.4668	675	56
5	.37595	.40572	2.4648	.92664	55
6	622	606	.4627	653	54
7	649	640	.4606	642	53
8	676	674	.4586	631	52
9	703	707	.4566	620	51
10	.37730	.40741	2.4545	.92609	50
11	757	775	.4525	598	49
12	784	809	.4504	587	48
13	811	843	.4484	576	47
14	838	877	.4464	565	46
15	.37865	.40911	2.4443	.92554	45
16	892	945	.4423	543	44
17	919	.40979	.4403	532	43
18	946	.41013	.4383	521	42
19	973	047	.4362	510	41
20	.37999	.41081	2.4342	.92499	40
21	.38026	115	.4322	488	39
22	053	149	.4302	477	38
23	080	183	.4282	466	37
24	107	217	.4262	455	36
25	.38134	.41251	2.4242	.92444	35
26	161	285	.4222	432	34
27	188	319	.4202	421	33
28	215	353	.4182	410	32
29	241	387	.4162	399	31
30	.38268	.41421	2.4142	.92388	30
31	295	455	.4122	377	29
32	322	490	.4102	366	28
33	349	524	.4083	355	27
34	376	558	.4063	343	26
35	.38403	.41592	2.4043	.92332	25
36	430	626	.4023	321	24
37	456	660	.4004	310	23
38	483	694	.3984	299	22
39	510	728	.3964	287	21
40	.38537	.41763	2.3945	.92276	20
41	564	797	.3925	265	19
42	591	831	.3906	˙254	18
43	617	865	.3886	243	17
44	644	899	.3867	231	16
45	.38671	.41933	2.3847	.92220	15
46	698	.41968	.3828	209	14
47	725	.42002	.3808	198	13
48	752	036	.3789	186	12
49	778	070	.3770	175	11
50	.38805	.42105	2.3750	.92164	10
51	832	139	.3731	152	9
52	859	173	.3712	141	8
53	886	207	.3693	130	7
54	912	242	.3673	119	6
55	.38939	.42276	2.3654	.92107	5
56	966	310	.3635	096	4
57	.38993	345	.3616	085	3
58	.39020	379	.3597	073	2
59	046	413	.3578	062	1
60	.39073	.42447	2.3559	.92050	0
	Cos	Cot	Tan	Sin	′

67°

′	Sin	Tan	Cot	Cos	
0	.39073	.42447	2.3559	.92050	60
1	100	482	.3539	039	59
2	127	516	.3520	028	58
3	153	551	.3501	016	57
4	180	585	.3483	.92005	56
5	.39207	.42619	2.3464	.91994	55
6	234	654	.3445	982	54
7	260	688	.3426	971	53
8	287	722	.3407	959	52
9	314	757	.3388	948	51
10	.39341	.42791	2.3369	.91936	50
11	367	826	.3351	925	49
12	394	860	.3332	914	48
13	421	894	.3313	902	47
14	448	929	.3294	891	46
15	.39474	.42963	2.3276	.91879	45
16	501	.42998	.3257	868	44
17	528	.43032	.3238	856	43
18	555	067	.3220	845	42
19	581	101	.3201	833	41
20	.39608	.43136	2.3183	.91822	40
21	635	170	.3164	810	39
22	661	205	.3146	799	38
23	688	239	.3127	787	37
24	715	274	.3109	775	36
25	.39741	.43308	2.3090	.91764	35
26	768	343	.3072	752	34
27	795	378	.3053	741	33
28	822	412	.3035	729	32
29	848	447	.3017	718	31
30	.39875	.43481	2.2998	.91706	30
31	902	516	.2980	694	29
32	928	550	.2962	683	28
33	955	585	.2944	671	27
34	.39982	620	.2925	660	26
35	.40008	.43654	2.2907	.91648	25
36	035	689	.2889	636	24
37	062	724	.2871	625	23
38	088	758	.2853	613	22
39	115	793	.2835	601	21
40	.40141	.43828	2.2817	.91590	20
41	168	862	.2799	578	19
42	195	897	.2781	566	18
43	221	932	.2763	555	17
44	248	.43966	.2745	543	16
45	.40275	.44001	2.2727	.91531	15
46	301	036	.2709	519	14
47	328	071	.2691	508	13
48	355	105	.2673	496	12
49	381	140	.2655	484	11
50	.40408	.44175	2.2637	.91472	10
51	434	210	.2620	461	9
52	461	244	.2602	449	8
53	488	279	.2584	437	7
54	514	314	.2566	425	6
55	.40541	.44349	2.2549	.91414	5
56	567	384	.2531	402	4
57	594	418	.2513	390	3
58	621	453	.2496	378	2
59	647	488	.2478	366	1
60	.40674	.44523	2.2460	.91355	0
	Cos	Cot	Tan	Sin	′

66°

′	Sin	Tan	Cot	Cos	
0	.40674	.44523	2.2460	.91355	60
1	700	558	.2443	343	59
2	727	593	.2425	331	58
3	753	627	.2408	319	57
4	780	662	.2390	307	56
5	.40806	.44697	2.2373	.91295	55
6	833	732	.2355	283	54
7	860	767	.2338	272	53
8	886	802	.2320	260	52
9	913	837	.2303	248	51
10	.40939	.44872	2.2286	.91236	50
11	966	907	.2268	224	49
12	.40992	942	.2251	212	48
13	.41019	.44977	.2234	200	47
14	045	.45012	.2216	188	46
15	.41072	.45047	2.2199	.91176	45
16	098	082	.2182	164	44
17	125	117	.2165	152	43
18	151	152	.2148	140	42
19	178	187	.2130	128	41
20	.41204	.45222	2.2113	.91116	40
21	231	257	.2096	104	39
22	257	292	.2079	092	38
23	284	327	.2062	080	37
24	310	362	.2045	068	36
25	.41337	.45397	2.2028	.91056	35
26	363	432	.2011	044	34
27	390	467	.1994	032	33
28	416	502	.1977	020	32
29	443	538	.1960	.91008	31
30	.41469	.45573	2.1943	.90996	30
31	496	608	.1926	984	29
32	522	643	.1909	972	28
33	549	678	.1892	960	27
34	575	713	.1876	948	26
35	.41602	.45748	2.1859	.90936	25
36	628	784	.1842	924	24
37	655	819	.1825	911	23
38	681	854	.1808	899	22
39	707	889	.1792	887	21
40	.41734	.45924	2.1775	.90875	20
41	760	960	.1758	863	19
42	787	.45995	.1742	851	18
43	813	.46030	.1725	839	17
44	840	065	.1708	826	16
45	.41866	.46101	2.1692	.90814	15
46	892	136	.1675	802	14
47	919	171	.1659	790	13
48	945	206	.1642	778	12
49	972	242	.1625	766	11
50	.41998	.46277	2.1609	.90753	10
51	.42024	312	.1592	741	9
52	051	348	.1576	729	8
53	077	383	.1560	717	7
54	104	418	.1543	704	6
55	.42130	.46454	2.1527	.90692	5
56	156	489	.1510	680	4
57	183	525	.1494	668	3
58	209	560	.1478	655	2
59	235	595	.1461	643	1
60	.42262	.46631	2.1445	.90631	0
	Cos	Cot	Tan	Sin	′

65°

′	Sin	Tan	Cot	Cos	
0	.42262	.46631	2.1445	.90631	60
1	288	666	.1429	618	59
2	315	702	.1413	606	58
3	341	737	.1396	594	57
4	367	772	.1380	582	56
5	.42394	.46808	2.1364	.90569	55
6	420	843	.1348	557	54
7	446	879	.1332	545	53
8	473	914	.1315	532	52
9	499	950	.1299	520	51
10	.42525	.46985	2.1283	.90507	50
11	552	.47021	.1267	495	49
12	578	056	.1251	483	48
13	604	092	.1235	470	47
14	631	128	.1219	458	46
15	.42657	.47163	2.1203	.90446	45
16	683	199	.1187	433	44
17	709	234	.1171	421	43
18	736	270	.1155	408	42
19	762	305	.1139	396	41
20	.42788	.47341	2.1123	.90383	40
21	815	377	.1107	371	39
22	841	412	.1092	358	38
23	867	448	.1076	346	37
24	894	483	.1060	334	36
25	.42920	.47519	2.1044	.90321	35
26	946	555	.1028	309	34
27	972	590	.1013	296	33
28	.42999	626	.0997	284	32
29	.43025	662	.0981	271	31
30	.43051	.47698	2.0965	.90259	30
31	077	733	.0950	246	29
32	104	769	.0934	233	28
33	130	805	.0918	221	27
34	156	840	.0903	208	26
35	.43182	.47876	2.0887	.90196	25
36	209	912	.0872	183	24
37	235	948	.0856	171	23
38	261	.47984	.0840	158	22
39	287	.48019	.0825	146	21
40	.43313	.48055	2.0809	.90133	20
41	340	091	.0794	120	19
42	366	127	.0778	108	18
43	392	163	.0763	095	17
44	418	198	.0748	082	16
45	.43445	.48234	2.0732	.90070	15
46	471	270	.0717	057	14
47	497	306	.0701	045	13
48	523	342	.0686	032	12
49	549	378	.0671	019	11
50	.43575	.48414	2.0655	.90007	10
51	602	450	.0640	.89994	9
52	628	486	.0625	981	8
53	654	521	.0609	968	7
54	680	557	.0594	956	6
55	.43706	.48593	2.0579	.89943	5
56	733	629	.0564	930	4
57	759	665	.0549	918	3
58	785	701	.0533	905	2
59	811	737	.0518	892	1
60	.43837	.48773	2.0503	.89879	0
	Cos	Cot	Tan	Sin	′

64°

′	Sin	Tan	Cot	Cos		′	Sin	Tan	Cot	Cos	
0	.43837	.48773	2.0503	.89879	60	0	.45399	.50953	1.9626	.89101	60
1	863	809	.0488	867	59	1	425	.50989	.9612	087	59
2	889	845	.0473	854	58	2	451	.51026	.9598	074	58
3	916	881	.0458	841	57	3	477	063	.9584	061	57
4	942	917	.0443	828	56	4	503	099	.9570	048	56
5	.43968	.48953	2.0428	.89816	55	5	.45529	.51136	1.9556	.89035	55
6	.43994	.48989	.0413	803	54	6	554	173	.9542	021	54
7	.44020	.49026	.0398	790	53	7	580	209	.9528	.89008	53
8	046	062	.0383	777	52	8	606	246	.9514	.88995	52
9	072	098	.0368	764	51	9	632	283	.9500	981	51
10	.44098	.49134	2.0353	.89752	50	10	.45658	.51319	1.9486	.88968	50
11	124	170	.0338	739	49	11	684	356	.9472	955	49
12	151	206	.0323	726	48	12	710	393	.9458	942	48
13	177	242	.0308	713	47	13	736	430	.9444	928	47
14	203	278	.0293	700	46	14	762	467	.9430	915	46
15	.44229	.49315	2.0278	.89687	45	15	.45787	.51503	1.9416	.88902	45
16	255	351	.0263	674	44	16	813	540	.9402	888	44
17	281	387	.0248	662	43	17	839	577	.9388	875	43
18	307	423	.0233	649	42	18	865	614	.9375	862	42
19	333	459	.0219	636	41	19	891	651	.9361	848	41
20	.44359	.49495	2.0204	.89623	40	20	.45917	.51688	1.9347	.88835	40
21	385	532	.0189	610	39	21	942	724	.9333	822	39
22	411	568	.0174	597	38	22	968	761	.9319	808	38
23	437	604	.0160	584	37	23	.45994	798	.9306	795	37
24	464	640	.0145	571	36	24	.46020	835	.9292	782	36
25	.44490	.49677	2.0130	.89558	35	25	.46046	.51872	1.9278	.88768	35
26	516	713	.0115	545	34	26	072	909	.9265	755	34
27	542	749	.0101	532	33	27	097	946	.9251	741	33
28	568	786	.0086	519	32	28	123	.51983	.9237	728	32
29	594	822	.0072	506	31	29	149	.52020	.9223	715	31
30	.44620	.49858	2.0057	.89493	30	30	.46175	.52057	1.9210	.88701	30
31	646	894	.0042	480	29	31	201	094	.9196	688	29
32	672	931	.0028	467	28	32	226	131	.9183	674	28
33	698	.49967	2.0013	454	27	33	252	168	.9169	661	27
34	724	.50004	1.9999	441	26	34	278	205	.9155	647	26
35	.44750	.50040	1.9984	.89428	25	35	.46304	.52242	1.9142	.88634	25
36	776	076	.9970	415	24	36	330	279	.9128	620	24
37	802	113	.9955	402	23	37	355	316	.9115	607	23
38	828	149	.9941	389	22	38	381	353	.9101	593	22
39	854	185	.9926	376	21	39	407	390	.9088	580	21
40	.44880	.50222	1.9912	.89363	20	40	.46433	.52427	1.9074	.88566	20
41	906	258	.9897	350	19	41	458	464	.9061	553	19
42	932	295	.9883	337	18	42	484	501	.9047	539	18
43	958	331	.9868	324	17	43	510	538	.9034	526	17
44	.44984	368	.9854	311	16	44	536	575	.9020	512	16
45	.45010	.50404	1.9840	.89298	15	45	.46561	.52613	1.9007	.88499	15
46	036	441	.9825	285	14	46	587	650	.8993	485	14
47	062	477	.9811	272	13	47	613	687	.8980	472	13
48	088	514	.9797	259	12	48	639	724	.8967	458	12
49	114	550	.9782	245	11	49	664	761	.8953	445	11
50	.45140	.50587	1.9768	.89232	10	50	.46690	.52798	1.8940	.88431	10
51	166	623	.9754	219	9	51	716	836	.8927	417	9
52	192	660	.9740	206	8	52	742	873	.8913	404	8
53	218	696	.9725	193	7	53	767	910	.8900	390	7
54	243	733	.9711	180	6	54	793	947	.8887	377	6
55	.45269	.50769	1.9697	.89167	5	55	.46819	.52985	1.8873	.88363	5
56	295	806	.9683	153	4	56	844	.53022	.8860	349	4
57	321	843	.9669	140	3	57	870	059	.8847	336	3
58	347	879	.9654	127	2	58	896	096	.8834	322	2
59	373	916	.9640	114	1	59	921	134	.8820	308	1
60	.45399	.50953	1.9626	.89101	0	60	.46947	.53171	1.8807	.88295	0
	Cos	Cot	Tan	Sin	′		Cos	Cot	Tan	Sin	′

′	Sin	Tan	Cot	Cos		′	Sin	Tan	Cot	Cos	
0	.46947	.53171	1.8807	.88295	60	0	.48481	.55431	1.8040	.87462	60
1	973	208	.8794	281	59	1	506	469	.8028	448	59
2	.46999	246	.8781	267	58	2	532	507	.8016	434	58
3	.47024	283	.8768	254	57	3	557	545	.8003	420	57
4	050	320	.8755	240	56	4	583	583	.7991	406	56
5	.47076	.53358	1.8741	.88226	55	5	.48608	.55621	1.7979	.87391	55
6	101	395	.8728	213	54	6	634	659	.7966	377	54
7	127	432	.8715	199	53	7	659	697	.7954	363	53
8	153	470	.8702	185	52	8	684	736	.7942	349	52
9	178	507	.8689	172	51	9	710	774	.7930	335	51
10	.47204	.53545	1.8676	.88158	50	10	.48735	.55812	1.7917	.87321	50
11	229	582	.8663	144	49	11	761	850	.7905	306	49
12	255	620	.8650	130	48	12	786	888	.7893	292	48
13	281	657	.8637	117	47	13	811	926	.7881	278	47
14	306	694	.8624	103	46	14	837	.55964	.7868	264	46
15	.47332	.53732	1.8611	.88089	45	15	.48862	.56003	1.7856	.87250	45
16	358	769	.8598	075	44	16	888	041	.7844	235	44
17	383	807	.8585	062	43	17	913	079	.7832	221	43
18	409	844	.8572	048	42	18	938	117	.7820	207	42
19	434	882	.8559	034	41	19	964	156	.7808	193	41
20	.47460	.53920	1.8546	.88020	40	20	.48989	.56194	1.7796	.87178	40
21	486	957	.8533	.88006	39	21	.49014	232	.7783	164	39
22	511	.53995	.8520	.87993	38	22	040	270	.7771	150	38
23	537	.54032	.8507	979	37	23	065	309	.7759	136	37
24	562	070	.8495	965	36	24	090	347	.7747	121	36
25	.47588	.54107	1.8482	.87951	35	25	.49116	.56385	1.7735	.87107	35
26	614	145	.8469	937	34	26	141	424	.7723	093	34
27	639	183	.8456	923	33	27	166	462	.7711	079	33
28	665	220	.8443	909	32	28	192	501	.7699	064	32
29	690	258	.8430	896	31	29	217	539	.7687	050	31
30	.47716	.54296	1.8418	.87882	30	30	.49242	.56577	1.7675	.87036	30
31	741	333	.8405	868	29	31	268	616	.7663	021	29
32	767	371	.8392	854	28	32	293	654	.7651	.87007	28
33	793	409	.8379	840	27	33	318	693	.7639	.86993	27
34	818	446	.8367	826	26	34	344	731	.7627	978	26
35	.47844	.54484	1.8354	.87812	25	35	.49369	.56769	1.7615	.86964	25
36	869	522	.8341	798	24	36	394	808	.7603	949	24
37	895	560	.8329	784	23	37	419	846	.7591	935	23
38	920	597	.8316	770	22	38	445	885	.7579	921	22
39	946	635	.8303	756	21	39	470	923	.7567	906	21
40	.47971	.54673	1.8291	.87743	20	40	.49495	.56962	1.7556	.86892	20
41	.47997	711	.8278	729	19	41	521	.57000	.7544	878	19
42	.48022	748	.8265	715	18	42	546	039	.7532	863	18
43	048	786	.8253	701	17	43	571	078	.7520	849	17
44	073	824	.8240	687	16	44	596	116	.7508	834	16
45	.48099	.54862	1.8228	.87673	15	45	.49622	.57155	1.7496	.86820	15
46	124	900	.8215	659	14	46	647	193	.7485	805	14
47	150	938	.8202	645	13	47	672	232	.7473	791	13
48	175	.54975	.8190	631	12	48	697	271	.7461	777	12
49	201	.55013	.8177	617	11	49	723	309	.7449	762	11
50	.48226	.55051	1.8165	.87603	10	50	.49748	.57348	1.7437	.86748	10
51	252	089	.8152	589	9	51	773	386	.7426	733	9
52	277	127	.8140	575	8	52	798	425	.7414	719	8
53	303	165	.8127	561	7	53	824	464	.7402	704	7
54	328	203	.8115	546	6	54	849	503	.7391	690	6
55	.48354	.55241	1.8103	.87532	5	55	.49874	.57541	1.7379	.86675	5
56	379	279	.8090	518	4	56	899	580	.7367	661	4
57	405	317	.8078	504	3	57	924	619	.7355	646	3
58	430	355	.8065	490	2	58	950	657	.7344	632	2
59	456	393	.8053	476	1	59	.49975	696	.7332	617	1
60	.48481	.55431	1.8040	.87462	0	60	.50000	.57735	1.7321	.86603	0
	Cos	Cot	Tan	Sin	′		Cos	Cot	Tan	Sin	′

61°   60°

′	Sin	Tan	Cot	Cos		′	Sin	Tan	Cot	Cos	
0	.50000	.57735	1.7321	.86603	60	0	.51504	.60086	1.6643	.85717	60
1	025	774	.7309	588	59	1	529	126	.6632	702	59
2	050	813	.7297	573	58	2	554	165	.6621	687	58
3	076	851	.7286	559	57	3	579	205	.6610	672	57
4	101	890	.7274	544	56	4	604	245	.6599	657	56
5	.50126	.57929	1.7262	.86530	55	5	.51628	.60284	1.6588	.85642	55
6	151	.57968	.7251	515	54	6	653	324	.6577	627	54
7	176	.58007	.7239	501	53	7	678	364	.6566	612	53
8	201	046	.7228	486	52	8	703	403	.6555	597	52
9	227	085	.7216	471	51	9	728	443	.6545	582	51
10	.50252	.58124	1.7205	.86457	50	10	.51753	.60483	1.6534	.85567	50
11	277	162	.7193	442	49	11	778	522	.6523	551	49
12	302	201	.7182	427	48	12	803	562	.6512	536	48
13	327	240	.7170	413	47	13	828	602	.6501	521	47
14	352	279	.7159	398	46	14	852	642	.6490	506	46
15	.50377	.58318	1.7147	.86384	45	15	.51877	.60681	1.6479	.85491	45
16	403	357	.7136	369	44	16	902	721	.6469	476	44
17	428	396	.7124	354	43	17	927	761	.6458	461	43
18	453	435	.7113	340	42	18	952	801	.6447	446	42
19	478	474	.7102	325	41	19	.51977	841	.6436	431	41
20	.50503	.58513	1.7090	.86310	40	20	.52002	.60881	1.6426	.85416	40
21	528	552	.7079	295	39	21	026	921	.6415	401	39
22	553	591	.7067	281	38	22	051	.60960	.6404	385	38
23	578	631	.7056	266	37	23	076	.61000	.6393	370	37
24	603	670	.7045	251	36	24	101	040	.6383	355	36
25	.50628	.58709	1.7033	.86237	35	25	.52126	.61080	1.6372	.85340	35
26	654	748	.7022	222	34	26	151	120	.6361	325	34
27	679	787	.7011	207	33	27	175	160	.6351	310	33
28	704	826	.6999	192	32	28	200	200	.6340	294	32
29	729	865	.6988	178	31	29	225	240	.6329	279	31
30	.50754	.58905	1.6977	.86163	30	30	.52250	.61280	1.6319	.85264	30
31	779	944	.6965	148	29	31	275	320	.6308	249	29
32	804	.58983	.6954	133	28	32	299	360	.6297	234	28
33	829	.59022	.6943	119	27	33	324	400	.6287	218	27
34	854	061	.6932	104	26	34	349	440	.6276	203	26
35	.50879	.59101	1.6920	.86089	25	35	.52374	.61480	1.6265	.85188	25
36	904	140	.6909	074	24	36	399	520	.6255	173	24
37	929	179	.6898	059	23	37	423	561	.6244	157	23
38	954	218	.6887	045	22	38	448	601	.6234	142	22
39	.50979	258	.6875	030	21	39	473	641	.6223	127	21
40	.51004	.59297	1.6864	.86015	20	40	.52498	.61681	1.6212	.85112	20
41	029	336	.6853	.86000	19	41	522	721	.6202	096	19
42	054	376	.6842	.85985	18	42	547	761	.6191	081	18
43	079	415	.6831	970	17	43	572	801	.6181	066	17
44	104	454	.6820	956	16	44	597	842	.6170	051	16
45	.51129	.59494	1.6808	.85941	15	45	.52621	.61882	1.6160	.85035	15
46	154	533	.6797	926	14	46	646	922	.6149	020	14
47	179	573	.6786	911	13	47	671	.61962	.6139	.85005	13
48	204	612	.6775	896	12	48	696	.62003	.6128	.84989	12
49	229	651	.6764	881	11	49	720	043	.6118	974	11
50	.51254	.59691	1.6753	.85866	10	50	.52745	.62083	1.6107	.84959	10
51	279	730	.6742	851	9	51	770	124	.6097	943	9
52	304	770	.6731	836	8	52	794	164	.6087	928	8
53	329	809	.6720	821	7	53	819	204	.6076	913	7
54	354	849	.6709	806	6	54	844	245	.6066	897	6
55	.51379	.59888	1.6698	.85792	5	55	.52869	.62285	1.6055	.84882	5
56	404	928	.6687	777	4	56	893	325	.6045	866	4
57	429	.59967	.6676	762	3	57	918	366	.6034	851	3
58	454	.60007	.6665	747	2	58	943	406	.6024	836	2
59	479	046	.6654	732	1	59	967	446	.6014	820	1
60	.51504	.60086	1.6643	.85717	0	60	.52992	.62487	1.6003	.84805	0
	Cos	Cot	Tan	Sin	′		Cos	Cot	Tan	Sin	′

′	Sin	Tan	Cot	Cos			∴	Sin	Tan	Cot	Cos	
0	.52992	.62487	1.6003	.84805	60		0	.54464	.64941	1.5399	.83867	60
1	.53017	527	.5993	789	59		1	488	.64982	.5389	851	59
2	041	568	.5983	774	58		2	513	.65024	.5379	835	58
3	066	608	.5972	759	57		3	537	065	.5369	819	57
4	091	649	.5962	743	56		4	561	106	.5359	804	56
5	.53115	.62689	1.5952	.84728	55		5	.54586	.65148	1.5350	.83788	55
6	140	730	.5941	712	54		6	610	189	.5340	772	54
7	164	770	.5931	697	53		7	635	231	.5330	756	53
8	189	811	.5921	681	52		8	659	272	.5320	740	52
9	214	852	.5911	666	51		9	683	314	.5311	724	51
10	.53238	.62892	1.5900	.84650	50		10	.54708	.65355	1.5301	.83708	50
11	263	933	.5890	635	49		11	732	397	.5291	692	49
12	288	.62973	.5880	619	48		12	756	438	.5282	676	48
13	312	.63014	.5869	604	47		13	781	480	.5272	660	47
14	337	055	.5859	588	46		14	805	521	.5262	645	46
15	.53361	.63095	1.5849	.84573	45		15	.54829	.65563	1.5253	.83629	45
16	386	136	.5839	557	44		16	854	604	.5243	613	44
17	411	177	.5829	542	43		17	878	646	.5233	597	43
18	435	217	.5818	526	42		18	902	688	.5224	581	42
19	460	258	.5808	511	41		19	927	729	.5214	565	41
20	.53484	.63299	1.5798	.84495	40		20	.54951	.65771	1.5204	.83549	40
21	509	340	.5788	480	39		21	975	813	.5195	533	39
22	534	380	.5778	464	38		22	.54999	854	.5185	517	38
23	558	421	.5768	448	37		23	.55024	896	.5175	501	37
24	583	462	.5757	433	36		24	048	938	.5166	485	36
25	.53607	.63503	1.5747	.84417	35		25	.55072	.65980	1.5156	.83469	35
26	632	544	.5737	402	34		26	097	.66021	.5147	453	34
27	656	584	.5727	386	33		27	121	063	.5137	437	33
28	681	625	.5717	370	32		28	145	105	.5127	421	32
29	705	666	.5707	355	31		29	169	147	.5118	405	31
30	.53730	.63707	1.5697	.84339	30		30	.55194	.66189	1.5108	.83389	30
31	754	748	.5687	324	29		31	218	230	.5099	373	29
32	779	789	.5677	308	28		32	242	272	.5089	356	28
33	804	830	.5667	292	27		33	266	314	.5080	340	27
34	828	871	.5657	277	26		34	291	356	.5070	324	26
35	.53853	.63912	1.5647	.84261	25		35	.55315	.66398	1.5061	.83308	25
36	877	953	.5637	245	24		36	339	440	.5051	292	24
37	902	.63994	.5627	230	23		37	363	482	.5042	276	23
38	926	.64035	.5617	214	22		38	388	524	.5032	260	22
39	951	076	.5607	198	21		39	412	566	.5023	244	21
40	.53975	.64117	1.5597	.84182	20		40	.55436	.66608	1.5013	.83228	20
41	.54000	158	.5587	167	19		41	460	650	.5004	212	19
42	024	199	.5577	151	18		42	484	692	.4994	195	18
43	049	240	.5567	135	17		43	509	734	.4985	179	17
44	073	281	.5557	120	16		44	533	776	.4975	163	16
45	.54097	.64322	1.5547	.84104	15		45	.55557	.66818	1.4966	.83147	15
46	122	363	.5537	088	14		46	581	860	.4957	131	14
47	146	404	.5527	072	13		47	605	902	.4947	115	13
48	171	446	.5517	057	12		48	630	944	.4938	098	12
49	195	487	.5507	041	11		49	654	.66986	.4928	082	11
50	.54220	.64528	1.5497	.84025	10		50	.55678	.67028	1.4919	.83066	10
51	244	569	.5487	.84009	9		51	702	071	.4910	050	9
52	269	610	.5477	.83994	8		52	726	113	.4900	034	8
53	293	652	.5468	978	7		53	750	155	.4891	017	7
54	317	693	.5458	962	6		54	775	197	.4882	.83001	6
55	.54342	.64734	1.5448	.83946	5		55	.55799	.67239	1.4872	.82985	5
56	366	775	.5438	930	4		56	823	282	.4863	969	4
57	391	817	.5428	915	3		57	847	324	.4854	953	3
58	415	858	.5418	899	2		58	871	366	.4844	936	2
59	440	899	.5408	883	1		59	895	409	.4835	920	1
60	54464	.64941	1.5399	.83867	0		60	.55919	.67451	1.4826	.82904	0
	Cos	Cot	Tan	Sin	′			Cos	Cot	Tan	Sin	′

′	Sin	Tan	Cot	Cos		′	Sin	Tan	Cot	Cos	
0	.55919	.67451	1.4826	.82904	**60**	**0**	.57358	.70021	1.4281	.81915	**60**
1	943	493	.4816	887	59	1	381	064	.4273	899	59
2	968	536	.4807	871	58	2	405	107	.4264	882	58
3	.55992	578	.4798	855	57	3	429	151	.4255	865	57
4	.56016	620	.4788	839	56	4	453	194	.4246	848	56
5	.56040	.67663	1.4779	.82822	**55**	**5**	.57477	.70238	1.4237	.81832	**55**
6	064	705	.4770	806	54	6	501	281	.4229	815	54
7	088	748	.4761	790	53	7	524	325	.4220	798	53
8	112	790	.4751	773	52	8	548	368	.4211	782	52
9	136	832	.4742	757	51	9	572	412	.4202	765	51
10	.56160	.67875	1.4733	.82741	**50**	**10**	.57596	.70455	1.4193	.81748	**50**
11	184	917	.4724	724	49	11	619	499	.4185	731	49
12	208	.67960	.4715	708	48	12	643	542	.4176	714	48
13	232	.68002	.4705	692	47	13	667	586	.4167	698	47
14	256	045	.4696	675	46	14	691	629	.4158	681	46
15	.56280	.68088	1.4687	.82659	**45**	**15**	.57715	.70673	1.4150	.81664	**45**
16	305	130	.4678	643	44	16	738	717	.4141	647	44
17	329	173	.4669	626	43	17	762	760	.4132	631	43
18	353	215	.4659	610	42	18	786	804	.4124	614	42
19	377	258	.4650	593	41	19	810	848	.4115	597	41
20	.56401	.68301	1.4641	.82577	**40**	**20**	.57833	.70891	1.4106	.81580	**40**
21	425	343	.4632	561	39	21	857	935	.4097	563	39
22	449	386	.4623	544	38	22	881	.70979	.4089	546	38
23	473	429	.4614	528	37	23	904	.71023	.4080	530	37
24	497	471	.4605	511	36	24	928	066	.4071	513	36
25	.56521	.68514	1.4596	.82495	**35**	**25**	.57952	.71110	1.4063	.81496	**35**
26	545	557	.4586	478	34	26	976	154	.4054	479	34
27	569	600	.4577	462	33	27	.57999	198	.4045	462	33
28	593	642	.4568	446	32	28	.58023	242	.4037	445	32
29	617	685	.4559	429	31	29	047	285	.4028	428	31
30	.56641	.68728	1.4550	.82413	**30**	**30**	.58070	.71329	1.4019	.81412	**30**
31	665	771	.4541	396	29	31	094	373	.4011	395	29
32	689	814	.4532	380	28	32	118	417	.4002	378	28
33	713	857	.4523	363	27	33	141	461	.3994	361	27
34	736	900	.4514	347	26	34	165	505	.3985	344	26
35	.56760	.68942	1.4505	.82330	**25**	**35**	.58189	.71549	1.3976	.81327	**25**
36	784	.68985	.4496	314	24	36	212	593	.3968	310	24
37	808	.69028	.4487	297	23	37	236	637	.3959	293	23
38	832	071	.4478	281	22	38	260	681	.3951	276	22
39	856	114	.4469	264	21	39	283	725	.3942	259	21
40	.56880	.69157	1.4460	.82248	**20**	**40**	.58307	.71769	1.3934	.81242	**20**
41	904	200	.4451	231	19	41	330	813	.3925	225	19
42	928	243	.4442	214	18	42	354	857	.3916	208	18
43	952	286	.4433	198	17	43	378	901	.3908	191	17
44	.56976	329	.4424	181	16	44	401	946	.3899	174	16
45	.57000	.69372	1.4415	.82165	**15**	**45**	.58425	.71990	1.3891	.81157	**15**
46	024	416	.4406	148	14	46	449	.72034	.3882	140	14
47	047	459	.4397	132	13	47	472	078	.3874	123	13
48	071	502	.4388	115	12	48	496	122	.3865	106	12
49	095	545	.4379	098	11	49	519	167	.3857	089	11
50	.57119	.69588	1.4370	.82082	**10**	**50**	.58543	.72211	1.3848	.81072	**10**
51	143	631	.4361	065	9	51	567	255	.3840	055	9
52	167	675	.4352	048	8	52	590	299	.3831	038	8
53	191	718	.4344	032	7	53	614	344	.3823	021	7
54	215	761	.4335	.82015	6	54	637	388	.3814	.81004	6
55	.57238	.69804	1.4326	.81999	**5**	**55**	.58661	.72432	1.3806	.80987	**5**
56	262	847	.4317	982	4	56	684	477	.3798	970	4
57	286	891	.4308	965	3	57	708	521	.3789	953	3
58	310	934	.4299	949	2	58	731	565	.3781	936	2
59	334	.69977	.4290	932	1	59	755	610	.3772	919	1
60	.57358	.70021	1.4281	.81915	**0**	**60**	.58779	.72654	1.3764	.80902	**0**
	Cos	Cot	Tan	Sin	′		Cos	Cot	Tan	Sin	′

55°   **54°**

′	Sin	Tan	Cot	Cos	
0	.58779	.72654	1.3764	.80902	60
1	802	699	.3755	885	59
2	826	743	.3747	867	58
3	849	788	.3739	850	57
4	873	832	.3730	833	56
5	.58896	.72877	1.3722	.80816	55
6	920	921	.3713	799	54
7	943	.72966	.3705	782	53
8	967	.73010	.3697	765	52
9	.58990	055	.3688	748	51
10	.59014	.73100	1.3680	.80730	50
11	037	144	.3672	713	49
12	061	189	.3663	696	48
13	084	234	.3655	679	47
14	108	278	.3647	662	46
15	.59131	.73323	1.3638	.80644	45
16	154	368	.3630	627	44
17	178	413	.3622	610	43
18	201	457	.3613	593	42
19	225	502	.3605	576	41
20	.59248	.73547	1.3597	.80558	40
21	272	592	.3588	541	39
22	295	637	.3580	524	38
23	318	681	.3572	507	37
24	342	726	.3564	489	36
25	.59365	.73771	1.3555	.80472	35
26	389	816	.3547	455	34
27	412	861	.3539	438	33
28	436	906	.3531	420	32
29	459	951	.3522	403	31
30	.59482	.73996	1.3514	.80386	30
31	506	.74041	.3506	368	29
32	529	086	.3498	351	28
33	552	131	.3490	334	27
34	576	176	.3481	316	26
35	.59599	.74221	1.3473	.80299	25
36	622	267	.3465	282	24
37	646	312	.3457	264	23
38	669	357	.3449	247	22
39	693	402	.3440	230	21
40	.59716	.74447	1.3432	.80212	20
41	739	492	.3424	195	19
42	763	538	.3416	178	18
43	786	583	.3408	160	17
44	809	628	.3400	143	16
45	.59832	.74674	1.3392	.80125	15
46	856	719	.3384	108	14
47	879	764	.3375	091	13
48	902	810	.3367	073	12
49	926	855	.3359	056	11
50	.59949	.74900	1.3351	.80038	10
51	972	946	.3343	021	9
52	.59995	.74991	.3335	.80003	8
53	.60019	.75037	.3327	.79986	7
54	042	082	.3319	968	6
55	.60065	.75128	1.3311	.79951	5
56	089	173	.3303	934	4
57	112	219	.3295	916	3
58	135	264	.3287	899	2
59	158	310	.3278	881	1
60	.60182	.75355	1.3270	.79864	0
	Cos	Cot	Tan	Sin	′

53°

′	Sin	Tan	Cot	Cos	
0	.60182	.75355	1.3270	.79864	60
1	205	401	.3262	846	59
2	228	447	.3254	829	58
3	251	492	.3246	811	57
4	274	538	.3238	793	56
5	.60298	.75584	1.3230	.79776	55
6	321	629	.3222	758	54
7	344	675	.3214	741	53
8	367	721	.3206	723	52
9	390	767	.3198	706	51
10	.60414	.75812	1.3190	.79688	50
11	437	858	.3182	671	49
12	460	904	.3175	653	48
13	483	950	.3167	635	47
14	506	.75996	.3159	618	46
15	.60529	.76042	1.3151	.79600	45
16	553	088	.3143	583	44
17	576	134	.3135	565	43
18	599	180	.3127	547	42
19	622	226	.3119	530	41
20	.60645	.76272	1.3111	.79512	40
21	668	318	.3103	494	39
22	691	364	.3095	477	38
23	714	410	.3087	459	37
24	738	456	.3079	441	36
25	.60761	.76502	1.3072	.79424	35
26	784	548	.3064	406	34
27	807	594	.3056	388	33
28	830	640	.3048	371	32
29	853	686	.3040	353	31
30	.60876	.76733	1.3032	.79335	30
31	899	779	.3024	318	29
32	922	825	.3017	300	28
33	945	871	.3009	282	27
34	968	918	.3001	264	26
35	.60991	.76964	1.2993	.79247	25
36	.61015	.77010	.2985	229	24
37	038	057	.2977	211	23
38	061	103	.2970	193	22
39	084	149	.2962	176	21
40	.61107	.77196	1.2954	.79158	20
41	130	242	.2946	140	19
42	153	289	.2938	122	18
43	176	335	.2931	105	17
44	199	382	.2923	087	16
45	.61222	.77428	1.2915	.79069	15
46	245	475	.2907	051	14
47	268	521	.2900	033	13
48	291	568	.2892	.79016	12
49	314	615	.2884	.78998	11
50	.61337	.77661	1.2876	.78980	10
51	360	708	.2869	962	9
52	383	754	.2861	944	8
53	406	801	.2853	926	7
54	429	848	.2846	908	6
55	.61451	.77895	1.2838	.78891	5
56	474	941	.2830	873	4
57	497	.77988	.2822	855	3
58	520	.78035	.2815	837	2
59	543	082	.2807	819	1
60	.61566	.78129	1.2799	.78801	0
	Cos	Cot	Tan	Sin	′

52°

′	Sin	Tan	Cot	Cos	
0	.61566	.78129	1.2799	.78801	60
1	589	175	.2792	783	59
2	612	222	.2784	765	58
3	635	269	.2776	747	57
4	658	316	.2769	729	56
5	.61681	.78363	1.2761	.78711	55
6	704	410	.2753	694	54
7	726	457	.2746	676	53
8	749	504	.2738	658	52
9	772	551	.2731	640	51
10	.61795	.78598	1.2723	.78622	50
11	818	645	.2715	604	49
12	841	692	.2708	586	48
13	864	739	.2700	568	47
14	887	786	.2693	550	46
15	.61909	.78834	1.2685	.78532	45
16	932	881	.2677	514	44
17	955	928	.2670	496	43
18	.61978	.78975	.2662	478	42
19	.62001	.79022	.2655	460	41
20	.62024	.79070	1.2647	.78442	40
21	046	117	.2640	424	39
22	069	164	.2632	405	38
23	092	212	.2624	387	37
24	115	259	.2617	369	36
25	.62138	.79306	1.2609	.78351	35
26	160	354	.2602	333	34
27	183	401	.2594	315	33
28	206	449	.2587	297	32
29	229	496	.2579	279	31
30	.62251	.79544	1.2572	.78261	30
31	274	591	.2564	243	29
32	297	639	.2557	225	28
33	320	686	.2549	206	27
34	342	734	.2542	188	26
35	.62365	.79781	1.2534	.78170	25
36	388	829	.2527	152	24
37	411	877	.2519	134	23
38	433	924	.2512	116	22
39	456	.79972	.2504	098	21
40	.62479	.80020	1.2497	.78079	20
41	502	067	.2489	061	19
42	524	115	.2482	043	18
43	547	163	.2475	025	17
44	570	211	.2467	.78007	16
45	.62592	.80258	1.2460	.77988	15
46	615	306	.2452	970	14
47	638	354	.2445	952	13
48	660	402	.2437	934	12
49	683	450	.2430	916	11
50	.62706	.80498	1.2423	.77897	10
51	728	546	.2415	879	9
52	751	594	.2408	861	8
53	774	642	.2401	843	7
54	796	690	.2393	824	6
55	.62819	.80738	1.2386	.77806	5
56	842	786	.2378	788	4
57	864	834	.2371	769	3
58	887	882	.2364	751	2
59	909	930	.2356	733	1
60	.62932	.80978	1.2349	.77715	0
	Cos	Cot	Tan	Sin	′

51°

′	Sin	Tan	Cot	Cos	
0	.62932	.80978	1.2349	.77715	60
1	955	.81027	.2342	696	59
2	.62977	075	.2334	678	58
3	.63000	123	.2327	660	57
4	022	171	.2320	641	56
5	.63045	.81220	1.2312	.77623	55
6	068	268	.2305	605	54
7	090	316	.2298	586	53
8	113	364	.2290	568	52
9	135	413	.2283	550	51
10	.63158	.81461	1.2276	.77531	50
11	180	510	.2268	513	49
12	203	558	.2261	494	48
13	225	606	.2254	476	47
14	248	655	.2247	458	46
15	.63271	.81703	1.2239	.77439	45
16	293	752	.2232	421	44
17	316	800	.2225	402	43
18	338	849	.2218	384	42
19	361	898	.2210	366	41
20	.63383	.81946	1.2203	.77347	40
21	406	.81995	.2196	329	39
22	428	.82044	.2189	310	38
23	451	092	.2181	292	37
24	473	141	.2174	273	36
25	.63496	.82190	1.2167	.77255	35
26	518	238	.2160	236	34
27	540	287	.2153	218	33
28	563	336	.2145	199	32
29	585	385	.2138	181	31
30	.63608	.82434	1.2131	.77162	30
31	630	483	.2124	144	29
32	653	531	.2117	125	28
33	675	580	.2109	107	27
34	698	629	.2102	088	26
35	.63720	.82678	1.2095	.77070	25
36	742	727	.2088	051	24
37	765	776	.2081	033	23
38	787	825	.2074	.77014	22
39	810	874	.2066	.76996	21
40	.63832	.82923	1.2059	.76977	20
41	854	.82972	.2052	959	19
42	877	.83022	.2045	940	18
43	899	071	.2038	921	17
44	922	120	.2031	903	16
45	.63944	.83169	1.2024	.76884	15
46	966	218	.2017	866	14
47	.63989	268	.2009	847	13
48	.64011	317	.2002	828	12
49	033	366	.1995	810	11
50	.64056	.83415	1.1988	.76791	10
51	078	465	.1981	772	9
52	100	514	.1974	754	8
53	123	564	.1967	735	7
54	145	613	.1960	717	6
55	.64167	.83662	1.1953	.76698	5
56	190	712	.1946	679	4
57	212	761	.1939	661	3
58	234	811	.1932	642	2
59	256	860	.1925	623	1
60	.64279	.83910	1.1918	.76604	0
	Cos	Cot	Tan	Sin	′

50°

′	Sin	Tan	Cot	Cos		′	Sin	Tan	Cot	Cos	
0	.64279	.83910	1.1918	.76604	**60**	**0**	.65606	.86929	1.1504	.75471	**60**
1	301	.83960	.1910	586	59	1	628	.86980	.1497	452	59
2	323	.84009	.1903	567	58	2	650	.87031	.1490	433	58
3	346	059	.1896	548	57	3	672	082	.1483	414	57
4	368	108	.1889	530	56	4	694	133	.1477	395	56
5	.64390	.84158	1.1882	.76511	**55**	**5**	.65716	.87184	1.1470	.75375	**55**
6	412	208	.1875	492	54	6	738	236	.1463	356	54
7	435	258	.1868	473	53	7	759	287	.1456	337	53
8	457	307	.1861	455	52	8	781	338	.1450	318	52
9	479	357	.1854	436	51	9	803	389	.1443	299	51
10	.64501	.84407	1.1847	.76417	**50**	**10**	.65825	.87441	1.1436	.75280	**50**
11	524	457	.1840	398	49	11	847	492	.1430	261	49
12	546	507	.1833	380	48	12	869	543	.1423	241	48
13	568	556	.1826	361	47	13	891	595	.1416	222	47
14	590	606	.1819	342	46	14	913	646	.1410	203	46
15	.64612	.84656	1.1812	.76323	**45**	**15**	.65935	.87698	1.1403	.75184	**45**
16	635	706	.1806	304	44	16	956	749	.1396	165	44
17	657	756	.1799	286	43	17	.65978	801	.1389	146	43
18	679	806	.1792	267	42	18	.66000	852	.1383	126	42
19	701	856	.1785	248	41	19	022	904	.1376	107	41
20	.64723	.84906	1.1778	.76229	**40**	**20**	.66044	.87955	1.1369	.75088	**40**
21	746	.84956	.1771	210	39	21	066	.88007	.1363	069	39
22	768	.85006	.1764	192	38	22	088	059	.1356	050	38
23	790	057	.1757	173	37	23	109	110	.1349	030	37
24	812	107	.1750	154	36	24	131	162	.1343	.75011	36
25	.64834	.85157	1.1743	.76135	**35**	**25**	.66153	.88214	1.1336	.74992	**35**
26	856	207	.1736	116	34	26	175	265	.1329	973	34
27	878	257	.1729	097	33	27	197	317	.1323	953	33
28	901	308	.1722	078	32	28	218	369	.1316	934	32
29	923	358	.1715	059	31	29	240	421	.1310	915	31
30	.64945	.85408	1.1708	.76041	**30**	**30**	.66262	.88473	1.1303	.74896	**30**
31	967	458	.1702	022	29	31	284	524	.1296	876	29
32	.64989	509	.1695	.76003	28	32	306	576	.1290	857	28
33	.65011	559	.1688	.75984	27	33	327	628	.1283	838	27
34	033	609	.1681	965	26	34	349	680	.1276	818	26
35	.65055	.85660	1.1674	.75946	**25**	**35**	.66371	.88732	1.1270	.74799	**25**
36	077	710	.1667	927	24	36	393	784	.1263	780	24
37	100	761	.1660	908	23	37	414	836	.1257	760	23
38	122	811	.1653	889	22	38	436	888	.1250	741	22
39	144	862	.1647	870	21	39	458	940	.1243	722	21
40	.65166	.85912	1.1640	.75851	**20**	**40**	.66480	.88992	1.1237	.74703	**20**
41	188	.85963	.1633	832	19	41	501	.89045	.1230	683	19
42	210	.86014	.1626	813	18	42	523	097	.1224	664	18
43	232	064	.1619	794	17	43	545	149	.1217	644	17
44	254	115	.1612	775	16	44	566	201	.1211	625	16
45	.65276	.86166	1.1606	.75756	**15**	**45**	.66588	.89253	1.1204	.74606	**15**
46	298	216	.1599	738	14	46	610	306	.1197	586	14
47	320	267	.1592	719	13	47	632	358	.1191	567	13
48	342	318	.1585	700	12	48	653	410	.1184	548	12
49	364	368	.1578	680	11	49	675	463	.1178	528	11
50	.65386	.86419	1.1571	.75661	**10**	**50**	.66697	.89515	1.1171	.74509	**10**
51	408	470	.1565	642	9	51	718	567	.1165	489	9
52	430	521	.1558	623	8	52	740	620	.1158	470	8
53	452	572	.1551	604	7	53	762	672	.1152	451	7
54	474	623	.1544	585	6	54	783	725	.1145	431	6
55	.65496	.86674	1.1538	.75566	**5**	**55**	.66805	.89777	1.1139	.74412	**5**
56	518	725	.1531	547	4	56	827	830	.1132	392	4
57	540	776	.1524	528	3	57	848	883	.1126	373	3
58	562	827	.1517	509	2	58	870	935	.1119	353	2
59	584	878	.1510	490	1	59	891	.89988	.1113	334	1
60	.65606	.86929	1.1504	.75471	**0**	**60**	.66913	.90040	1.1106	.74314	**0**
	Cos	Cot	Tan	Sin	′		Cos	Cot	Tan	Sin	′

′	Sin	Tan	Cot	Cos		′	Sin	Tan	Cot	Cos	
0	.66913	.90040	1.1106	.74314	**60**	**0**	.68200	.93252	1.0724	.73135	**60**
1	935	093	.1100	295	59	1	221	306	.0717	116	59
2	956	146	.1093	276	58	2	242	360	.0711	096	58
3	978	199	.1087	256	57	3	264	415	.0705	076	57
4	.66999	251	.1080	237	56	4	285	469	.0699	056	56
5	.67021	.90304	1.1074	.74217	**55**	**5**	.68306	.93524	1.0692	.73036	**55**
6	043	357	.1067	198	54	6	327	578	.0686	.73016	54
7	064	410	.1061	178	53	7	349	633	.0680	.72996	53
8	086	463	.1054	159	52	8	370	688	.0674	976	52
9	107	516	.1048	139	51	9	391	742	.0668	957	51
10	.67129	.90569	1.1041	.74120	**50**	**10**	.68412	.93797	1.0661	.72937	**50**
11	151	621	.1035	100	49	11	434	852	.0655	917	49
12	172	674	.1028	080	48	12	455	906	.0649	897	48
13	194	727	.1022	061	47	13	476	.93961	.0643	877	47
14	215	781	.1016	041	46	14	497	.94016	.0637	857	46
15	.67237	.90834	1.1009	.74022	**45**	**15**	.68518	.94071	1.0630	.72837	**45**
16	258	887	.1003	.74002	44	16	539	125	.0624	817	44
17	280	940	.0996	.73983	43	17	561	180	.0618	797	43
18	301	.90993	.0990	963	42	18	582	235	.0612	777	42
19	323	.91046	.0983	944	41	19	603	290	.0606	757	41
20	.67344	.91099	1.0977	.73924	**40**	**20**	.68624	.94345	1.0599	.72737	**40**
21	366	153	.0971	904	39	21	645	400	.0593	717	39
22	387	206	.0964	885	38	22	666	455	.0587	697	38
23	409	259	.0958	865	37	23	688	510	.0581	677	37
24	430	313	.0951	846	36	24	709	565	.0575	657	36
25	.67452	.91366	1.0945	.73826	**35**	**25**	.68730	.94620	1.0569	.72637	**35**
26	473	419	.0939	806	34	26	751	676	.0562	617	34
27	495	473	.0932	787	33	27	772	731	.0556	597	33
28	516	526	.0926	767	32	28	793	786	.0550	577	32
29	538	580	.0919	747	31	29	814	841	.0544	557	31
30	.67559	.91633	1.0913	.73728	**30**	**30**	.68835	.94896	1.0538	.72537	**30**
31	580	687	.0907	708	29	31	857	.94952	.0532	517	29
32	602	740	.0900	688	28	32	878	.95007	.0526	497	28
33	623	794	.0894	669	27	33	899	062	.0519	477	27
34	645	847	.0888	649	26	34	920	118	.0513	457	26
35	.67666	.91901	1.0881	.73629	**25**	**35**	.68941	.95173	1.0507	.72437	**25**
36	688	.91955	.0875	610	24	36	962	229	.0501	417	24
37	709	.92008	.0869	590	23	37	.68983	284	.0495	397	23
38	730	062	.0862	570	22	38	.69004	340	.0489	377	22
39	752	116	.0856	551	21	39	025	395	.0483	357	21
40	.67773	.92170	1.0850	.73531	**20**	**40**	.69046	.95451	1.0477	.72337	**20**
41	795	224	.0843	511	19	41	067	506	.0470	317	19
42	816	277	.0837	491	18	42	088	562	.0464	297	18
43	837	331	.0831	472	17	43	109	618	.0458	277	17
44	859	385	.0824	452	16	44	130	673	.0452	257	16
45	.67880	.92439	1.0818	.73432	**15**	**45**	.69151	.95729	1.0446	.72236	**15**
46	901	493	.0812	413	14	46	172	785	.0440	216	14
47	923	547	.0805	393	13	47	193	841	.0434	196	13
48	944	601	.0799	373	12	48	214	897	.0428	176	12
49	965	655	.0793	353	11	49	235	.95952	.0422	156	11
50	.67987	.92709	1.0786	.73333	**10**	**50**	.69256	.96008	1.0416	.72136	**10**
51	.68008	763	.0780	314	9	51	277	064	.0410	116	9
52	029	817	.0774	294	8	52	298	120	.0404	095	8
53	051	872	.0768	274	7	53	319	176	.0398	075	7
54	072	926	.0761	254	6	54	340	232	.0392	055	6
55	.68093	.92980	1.0755	.73234	**5**	**55**	.69361	.96288	1.0385	.72035	**5**
56	115	.93034	.0749	215	4	56	382	344	.0379	.72015	4
57	136	088	.0742	195	3	57	403	400	.0373	.71995	3
58	157	143	.0736	175	2	58	424	457	.0367	974	2
59	179	197	.0730	155	1	59	445	513	.0361	954	1
60	.68200	.93252	1.0724	.73135	**0**	**60**	.69466	.96569	1.0355	.71934	**0**
	Cos	Cot	Tan	Sin	′		Cos	Cot	Tan	Sin	′

′	Sin	Tan	Cot	Cos	
0	.69466	.96569	1.0355	.71934	60
1	487	625	.0349	914	59
2	508	681	.0343	894	58
3	529	738	.0337	873	57
4	549	794	.0331	853	56
5	.69570	.96850	1.0325	.71833	55
6	591	907	.0319	813	54
7	612	.96963	.0313	792	53
8	633	.97020	.0307	772	52
9	654	076	.0301	752	51
10	.69675	.97133	1.0295	.71732	50
11	696	189	.0289	711	49
12	717	246	.0283	691	48
13	737	302	.0277	671	47
14	758	359	.0271	650	46
15	.69779	.97416	1.0265	.71630	45
16	800	472	.0259	610	44
17	821	529	.0253	590	43
18	842	586	.0247	569	42
19	862	643	.0241	549	41
20	.69883	.97700	1.0235	.71529	40
21	904	756	.0230	508	39
22	925	813	.0224	488	38
23	946	870	.0218	468	37
24	966	927	.0212	447	36
25	.69987	.97984	1.0206	.71427	35
26	.70008	.98041	.0200	407	34
27	029	098	.0194	386	33
28	049	155	.0188	366	32
29	070	213	.0182	345	31
30	.70091	.98270	1.0176	.71325	30
31	112	327	.0170	305	29
32	132	384	.0164	284	28
33	153	441	.0158	264	27
34	174	499	.0152	243	26
35	.70195	.98556	1.0147	.71223	25
36	215	613	.0141	203	24
37	236	671	.0135	182	23
38	257	728	.0129	162	22
39	277	786	.0123	141	21
40	.70298	.98843	1.0117	.71121	20
41	319	901	.0111	100	19
42	339	.98958	.0105	080	18
43	360	.99016	.0099	059	17
44	381	073	.0094	039	16
45	.70401	.99131	1.0088	.71019	15
46	422	189	.0082	.70998	14
47	443	247	.0076	978	13
48	463	304	.0070	957	12
49	484	362	.0064	937	11
50	.70505	.99420	1.0058	.70916	10
51	525	478	.0052	896	9
52	546	536	.0047	875	8
53	567	594	.0041	855	7
54	587	652	.0035	834	6
55	.70608	.99710	1.0029	.70813	5
56	628	768	.0023	793	4
57	649	826	.0017	772	3
58	670	884	.0012	752	2
59	690	.99942	.0006	731	1
60	.70711	1.0000	1.0000	.70711	0
	Cos	Cot	Tan	Sin	′

Degrees	Sine Value	Sine Log	Tangent Value	Tangent Log	Cotangent Value	Cotangent Log	Cosine Value	Cosine Log	
0° 00′	.0000	—	.0000	—	—	—	1.0000	0.0000	90° 00′
10	.0029	7.4637	.0029	7.4637	343.77	2.5363	1.0000	0.0000	50
20	.0058	7.7648	.0058	7.7648	171.89	2.2352	1.0000	0.0000	40
30	.0087	7.9408	.0087	7.9409	114.59	2.0591	1.0000	0.0000	30
40	.0116	8.0658	.0116	8.0658	85.940	1.9342	.9999	9.0000	20
50	.0145	8.1627	.0145	8.1627	68.750	1.8373	.9999	9.0000	10
1° 00′	.0175	8.2419	.0175	8.2419	57.290	1.7581	.9998	9.9999	89° 00′
10	.0204	8.3088	.0204	8.3089	49.104	1.6911	.9998	9.9999	50
20	.0233	8.3668	.0233	8.3669	42.964	1.6331	.9997	9.9999	40
30	.0262	8.4179	.0262	8.4181	38.188	1.5819	.9997	9.9999	30
40	.0291	8.4637	.0291	8.4638	34.368	1.5362	.9996	9.9998	20
50	.0320	8.5050	.0320	8.5053	31.242	1.4947	.9995	9.9998	10
2° 00′	.0349	8.5428	.0349	8.5431	28.636	1.4569	.9994	9.9997	88° 00′
10	.0378	8.5776	.0378	8.5779	26.432	1.4221	.9993	9.9997	50
20	.0407	8.6097	.0407	8.6101	24.542	1.3899	.9992	9.9996	40
30	.0436	8.6397	.0437	8.6401	22.904	1.3599	.9990	9.9996	30
40	.0465	8.6677	.0466	8.6682	21.470	1.3318	.9989	9.9995	20
50	.0494	8.6940	.0495	8.6945	20.206	1.3055	.9988	9.9995	10
3° 00′	.0523	8.7188	.0524	8.7194	19.081	1.2806	.9986	9.9994	87° 00′
10	.0552	8.7423	.0553	8.7429	18.075	1.2571	.9985	9.9993	50
20	.0581	8.7645	.0582	8.7652	17.169	1.2348	.9983	9.9993	40
30	.0610	8.7857	.0612	8.7865	16.350	1.2135	.9981	9.9992	30
40	.0640	8.8059	.0641	8.8067	15.605	1.1933	.9980	9.9991	20
50	.0669	8.8251	.0670	8.8261	14.924	1.1739	.9978	9.9990	10
4° 00′	.0698	8.8436	.0699	8.8446	14.301	1.1554	.9976	9.9989	86° 00′
10	.0727	8.8613	.0729	8.8624	13.727	1.1376	.9974	9.9989	50
20	.0756	8.8783	.0758	8.8795	13.197	1.1205	.9971	9.9988	40
30	.0785	8.8946	.0787	8.8960	12.706	1.1040	.9969	9.9987	30
40	.0814	8.9104	.0816	8.9118	12.251	1.0882	.9967	9.9986	20
50	.0843	8.9256	.0846	8.9272	11.826	1.0728	.9964	9.9985	10
5° 00′	.0872	8.9403	.0875	8.9420	11.430	1.0580	.9962	9.9983	85° 00′
10	.0901	8.9545	.0904	8.9563	11.059	1.0437	.9959	9.9982	50
20	.0929	8.9682	.0934	8.9701	10.712	1.0299	.9957	9.9981	40
30	.0958	8.9816	.0963	8.9836	10.385	1.0164	.9954	9.9980	30
40	.0987	8.9945	.0992	8.9966	10.078	1.0034	.9951	9.9979	20
50	.1016	9.0070	.1022	9.0093	9.7882	0.9907	.9948	9.9977	10
6° 00′	.1045	9.0192	.1051	9.0216	9.5144	0.9784	.9945	9.9976	84° 00′
10	.1074	9.0311	.1080	9.0336	9.2553	0.9664	.9942	9.9975	50
20	.1103	9.0426	.1110	9.0453	9.0098	0.9547	.9939	9.9973	40
30	.1132	9.0539	.1139	9.0567	8.7769	0.9433	.9936	9.9972	30
40	.1161	9.0648	.1169	9.0678	8.5555	0.9322	.9932	9.9971	20
50	.1190	9.0755	.1198	9.0786	8.3450	0.9214	.9929	9.9969	10
7° 00′	.1219	9.0859	.1228	9.0891	8.1443	0.9109	.9925	9.9968	83° 00′
10	.1248	9.0961	.1257	9.0995	7.9530	0.9005	.9922	9.9966	50
20	.1276	9.1060	.1287	9.1096	7.7704	0.8904	.9918	9.9964	40
30	.1305	9.1157	.1317	9.1194	7.5958	0.8806	.9914	9.9963	30
40	.1334	9.1252	.1346	9.1291	7.4287	0.8709	.9911	9.9961	20
50	.1363	9.1345	.1376	9.1385	7.2687	0.8615	.9907	9.9959	10
8° 00′	.1392	9.1436	.1405	9.1478	7.1154	0.8522	.9903	9.9958	82° 00′
10	.1421	9.1525	.1435	9.1569	6.9682	0.8431	.9899	9.9956	50
20	.1449	9.1612	.1465	9.1658	6.8269	0.8342	.9894	9.9954	40
30	.1478	9.1697	.1495	9.1745	6.6912	0.8255	.9890	9.9952	30
40	.1507	9.1781	.1524	9.1831	6.5606	0.8169	.9886	9.9950	20
50	.1536	9.1863	.1554	9.1915	6.4348	0.8085	.9881	9.9948	10
9° 00′	.1564	9.1943	.1584	9.1997	6.3138	0.8003	.9877	9.9946	81° 00′
	Value	Log	Value	Log	Value	Log	Value	Log	Degrees
	Cosine		Cotangent		Tangent		Sine		

Degrees	Sine		Tangent		Cotangent		Cosine		
	Value	Log	Value	Log	Value	Log	Value	Log	
9° 00′	.1564	9.1943	.1584	9.1997	6.3138	0.8003	.9877	9.9946	81° 00′
10	.1593	9.2022	.1614	9.2078	6.1970	0.7922	.9872	9.9944	50′
20	.1622	9.2100	.1644	9.2158	6.0844	0.7842	.9868	9.9942	40
30	.1650	9.2176	.1673	9.2236	5.9758	0.7764	.9863	9.9940	30
40	.1679	9.2251	.1703	9.2313	5.8708	0.7687	.9858	9.9938	20
50	.1708	9.2324	.1733	9.2389	5.7694	0.7611	.9853	9.9936	10
10° 00′	.1736	9.2397	.1763	9.2463	5.6713	0.7537	.9848	9.9934	80° 00′
10	.1765	9.2468	.1793	9.2536	5.5764	0.7464	.9843	9.9931	50
20	.1794	9.2538	.1823	9.2609	5.4845	0.7391	.9838	9.9929	40
30	.1822	9.2606	.1853	9.2680	5.3955	0.7320	.9833	9.9927	30
40	.1851	9.2674	.1883	9.2750	5.3093	0.7250	.9827	9.9924	20
50	.1880	9.2740	.1914	9.2819	5.2257	0.7181	.9822	9.9922	10
11° 00′	.1908	9.2806	.1944	9.2887	5.1446	0.7113	.9816	9.9919	79° 00′
10	.1937	9.2870	.1974	9.2953	5.0658	0.7047	.9811	9.9917	50
20	.1965	9.2934	.2004	9.3020	4.9894	0.6980	.9805	9.9914	40
30	.1994	9.2997	.2035	9.3085	4.9152	0.6915	.9799	9.9912	30
40	.2022	9.3058	.2065	9.3149	4.8430	0.6851	.9793	9.9909	20
50	.2051	9.3119	.2095	9.3212	4.7729	0.6788	.9787	9.9907	10
12° 00′	.2079	9.3179	.2126	9.3275	4.7046	0.6725	.9781	9.9904	78° 00′
10	.2108	9.3238	.2156	9.3336	4.6382	0.6664	.9775	9.9901	50
20	.2136	9.3296	.2186	9.3397	4.5736	0.6603	.9769	9.9899	40
30	.2164	9.3353	.2217	9.3458	4.5107	0.6542	.9763	9.9896	30
40	.2193	9.3410	.2247	9.3517	4.4494	0.6483	.9757	9.9893	20
50	.2221	9.3466	.2278	9.3576	4.3897	0.6424	.9750	9.9890	10
13° 00′	.2250	9.3521	.2309	9.3634	4.3315	0.6366	.9744	9.9887	77° 00′
10	.2278	9.3575	.2339	9.3691	4.2747	0.6309	.9737	9.9884	50
20	.2306	9.3629	.2370	9.3748	4.2193	0.6252	.9730	9.9881	40
30	.2334	9.3682	.2401	9.3804	4.1653	0.6196	.9724	9.9878	30
40	.2363	9.3734	.2432	9.3859	4.1126	0.6141	.9717	9.9875	20
50	.2391	9.3786	.2462	9.3914	4.0611	0.6086	.9710	9.9872	10
14° 00′	.2419	9.3837	.2493	9.3968	4.0108	0.6032	.9703	9.9869	76° 00′
10	.2447	9.3887	.2524	9.4021	3.9617	0.5979	.9696	9.9866	50
20	.2476	9.3937	.2555	9.4074	3.9136	0.5926	.9689	9.9863	40
30	.2504	9.3986	.2586	9.4127	3.8667	0.5873	.9681	9.9859	30
40	.2532	9.4035	.2617	9.4178	3.8208	0.5822	.9674	9.9856	20
50	.2560	9.4083	.2648	9.4230	3.7760	0.5770	.9667	9.9853	10
15° 00′	.2588	9.4130	.2679	9.4281	3.7321	0.5719	.9659	9.9849	75° 00′
10	.2616	9.4177	.2711	9.4331	3.6891	0.5669	.9652	9.9846	50
20	.2644	9.4223	.2742	9.4381	3.6470	0.5619	.9644	9.9843	40
30	.2672	9.4269	.2773	9.4430	3.6059	0.5570	.9636	9.9839	30
40	.2700	9.4314	.2805	9.4479	3.5656	0.5521	.9628	9.9836	20
50	.2728	9.4359	.2836	9.4527	3.5261	0.5473	.9621	9.9832	10
16° 00′	.2756	9.4403	.2867	9.4575	3.4874	0.5425	.9613	9.9828	74° 00′
10	.2784	9.4447	.2899	9.4622	3.4495	0.5378	.9605	9.9825	50
20	.2812	9.4491	.2931	9.4669	3.4124	0.5331	.9596	9.9821	40
30	.2840	9.4533	.2962	9.4716	3.3759	0.5284	.9588	9.9817	30
40	.2868	9.4576	.2994	9.4762	3.3402	0.5238	.9580	9.9814	20
50	.2896	9.4618	.3026	9.4808	3.3052	0.5192	.9572	9.9810	10
17° 00′	.2924	9.4659	.3057	9.4853	3.2709	0.5147	.9563	9.9806	73° 00′
10	.2952	9.4700	.3089	9.4898	3.2371	0.5102	.9555	9.9802	50
20	.2979	9.4741	.3121	9.4943	3.2041	0.5057	.9546	9.9798	40
30	.3007	9.4781	.3153	9.4987	3.1716	0.5013	.9537	9.9794	30
40	.3035	9.4821	.3185	9.5031	3.1397	0.4969	.9528	9.9790	20
50	.3062	9.4861	.3217	9.5075	3.1084	0.4925	.9520	9.9786	10
18° 00′	.3090	9.4900	.3249	9.5118	3.0777	0.4882	.9511	9.9782	72° 00′
	Value	Log	Value	Log	Value	Log	Value	Log	
	Cosine		Cotangent		Tangent		Sine		Degrees

Degrees	Sine Value	Sine Log	Tangent Value	Tangent Log	Cotangent Value	Cotangent Log	Cosine Value	Cosine Log	
18° 00′	.3090	9.4900	.3249	9.5118	3.0777	0.4882	.9511	9.9782	72° 00′
10	.3118	9.4939	.3281	9.5161	3.0475	0.4839	.9502	9.9778	50
20	.3145	9.4977	.3314	9.5203	3.0178	0.4797	.9492	9.9774	40
30	.3173	9.5015	.3346	9.5245	2.9887	0.4755	.9483	9.9770	30
40	.3201	9.5052	.3378	9.5287	2.9600	0.4713	.9474	9.9765	20
50	.3228	9.5090	.3411	9.5329	2.9319	0.4671	.9465	9.9761	10
19° 00′	.3256	9.5126	.3443	9.5370	2.9042	0.4630	.9455	9.9757	71° 00′
10	.3283	9.5163	.3476	9.5411	2.8770	0.4589	.9446	9.9752	50
20	.3311	9.5199	.3508	9.5451	2.8502	0.4549	.9436	9.9748	40
30	.3338	9.5235	.3541	9.5491	2.8239	0.4509	.9426	9.9743	30
40	.3365	9.5270	.3574	9.5531	2.7980	0.4469	.9417	9.9739	20
50	.3393	9.5306	.3607	9.5571	2.7725	0.4429	.9407	9.9734	10
20° 00′	.3420	9.5341	.3640	9.5611	2.7475	0.4389	.9397	9.9730	70° 00′
10	.3448	9.5375	.3673	9.5650	2.7228	0.4350	.9387	9.9725	50
20	.3475	9.5409	.3706	9.5689	2.6985	0.4311	.9377	9.9721	40
30	.3502	9.5443	.3739	9.5727	2.6746	0.4273	.9367	9.9716	30
40	.3529	9.5477	.3772	9.5766	2.6511	0.4234	.9356	9.9711	20
50	.3557	9.5510	.3805	9.5804	2.6279	0.4196	.9346	9.9706	10
21° 00′	.3584	9.5543	.3839	9.5842	2.6051	0.4158	.9336	9.9702	69° 00′
10	.3611	9.5576	.3872	9.5879	2.5826	0.4121	.9325	9.9697	50
20	.3638	9.5609	.3906	9.5917	2.5605	0.4083	.9315	9.9692	40
30	.3665	9.5641	.3939	9.5954	2.5386	0.4046	.9304	9.9687	30
40	.3692	9.5673	.3973	9.5991	2.5172	0.4009	.9293	9.9682	20
50	.3719	9.5704	.4006	9.6028	2.4960	0.3972	.9283	9.9677	10
22° 00′	.3746	9.5736	.4040	9.6064	2.4751	0.3936	.9272	9.9672	68° 00′
10	.3773	9.5767	.4074	9.6100	2.4545	0.3900	.9261	9.9667	50
20	.3800	9.5798	.4108	9.6136	2.4342	0.3864	.9250	9.9661	40
30	.3827	9.5828	.4142	9.6172	2.4142	0.3828	.9239	9.9656	30
40	.3854	9.5859	.4176	9.6208	2.3945	0.3792	.9228	9.9651	20
50	.3881	9.5889	.4210	9.6243	2.3750	0.3757	.9216	9.9646	10
23° 00′	.3907	9.5919	.4245	9.6279	2.3559	0.3721	.9205	9.9640	67° 00′
10	.3934	9.5948	.4279	9.6314	2.3369	0.3686	.9194	9.9635	50
20	.3961	9.5978	.4314	9.6348	2.3183	0.3652	.9182	9.9629	40
30	.3987	9.6007	.4348	9.6383	2.2998	0.3617	.9171	9.9624	30
40	.4014	9.6036	.4383	9.6417	2.2817	0.3583	.9159	9.9618	20
50	.4041	9.6065	.4417	9.6452	2.2637	0.3548	.9147	9.9613	10
24° 00′	.4067	9.6093	.4452	9.6486	2.2460	0.3514	.9135	9.9607	66° 00′
10	.4094	9.6121	.4487	9.6520	2.2286	0.3480	.9124	9.9602	50
20	.4120	9.6149	.4522	9.6553	2.2113	0.3447	.9112	9.9596	40
30	.4147	9.6177	.4557	9.6587	2.1943	0.3413	.9100	9.9590	30
40	.4173	9.6205	.4592	9.6620	2.1775	0.3380	.9088	9.9584	20
50	.4200	9.6232	.4628	9.6654	2.1609	0.3346	.9075	9.9579	10
25° 00′	.4226	9.6259	.4663	9.6687	2.1445	0.3313	.9063	9.9573	65° 00′
10	.4253	9.6286	.4699	9.6720	2.1283	0.3280	.9051	9.9567	50
20	.4279	9.6313	.4734	9.6752	2.1123	0.3248	.9038	9.9561	40
30	.4305	9.6340	.4770	9.6785	2.0965	0.3215	.9026	9.9555	30
40	.4331	9.6366	.4806	9.6817	2.0809	0.3183	.9013	9.9549	20
50	.4358	9.6392	.4841	9.6850	2.0655	0.3150	.9001	9.9543	10
26° 00′	.4384	9.6418	.4877	9.6882	2.0503	0.3118	.8988	9.9537	64° 00′
10	.4410	9.6444	.4913	9.6914	2.0353	0.3086	.8975	9.9530	50
20	.4436	9.6470	.4950	9.6946	2.0204	0.3054	.8962	9.9524	40
30	.4462	9.6495	.4986	9.6977	2.0057	0.3023	.8949	9.9518	30
40	.4488	9.6521	.5022	9.7009	1.9912	0.2991	.8936	9.9512	20
50	.4514	9.6546	.5059	9.7040	1.9768	0.2960	.8923	9.9505	10
27° 00′	.4540	9.6570	.5095	9.7072	1.9626	0.2928	.8910	9.9499	63° 00′
	Value	Log	Value	Log	Value	Log	Value	Log	
	Cosine		Cotangent		Tangent		Sine		Degrees

Degrees	Sine		Tangent		Cotangent		Cosine		
	Value	Log	Value	Log	Value	Log	Value	Log	
27° 00'	.4540	9.6570	.5095	9.7072	1.9626	0.2928	.8910	9.9499	63° 00'
10	.4566	9.6595	.5132	9.7103	1.9456	0.2897	.8897	9.9492	50
20	.4592	9.6620	.5169	9.7134	1.9347	0.2866	.8884	9.9486	40
30	.4617	9.6644	.5206	9.7165	1.9210	0.2835	.8870	9.9479	30
40	.4643	9.6668	.5243	9.7196	1.9074	0.2804	.8857	9.9473	20
50	.4669	9.6692	.5280	9.7226	1.8940	0.2774	.8843	9.9466	10
28° 00'	.4695	9.6716	.5317	9.7257	1.8807	0.2743	.8829	9.9459	62° 00'
10	.4720	9.6740	.5354	9.7287	1.8676	0.2713	.8816	9.9453	50
20	.4746	9.6763	.5392	9.7317	1.8546	0.2683	.8802	9.944	40
30	.4772	9.6787	.5430	9.7348	1.8418	0.2652	.8788	9.9439	30
40	.4797	9.6810	.5467	9.7378	1.8291	0.2622	.8774	9.9432	20
50	.4823	9.6833	.5505	9.7408	1.8165	0.2592	.8760	9.9425	10
29° 00'	.4848	9.6856	.5543	9.7438	1.8040	0.2562	.8746	9.9418	61° 00'
10	.4874	9.6878	.5581	9.7467	1.7917	0.2533	.8732	9.9411	50
20	.4899	9.6901	.5619	9.7497	1.7796	0.2503	.8718	9.9404	40
30	.4924	9.6923	.5658	9.7526	1.7675	0.2474	.8704	9.9397	30
40	.4950	9.6946	.5696	9.7556	1.7556	0.2444	.8689	9.9390	20
50	.4975	9.6968	.5735	9.7585	1.7437	0.2415	.8675	9.9383	10
30° 00'	.5000	9.6990	.5774	9.7614	1.7321	0.2386	.8660	9.9375	60° 00'
10	.5025	9.7012	.5812	9.7644	1.7205	0.2356	.8646	9.9368	50
20	.5050	9.7033	.5851	9.7673	1.7090	0.2327	.8631	9.9361	40
30	.5075	9.7055	.5890	9.7701	1.6977	0.2299	.8616	9.9353	30
40	.5100	9.7076	.5930	9.7730	1.6864	0.2270	.8601	9.9346	20
50	.5125	9.7097	.5969	9.7759	1.6753	0.2241	.8587	9.9338	10
31° 00'	.5150	9.7118	.6009	9.7788	1.6643	0.2212	.8572	9.9331	59° 00'
10	.5175	9.7139	.6048	9.7816	1.6534	0.2184	.8557	9.9323	50
20	.5200	9.7160	.6088	9.7845	1.6426	0.2155	.8542	9.9315	40
30	.5225	9.7181	.6128	9.7873	1.6319	0.2127	.8526	9.9308	30
40	.5250	9.7201	.6168	9.7902	1.6212	0.2098	.8511	9.9300	20
50	.5275	9.7222	.6208	9.7930	1.6107	0.2070	.8496	9.9292	10
32° 00'	.5299	9.7242	.6249	9.7958	1.6003	0.2042	.8480	9.9284	58° 00'
10	.5324	9.7262	.6289	9.7986	1.5900	0.2014	.8465	9.9276	50
20	.5348	9.7282	.6330	9.8014	1.5798	0.1986	.8450	9.9268	40
30	.5373	9.7302	.6371	9.8042	1.5697	0.1958	.8434	9.9260	30
40	.5398	9.7322	.6412	9.8070	1.5597	0.1930	.8418	9.9252	20
50	.5422	9.7342	.6453	9.8097	1.5497	0.1903	.8403	9.9244	10
33° 00'	.5446	9.7361	.6494	9.8125	1.5399	0.1875	.8387	9.9236	57° 00'
10	.5471	9.7380	.6536	9.8153	1.5301	0.1847	.8371	9.9228	50
20	.5495	9.7400	.6577	9.8180	1.5204	0.1820	.8355	9.9219	40
30	.5519	9.7419	.6619	9.8208	1.5108	0.1792	.8339	9.9211	30
40	.5544	9.7438	.6661	9.8235	1.5013	0.1765	.8323	9.9203	20
50	.5568	9.7457	.6703	9.8263	1.4919	0.1737	.8307	9.9194	10
34° 00'	.5592	9.7476	.6745	9.8290	1.4826	0.1710	.8290	9.9186	56° 00'
10	.5616	9.7494	.6787	9.8317	1.4733	0.1683	.8274	9.9177	50
20	.5640	9.7513	.6830	9.8344	1.4641	0.1656	.8258	9.9169	40
30	.5664	9.7531	.6873	9.8371	1.4550	0.1629	.8241	9.9160	30
40	.5688	9.7550	.6916	9.8398	1.4460	0.1602	.8225	9.9151	20
50	.5712	9.7568	.6959	9.8425	1.4370	0.1575	.8208	9.9142	10
35° 00'	.5736	9.7586	.7002	9.8452	1.4281	0.1548	.8192	9.9134	55° 00'
10	.5760	9.7604	.7046	9.8479	1.4193	0.1521	.8175	9.9125	50
20	.5783	9.7622	.7089	9.8506	1.4106	0.1494	.8158	9.9116	40
30	.5807	9.7640	.7133	9.8533	1.4019	0.1467	.8141	9.9107	30
40	.5831	9.7657	.7177	9.8559	1.3934	0.1441	.8124	9.9098	20
50	.5854	9.7675	.7221	9.8586	1.3848	0.1414	.8107	9.9089	10
36° 00'	.5878	9.7692	.7265	9.8613	1.3764	0.1387	.8090	9.9080	54° 00'
	Value	Log	Value	Log	Value	Log	Value	Log	
	Cosine		Cotangent		Tangent		Sine		Degrees

Degrees	Sine		Tangent		Cotangent		Cosine		
	Value	Log	Value	Log	Value	Log	Value	Log	
36° 00′	.5878	9.7692	.7265	9.8613	1.3764	0.1387	.8090	9.9080	54° 00′
10	.5901	9.7710	.7310	9.8639	1.3680	0.1361	.8073	9.9070	50
20	.5925	9.7727	.7355	9.8666	1.3597	0.1334	.8056	9.9061	0
30	.5948	9.7744	.7400	9.8692	1.3514	0.1308	.8039	9.9052	30
40	.5972	9.7761	.7445	9.8718	1.3432	0.1282	.8021	9.9042	20
50	.5995	9.7778	.7490	9.8745	1.3351	0.1255	.8004	9.9033	10
37° 00′	.6018	9.7795	.7536	9.8771	1.3270	0.1229	.7986	9.9023	53° 00′
10	.6041	9.7811	.7581	9.8797	1.3190	0.1203	.7969	9.9014	50
20	.6065	9.7828	.7627	9.8824	1.3111	0.1176	.7951	9.9004	40
30	.6088	9.7844	.7673	9.8850	1.3032	0.1150	.7934	9.8995	30
40	.6111	9.7861	.7720	9.8876	1.2954	0.1124	.7916	9.8985	20
50	.6134	9.7877	.7766	9.8902	1.2876	0.1098	.7898	9.8975	10
38° 00′	.6157	9.7893	.7813	9.8928	1.2799	0.1072	.7880	9.8965	52° 00′
10	.6180	9.7910	.7860	9.8954	1.2723	0.1046	.7862	9.8955	50
20	.6202	9.7926	.7907	9.8980	1.2647	0.1020	.7844	9.8945	40
30	.6225	9.7941	.7954	9.9006	1.2572	0.0994	.7826	9.8935	30
40	.6248	9.7957	.8002	9.9032	1.2497	0.0968	.7808	9.8925	20
50	.6271	9.7973	.8050	9.9058	1.2423	0.0942	.7790	9.8915	10
39° 00′	.6293	9.7989	.8098	9.9084	1.2349	0.0916	.7771	9.8905	51° 00′
10	.6316	9.8004	.8146	9.9110	1.2276	0.0890	.7753	9.8895	50
20	.6338	9.8020	.8195	9.9135	1.2203	0.0865	.7735	9.8884	40
30	.6361	9.8035	.8243	9.9161	1.2131	0.0839	.7716	9.8874	30
40	.6383	9.8050	.8292	9.9187	1.2059	0.0813	.7698	9.8864	20
50	.6406	9.8066	.8342	9.9212	1.1988	0.0788	.7679	9.8853	10
40° 00′	.6428	9.8081	.8391	9.9238	1.1918	0.0762	.7660	9.8843	50° 00′
10	.6450	9.8096	.8441	9.9264	1.1847	0.0736	.7642	9.8832	50
20	.6472	9.8111	.8491	9.9289	1.1778	0.0711	.7623	9.8821	40
30	.6494	9.8125	.8541	9.9315	1.1708	0.0685	.7604	9.8810	30
40	.6517	9.8140	.8591	9.9341	1.1640	0.0659	.7585	9.8800	20
50	.6539	9.8155	.8642	9.9366	1.1571	0.0634	.7566	9.8789	10
41° 00′	.6561	9.8169	.8693	9.9392	1.1504	0.0608	.7547	9.8778	49° 00′
10	.6583	9.8184	.8744	9.9417	1.1436	0.0583	.7528	9.8767	50
20	.6604	9.8198	.8796	9.9443	1.1369	0.0557	.7509	9.8756	40
30	.6626	9.8213	.8847	9.9468	1.1303	0.0532	.7490	9.8745	30
40	.6648	9.8227	.8899	9.9494	1.1237	0.0506	.7470	9.8733	20
50	.6670	9.8241	.8952	9.9519	1.1171	0.0481	.7451	9.8722	10
42° 00′	.6691	9.8255	.9004	9.9544	1.1106	0.0456	.7431	9.8711	48° 00′
10	.6713	9.8269	.9057	9.9570	1.1041	0.0430	.7412	9.8699	50
20	.6734	9.8283	.9110	9.9595	1.0977	0.0405	.7392	9.8688	40
30	.6756	9.8297	.9163	9.9621	1.0913	0.0379	.7373	9.8676	30
40	.6777	9.8311	.9217	9.9646	1.0850	0.0354	.7353	9.8665	20
50	.6799	9.8324	.9271	9.9671	1.0786	0.0329	.7333	9.8653	10
43° 00′	.6820	9.8338	.9325	9.9697	1.0724	0.0303	.7314	9.8641	47° 00′
10	.6841	9.8351	.9380	9.9722	1.0661	0.0278	.7294	9.8629	50
20	.6862	9.8365	.9435	9.9747	1.0599	0.0253	.7274	9.8618	40
30	.6884	9.8378	.9490	9.9772	1.0538	0.0228	.7254	9.8606	30
40	.6905	9.8391	.9545	9.9798	1.0477	0.0202	.7234	9.8594	20
50	.6926	9.8405	.9601	9.9823	1.0416	0.0177	.7214	9.8582	10
44° 00′	.6947	9.8418	.9657	9.9848	1.0355	0.0152	.7193	9.8569	46° 00′
10	.6967	9.8431	.9713	9.9874	1.0295	0.0126	.7173	9.8557	50
20	.6988	9.8444	.9770	9.9899	1.0235	0.0101	.7153	9.8545	40
30	.7009	9.8457	.9827	9.9924	1.0176	0.0076	.7133	9.8532	30
40	.7030	9.8469	.9884	9.9949	1.0117	0.0051	.7112	9.8520	20
50	.7050	9.8482	.9942	9.9975	1.0058	0.0025	.7092	9.8507	10
45° 00′	.7071	9.8495	1.0000	0.0000	1.0000	0.0000	.7071	9.8495	45° 00′
	Value	Log	Value	Log	Value	Log	Value	Log	
	Cosine		Cotangent		Tangent		Sine		Degrees

Useful Geometrical Formulas

Circle.
Circumference $= 2\pi r = \pi D$.

Area $= \pi r^2$.

Area of sector $= \frac{1}{2}r \times \text{arc} = \frac{1}{2}r^2\theta$.

Trapezoid.
Area $= \frac{1}{2}h(b + b')$.

Pyramid.
Volume $= \frac{1}{3}bh$.

Volume of frustum $= \frac{1}{3}h(b + b' + \sqrt{bb'})$.

Cone of Revolution.
Lateral area $= \pi r \times$ slant height.

Lateral area of frustum $= \pi(R + r) \times$ slant height.

Volume $= \frac{1}{3}\pi r^2 h$.

Volume of frustum $= \frac{1}{3}\pi h(R^2 + r^2 + R \cdot r)$.

Prismatoid.
Volume $= \frac{1}{6}h(b + b' + 4M)$, $M =$ area of midsection.

Sphere.
Area of surface $= 4\pi r^2$.

Area of zone $= 2\pi r \times$ altitude.

Volume of sphere $= \frac{4}{3}\pi r^3$.

Volume of sector $= \frac{2}{3}\pi r^2 h$, $h =$ altitude of zone.

Volume of segment (one base) $= \frac{1}{2}\pi a^2 h + \frac{1}{6}\pi h^3$,

Volume of segment (two bases) $= \frac{1}{2}\pi h(a^2 + a'^2) + \frac{1}{6}\pi h^3$,

where $h =$ altitude, and a and $a' =$ radii of bases.

The proportional parts of the tabular difference for each line are given under PROP. PARTS. To interpolate between two logarithms add to the smaller one the proper prop. part found in the same line.

N.	0	1	2	3	4	5	6	7	8	9	1 2 3	4 5 6	7 8 9
10	0000	0043	0086	0128	0170	0212	0253	0294	0334	0374	4 8 12	17 21 25	29 33 37
11	0414	0453	0492	0531	0569	0607	0645	0682	0719	0755	4 8 11	15 19 23	26 30 34
12	0792	0828	0864	0899	0934	0969	1004	1038	1072	1106	3 7 10	14 17 21	24 28 31
13	1139	1173	1206	1239	1271	1303	1335	1367	1399	1430	3 6 10	13 16 19	23 26 29
14	1461	1492	1523	1553	1584	1614	1644	1673	1703	1732	3 6 9	12 15 18	21 24 27
15	1761	1790	1818	1847	1875	1903	1931	1959	1987	2014	3 6 8	11 14 17	20 22 25
16	2041	2068	2095	2122	2148	2175	2201	2227	2253	2279	3 5 8	11 13 16	18 21 24
17	2304	2330	2355	2380	2405	2430	2455	2480	2504	2529	2 5 7	10 12 15	17 20 22
18	2553	2577	2601	2625	2648	2672	2695	2718	2742	2765	2 5 7	9 12 14	16 19 21
19	2788	2810	2833	2856	2878	2900	2923	2945	2967	2989	2 4 7	9 11 13	16 18 20
20	3010	3032	3054	3075	3096	3118	3139	3160	3181	3201	2 4 6	8 11 13	15 17 19
21	3222	3243	3263	3284	3304	3324	3345	3365	3385	3404	2 4 6	8 10 12	14 16 18
22	3424	3444	3464	3483	3502	3522	3541	3560	3579	3598	2 4 6	8 10 12	14 16 17
23	3617	3636	3655	3674	3692	3711	3729	3747	3766	3784	2 4 6	7 9 11	13 15 17
24	3802	3820	3838	3856	3874	3892	3909	3927	3945	3962	2 4 5	7 9 11	12 14 16
25	3979	3997	4014	4031	4048	4065	4082	4099	4116	4133	2 3 5	7 9 10	12 14 16
26	4150	4166	4183	4200	4216	4232	4249	4265	4281	4298	2 3 5	7 8 10	11 13 15
27	4314	4330	4346	4362	4378	4393	4409	4425	4440	4456	2 3 5	6 8 9	11 13 14
28	4472	4487	4502	4518	4533	4548	4564	4579	4594	4609	2 3 5	6 8 9	11 12 14
29	4624	4639	4654	4669	4683	4698	4713	4728	4742	4757	1 3 4	6 7 9	10 12 13
30	4771	4786	4800	4814	4829	4843	4857	4871	4886	4900	1 3 4	6 7 9	10 11 13
31	4914	4928	4942	4955	4969	4983	4997	5011	5024	5038	1 3 4	5 7 8	10 11 12
32	5051	5065	5079	5092	5105	5119	5132	5145	5159	5172	1 3 4	5 7 8	9 11 12
33	5185	5198	5211	5224	5237	5250	5263	5276	5289	5302	1 3 4	5 6 8	9 10 12
34	5315	5328	5340	5353	5366	5378	5391	5403	5416	5428	1 2 4	5 6 8	9 10 11
35	5441	5453	5465	5478	5490	5502	5514	5527	5539	5551	1 2 4	5 6 7	9 10 11
36	5563	5575	5587	5599	5611	5623	5635	5647	5658	5670	1 2 4	5 6 7	8 10 11
37	5682	5694	5705	5717	5729	5740	5752	5763	5775	5786	1 2 3	5 6 7	8 9 11
38	5798	5809	5821	5832	5843	5855	5866	5877	5888	5899	1 2 3	5 6 7	8 9 10
39	5911	5922	5933	5944	5955	5966	5977	5988	5999	6010	1 2 3	4 6 7	8 9 10
40	6021	6031	6042	6053	6064	6075	6085	6096	6107	6117	1 2 3	4 5 6	7 9 10
41	6128	6138	6149	6160	6170	6180	6191	6201	6212	6222	1 2 3	4 5 6	7 8 9
42	6232	6243	6253	6263	6274	6284	6294	6304	6314	6325	1 2 3	4 5 6	7 8 9
43	6335	6345	6355	6365	6375	6385	6395	6405	6415	6425	1 2 3	4 5 6	7 8 9
44	6435	6444	6454	6464	6474	6484	6493	6503	6513	6522	1 2 3	4 5 6	7 8 9
45	6532	6542	6551	6561	6571	6580	6590	6599	6609	6618	1 2 3	4 5 6	7 8 9
46	6628	6637	6646	6656	6665	6675	6684	6693	6702	6712	1 2 3	4 5 6	7 7 8
47	6721	6730	6739	6749	6758	6767	6776	6785	6794	6803	1 2 3	4 5 6	7 7 8
48	6812	6821	6830	6839	6848	6857	6866	6875	6884	6893	1 2 3	4 4 5	6 7 8
49	6902	6911	6920	6928	6937	6946	6955	6964	6972	6981	1 2 3	4 4 5	6 7 8
50	6990	6998	7007	7016	7024	7033	7042	7050	7059	7067	1 2 3	3 4 5	6 7 8
51	7076	7084	7093	7101	7110	7118	7126	7135	7143	7152	1 2 3	3 4 5	6 7 8
52	7160	7168	7177	7185	7193	7202	7210	7218	7226	7235	1 2 2	3 4 5	6 7 7
53	7243	7251	7259	7267	7275	7284	7292	7300	7308	7316	1 2 2	3 4 5	6 6 7
54	7324	7332	7340	7348	7356	7364	7372	7380	7388	7396	1 2 2	3 4 5	6 6 7
N.	0	1	2	3	4	5	6	7	8	9	1 2 3	4 5 6	7 8 9

Prop. Parts

The proportional parts of the tabular difference for each line are given under Prop. Parts. To interpolate between two logarithms add to the smaller one the proper prop. part found in the same line.

N.	0	1	2	3	4	5	6	7	8	9	1 2 3	4 5 6	7 8 9
55	7404	7412	7419	7427	7435	7443	7451	7459	7466	7474	1 2 2	3 4 5	5 6 7
56	7482	7490	7497	7505	7513	7520	7528	7536	7543	7551	1 2 2	3 4 5	5 6 7
57	7559	7566	7574	7582	7589	7597	7604	7612	7619	7627	1 2 2	3 4 4	5 6 7
58	7634	7642	7649	7657	7664	7672	7679	7686	7694	7701	1 1 2	3 4 4	5 6 7
59	7709	7716	7723	7731	7738	7745	7752	7760	7767	7774	1 1 2	3 4 4	5 6 7
60	7782	7789	7796	7803	7810	7818	7825	7832	7839	7846	1 1 2	3 4 4	5 6 6
61	7853	7860	7868	7875	7882	7889	7896	7903	7910	7917	1 1 2	3 4 4	5 6 6
62	7924	7931	7938	7945	7952	7959	7966	7973	7980	7987	1 1 2	3 3 4	5 5 6
63	7993	8000	8007	8014	8021	8028	8035	8041	8048	8055	1 1 2	3 3 4	5 5 6
64	8062	8069	8075	8082	8089	8096	8102	8109	8116	8122	1 1 2	3 3 4	5 5 6
65	8129	8136	8142	8149	8156	8162	8169	8176	8182	8189	1 1 2	3 3 4	5 5 6
66	8195	8202	8209	8215	8222	8228	8235	8241	8248	8254	1 1 2	3 3 4	5 5 6
67	8261	8267	8274	8280	8287	8293	8299	8306	8312	8319	1 1 2	3 3 4	4 5 6
68	8325	8331	8338	8344	8351	8357	8363	8370	8376	8382	1 1 2	3 3 4	4 5 6
69	8388	8395	8401	8407	8414	8420	8426	8432	8439	8445	1 1 2	3 3 4	4 5 6
70	8451	8457	8463	8470	8476	8482	8488	8494	8500	8506	1 1 2	2 3 4	4 5 6
71	8513	8519	8525	8531	8537	8543	8549	8555	8561	8567	1 1 2	2 3 4	4 5 6
72	8573	8579	8585	8591	8597	8603	8609	8615	8621	8627	1 1 2	2 3 4	4 5 6
73	8633	8639	8645	8651	8657	8663	8669	8675	8681	8686	1 1 2	2 3 4	4 5 5
74	8692	8698	8704	8710	8716	8722	8727	8733	8739	8745	1 1 2	2 3 4	4 5 5
75	8751	8756	8762	8768	8774	8779	8785	8791	8797	8802	1 1 2	2 3 3	4 5 5
76	8808	8814	8820	8825	8831	8837	8842	8848	8854	8859	1 1 2	2 3 3	4 5 5
77	8865	8871	8876	8882	8887	8893	8899	8904	8910	8915	1 1 2	2 3 3	4 4 5
78	8921	8927	8932	8938	8943	8949	8954	8960	8965	8971	1 1 2	2 3 3	4 4 5
79	8976	8982	8987	8993	8998	9004	9009	9015	9020	9025	1 1 2	2 3 3	4 4 5
80	9031	9036	9042	9047	9053	9058	9063	9069	9074	9079	1 1 2	2 3 3	4 4 5
81	9085	9090	9096	9101	9106	9112	9117	9122	9128	9133	1 1 2	2 3 3	4 4 5
82	9138	9143	9149	9154	9159	9165	9170	9175	9180	9186	1 1 2	2 3 3	4 4 5
83	9191	9196	9201	9206	9212	9217	9222	9227	9232	9238	1 1 2	2 3 3	4 4 5
84	9243	9248	9253	9258	9263	9269	9274	9279	9284	9289	1 1 2	2 3 3	4 4 5
85	9294	9299	9304	9309	9315	9320	9325	9330	9335	9340	1 1 2	2 3 3	4 4 5
86	9345	9350	9355	9360	9365	9370	9375	9380	9385	9390	1 1 2	2 3 3	4 4 5
87	9395	9400	9405	9410	9415	9420	9425	9430	9435	9440	0 1 2	2 3 3	4 4 4
88	9445	9450	9455	9460	9465	9469	9474	9479	9484	9489	0 1 1	2 2 3	3 4 4
89	9494	9499	9504	9509	9513	9518	9523	9528	9533	9538	0 1 1	2 2 3	3 4 4
90	9542	9547	9552	9557	9562	9566	9571	9576	9581	9586	0 1 1	2 2 3	3 4 4
91	9590	9595	9600	9605	9609	9614	9619	9624	9628	9633	0 1 1	2 2 3	3 4 4
92	9638	9643	9647	9652	9657	9661	9666	9671	9675	9680	0 1 1	2 2 3	3 4 4
93	9685	9689	9694	9699	9703	9708	9713	9717	9722	9727	0 1 1	2 2 3	3 4 4
94	9731	9736	9741	9745	9750	9754	9759	9763	9768	9773	0 1 1	2 2 3	3 4 4
95	9777	9782	9786	9791	9795	9800	9805	9809	9814	9818	0 1 1	2 2 3	3 4 4
96	9823	9827	9832	9836	9841	9845	9850	9854	9859	9863	0 1 1	2 2 3	3 4 4
97	9868	9872	9877	9881	9886	9890	9894	9899	9903	9908	0 1 1	2 2 3	3 4 4
98	9912	9917	9921	9926	9930	9934	9939	9943	9948	9952	0 1 1	2 2 3	3 4 4
99	9956	9961	9965	9969	9974	9978	9983	9987	9991	9996	0 1 1	2 2 3	3 4 4
N.	**0**	**1**	**2**	**3**	**4**	**5**	**6**	**7**	**8**	**9**	1 2 3	4 5 6	7 8 9

Prop. Parts

Angle Rad.	Degrees	Sin	Cos	Tan	Angle Rad.	Degrees	Sin	Cos	Tan
.00	0° 00.0'	.00000	1.0000	.00000	.60	34° 22.6'	.56464	.82534	.68414
.01	0° 34.4'	.01000	.99995	.01000	.61	34° 57.0'	.57287	.81965	.69892
.02	1° 08.8'	.02000	.99980	.02000	.62	35° 31.4'	.58104	.81388	.71391
.03	1° 43.1'	.03000	.99955	.03001	.63	36° 05.8'	.58914	.80803	.72911
.04	2° 17.5'	.03999	.99920	.04002	.64	36° 40.2'	.59720	.80210	.74454
.05	2° 51.9'	.04998	.99875	.05004	.65	37° 14.5'	.60519	.79608	.76020
.06	3° 26.3'	.05996	.99820	.06007	.66	37° 48.9'	.61312	.78999	.77610
.07	4° 00.6'	.06994	.99755	.07011	.67	38° 23.3'	.62099	.78382	.79225
.08	4° 35.0'	.07991	.99680	.08017	.68	38° 57.7'	.62879	.77757	.80866
.09	5° 09.4'	.08988	.99595	.09024	.69	39° 32.0'	.63654	.77125	.82533
.10	5° 43.8'	.09983	.99500	.10033	.70	40° 06.4'	.64422	.76484	.84229
.11	6° 18.2'	.10978	.99396	.11045	.71	40° 40.8'	.65183	.75836	.85953
.12	6° 52.5'	.11971	.99281	.12058	.72	41° 15.2'	.65938	.75181	.87707
.13	7° 26.9'	.12963	.99156	.13074	.73	41° 49.6'	.66687	.74517	.89492
.14	8° 01.3'	.13954	.99022	.14092	.74	42° 23.9'	.67429	.73847	.91309
.15	8° 35.7'	.14944	.98877	.15114	.75	42° 58.3'	.68164	.73169	.93160
.16	9° 10.0'	.15932	.98723	.16138	.76	43° 32.7'	.68892	.72484	.95055
.17	9° 44.4'	.16918	.98558	.17166	.77	44° 07.1'	.69614	.71791	.96967
.18	10° 18.8'	.17903	.98384	.18197	.78	44° 41.4'	.70328	.71091	.98926
.19	10° 53.2'	.18886	.98200	.19232	.79	45° 15.8'	.71035	.70385	1.0092
.20	11° 27.5'	.19867	.98007	.20271	.80	45° 50.2'	.71736	.69671	1.0296
.21	12° 01.9'	.20846	.97803	.21314	.81	46° 24.6'	.72429	.68950	1.0505
.22	12° 36.3'	.21823	.97590	.22362	.82	46° 59.0'	.73115	.68222	1.0717
.23	13° 10.7'	.22798	.97367	.23414	.83	47° 33.3'	.73793	.67488	1.0934
.24	13° 45.1'	.23770	.97134	.24472	.84	48° 07.7'	.74464	.66746	1.1156
.25	14° 19.4'	.24740	.96891	.25534	.85	48° 42.1'	.75128	65998	1.1383
.26	14° 53.8'	.25708	.96639	.26602	.86	49° 16.5'	.75784	.65244	1.1616
.27	15° 28.2'	.26673	.96377	.27676	.87	49° 50.8'	.76433	.64483	1.1853
.28	16° 02.6'	.27636	.96106	.28755	.88	50° 25.2'	.77074	.63715	1.2097
.29	16° 36.9'	.28595	.95824	.29841	.89	50° 59.6'	.77707	.62941	1.2346
.30	17° 11.3'	.29552	.95534	.30934	.90	51° 34.0'	.78333	.62161	1.2602
.31	17° 45.7'	.30506	.95233	.32033	.91	52° 08.3'	.78950	.61375	1.2864
.32	18° 20.1'	.31457	.94924	.33139	.92	52° 42.7'	.79560	.60582	1.3133
.33	18° 54.5'	.32404	.94604	.34252	.93	53° 17.1'	.80162	.59783	1.3409
.34	19° 28.8'	.33349	.94275	.35374	.94	53° 51.5'	.80756	.58979	1.3692
.35	20° 03.2'	.34290	.93937	.36503	.95	54° 25.9'	.81342	.58168	1.3984
.36	20° 37.6'	.35227	.93590	.37640	.96	55° 00.2'	.81919	.57352	1.4284
.37	21° 12.0'	.36162	.93233	.38786	.97	55° 34.6'	.82489	.56530	1.4592
.38	21° 46.3'	.37092	.92866	.39941	.98	56° 09.0'	.83050	.55702	1.4910
.39	22° 20.7'	.38019	.92491	.41106	.99	56° 43.4'	.83603	.54869	1.5237
.40	22° 55.1'	.38942	.92106	.42279	1.00	57° 17.7'	.84147	.54030	1.5574
.41	23° 29.5'	.39861	.91712	.43463	1.01	57° 52.1'	.84683	.53186	1.5922
.42	24° 03.9'	.40776	.91309	.44657	1.02	58° 26.5'	.85211	.52337	1.6281
.43	24° 38.2'	.41687	.90897	.45862	1.03	59° 00.9'	.85730	.51482	1.6652
.44	25° 12.6'	.42594	.90475	.47078	1.04	59° 35.3'	.86240	.50622	1.7036
.45	25° 47.0'	.43497	.90045	.48305	1.05	60° 09.6'	.86742	.49757	1.7433
.46	26° 21.4'	.44395	.89605	.49545	1.06	60° 44.0'	.87236	.48887	1.7844
.47	26° 55.7'	.45289	.89157	.50795	1.07	61° 18.4'	.87720	.48012	1.8270
.48	27° 30.1'	.46178	.88699	.52061	1.08	61° 52.8'	.88196	.47133	1.8712
.49	28° 04.5'	.47063	.88233	.53339	1.09	62° 27.1'	.88663	.46249	1.9171
.50	28° 38.9'	.47943	.87758	.54630	1.10	63° 01.5'	.89121	.45360	1.9648
.51	29° 13.3'	.48818	.87274	.55936	1.11	63° 35.9'	.89570	.44466	2.0143
.52	29° 47.6'	.49688	.86782	.57256	1.12	64° 10.3'	.90010	.43568	2.0660
.53	30° 22.0'	.50553	.86281	.58592	1.13	64° 44.7'	.90441	.42666	2.1198
.54	30° 56.4'	.51414	.85771	.59943	1.14	65° 19.0'	.90863	.41759	2.1759
.55	31° 30.8'	.52269	.85252	.61311	1.15	65° 53.4'	.91276	.40849	2.2345
.56	32° 05.1'	.53119	.84726	.62695	1.16	66° 27.8'	.91680	.39934	2.2958
.57	32° 39.5'	.53963	.84190	.64097	1.17	67° 02.2'	.92075	.39015	2.3600
.58	33° 13.9'	.54802	.83646	.65517	1.18	67° 36.5'	.92461	.38092	2.4273
.59	33° 48.3'	.55636	.83094	.66956	1.19	68° 10.9'	.92837	.37166	2.4979
.60	34° 22.6'	.56464	.82534	.68414	1.20	68° 45.3'	.93204	.36236	2.5722

Angle		Sin	Cos	Tan	Angle		Sin	Cos	Tan
Rad.	Degrees				Rad.	Degrees			
1.20	68° 45.3′	.93204	.36236	2.5722	**1.40**	80° 12.8′	.98545	.16997	5.7979
1.21	69° 19.7′	.93562	.35302	2.6503	1.41	80° 47.2′	.98710	.16010	6.1654
1.22	69° 54.1′	.93910	.34365	2.7328	1.42	81° 21.6′	.98865	.15023	6.5811
1.23	70° 28.4′	.94249	.33424	2.8198	1.43	81° 56.0′	.99010	.14033	7.0555
1.24	71° 02.8′	.94578	.32480	2.9119	1.44	82° 30.4′	.99146	.13042	7.6018
1.25	71° 37.2′	.94898	.31532	3.0096	**1.45**	83° 04.7′	.99271	.12050	8.2381
1.26	72° 11.6′	.95209	.30582	3.1133	1.46	83° 39.1′	.99387	.11057	8.9886
1.27	72° 45.9′	.95510	.29628	3.2236	1.47	84° 13.5′	.99492	.10063	9.8874
1.28	73° 20.3′	.95802	.28672	3.3413	1.48	84° 47.9′	.99588	.09067	10.983
1.29	73° 54.7′	.96084	.27712	3.4672	1.49	85° 22.2′	.99674	.08071	12.350
1.30	74° 29.1′	.96356	.26750	3.6021	**1.50**	85° 56.6′	.99749	.07074	14.101
1.31	75° 03.4′	.96618	.25785	3.7470	1.51	86° 31.0′	.99815	.06076	16.428
1.32	75° 37.8′	.96872	.24818	3.9033	1.52	87° 05.4′	.99871	.05077	19.670
1.33	76° 12.2′	.97115	.23848	4.0723	1.53	87° 39.8′	.99917	.04079	24.498
1.34	76° 46.6′	.97348	.22875	4.2556	1.54	88° 14.1′	.99953	.03079	32.461
1.35	77° 21.0′	.97572	.21901	4.4552	**1.55**	88° 48.5′	.99978	.02079	48.078
1.36	77° 55.3′	.97786	.20924	4.6734	1.56	89° 22.9′	.99994	.01080	92.621
1.37	78° 29.7′	.97991	.19945	4.9131	1.57	89° 57.3′	1.0000	.00080	1255.8
1.38	79° 04.1′	.98185	.18964	5.1774	1.58	90° 31.6′	.99996	−.00920	−108.65
1.39	79° 38.5′	.98370	.17981	5.4707	1.59	91° 06.0′	.99982	−.01920	−52.067
1.40	80° 12.8′	.98545	.16997	5.7979	**1.60**	91° 40.4′	.99957	−.02920	−34.233

Degrees in Radians

0°	0.00000	**15°**	0.26180	**30°**	0.52360	**45°**	0.78540	**60°**	1.04720	**75°**	1.30900
1	0.01745	16	0.27925	31	0.54105	46	0.80285	61	1.06465	76	1.32645
2	0.03491	17	0.29671	32	0.55851	47	0.82030	62	1.08210	77	1.34390
3	0.05236	18	0.31416	33	0.57596	48	0.83776	63	1.09956	78	1.36136
4	0.06981	19	0.33161	34	0.59341	49	0.85521	64	1.11701	79	1.37881
5	0.08727	**20**	0.34907	**35**	0.61087	**50**	0.87266	**65**	1.13446	**80**	1.39626
6	0.10472	21	0.36652	36	0.62832	51	0.89012	66	1.15192	81	1.41372
7	0.12217	22	0.38397	37	0.64577	52	0.90757	67	1.16937	82	1.43117
8	0.13963	23	0.40143	38	0.66323	53	0.92502	68	1.18682	83	1.44862
9	0.15708	24	0.41888	39	0.68068	54	0.94248	69	1.20428	84	1.46608
10	0.17453	**25**	0.43633	**40**	0.69813	**55**	0.95993	**70**	1.22173	**85**	1.48353
11	0.19199	26	0.45379	41	0.71558	56	0.97738	71	1.23918	86	1.50098
12	0.20944	27	0.47124	42	0.73304	57	0.99484	72	1.25664	87	1.51844
13	0.22689	28	0.48869	43	0.75049	58	1.01229	73	1.27409	88	1.53589
14	0.24435	29	0.50615	44	0.76794	59	1.02974	74	1.29154	89	1.55334
15	0.26180	**30**	0.52360	**45**	0.78540	**60**	1.04720	**75**	1.30900	**90**	1.57080

Minutes in Radians

0′	0.00000	**10′**	0.00291	**20′**	0.00582	**30′**	0.00873	**40′**	0.01164	**50′**	0.01454
1	0.00029	11	0.00320	21	0.00611	31	0.00902	41	0.01193	51	0.01484
2	0.00058	12	0.00349	22	0.00640	32	0.00931	42	0.01222	52	0.01513
3	0.00087	13	0.00378	23	0.00669	33	0.00960	43	0.01251	53	0.01542
4	0.00116	14	0.00407	24	0.00698	34	0.00989	44	0.01280	54	0.01571
5	0.00145	**15**	0.00436	**25**	0.00727	**35**	0.01018	**45**	0.01309	**55**	0.01600
6	0.00174	16	0.00465	26	0.00756	36	0.01047	46	0.01338	56	0.01629
7	0.00204	17	0.00495	27	0.00785	37	0.01076	47	0.01367	57	0.01658
8	0.00233	18	0.00524	28	0.00814	38	0.01105	48	0.01396	58	0.01687
9	0.00262	19	0.00553	29	0.00844	39	0.01134	49	0.01425	59	0.01716
10	0.00291	**20**	0.00582	**30**	0.00873	**40**	0.01164	**50**	0.01454	**60**	0.01745

n	n^2	$\sqrt{n}$	$\sqrt{10n}$	$1/n$	n	n^2	$\sqrt{n}$	$\sqrt{10n}$	$1/n$
1.00	1.0000	1.00000	3.16228	1.00000	**1.50**	2.2500	1.22474	3.87298	.666667
1.01	1.0201	1.00499	3.17805	.990099	1.51	2.2801	1.22882	3.88587	.662252
1.02	1.0404	1.00995	3.19374	.980392	1.52	2.3104	1.23288	3.89872	.657895
1.03	1.0609	1.01489	3.20936	.970874	1.53	2.3409	1.23693	3.91152	.653595
1.04	1.0816	1.01980	3.22490	.961538	1.54	2.3716	1.24097	3.92428	.649351
1.05	1.1025	1.02470	3.24037	.952381	1.55	2.4025	1.24499	3.93700	.645161
1.06	1.1236	1.02956	3.25576	.943396	1.56	2.4336	1.24900	3.94968	.641026
1.07	1.1449	1.03441	3.27109	.934579	1.57	2.4649	1.25300	3.96232	.636943
1.08	1.1664	1.03923	3.28634	.925926	1.58	2.4964	1.25698	3.97492	.632911
1.09	1.1881	1.04403	3.30151	.917431	1.59	2.5281	1.26095	3.98748	.628931
1.10	1.2100	1.04881	3.31662	.909091	**1.60**	2.5600	1.26491	4.00000	.625000
1.11	1.2321	1.05357	3.33167	.900901	1.61	2.5921	1.26886	4.01248	.621118
1.12	1.2544	1.05830	3.34664	.892857	1.62	2.6244	1.27279	4.02492	.617284
1.13	1.2769	1.06301	3.36155	.884956	1.63	2.6569	1.27671	4.03733	.613497
1.14	1.2996	1.06771	3.37639	.877193	1.64	2.6896	1.28062	4.04969	.609756
1.15	1.3225	1.07238	3.39116	.869565	1.65	2.7225	1.28452	4.06202	.606061
1.16	1.3456	1.07703	3.40588	.862069	1.66	2.7556	1.28841	4.07431	.602410
1.17	1.3689	1.08167	3.42053	.854701	1.67	2.7889	1.29228	4.08656	.598802
1.18	1.3924	1.08628	3.43511	.847458	1.68	2.8224	1.29615	4.09878	.595238
1.19	1.4161	1.09087	3.44964	.840336	1.69	2.8561	1.30000	4.11096	.591716
1.20	1.4400	1.09545	3.46410	.833333	**1.70**	2.8900	1.30384	4.12311	.588235
1.21	1.4641	1.10000	3.47851	.826446	1.71	2.9241	1.30767	4.13521	.584795
1.22	1.4884	1.10454	3.49285	.819672	1.72	2.9584	1.31149	4.14729	.581395
1.23	1.5129	1.10905	3.50714	.813008	1.73	2.9929	1.31529	4.15933	.578035
1.24	1.5376	1.11355	3.52136	.806452	1.74	3.0276	1.31909	4.17133	.574713
1.25	1.5625	1.11803	3.53553	.800000	1.75	3.0625	1.32288	4.18330	.571429
1.26	1.5876	1.12250	3.54965	.793651	1.76	3.0976	1.32665	4.19524	.568182
1.27	1.6129	1.12694	3.56371	.787402	1.77	3.1329	1.33041	4.20714	.564972
1.28	1.6384	1.13137	3.57771	.781250	1.78	3.1684	1.33417	4.21900	.561798
1.29	1.6641	1.13578	3.59166	.775194	1.79	3.2041	1.33791	4.23084	.558659
1.30	1.6900	1.14018	3.60555	.769231	**1.80**	3.2400	1.34164	4.24264	.555556
1.31	1.7161	1.14455	3.61939	.763359	1.81	3.2761	1.34536	4.25441	.552486
1.32	1.7424	1.14891	3.63318	.757576	1.82	3.3124	1.34907	4.26615	.549451
1.33	1.7689	1.15326	3.64692	.751880	1.83	3.3489	1.35277	4.27785	.546448
1.34	1.7956	1.15758	3.66060	.746269	1.84	3.3856	1.35647	4.28952	.543478
1.35	1.8225	1.16190	3.67423	.740741	1.85	3.4225	1.36015	4.30116	.540541
1.36	1.8496	1.16619	3.68782	.735294	1.86	3.4596	1.36382	4.31277	.537634
1.37	1.8769	1.17047	3.70135	.729927	1.87	3.4969	1.36748	4.32435	.534759
1.38	1.9044	1.17473	3.71484	.724638	1.88	3.5344	1.37113	4.33590	.531915
1.39	1.9321	1.17898	3.72827	.719424	1.89	3.5721	1.37477	4.34741	.529101
1.40	1.9600	1.18322	3.74166	.714286	**1.90**	3.6100	1.37840	4.35890	.526316
1.41	1.9881	1.18743	3.75500	.709220	1.91	3.6481	1.38203	4.37035	.523560
1.42	2.0164	1.19164	3.76829	.704225	1.92	3.6864	1.38564	4.38178	.520833
1.43	2.0449	1.19583	3.78153	.699301	1.93	3.7249	1.38924	4.39318	.518135
1.44	2.0736	1.20000	3.79473	.694444	1.94	3.7636	1.39284	4.40454	.515464
1.45	2.1025	1.20416	3.80789	.689655	1.95	3.8025	1.39642	4.41588	.512821
1.46	2.1316	1.20830	3.82099	.684932	1.96	3.8416	1.40000	4.42719	.510204
1.47	2.1609	1.21244	3.83406	.680272	1.97	3.8809	1.40357	4.43847	.507614
1.48	2.1904	1.21655	3.84708	.675676	1.98	3.9204	1.40712	4.44972	.505051
1.49	2.2201	1.22066	3.86005	.671141	1.99	3.9601	1.41067	4.46094	.502513
1.50	2.2500	1.22474	3.87298	.666667	**2.00**	4.0000	1.41421	4.47214	.500000
n	n^2	$\sqrt{n}$	$\sqrt{10n}$	$1/n$	n	n^2	$\sqrt{n}$	$\sqrt{10n}$	$1/n$

n	n^2	$\sqrt{n}$	$\sqrt{10n}$	$1/n$	n	n^2	$\sqrt{n}$	$\sqrt{10n}$	$1/n$
2.00	4.0000	1.41421	4.47214	.500000	**2.50**	6.2500	1.58114	**5.00000**	.400000
2.01	4.0401	1.41774	4.48330	.497512	2.51	6.3001	1.58430	5.00999	.398406
2.02	4.0804	1.42127	4.49444	.495050	2.52	6.3504	1.58745	5.01996	.396825
2.03	4.1209	1.42478	4.50555	.492611	2.53	6.4009	1.59060	5.02991	.395257
2.04	4.1616	1.42829	4.51664	.490196	2.54	6.4516	1.59374	5.03984	.393701
2.05	4.2025	1.43178	4.52769	.487805	2.55	6.5025	1.59687	5.04975	.392157
2.06	4.2436	1.43527	4.53872	.485437	2.56	6.5536	1.60000	5.05964	.390625
2.07	4.2849	1.43875	4.54973	.483092	2.57	6.6049	1.60312	5.06952	.389105
2.08	4.3264	1.44222	4.56070	.480769	2.58	6.6564	1.60624	5.07937	.387597
2.09	4.3681	1.44568	4.57165	.478469	2.59	6.7081	1.60935	5.08920	.386100
2.10	4.4100	1.44914	4.58258	.476190	**2.60**	6.7600	1.61245	5.09902	.384615
2.11	4.4521	1.45258	4.59347	.473934	2.61	6.8121	1.61555	5.10882	.383142
2.12	4.4944	1.45602	4.60435	.471698	2.62	6.8644	1.61864	5.11859	.381679
2.13	4.5369	1.45945	4.61519	.469434	2.63	6.9169	1.62173	5.12835	.380228
2.14	4.5796	1.46287	4.62601	.467290	2.64	6.9696	1.62481	5.13809	.378788
2.15	4.6225	1.46629	4.63681	.465116	2.65	7.0225	1.62788	5.14782	.377358
2.16	4.6656	1.46969	4.64758	.462963	2.66	7.0756	1.63095	5.15752	.375940
2.17	4.7089	1.47309	4.65833	.460829	2.67	7.1289	1.63401	5.16720	.374532
2.18	4.7524	1.47648	4.66905	.458716	2.68	7.1824	1.63707	5.17687	.373134
2.19	4.7961	1.47986	4.67974	.456621	2.69	7.2361	1.64012	5.18652	.371747
2.20	4.8400	1.48324	4.69042	.454545	**2.70**	7.2900	1.64317	5.19615	.370370
2.21	4.8841	1.48661	4.70106	.452489	2.71	7.3441	1.64621	5.20577	.369004
2.22	4.9284	1.48997	4.71169	.450450	2.72	7.3984	1.64924	5.21536	.367647
2.23	4.9729	1.49332	4.72229	.448430	2.73	7.4529	1.65227	5.22494	.366300
2.24	5.0176	1.49666	4.73286	.446429	2.74	7.5076	1.65529	5.23450	.364964
2.25	5.0625	1.50000	4.74342	.444444	2.75	7.5625	1.65831	5.24404	.363636
2.26	5.1076	1.50333	4.75395	.442478	2.76	7.6176	1.66132	5.25357	.362319
2.27	5.1529	1.50665	4.76445	.440529	2.77	7.6729	1.66433	5.26308	.361011
2.28	5.1984	1.50997	4.77493	.438596	2.78	7.7284	1.66733	5.27257	.359712
2.29	5.2441	1.51327	4.78539	.436681	2.79	7.7841	1.67033	5.28205	.358423
2.30	5.2900	1.51658	4.79583	.434783	**2.80**	7.8400	1.67332	5.29150	.357143
2.31	5.3361	1.51987	4.80625	.432900	2.81	7.8961	1.67631	5.30094	.355872
2.32	5.3824	1.52315	4.81664	.431034	2.82	7.9524	1.67929	5.31037	.354610
2.33	5.4289	1.52643	4.82701	.429185	2.83	8.0089	1.68226	5.31977	.353357
2.34	5.4756	1.52971	4.83735	.427350	2.84	8.0656	1.68523	5.32917	.352113
2.35	5.5225	1.53297	4.84768	.425532	2.85	8.1225	1.68819	5.33854	.350877
2.36	5.5696	1.53623	4.85798	.423729	2.86	8.1796	1.69115	5.34790	.349650
2.37	5.6169	1.53948	4.86826	.421941	2.87	8.2369	1.69411	5.35724	.348432
2.38	5.6644	1.54272	4.87852	.420168	2.88	8.2944	1.69706	5.36656	.347222
2.39	5.7121	1.54596	4.88876	.418410	2.89	8.3521	1.70000	5.37587	.346021
2.40	5.7600	1.54919	4.89898	.416667	**2.90**	8.4100	1.70294	5.38516	.344828
2.41	5.8081	1.55242	4.90918	.414938	2.91	8.4681	1.70587	5.39444	.343643
2.42	5.8564	1.55563	4.91935	.413223	2.92	8.5264	1.70880	5.40370	.342466
2.43	5.9049	1.55885	4.92950	.411523	2.93	8.5849	1.71172	5.41295	.341297
2.44	5.9536	1.56205	4.93964	.409836	2.94	8.6436	1.71464	5.42218	3.40136
2.45	6.0025	1.56525	4.94975	.408163	2.95	8.7025	1.71756	5.43139	.338983
2.46	6.0516	1.56844	4.95984	.406504	2.96	8.7616	1.72047	5.44059	.337838
2.47	6.1009	1.57162	4.96991	.404858	2.97	8.8209	1.72337	5.44977	.336700
2.48	6.1504	1.57480	4.97996	.403226	2.98	8.8804	1.72627	5.45894	.335570
2.49	6.2001	1.57797	4.98999	.401606	2.99	8.9401	1.72916	5.46809	.334448
2.50	6.2500	1.58114	5.00000	.400000	**3.00**	9.0000	1.73205	5.47723	.333333
n	n^2	$\sqrt{n}$	$\sqrt{10n}$	$1/n$	n	n^2	$\sqrt{n}$	$\sqrt{10n}$	$1/n$

TABLE VII

n	n^2	$\sqrt{n}$	$\sqrt{10n}$	$1/n$	n	n^2	$\sqrt{n}$	$\sqrt{10n}$	$1/n$
3.00	9.0000	1.73205	5.47723	.333333	**3.50**	12.2500	1.87083	5.91608	.285714
3.01	9.0601	1.73494	5.48635	.332226	3.51	12.3201	1.87350	5.92453	.284900
3.02	9.1204	1.73781	5.49545	.331126	3.52	12.3904	1.87617	5.93296	.284091
3.03	9.1809	1.74069	5.50454	.330033	3.53	12.4609	1.87883	5.94138	.283286
3.04	9.2416	1.74356	5.51362	.328947	3.54	12.5316	1.88149	5.94979	.282486
3.05	9.3025	1.74642	5.52268	.327869	3.55	12.6025	1.88414	5.95819	.281690
3.06	9.3636	1.74929	5.53173	.326797	3.56	12.6736	1.88680	5.96657	.280899
3.07	9.4249	1.75214	5.54076	.325733	3.57	12.7449	1.88944	5.97495	.280112
3.08	9.4864	1.75499	5.54977	.324675	3.58	12.8164	1.89209	5.98331	.279330
3.09	9.5481	1.75784	5.55878	.323625	3.59	12.8881	1.89473	5.99166	.278552
3.10	9.6100	1.76068	5.56776	.322581	**3.60**	12.9600	1.89737	6.00000	.277778
3.11	9.6721	1.76352	5.57674	.321543	3.61	13.0321	1.90000	6.00833	.277008
3.12	9.7344	1.76635	5.58570	.320513	3.62	13.1044	1.90263	6.01664	.276243
3.13	9.7969	1.76918	5.59464	.319489	3.63	13.1769	1.90526	6.02495	.275482
3.14	9.8596	1.77200	5.60357	.318471	3.64	13.2496	1.90788	6.03324	.274725
3.15	9.9225	1.77482	5.61249	.317460	3.65	13.3225	1.91050	6.04152	.273973
3.16	9.9856	1.77764	5.62139	.316456	3.66	13.3956	1.91311	6.04979	.273224
3.17	10.0489	1.78045	5.63028	.315457	3.67	13.4689	1.91572	6.05805	.272480
3.18	10.1124	1.78326	5.63915	.314465	3.68	13.5424	1.91833	6.06630	.271739
3.19	10.1761	1.78606	5.64801	.313480	3.69	13.6161	1.92094	6.07454	.271003
3.20	10.2400	1.78885	5.65685	.312500	**3.70**	13.6900	1.92354	6.08276	.270270
3.21	10.3041	1.79165	5.66569	.311526	3.71	13.7641	1.92614	6.09098	.269542
3.22	10.3684	1.79444	5.67450	.310559	3.72	13.8384	1.92873	6.09918	.268817
3.23	10.4329	1.79722	5.68331	.309598	3.73	13.9129	1.93132	6.10737	.268097
3.24	10.4976	1.80000	5.69210	.308642	3.74	13.9876	1.93391	6.11555	.267380
3.25	10.5625	1.80278	5.70088	.307692	3.75	14.0625	1.93649	6.12372	.266667
3.26	10.6276	1.80555	5.70964	.306748	3.76	14.1376	1.93907	6.13188	.265957
3.27	10.6929	1.80831	5.71839	.305810	3.77	14.2129	1.94165	6.14003	.265252
3.28	10.7584	1.81108	5.72713	.304878	3.78	14.2884	1.94422	6.14817	.264550
3.29	10.8241	1.81384	5.73585	.303951	3.79	14.3641	1.94679	6.15630	.263852
3.30	10.8900	1.81659	5.74456	.303030	**3.80**	14.4400	1.94936	6.16441	.263158
3.31	10.9561	1.81934	5.75326	.302115	3.81	14.5161	1.95192	6.17252	.262467
3.32	11.0224	1.82209	5.76194	.301205	3.82	14.5924	1.95448	6.18061	.261780
3.33	11.0889	1.82483	5.77062	.300300	3.83	14.6689	1.95704	6.18870	.261097
3.34	11.1556	1.82757	5.77927	.299401	3.84	14.7456	1.95959	6.19677	.260417
3.35	11.2225	1.83030	5.78792	.298507	3.85	14.8225	1.96214	6.20484	.259740
3.36	11.2896	1.83303	5.79655	.297619	3.86	14.8996	1.96469	6.21289	.259067
3.37	11.3569	1.83576	5.80517	.296736	3.87	14.9769	1.96723	6.22093	.258398
3.38	11.4244	1.83848	5.81378	.295858	3.88	15.0544	1.96977	6.22896	.257732
3.39	11.4921	1.84120	5.82237	.294985	3.89	15.1321	1.97231	6.23699	.257069
3.40	11.5600	1.84391	5.83095	.294118	**3.90**	15.2100	1.97484	6.24500	.256410
3.41	11.6281	1.84662	5.83952	.293255	3.91	15.2881	1.97737	6.25300	.255754
3.42	11.6964	1.84932	5.84808	.292398	3.92	15.3664	1.97990	6.26099	.255102
3.43	11.7649	1.85203	5.85662	.291545	3.93	15.4449	1.98242	6.26897	.254453
3.44	11.8336	1.85472	5.86515	.290698	3.94	15.5236	1.98494	6.27694	.253807
3.45	11.9025	1.85742	5.87367	.289855	3.95	15.6025	1.98746	6.28490	.253165
3.46	11.9716	1.86011	5.88218	.289017	3.96	15.6816	1.98997	6.29285	.252525
3.47	12.0409	1.86279	5.89067	.288184	3.97	15.7609	1.99249	6.30079	.251889
3.48	12.1104	1.86548	5.89915	.287356	3.98	15.8404	1.99499	6.30872	.251256
3.49	12.1801	1.86815	5.90762	.286533	3.99	15.9201	1.99750	6.31664	.250627
3.50	12.2500	1.87083	5.91608	.285714	**4.00**	16.0000	2.00000	6.32456	.250000
n	n^2	$\sqrt{n}$	$\sqrt{10n}$	$1/n$	n	n^2	$\sqrt{n}$	$\sqrt{10n}$	$1/n$

n	n^2	$\sqrt{n}$	$\sqrt{10n}$	$1/n$	n	n^2	$\sqrt{n}$	$\sqrt{10n}$	$1/n$
4.00	16.0000	2.00000	6.32456	.250000	**4.50**	20.2500	2.12132	6.70820	.222222
4.01	16.0801	2.00250	6.33246	.249377	4.51	20.3401	2.12368	6.71565	.221729
4.02	16.1604	2.00499	6.34035	.248756	4.52	20.4304	2.12603	6.72309	.221239
4.03	16.2409	2.00749	6.34823	.248139	4.53	20.5209	2.12838	6.73053	.220751
4.04	16.3216	2.00998	6.35610	.247525	4.54	20.6116	2.13073	6.73795	.220264
4.05	16.4025	2.01246	6.36396	.246914	4.55	20.7025	2.13307	6.74537	.219780
4.06	16.4836	2.01494	6.37181	.246305	4.56	20.7936	2.13542	6.75278	.219298
4.07	16.5649	2.01742	6.37966	.245700	4.57	20.8849	2.13776	6.76018	.218818
4.08	16.6464	2.01990	6.38749	.245098	4.58	20.9764	2.14009	6.76757	.218341
4.09	16.7281	2.02237	6.39531	.244499	4.59	21.0681	2.14243	6.77495	.217865
4.10	16.8100	2.02485	6.40312	.243902	**4.60**	21.1600	2.14476	6.78233	.217391
4.11	16.8921	2.02731	6.41093	.243309	4.61	21.2521	2.14709	6.78970	.216920
4.12	16.9744	2.02978	6.41872	.242718	4.62	21.3444	2.14942	6.79706	.216450
4.13	17.0569	2.03224	6.42651	.242131	4.63	21.4369	2.15174	6.80441	.215983
4.14	17.1396	2.03470	6.43428	.241546	4.64	21.5296	2.15407	6.81175	.215517
4.15	17.2225	2.03715	6.44205	.240964	4.65	21.6225	2.15639	6.81909	.215054
4.16	17.3056	2.03961	6.44981	.240385	4.66	21.7156	2.15870	6.82642	.214592
4.17	17.3889	2.04206	6.45755	.239808	4.67	21.8089	2.16102	6.83374	.214133
4.18	17.4724	2.04450	6.46529	.239234	4.68	21.9024	2.16333	6.84105	.213675
4.19	17.5561	2.04695	6.47302	.238663	4.69	21.9961	2.16564	6.84836	.213220
4.20	17.6400	2.04939	6.48074	.238095	**4.70**	22.0900	2.16795	6.85565	.212766
4.21	17.7241	2.05183	6.48845	.237530	4.71	22.1841	2.17025	6.86294	.212314
4.22	17.8084	2.05426	6.49615	.236967	4.72	22.2784	2.17256	6.87023	.211864
4.23	17.8929	2.05670	6.50384	.236407	4.73	22.3729	2.17486	6.87750	.211416
4.24	17.9776	2.05913	6.51153	.235849	4.74	22.4676	2.17715	6.88477	.210970
4.25	18.0625	2.06155	6.51920	.235294	4.75	22.5625	2.17945	6.89202	.210526
4.26	18.1476	2.06398	6.52687	.234742	4.76	22.6576	2.18174	6.89928	.210084
4.27	18.2329	2.06640	6.53452	.234192	4.77	22.7529	2.18403	6.90652	.209644
4.28	18.3184	2.06882	6.54217	.233645	4.78	22.8484	2.18632	6.91375	.209205
4.29	18.4041	2.07123	6.54981	.233100	4.79	22.9441	2.18861	6.92098	.208768
4.30	18.4900	2.07364	6.55744	.232558	**4.80**	23.0400	2.19089	6.92820	.208333
4.31	18.5761	2.07605	6.56506	.232019	4.81	23.1361	2.19317	6.93542	.207900
4.32	18.6624	2.07846	6.57267	.231481	4.82	23.2324	2.19545	6.94262	.207469
4.33	18.7489	2.08087	6.58027	.230947	4.83	23.3289	2.19773	6.94982	.207039
4.34	18.8356	2.08327	6.58787	.230415	4.84	23.4256	2.20000	6.95701	.206612
4.35	18.9225	2.08567	6.59545	.229885	4.85	23.5225	2.20227	6.96419	.206186
4.36	19.0096	2.08806	6.60303	.229358	4.86	23.6196	2.20454	6.97137	.205761
4.37	19.0969	2.09045	6.61060	.228833	4.87	23.7169	2.20681	6.97854	.205339
4.38	19.1844	2.09284	6.61816	.228311	4.88	23.8144	2.20907	6.98570	.204918
4.39	19.2721	2.09523	6.62571	.227790	4.89	23.9121	2.21133	6.99285	.204499
4.40	19.3600	2.09762	6.63325	.227273	**4.90**	24.0100	2.21359	7.00000	.204082
4.41	19.4481	2.10000	6.64078	.226757	4.91	24.1081	2.21585	7.00714	.203666
4.42	19.5364	2.10238	6.64831	.226244	4.92	24.2064	2.21811	7.01427	.203252
4.43	19.6249	2.10476	6.65582	.225734	4.93	24.3049	2.22036	7.02140	.202840
4.44	19.7136	2.10713	6.66333	.225225	4.94	24.4036	2.22261	7.02851	.202429
4.45	19.8025	2.10950	6.67083	.224719	4.95	24.5025	2.22486	7.03562	.202020
4.46	19.8916	2.11187	6.67832	.224215	4.96	24.6016	2.22711	7.04273	.201613
4.47	19.9809	2.11424	6.68581	.223714	4.97	24.7009	2.22935	7.04982	.201207
4.48	20.0704	2.11660	6.69328	.223214	4.98	24.8004	2.23159	7.05691	.200803
4.49	20.1601	2.11896	6.70075	.222717	4.99	24.9001	2.23383	7.06399	.200401
4.50	20.2500	2.12132	6.70820	.222222	**5.00**	25.0000	2.23607	7.07107	.200000
n	n^2	$\sqrt{n}$	$\sqrt{10n}$	$1/n$	n	n^2	$\sqrt{n}$	$\sqrt{10n}$	$1/n$

TABLE VII

n	n^2	$\sqrt{n}$	$\sqrt{10n}$	$1/n$	n	n^2	$\sqrt{n}$	$\sqrt{10n}$	$1/n$
5.00	25.0000	2.23607	7.07107	.200000	**5.50**	30.2500	2.34521	7.41620	.181818
5.01	25.1001	2.23830	7.07814	.199601	5.51	30.3601	2.34734	7.42294	.181488
5.02	25.2004	2.24054	7.08520	.199203	5.52	30.4704	2.34947	7.42967	.181159
5.03	25.3009	2.24277	7.09225	.198807	5.53	30.5809	2.35160	7.43640	.180832
5.04	25.4016	2.24499	7.09930	.198413	5.54	30.6916	2.35372	7.44312	.180505
5.05	25.5025	2.24722	7.10634	.198020	5.55	30.8025	2.35584	7.44983	.180180
5.06	25.6036	2.24944	7.11337	.197628	5.56	30.9136	2.35797	7.45654	.179856
5.07	25.7049	2.25167	7.12039	.197239	5.57	31.0249	2.36008	7.46324	.179533
5.08	25.8064	2.25389	7.12741	.196850	5.58	31.1364	2.36220	7.46994	.179211
5.09	25.9081	2.25610	7.13442	.196464	5.59	31.2481	2.36432	7.47663	.178891
5.10	26.0100	2.25832	7.14143	.196078	**5.60**	31.3600	2.36643	7.48331	.178571
5.11	26.1121	2.26053	7.14843	.195695	5.61	31.4721	2.36854	7.48999	.178253
5.12	26.2144	2.26274	7.15542	.195312	5.62	31.5844	2.37065	7.49667	.177936
5.13	26.3169	2.26495	7.16240	.194932	5.63	31.6969	2.37276	7.50333	.177620
5.14	26.4196	2.26716	7.16938	.194553	5.64	31.8096	2.37487	7.50999	.177305
5.15	26.5225	2.26936	7.17635	.194175	5.65	31.9225	2.37697	7.51665	.176991
5.16	26.6256	2.27156	7.18331	.193798	5.66	32.0356	2.37908	7.52330	.176678
5.17	26.7289	2.27376	7.19027	.193424	5.67	32.1489	2.38118	7.52994	.176367
5.18	26.8324	2.27596	7.19722	.193050	5.68	32.2624	2.38328	7.53658	.176056
5.19	26.9361	2.27816	7.20417	.192678	5.69	32.3761	2.38537	7.54321	.175747
5.20	27.0400	2.28035	7.21110	.192308	**5.70**	32.4900	2.38747	7.54983	.175439
5.21	27.1441	2.28254	7.21803	.191939	5.71	32.6041	2.38956	7.55645	.175131
5.22	27.2484	2.28473	7.22496	.191571	5.72	32.7184	2.39165	7.56307	.174825
5.23	27.3529	2.28692	7.23187	.191205	5.73	32.8329	2.39374	7.56968	.174520
5.24	27.4576	2.28910	7.23878	.190840	5.74	32.9476	2.39583	7.57628	.174216
5.25	27.5625	2.29129	7.24569	.190476	5.75	33.0625	2.39792	7.58288	.173913
5.26	27.6676	2.29347	7.25259	.190114	5.76	33.1776	2.40000	7.58947	.173611
5.27	27.7729	2.29565	7.25948	.189753	5.77	33.2929	2.40208	7.59605	.173310
5.28	27.8784	2.29783	7.26636	.189394	5.78	33.4084	2.40416	7.60263	.173010
5.29	27.9841	2.30000	7.27324	.189036	5.79	33.5241	2.40624	7.60920	.172712
5.30	28.0900	2.30217	7.28011	.188679	**5.80**	33.6400	2.40832	7.61577	.172414
5.31	28.1961	2.30434	7.28697	.188324	5.81	33.7561	2.41039	7.62234	.172117
5.32	28.3024	2.30651	7.29383	.187970	5.82	33.8724	2.41247	7.62889	.171821
5.33	28.4089	2.30868	7.30068	.187617	5.83	33.9889	2.41454	7.63544	.171527
5.34	28.5156	2.31084	7.30753	.187266	5.84	34.1056	2.41661	7.64199	.171233
5.35	28.6225	2.31301	7.31437	.186916	5.85	34.2225	2.41868	7.64853	.170940
5.36	28.7296	2.31517	7.32120	.186567	5.86	34.3396	2.42074	7.65506	.170649
5.37	28.8369	2.31733	7.32803	.186220	5.87	34.4569	2.42281	7.66159	.170358
5.38	28.9444	2.31948	7.33485	.185874	5.88	34.5744	2.42487	7.66812	.170068
5.39	29.0521	2.32164	7.34166	.185529	5.89	34.6921	2.42693	7.67463	.169779
5.40	29.1600	2.32379	7.34847	.185185	**5.90**	34.8100	2.42899	7.68115	.169492
5.41	29.2681	2.32594	7.35527	.184843	5.91	34.9281	2.43105	7.68765	.169205
5.42	29.3764	2.32809	7.36206	.184502	5.92	35.0464	2.43311	7.69415	.168919
5.43	29.4849	2.33024	7.36885	.184162	5.93	35.1649	2.43516	7.70065	.168634
5.44	29.5936	2.33238	7.37564	.183824	5.94	35.2836	2.43721	7.70714	.168350
5.45	29.7025	2.33452	7.38241	.183486	5.95	35.4025	2.43926	7.71362	.168067
5.46	29.8116	2.33666	7.38918	.183150	5.96	35.5216	2.44131	7.72010	.167785
5.47	29.9209	2.33880	7.39594	.182815	5.97	35.6409	2.44336	7.72658	.167504
5.48	30.0304	2.34094	7.40270	.182482	5.98	35.7604	2.44540	7.73305	.167224
5.49	30.1401	2.34307	7.40945	.182149	5.99	35.8801	2.44745	7.73951	.166945
5.50	30.2500	2.34521	7.41620	.181818	**6.00**	36.0000	2.44949	7.74597	.166667
n	n^2	$\sqrt{n}$	$\sqrt{10n}$	$1/n$	n	n^2	$\sqrt{n}$	$\sqrt{10n}$	$1/n$

n	n^2	$\sqrt{n}$	$\sqrt{10n}$	$1/n$	n	n^2	$\sqrt{n}$	$\sqrt{10n}$	$1/n$
6.00	36.0000	2.44949	7.74597	.166667	**6.50**	42.2500	2.54951	8.06226	.153846
6.01	36.1201	2.45153	7.75242	.166389	6.51	42.3801	2.55147	8.06846	.153610
6.02	36.2404	2.45357	7.75887	.166113	6.52	42.5104	2.55343	8.07465	.153374
6.03	36.3609	2.45561	7.76531	.165837	6.53	42.6409	2.55539	8.08084	.153139
6.04	36.4816	2.45764	7.77174	.165563	6.54	42.7716	2.55734	8.08703	.152905
6.05	36.6025	2.45967	7.77817	.165289	6.55	42.9025	2.55930	8.09321	.152672
6.06	36.7236	2.46171	7.78460	.165017	6.56	43.0336	2.56125	8.09938	.152439
6.07	36.8449	2.46374	7.79102	.164745	6.57	43.1649	2.56320	8.10555	.152207
6.08	36.9664	2.46577	7.79744	.164474	6.58	43.2964	2.56515	8.11172	.151976
6.09	37.0881	2.46779	7.80385	.164204	6.59	43.4281	2.56710	8.11788	.151745
6.10	37.2100	2.46982	7.81025	.163934	**6.60**	43.5600	2.56905	8.12404	.151515
6.11	37.3321	2.47184	7.81665	.163666	6.61	43.6921	2.57099	8.13019	.151286
6.12	37.4544	2.47386	7.82304	.163399	6.62	43.8244	2.57294	8.13634	.151057
6.13	37.5769	2.47588	7.82943	.163132	6.63	43.9569	2.57488	8.14248	.150830
6.14	37.6996	2.47790	7.83582	.162866	6.64	44.0896	2.57682	8.14862	.150602
6.15	37.8225	2.47992	7.84219	.162602	6.65	44.2225	2.57876	8.15475	.150376
6.16	37.9456	2.48193	7.84857	.162338	6.66	44.3556	2.58070	8.16088	.150150
6.17	38.0689	2.48395	7.85493	.162075	6.67	44.4889	2.58263	8.16701	.149925
6.18	38.1924	2.48596	7.86130	.161812	6.68	44.6224	2.58457	8.17313	.149701
6.19	38.3161	2.48797	7.86766	.161551	6.69	44.7561	2.58650	8.17924	.149477
6.20	38.4400	2.48998	7.87401	.161290	**6.70**	44.8900	2.58844	8.18535	.149254
6.21	38.5641	2.49199	7.88036	.161031	6.71	45.0241	2.59037	8.19146	.149031
6.22	38.6884	2.49399	7.88670	.160772	6.72	45.1584	2.59230	8.19756	.148810
6.23	38.8129	2.49600	7.89303	.160514	6.73	45.2929	2.59422	8.20366	.148588
6.24	38.9376	2.49800	7.89937	.160256	6.74	45.4276	2.59615	8.20975	.148368
6.25	39.0625	2.50000	7.90569	.160000	6.75	45.5625	2.59808	8.21584	.148148
6.26	39.1876	2.50200	7.91202	.159744	6.76	45.6976	2.60000	8.22192	.147929
6.27	39.3129	2.50400	7.91833	.159490	6.77	45.8329	2.60192	8.22800	.147710
6.28	39.4384	2.50599	7.92465	.159236	6.78	45.9684	2.60384	8.23408	.147493
6.29	39.5641	2.50799	7.93095	.158983	6.79	46.1041	2.60576	8.24015	.147275
6.30	39.6900	2.50998	7.93725	.158730	**6.80**	46.2400	2.60768	8.24621	.147059
6.31	39.8161	2.51197	7.94355	.158479	6.81	46.3761	2.60960	8.25227	.146843
6.32	39.9424	2.51396	7.94984	.158228	6.82	46.5124	2.61151	8.25833	.146628
6.33	40.0689	2.51595	7.95613	.157978	6.83	46.6489	2.61343	8.26438	.146413
6.34	40.1956	2.51794	7.96241	.157729	6.84	46.7856	2.61534	8.27043	.146199
6.35	40.3225	2.51992	7.96869	.157480	6.85	46.9225	2.61725	8.27647	.145985
6 36	40.4496	2.52190	7.97496	.157233	6.86	47.0596	2.61916	8.28251	.145773
6.37	40.5769	2.52389	7.98123	.156986	6.87	47.1969	2.62107	8.28855	.145560
6.38	40.7044	2.52587	7.98749	.156740	6.88	47.3344	2.62298	8.29458	.145349
6.39	40.8321	2.52784	7.99375	.156495	6.89	47.4721	2.62488	8.30060	.145138
6.40	40.9600	2.52982	8.00000	.156250	**6.90**	47.6100	2.62679	8.30662	.144928
6.41	41.0881	2.53180	8.00625	.156006	6.91	47.7481	2.62869	8.31264	.144718
6.42	41.2164	2.53377	8.01249	.155763	6.92	47.8864	2.63059	8.31865	.144509
6.43	41.3449	2.53574	8.01873	.155521	6.93	48.0249	2.63249	8.32466	.144300
6.44	41.4736	2.53772	8.02496	.155280	6.94	48.1636	2.63439	8.33067	.144092
6.45	41.6025	2.53969	8.03119	.155039	6.95	48.3025	2.63629	8.33667	.143885
6.46	41.7316	2.54165	8.03741	.154799	6.96	48.4416	2.63818	8.34266	.143678
6.47	41.8609	2.54362	8.04363	.154560	6.97	48.5809	2.64008	8.34865	.143472
6.48	41.9904	2.54558	8.04984	.154321	6.98	48.7204	2.64197	8.35464	.143266
6.49	42.1201	2.54755	8.05605	.154083	6.99	48.8601	2.64386	8.36062	.143062
6.50	42.2500	2.54951	8.06226	.153846	**7.00**	49.0000	2.64575	8.36660	.142857
n	n^2	$\sqrt{n}$	$\sqrt{10n}$	$1/n$	n	n^2	$\sqrt{n}$	$\sqrt{10n}$	$1/n$

TABLE VII

n	n^2	$\sqrt{n}$	$\sqrt{10n}$	$1/n$	n	n^2	$\sqrt{n}$	$\sqrt{10n}$	$1/n$
7.00	49.0000	2.64575	8.36660	.142857	7.50	56.2500	2.73861	8.66025	.133333
7.01	49.1401	2.64764	8.37257	.142653	7.51	56.4001	2.74044	8.66603	.133156
7.02	49.2804	2.64953	8.37854	.142450	7.52	56.5504	2.74226	8.67179	.132979
7.03	49.4209	2.65141	8.38451	.142248	7.53	56.7009	2.74408	8.67756	.132802
7.04	49.5616	2.65330	8.39047	.142045	7.54	56.8516	2.74591	8.68332	.132626
7.05	49.7025	2.65518	8.39643	.141844	7.55	57.0025	2.74773	8.68907	.132450
7.06	49.8436	2.65707	8.40238	.141643	7.56	57.1536	2.74955	8.69483	.132275
7.07	49.9849	2.65895	8.40833	.141443	7.57	57.3049	2.75136	8.70057	.132100
7.08	50.1264	2.66083	8.41427	.141243	7.58	57.4564	2.75318	8.70632	.131926
7.09	50.2681	2.66271	8.42021	.141044	7.59	57.6081	2.75500	8.71206	.131752
7.10	50.4100	2.66458	8.42615	.140845	7.60	57.7600	2.75681	8.71780	.131579
7.11	50.5521	2.66646	8.43208	.140647	7.61	57.9121	2.75862	8.72353	.131406
7.12	50.6944	2.66833	8.43801	.140449	7.62	58.0644	2.76043	8.72926	.131234
7.13	50.8369	2.67021	8.44393	.140252	7.63	58.2169	2.76225	8.73499	.131062
7.14	50.9796	2.67208	8.44985	.140056	7.64	58.3696	2.76405	8.74071	.130890
7.15	51.1225	2.67395	8.45577	.139860	7.65	58.5225	2.76586	8.74643	.130719
7.16	51.2656	2.67582	8.46168	.139665	7.66	58.6756	2.76767	8.75214	.130548
7.17	51.4089	2.67769	8.46759	.139470	7.67	58.8289	2.76948	8.75785	.130378
7.18	51.5524	2.67955	8.47349	.139276	7.68	58.9824	2.77128	8.76356	.130208
7.19	51.6961	2.68142	8.47939	.139082	7.69	59.1361	2.77308	8.76926	.130039
7.20	51.8400	2.68328	8.48528	.138889	7.70	59.2900	2.77489	8.77496	.129870
7.21	51.9841	2.68514	8.49117	.138696	7.71	59.4441	2.77669	8.78066	.129702
7.22	52.1284	2.68701	8.49706	.138504	7.72	59.5984	2.77849	8.78635	.129534
7.23	52.2729	2.68887	8.50294	.138313	7.73	59.7529	2.78029	8.79204	.129366
7.24	52.4176	2.69072	8.50882	.138122	7.74	59.9076	2.78209	8.79773	.129199
7.25	52.5625	2.69258	8.51469	.137931	7.75	60.0625	2.78388	8.80341	.129032
7.26	52.7076	2.69444	8.52056	.137741	7.76	60.2176	2.78568	8.80909	.128866
7.27	52.8529	2.69629	8.52643	.137552	7.77	60.3729	2.78747	8.81476	.128700
7.28	52.9984	2.69815	8.53229	.137363	7.78	60.5284	2.78927	8.82043	.128535
7.29	53.1441	2.70000	8.53815	.137174	7.79	60.6841	2.79106	8.82610	.128370
7.30	53.2900	2.70185	8.54400	.136986	7.80	60.8400	2.79285	8.83176	.128205
7.31	53.4361	2.70370	8.54985	.136799	7.81	60.9961	2.79464	8.83742	.128041
7.32	53.5824	2.70555	8.55570	.136612	7.82	61.1524	2.79643	8.84308	.127877
7.33	53.7289	2.70740	8.56154	.136426	7.83	61.3089	2.79821	8.84873	.127714
7.34	53.8756	2.70924	8.56738	.136240	7.84	61.4656	2.80000	8.85438	.127551
7.35	54.0225	2.71109	8.57321	.136054	7.85	61.6225	2.80179	8.86002	.127389
7.36	54.1696	2.71293	8.57904	.135870	7.86	61.7796	2.80357	8.86566	.127226
7.37	54.3169	2.71477	8.58487	.135685	7.87	61.9369	2.80535	8.87130	.127065
7.38	54.4644	2.71662	8.59069	.135501	7.88	62.0944	2.80713	8.87694	.126904
7.39	54.6121	2.71846	8.59651	.135318	7.89	62.2521	2.80891	8.88257	.126743
7.40	54.7600	2.72029	8.60233	.135135	7.90	62.4100	2.81069	8.88819	.126582
7.41	54.9081	2.72213	8.60814	.134953	7.91	62.5681	2.81247	8.89382	.126422
7.42	55.0564	2.72397	8.61394	.134771	7.92	62.7264	2.81425	8.89944	.126263
7.43	55.2049	2.72580	8.61974	.134590	7.93	62.8849	2.81603	8.90505	.126103
7.44	55.3536	2.72764	8.62554	.134409	7.94	63.0436	2.81780	8.91067	.125945
7.45	55.5025	2.72947	8.63134	.134228	7.95	63.2025	2.81957	8.91628	.125786
7.46	55.6516	2.73130	8.63713	.134048	7.96	63.3616	2.82135	8.92188	.125628
7.47	55.8009	2.73313	8.64292	.133869	7.97	63.5209	2.82312	8.92749	.125471
7.48	55.9504	2.73496	8.64870	.133690	7.98	63.6804	2.82489	8.93308	.125313
7.49	56.1001	2.73679	8.65448	.133511	7.99	63.8401	2.82666	8.93868	.125156
7.50	56.2500	2.73861	8.66025	.133333	8.00	64.0000	2.82843	8.94427	.125000
n	n^2	$\sqrt{n}$	$\sqrt{10n}$	$1/n$	n	n^2	$\sqrt{n}$	$\sqrt{10n}$	$1/n$

n	n^2	$\sqrt{n}$	$\sqrt{10n}$	$1/n$	n	n^2	$\sqrt{n}$	$\sqrt{10n}$	$1/n$
8.00	64.0000	2.82843	8.94427	.125000	**8.50**	72.2500	2.91548	9.21954	.117647
8.01	64.1601	2.83019	8.94986	.124844	8.51	72.4201	2.91719	9.22497	.117509
8.02	64.3204	2.83196	8.95545	.124688	8.52	72.5904	2.91890	9.23038	.117371
8.03	64.4809	2.83373	8.96103	.124533	8.53	72.7609	2.92062	9.23580	.117233
8.04	64.6416	2.83549	8.96660	.124378	8.54	72.9316	2.92233	9.24121	.117096
8.05	64.8025	2.83725	8.97218	.124224	8.55	73.1025	2.92404	9.24662	.116959
8.06	64.9636	2.83901	8.97775	.124069	8.56	73.2736	2.92575	9.25203	.116822
8.07	65.1249	2.84077	8.98332	.123916	8.57	73.4449	2.92746	9.25743	.116686
8.08	65.2864	2.84253	8.98888	.123762	8.58	73.6164	2.92916	9.26283	.116550
8.09	65.4481	2.84429	8.99444	.123609	8.59	73.7881	2.93087	9.26823	.116414
8.10	65.6100	2.84605	9.00000	.123457	**8.60**	73.9600	2.93258	9.27362	.116279
8.11	65.7721	2.84781	9.00555	.123305	8.61	74.1321	2.93428	9.27901	.116144
8.12	65.9344	2.84956	9.01110	.123153	8.62	74.3044	2.93598	9.28440	.116009
8.13	66.0969	2.85132	9.01665	.123001	8.63	74.4769	2.93769	9.28978	.115875
8.14	66.2596	2.85307	9.02219	.122850	8.64	74.6496	2.93939	9.29516	.115741
8.15	66.4225	2.85482	9.02774	.122699	8.65	74.8225	2.94109	9.30054	.115607
8.16	66.5856	2.85657	9.03327	.122549	8.66	74.9956	2.94279	9.30591	.115473
8.17	66.7489	2.85832	9.03881	.122399	8.67	75.1689	2.94449	9.31128	.115340
8.18	66.9124	2.86007	9.04434	.122249	8.68	75.3424	2.94618	9.31665	.115207
8.19	67.0761	2.86182	9.04986	.122100	8.69	75.5161	2.94788	9.32202	.115075
8.20	67.2400	2.86356	9.05539	.121951	**8.70**	75.6900	2.94958	9.32738	.114943
8.21	67.4041	2.86531	9.06091	.121803	8.71	75.8641	2.95127	9.33274	.114811
8.22	67.5684	2.86705	9.06642	.121655	8.72	76.0384	2.95296	9.33809	.114679
8.23	67.7329	2.86880	9.07193	.121507	8.73	76.2129	2.95466	9.34345	.114548
8.24	67.8976	2.87054	9.07744	.121359	8.74	76.3876	2.95635	9.34880	.114416
8.25	68.0625	2.87228	9.08295	.121212	8.75	76.5625	2.95804	9.35414	.114286
8.26	68.2276	2.87402	9.08845	.121065	8.76	76.7376	2.95973	9.35949	.114155
8.27	68.3929	2.87576	9.09395	.120919	8.77	76.9129	2.96142	9.36483	.114025
8.28	68.5584	2.87750	9.09945	.120773	8.78	77.0884	2.96311	9.37017	.113895
8.29	68.7241	2.87924	9.10494	.120627	8.79	77.2641	2.96479	9.37550	.113766
8.30	68.8900	2.88097	9.11043	.120482	**8.80**	77.4400	2.96648	9.38083	.113636
8.31	69.0561	2.88271	9.11592	.120337	8.81	77.6161	2.96816	9.38616	.113507
8.32	69.2224	2.88444	9.12140	.120192	8.82	77.7924	2.96985	9.39149	.113379
8.33	69.3889	2.88617	9.12688	.120048	8.83	77.9689	2.97153	9.39681	.113250
8.34	69.5556	2.88791	9.13236	.119904	8.84	78.1456	2.97321	9.40213	.113122
8.35	69.7225	2.88964	9.13783	.119760	8.85	78.3225	2.97489	9.40744	.112994
8.36	69.8896	2.89137	9.14330	.119617	8.86	78.4996	2.97658	9.41276	.112867
8.37	70.0569	2.89310	9.14877	.119474	8.87	78.6769	2.97825	9.41807	.112740
8.38	70.2244	2.89482	9.15423	.119332	8.88	78.8544	2.97993	9.42338	.112613
8.39	70.3921	2.89655	9.15969	.119190	8.89	79.0321	2.98161	9.42868	.112486
8.40	70.5600	2.89828	9.16515	.119048	**8.90**	79.2100	2.98329	9.43398	.112360
8.41	70.7281	2.90000	9.17061	.118906	8.91	79.3881	2.98496	9.43928	.112233
8.42	70.8964	2.90172	9.17606	.118765	8.92	79.5664	2.98664	9.44458	.112108
8.43	71.0649	2.90345	9.18150	.118624	8.93	79.7449	2.98831	9.44987	.111982
8.44	71.2336	2.90517	9.18695	.118483	8.94	79.9236	2.98998	9.45516	.111857
8.45	71.4025	2.90689	9.19239	.118343	8.95	80.1025	2.99166	9.46044	.111732
8.46	71.5716	2.90861	9.19783	.118203	8.96	80.2816	2.99333	9.46573	.111607
8.47	71.7409	2.91033	9.20326	.118064	8.97	80.4609	2.99500	9.47101	.111483
8.48	71.9104	2.91204	9.20869	.117925	8.98	80.6404	2.99666	9.47629	.111359
8.49	72.0801	2.91376	9.21412	.117786	8.99	80.8201	2.99833	9.48156	.111235
8.50	72.2500	2.91548	9.21954	.117647	**9.00**	81.0000	3.00000	9.48683	.111111
n	n^2	$\sqrt{n}$	$\sqrt{10n}$	$1/n$	n	n^2	$\sqrt{n}$	$\sqrt{10n}$	$1/n$

n	n²	√n	√10n	1/n	n	n²	√n	√10n	1/n
9.00	81.0000	3.00000	9.48683	.111111	**9.50**	90.2500	3.08221	9.74679	.105263
9.01	81.1801	3.00167	9.49210	.110988	9.51	90.4401	3.08383	9.75192	.105152
9.02	81.3604	3.00333	9.49737	.110865	9.52	90.6304	3.08545	9.75705	.105042
9.03	81.5409	3.00500	9.50263	.110742	9.53	90.8209	3.08707	9.76217	.104932
9.04	81.7216	3.00666	9.50789	.110619	9.54	91.0116	3.08869	9.76729	.104822
9.05	81.9025	3.00832	9.51315	.110497	9.55	91.2025	3.09031	9.77241	.104712
9.06	82.0836	3.00998	9.51840	.110375	9.56	91.3936	3.09192	9.77753	.104603
9.07	82.2649	3.01164	9.52365	.110254	9.57	91.5849	3.09354	9.78264	.104493
9.08	82.4464	3.01330	9.52890	.110132	9.58	91.7764	3.09516	9.78775	.104384
9.09	82.6281	3.01496	9.53415	.110011	9.59	91.9681	3.09677	9.79285	.104275
9.10	82.8100	3.01662	9.53939	.109890	**9.60**	92.1600	3.09839	9.79796	.104167
9.11	82.9921	3.01828	9.54463	.109769	9.61	92.3521	3.10000	9.80306	.104058
9.12	83.1744	3.01993	9.54987	.109649	9.62	92.5444	3.10161	9.80816	.103950
9.13	83.3569	3.02159	9.55510	.109529	9.63	92.7369	3.10322	9.81326	.103842
9.14	83.5396	3.02324	9.56033	.109409	9.64	92.9296	3.10483	9.81835	.103734
9.15	83.7225	3.02490	9.56556	.109290	9.65	93.1225	3.10644	9.82344	.103627
9.16	83.9056	3.02655	9.57079	.109170	9.66	93.3156	3.10805	9.82853	.103520
9.17	84.0889	3.02820	9.57601	.109051	9 67	93.5089	3.10966	9.83362	.103413
9.18	84.2724	3.02985	9.58123	.108932	9.68	93.7024	3.11127	9.83870	.103306
9.19	84.456į	3.03150	9.58645	.108814	9.69	93.8961	3.11288	9.84378	.103199
9.20	84.6400	3.03315	9.59166	.108696	**9.70**	94.0900	3.11448	9.84886	.103093
9.21	84.8241	3.03480	9.59687	.108578	9.71	94.2841	3.11609	9.85393	.102987
9.22	85.0084	3.03645	9.60208	.108460	9.72	94.4784	3.11769	9.85901	.102881
9.23	85.1929	3.03809	9.60729	.108342	9.73	94.6729	3.11929	9.86408	.102775
9.24	85.3776	3.03974	9.61249	.108225	9.74	94.8676	3.12090	9.86914	.102669
9.25	85.5625	3.04138	9.61769	.108108	9.75	95.0625	3.12250	9.87421	.102564
9.26	85.7476	3.04302	9.62289	.107991	9.76	95.2576	3.12410	9.87927	.102459
9.27	85.9329	3.04467	9.62808	.107875	9.77	95.4529	3.12570	9.88433	.102354
9.28	86.1184	3.04631	9.63328	.107759	9.78	95.6484	3.12730	9.88939	.102249
9.29	86.3041	3.04795	9.63846	.107643	9.79	95.8441	3.12890	9.89444	.102145
9.30	86.4900	3.04959	9.64365	.107527	**9.80**	96.0400	3.13050	9.89949	.102041
9.31	86.6761	3.05123	9.64883	.107411	9.81	96.2361	3.13209	9.90454	.101937
9.32	86.8624	3.05287	9.65401	.107296	9.82	96.4324	3.13369	9.90959	.101833
9.33	87.0489	3.05450	9.65919	.107181	9.83	96.6289	3.13528	9.91464	.101729
9.34	87.2356	3.05614	9.66437	.107066	9.84	96.8256	3.13688	9.91968	.101626
9.35	87.4225	3.05778	9.66954	.106952	9.85	97.0225	3.13847	9.92472	.101523
9.36	87.6096	3.05941	9.67471	.106838	9.86	97.2196	3.14006	9.92975	.101420
9.37	87.7969	3.06105	9.67988	.106724	9.87	97.4169	3.14166	9.93479	.101317
9.38	87.9844	3.06268	9.68504	.106610	9.88	97.6144	3.14325	9.93982	.101215
9.39	88.1721	3.06431	9.69020	.106496	9.89	97.8121	3.14484	9.94485	.101112
9.40	88.3600	3.06594	9.69536	.106383	**9.90**	98.0100	3.14643	9.94987	.101010
9.41	88.5481	3.06757	9.70052	.106270	9.91	98.2081	3.14802	9.95490	.100908
9.42	88.7364	3.06920	9.70567	.106157	9.92	98.4064	3.14960	9.95992	.100806
9.43	88.9249	3.07083	9.71082	.106045	9.93	98.6049	3.15119	9.96494	.100705
9.44	89.1136	3.07246	9.71597	.105932	9.94	98.8036	3.15278	9.96995	.100604
9.45	89.3025	3.07409	9.72111	.105820	9.95	99.0025	3.15436	9.97497	.100503
9.46	89.4916	3.07571	9.72625	.105708	9.96	99.2016	3.15595	9.97998	.100402
9.47	89.6809	3.07734	9.73139	.105597	9.97	99.4009	3.15753	9.98499	.100301
9.48	89.8704	3.07896	9.73653	.105485	9.98	99.6004	3.15911	9.98999	.100200
9.49	90.0601	3.08058	9.74166	.105374	9.99	99.8001	3.16070	9.99500	.100100
9.50	90.2500	3.08221	9.74679	.105263	**10.00**	100.000	3.16228	10.0000	.100000
n	n²	√n	√10n	1/n	n	n²	√n	√10n	1/n

Date Due